McDougal Littell

CLASSZONE

Visit classzone.com and get connected.

ClassZone resources provide instruction, practice and learning support for students and parents.

Help with the Math

- @Home Tutor enables students to focus on the math and be more prepared for class, using animated examples and instruction.
- Extra examples similar to those in the book provide additional support.

Games and Activities

- Crossword puzzles, memory games, and other activities help students connect to essential math concepts.
- Math Vocabulary Flipcards are a fun way to learn math terminology.

Assessment

- Section Quizzes show students what concepts they still need further practice on.
- Students can take Unit Tests online and then view test reports to see whether they need more practice.

Access the online version of your textbook at **classzone.com**

Your complete text is available for immediate use!

McDougal Littell

Where Great Lessons Begin

McDougal Littell

GEORGIA HIGH SCHOOL MATHEMATICS 1

McDougal Littell
A DIVISION OF HOUGHTON MIFFLIN COMPANY
Evanston, Illinois • Boston • Dallas

Cover Photo Credits: Clockwise from top: *Okefenokee Swamp* © Farrell Grehan/Corbis; *Peach* © Comstock Images/Age Fotostock; *St. Simons Island Lighthouse* © James Schwabel/Alamy; *Horse-drawn carriage, Savannah* © Bob Krist/Corbis; *The Rock Eagle Effigy Mound* © Tami Chappell/America 24-7/Getty Images; *Tybee Island boat marina* © Walter Bibikow/Age Fotostock; *Georgia State Capitol Building* © W. Cody/Corbis

ISBN-10: 0-618-92011-0
ISBN-13: 978-0-618-92011-2 23456789—DSV—11 10 09 08

Internet Web Site: http://www.mcdougallittell.com

About This Book

McDougal Littell Georgia High School Mathematics 1

The Georgia High School Mathematics 1 book covers all of the Georgia Performance Standards for Mathematics 1. Its content has been organized into a convenient sequence that corresponds to the strands of the Georgia Performance Standards. Georgia standards that correlate to the content of each lesson are given at point of use in the Student Edition and Teacher's Edition of *Georgia High School Mathematics 1.*

At the front of this book, you will find a complete listing of all the Georgia Performance Standards for Mathematics 1, along with a correlation of these standards to appropriate lessons in *Georgia High School Mathematics 1.*

Advisers and Reviewers

Curriculum Advisers and Reviewers

Michele Borror Long
Mathematics Teacher
LaGrange High School
LaGrange, GA

Sandye Ashley
Mathematics Teacher
Rome Middle School
Rome, GA

Georgia Panel

Ernest Adams
Mathematics Teacher,
Department Chair
Northview High School
Duluth, GA

Salvatore Angelica
Mathematics Teacher
Luella High School
Locust Grove, GA

Sandra Campagnone
Mathematics Teacher
Pebblebrook High School
Mableton, GA

Mack Graham
Mathematics Teacher
Benjamin E. Mays High School
Atlanta, GA

Debra Hodge
Mathematics Teacher
Dunwoody High School
Dunwoody, GA

Carletta Malcom
Mathematics Teacher,
Department Chair
Cedar Grove High School
Ellenwood, GA

Yvonne Pringle
Mathematics Teacher,
Department Chair
North Atlanta High School
Atlanta, GA

Maria Travitz
Mathematics Teacher
Kennesaw Mountain High School
Kennesaw, GA

Melissa Walker
Mathematics Teacher,
Department Chair
Martin Luther King, Jr. High School
Lithonia, GA

Contents

UNIT 1 Algebra: Linear Functions

UNIT 2 Algebra: Polynomials and Quadratic Functions

UNIT 3 Algebra: Cubic, Square Root, and Rational Functions

UNIT 4 Geometry: Reasoning and Proof, Lines, and Congruent Triangles

UNIT 5

Geometry: Relationships in Triangles and Quadrilaterals

UNIT 6

Data Analysis and Probability

Student Resources

Correlation to Standards

Correlation of *McDougal Littell Georgia High School Mathematics 1* to the Georgia Performance Standards for Mathematics 1

ALGEBRA

Students will explore functions and solve simple equations. Students will simplify and operate with radical, polynomial, and rational expressions.

Georgia Performance Standard		Lesson/Activity
MM1A1	**Students will explore and interpret the characteristics of functions, using graphs, tables, and simple algebraic techniques.**	
MM1A1a	Represent functions using function notation.	Lesson 1.7, Lesson 1.9, Lesson 2.11
MM1A1b	Graph the basic functions $f(x) = x^n$, where $n = 1$ to 3, $f(x) = \sqrt{x}$, $f(x) = \lvert x \rvert$, and $f(x) = \frac{1}{x}$.	Lesson 1.4, Lesson 1.6, Lesson 1.7, Investigating Math Activity 1.7, Lesson 1.9, Lesson 2.10, Investigating Math Activity 2.10, Lesson 3.1, Lesson 3.3, Lesson 3.6
MM1A1c	Graph transformations of basic functions including vertical shifts, stretches, and shrinks, as well as reflections across the x- and y-axes.	Lesson 1.7, Investigating Math Activity 1.7, Lesson 1.9, Lesson 2.10, Lesson 2.11, Lesson 3.1, Lesson 3.3, Investigating Math Activity 3.3, Lesson 3.6
MM1A1d	Investigate and explain the characteristics of a function: domain, range, zeros, intercepts, intervals of increase and decrease, maximum and minimum values, and end behavior.	Lesson 1.2, Lesson 1.3, Lesson 1.4, Lesson 1.6, Investigating Math Activity 1.6, Technology Activity 1.6, Lesson 1.8, Lesson 2.11, Problem Solving Workshop 2.11, Lesson 2.12, Lesson 3.1, Lesson 3.3, Lesson 3.6
MM1A1e	Relate to a given context the characteristics of a function, and use graphs and tables to investigate its behavior.	Lesson 2.10, Problem Solving Workshop 2.11
MM1A1f	Recognize sequences as functions with domains that are whole numbers.	Lesson 3.13
MM1A1g	Explore rates of change, comparing constant rates of change (i.e., slope) versus variable rates of change. Compare rates of change of linear, quadratic, square root, and other function families.	Lesson 1.5, Lesson 3.12
MM1A1h	Determine graphically and algebraically whether a function has symmetry and whether it is even, odd, or neither.	Lesson 3.1

Georgia Performance Standard		Lesson/Activity
MM1A1i	Understand that any equation in x can be interpreted as the equation $f(x) = g(x)$, and interpret the solutions of the equation as the x-value(s) of the intersection point(s) of the graphs of $y = f(x)$ and $y = g(x)$.	Lesson 3.12
MM1A2	**Students will simplify and operate with radical expressions, polynomials, and rational expressions.**	
MM1A2a	Simplify algebraic and numeric expressions involving square root.	Lesson 3.4
MM1A2b	Perform operations with square roots.	Lesson 3.4
MM1A2c	Add, subtract, multiply, and divide polynomials.	Lesson 2.1, Investigating Math Activity 2.1, Lesson 2.2, Investigating Math Activity 2.2, Lesson 2.3, Lesson 3.7, Lesson 3.8
MM1A2d	Expand binomials using the Binomial Theorem.	Lesson 2.4
MM1A2e	Add, subtract, multiply, and divide rational expressions.	Lesson 3.9, Technology Activity 3.9, Lesson 3.10, Problem Solving Workshop 3.10
MM1A2f	Factor expressions by greatest common factor, grouping, trial and error, and special products limited to the formulas below. $(x + y)^2 = x^2 + 2xy + y^2$ $(x - y)^2 = x^2 - 2xy + y^2$ $(x + y)(x - y) = x^2 - y^2$ $(x + a)(x + b) = x^2 + (a + b)x + ab$ $(x + y)^3 = x^3 + 3x^2y + 3xy^2 + y^3$ $(x - y)^3 = x^3 - 3x^2y + 3xy^2 - y^3$	Lesson 2.5, Lesson 2.6, Lesson 2.7, Lesson 2.8, Lesson 2.9, Lesson 3.2, Investigating Math Activity 3.10
MM1A2g	Use area and volume models for polynomial arithmetic.	Lesson 2.2, Investigating Math Activity 2.2
MM1A3	**Students will solve simple equations.**	
MM1A3a	Solve quadratic equations in the form $ax^2 + bx + c = 0$, where $a = 1$, by using factorization and finding square roots where applicable.	Lesson 2.6, Lesson 2.13
MM1A3b	Solve equations involving radicals such as $\sqrt{x} + b = c$, using algebraic techniques.	Lesson 3.5
MM1A3c	Use a variety of techniques, including technology, tables, and graphs to solve equations resulting from the investigation of $x^2 + bx + c = 0$.	Lesson 2.6, Lesson 2.12, Technology Activity 2.12
MM1A3d	Solve simple rational equations that result in linear equations or quadratic equations with leading coefficient of 1.	Lesson 3.11

GEOMETRY

Students will explore, understand, and use the formal language of reasoning and justification. Students will apply properties of polygons and determine distances and points of concurrence.

Georgia Performance Standard		Lesson/Activity
MM1G1	**Students will investigate properties of geometric figures in the coordinate plane.**	
MM1G1a	Determine the distance between two points.	Lesson 4.1, Lesson 5.9
MM1G1b	Determine the distance between a point and a line.	Lesson 4.7, Problem Solving Workshop 4.7
MM1G1c	Determine the midpoint of a segment.	Lesson 4.1, Lesson 5.1, Lesson 5.4
MM1G1d	Understand the distance formula as an application of the Pythagorean theorem.	Investigating Math Activity 4.1
MM1G1e	Use the coordinate plane to investigate properties of and verify conjectures related to triangles and quadrilaterals.	Lesson 4.8, Lesson 5.1, Problem Solving Workshop 5.2, Lesson 5.4, Lesson 5.8, Lesson 5.9, Lesson 5.11
MM1G2	**Students will understand and use the language of mathematical argument and justification.**	
MM1G2a	Use conjecture, inductive reasoning, deductive reasoning, counterexamples, and indirect proof as appropriate.	Lesson 4.2, Technology Activity 4.2, Lesson 4.4, Lesson 4.5, Lesson 4.6, Lesson 5.6
MM1G2b	Understand and use the relationships among a statement and its converse, inverse, and contrapositive.	Lesson 4.3
MM1G3	**Students will discover, prove, and apply properties of triangles, quadrilaterals, and other polygons.**	
MM1G3a	Determine the sum of interior and exterior angles in a polygon.	Lesson 5.7
MM1G3b	Understand and use the triangle inequality, the side-angle inequality, and the exterior-angle inequality.	Lesson 5.5, Technology Activity 5.5
MM1G3c	Understand and use congruence postulates and theorems for triangles (SSS, SAS, ASA, AAS, HL).	Lesson 4.8, Lesson 4.9, Lesson 4.10, Investigating Math Activity 4.10
MM1G3d	Understand, use, and prove properties of and relationships among special quadrilaterals: parallelogram, rectangle, rhombus, square, trapezoid, and kite.	Lesson 5.8, Lesson 5.9, Investigating Math Activity 5.9, Lesson 5.10, Lesson 5.11, Lesson 5.12
MM1G3e	Find and use points of concurrency in triangles: incenter, orthocenter, circumcenter, centroid.	Lesson 5.2, Problem Solving Workshop 5.2, Lesson 5.3, Investigating Math Activity 5.3, Lesson 5.4

DATA ANALYSIS AND PROBABILITY

Students will use counting techniques and determine probability. Students will demonstrate understanding of data analysis by posing questions to be answered by collecting data. Students will organize, represent, investigate, interpret, and make inferences from data.

Georgia Performance Standard		Lesson / Activity
MM1D1	**Students will determine the number of outcomes related to a given event.**	
MM1D1a	Apply the addition and multiplication principles of counting.	Lesson 6.1
MM1D1b	Calculate and use simple permutations and combinations.	Lesson 6.2, Lesson 6.3, Investigating Math Activity 6.3
MM1D2	**Students will use the basic laws of probability.**	
MM1D2a	Find the probabilities of mutually exclusive events.	Lesson 6.4
MM1D2b	Find the probabilities of dependent events.	Lesson 6.4
MM1D2c	Calculate conditional probabilities.	Lesson 6.4
MM1D2d	Use expected value to predict outcomes.	Lesson 6.5
MM1D3	**Students will relate samples to a population.**	
MM1D3a	Compare summary statistics (mean, median, quartiles, and interquartile range) from one sample data distribution to another sample data distribution in describing center and variability of the data distributions.	Lesson 6.8
MM1D3b	Compare the averages of the summary statistics from a large number of samples to the corresponding population parameters.	Lesson 6.8
MM1D3c	Understand that a random sample is used to improve the chance of selecting a representative sample.	Lesson 6.6
MM1D4	Students will explore variability of data by determining the mean absolute deviation (the average of the absolute values of the deviations).	Lesson 6.7, Technology Activity 6.7, Problem Solving Workshop 6.7

UNIT 1
Algebra: Linear Functions

LESSON 1.1

Use a Problem Solving Plan

Georgia Performance Standards: MM1P1d, MM1P3a

Goal Use a problem solving plan to solve problems.

Vocabulary

A **formula** is an equation that relates two or more quantities.

A Problem Solving Plan

STEP 1 **Read and Understand** Read the problem carefully. Identify what you know and what you want to find out.

STEP 2 **Make a Plan** Decide on the approach to solving the problem.

STEP 3 **Solve the Problem** Carry out your plan. Try a new approach if the first one isn't successful.

STEP 4 **Look Back** Once you obtain your answer, check to see that it is reasonable.

UNIT 1

Example 1 Read a problem and make a plan

A group of people go to a play. Adult tickets cost $8 and tickets for children under twelve years of age cost $5. There are 4 children under twelve. The group spends $44 for all the tickets. How many adults attended the play?

Solution

STEP 1 **Read and Understand**

What do you know?

You know the cost of each ticket, the number of children attending, and the total cost of the tickets.

What do you want to find out?

You want to find the number of adult tickets purchased.

STEP 2 **Make a Plan**

Use what you know to write a verbal model that represents what you want to find out. Then write an equation and solve it.

Guided Practice for Example 1

Identify what you know and what you need to find out. Do *not* solve the problem.

1. A salesman is reimbursed $50 a day for food and lodging. He also receives $.35 for each mile driven. He drives 124 miles and is reimbursed $193.40. How many days was the trip?

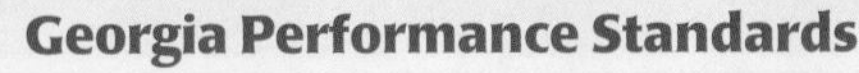

Georgia Performance Standards

MM1P1d Monitor and reflect on the process of mathematical problem solving. ☑

MM1P3a Organize and consolidate their mathematical thinking through communication. ☑

Example 2 Solve a problem and look back

Solve the problem in Example 1 by carrying out the plan. Then check your answer.

Solution

STEP 3 **Solve the Problem** Write a verbal model. Then write an equation. Let a be the number of adult tickets purchased.

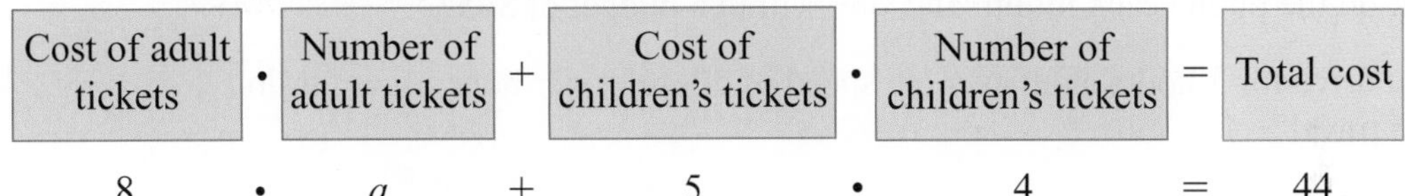

Cost of adult tickets
•
Number of adult tickets
+
Cost of children's tickets
•
Number of children's tickets
=
Total cost

$$8 \cdot a + 5 \cdot 4 = 44$$

The equation is $8a + 20 = 44$. One way to solve the equation is to use the strategy *guess*, *check* and *revise*.

Guess a number that seems reasonable considering the total cost of $44. Try 2.

$8a + 20 = 44$	Write equation.
$8(2) + 20 \stackrel{?}{=} 44$	Substitute 2 for a.
$36 \neq 44$ ✗	Simplify; 2 does not check.

Because $36 < 44$, try a larger number. Try 3.

$8a + 20 = 44$	Write equation.
$8(3) + 20 \stackrel{?}{=} 44$	Substitute 3 for a.
$44 = 44$ ✓	Simplify.

The group bought 3 adult tickets.

STEP 4 **Look Back** Each adult ticket purchase adds $8 to the total ticket cost. Make a table.

Number of adults	0	1	2	3	4
Total cost	$20	$28	$36	$44	$52

The total cost is $44 when 3 adult tickets are purchased. The answer in Step 3 is correct.

Guided Practice for Example 2

Use a problem solving plan to solve the problem.

2. You have saved $165 to buy a video camera that costs $300. You plan to save $15 each week. How many weeks will it take to save for the video camera?

UNIT 1

LESSON 1.1

Exercise Set A

MM1P1d Monitor and reflect on the process of mathematical problem solving.

MM1P3a Organize and consolidate their mathematical thinking through communication.

In Exercises 1–3, identify what you know and what you need to find out. You do *not* need to solve the problem.

1. You are making blueberry muffins for a bake sale and need to make enough muffins to fill 24 boxes of 6 muffins each. How many dozen muffins do you need to make?

2. The cellular phone plan you signed up for gives you 400 minutes a month for \$35 and charges \$.15 for each additional minute over 400 minutes. How long can you talk on the phone each month and stay within a budget of \$45?

3. You drive for 3 hours at an average speed of 50 miles per hour. How far do you travel?

In Exercises 4 and 5, state the formula that is needed to solve the problem. You do *not* need to solve the problem.

4. You invest \$200 into a savings account that earns 2% simple annual interest. How long will it take to earn \$50 in interest?

5. It takes you half an hour to travel 26 miles to work. What is your average speed?

6. **Sticker Collection** Your sticker collection consists of 175 stickers. Each sticker is either an animated cartoon character or an animal. There are 43 less stickers that are animated characters than stickers that are animals. Let x be the number of stickers that are animals. Which equation correctly models this situation?

   A. $x - 43 = 175$ **B.** $x + (x + 43) = 175$ **C.** $x + (x - 43) = 175$

7. **Candles** You sell candles for \$1 each. It costs you \$.60 to make each candle. What is your profit if you sell 200 candles?

8. **Bookshelf** You installed a bookshelf on the wall to organize some of your books. The books that you absolutely want on the shelf weigh a total of $6\frac{3}{4}$ pounds. The bookshelf can handle no more than 9 pounds. You plan on filling the rest of the shelf with your paperbacks that each weigh about $\frac{1}{8}$ pound. Assuming you won't run out of room, how many paperback books can you add to the shelf?

9. **Camping** You are responsible for buying supplies for an upcoming camping trip. You can buy packages of stew that just need water added and then are heated. Each package costs \$4.95 and contains enough stew for 2 people. You need to buy enough packages so that you can have stew for 3 days of the trip. There will be 8 people on the trip. How many packages do you need? What is the total cost?

10. **Banking** You are going to open a certificate of deposit (CD) that earns simple interest. One CD earns 2% annual interest on a \$500 deposit for 3 years. Another CD earns 3% annual interest on a \$250 deposit for 4 years. Which CD will earn more interest?

UNIT 1

LESSON 1.1

Exercise Set B

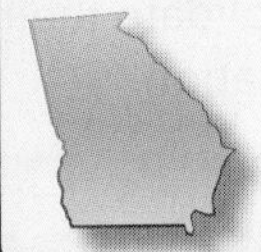

MM1P1d Monitor and reflect on the process of mathematical problem solving.

MM1P3a Organize and consolidate their mathematical thinking through communication.

1. **Stamp Collection** Your stamp collection consists of 145 stamps. Each stamp has either a cancellation mark or no cancellation mark. There are 93 more stamps with cancellation marks than stamps without cancellation marks. Let x be the number of stamps with cancellation marks. Which equation correctly models this situation?

   A. $x + 93 = 145$ **B.** $x + (x + 93) = 145$ **C.** $x + (x - 93) = 145$

In Exercises 2–4, write an equation that you can use to solve the problem. You do *not* need to solve the problem.

2. Your soccer team has raised \$400 for cleats and shin guards. It will cost \$41.50 for each of the 15 players to have a pair of cleats and shin guards. How much more money will each player have to pay to cover the cost?

3. You are putting tile on part of the walls in your kitchen. You use both plain and decorative tiles. You need to use a total of 500 tiles and you want to use three times as many plain tiles as decorative tiles. How many of each kind of tile will you need?

4. You buy 8 gifts. Some of the gifts are CDs for \$12 each and the others are DVDs for \$20 each. How many CDs do you buy if you spend a total of \$136?

In Exercises 5 and 6, write the formula that is needed to solve the problem and identify the values of the variables that are given. You do *not* need to solve the problem.

5. You are traveling 250 miles to your friend's house. It takes you 5 hours to get there. What was your average speed?

6. The savings account in which you initially invested \$250 has earned \$30 simple annual interest in 5 years. What is the annual interest rate of the account?

7. **Garden** You are putting fence around a rectangular garden whose length is twice its width. You use 90 feet of fencing. What are the dimensions of the garden?

8. **Party** You are responsible for buying the frozen lasagna for an upcoming birthday party. Each package of lasagna costs \$7.99 and serves 8. You need to buy enough packages so that each person can have two servings. There will be 17 people at the party. How many packages do you need? What is the total cost for the lasagna?

9. **Temperature** Last year, the low temperature in your town was 32°F. The high temperature for the year was 3 times this temperature. What were last year's high and low temperatures in degrees Celsius? Round your answers to the nearest tenth.

10. **Painting** You and your friend are painting a 150-foot long fence. You start at opposite ends at the same time and paint towards each other. You paint the fence at a rate of 1.75 feet per minute and your friend paints at a rate of 1.25 feet per minute.

    a. How long will it take both of you to complete the fence?

    b. How far from your beginning point will each of you be?

Georgia Performance Standards

MM1P1d	Monitor and reflect on the process of mathematical problem solving.	
MM1P3a	Organize and consolidate their mathematical thinking through communication.	

LESSON 1.1

Problem Solving Workshop

Problem You have saved \$95 to go on a school trip that costs \$275. You plan to save \$15 each week. How many weeks will it take you to save for the trip?

STEP 1 **Read and Understand**

What do you know? You know the school trip costs \$275, you have saved \$95, and you plan to save \$15 each week.

What do you want to find out? You want to find out the number of weeks it will take you to save \$275.

STEP 2 **Make a Plan** Use what you know to write a verbal model that represents what you want to find out. Then write an equation and solve it.

STEP 3 **Solve the Problem** Write a verbal model. Then write an equation. Let w be the number of weeks you save.

Money saved (dollars)	+	Money saved per week (dollars)	•	Number of weeks	=	Total cost of trip (dollars)
95	+	15	•	w	=	275

The equation is $95 + 15w = 275$. Solve the equation.

$95 + 15w = 275$ Write equation.

$15w = 180$ Subtract 95 from each side.

$w = 12$ Divide each side by 15.

It will take 12 weeks to save for the school trip.

STEP 4 **Look Back** Each two additional weeks you save add \$30 to the \$95 you have saved. Make a table.

Weeks	0	2	4	6	8	10	12
Total Saved	\$95	\$125	\$155	\$185	\$215	\$245	\$275

The total saved is \$275 when you have \$95 saved and you save \$15 per week for 12 weeks. The answer in Step 3 is correct.

Practice

1. **Television** Anne is saving money for a television that costs \$180. She makes \$8 an hour baby-sitting, and her parents will contribute \$60. How many hours does she need to baby-sit to buy the television?
2. **Aquarium** It takes 28 trips to fill a 14-gallon aquarium with a pitcher. How many trips with the same pitcher will you need to fill a 32-gallon aquarium?
3. **Piano** You practice piano for 1.5 hours each weekday and for 2.5 hours on each weekend day. How many hours per week do you practice?
4. **Lasagna** You are making lasagna for 25 people at a dinner. It takes 8 ounces of mozzarella cheese to make enough to serve 10 people. You have 12 ounces of mozzarella cheese. How many more ounces do you need?

LESSON 1.2

Represent Functions as Rules and Tables

Georgia Performance Standards: MM1A1d

Goal Represent functions as rules and as tables.

Vocabulary

A **function** consists of:

- A set called the **domain** containing numbers called **inputs,** and a set called the **range** containing numbers called **outputs.**
- A pairing of inputs with outputs such that each input is paired with exactly one output.

The input variable is called an **independent variable.**

The output variable is called the **dependent variable** because its value depends on the value of the input variable.

Example 1 Identify the domain and range of a function

The input-output table shows the price of various lobsters at a fish market. Identify the domain and range of the function.

Input (pounds)	1.5	2.3	3.1	4.2
Output (dollars)	\$7.80	\$11.96	\$16.12	\$21.82

Solution

The domain is the set of inputs: 1.5, 2.3, 3.1, and 4.2.

The range is the set of outputs: 7.80, 11.96, 16.12, and 21.82.

Guided Practice for Example 1

Identify the domain and range of the function.

1.

Input	2	5	7	8
Output	5	11	15	17

2.

Input	1	3	4	7
Output	2	8	11	20

3.

Input	3	5	9	11
Output	8	10	16	24

Georgia Performance Standards

MM1A1d Investigate and explain the characteristics of a function: domain, range, zeros, intercepts, intervals of increase and decrease, maximum and minimum values, and end behavior.

Example 2 Make a table for a function

The domain of the function $y = x - 3$ is 2, 5, 8, and 11. Make a table for the function, then identify the range of the function.

Solution

x	2	5	8	11
$y = x - 3$	$2 - 3 = -1$	$5 - 3 = 2$	$8 - 3 = 5$	$11 - 3 = 8$

The range of the function is -1, 2, 5, and 8.

Guided Practice for Example 2

Make a table for the function. Identify the range of the function.

4. $y = 4x$

Domain: 0, 3, 5, and 7

5. $y = 3x - 2$

Domain: 1, 2, 3, and 4

UNIT 1

Example 3 Write a function rule

Write a rule for the function.

Input	3	6	7	10
Output	15	30	35	50

Solution

Let x be the input, or independent variable, and let y be the output, or dependent variable. Notice that each output is 5 times the corresponding input. So, a rule for the function is $y = 5x$.

Guided Practice for Example 3

Write a rule for the function.

6.

Input	3	5	7	9
Output	14	16	18	20

7.

Input	6	7	8	9
Output	3	3.5	4	4.5

LESSON 1.2

Exercise Set A

MM1A1d Investigate and explain the characteristics of a function: domain, range, zeros, intercepts, intervals of increase and decrease, maximum and minimum values, and end behavior.

Copy and complete the sentence.

1. The input variable is called the __?__ variable.
2. The output variable is called the __?__ variable.

Tell whether the pairing is a function.

3.

Input	Output
1	15
3	20
5	15
7	20

4.

Input	Output
5	5
6	5
7	5
8	5

5.

Input	Output
6	3
12	4
12	1
18	2

Make a table for the function. Identify the range of the function.

6. $y = 4x - 2$

   Domain: 1, 2, 3, 4

7. $y = 0.1x + 3$

   Domain: 10, 20, 30, 40

8. $y = \frac{1}{2}x + 2$

   Domain: 6, 7, 8, 9

Write a rule for the function.

9.

Input, *x*	1	2	3	4
Output, *y*	5	10	15	20

10.

Input, *x*	10	11	12	13
Output, *y*	3	4	5	6

11. **Shoe Sizes** The table shows men's shoe sizes in the United States and Australia. Write a rule for the Australian size as a function of the United States' size.

U.S. size	5	6	7	8	9	10
Australian size	3	4	5	6	7	8

12. **Balloon Bunches** You are making balloon bunches to attach to tables for a charity event. You plan on using 8 balloons in each bunch. Write a rule for the total number of balloons used as a function of the number of bunches created. Identify the independent and dependent variables. How many balloons will you use if you make 10 bunches?

13. **Baking** A baker has baked 10 loaves of bread so far today and plans on baking 3 loaves more each hour for the rest of his shift. Write a rule for the total number of loaves baked as a function of the number of hours left in the baker's shift. Identify the independent and dependent variables. How many loaves will the baker make if he has 4 hours left in his shift?

LESSON 1.2

Exercise Set B

MM1A1d Investigate and explain the characteristics of a function: domain, range, zeros, intercepts, intervals of increase and decrease, maximum and minimum values, and end behavior.

Tell whether the pairing is a function.

1.

Input	Output
0.2	1.5
0.4	1.25
0.6	1.5
0.8	1.25

2.

Input	Output
5.1	4.3
5.2	4.3
5.3	4.2
5.4	4.1

3.

Input	Output
25	14
30	13
30	12
35	11

4. Error Analysis *Describe* and correct the error related to the pairing represented by the table.

Input, x	1	3	1	-3
Output, y	-1	4	1	5

The pairing is a function.

The range is -1, 4, 1, and 5.

Make a table for the function. Identify the range of the function.

5. $y = \frac{1}{3}x - 4$

Domain: 12, 15, 18, 21

6. $y = \frac{1}{4}x + \frac{3}{4}$

Domain: 1, 3, 5, 7

7. $y = \frac{0.1x + 2}{3}$

Domain: 10, 20, 30, 40

Write a rule for the function.

8.

Input, x	0	1	2	3
Output, y	3	5	7	9

9.

Input, x	16	14	12	10
Output, y	7	6	5	4

10. Shoe Sizes The table shows men's shoe sizes in the United States and Europe. Write a rule for the European size as a function of the United States' size. Then use your function to predict the European size of a U.S. size 11 shoe.

U.S. size	3.5	4	4.5	5	5.5	6
European size	35	35.5	36	36.5	37	37.5

11. Sandwich Rings A delicatessen worker has created 8 large sandwich rings in the first 2 hours of her shift. She plans on making sandwich rings at the same rate for the rest of her shift. Write a rule for the total number of sandwich rings made as a function of the number of hours left in the deli worker's shift. How many sandwich rings will the deli worker make if she has 6 hours left in her shift?

LESSON 1.3

Represent Functions as Graphs

Georgia Performance Standards: MM1A1d

Goal Represent functions as graphs.

Example 1 Graph a function

Graph the function $y = 3x$ with domain 0, 1, 2, 3, and 4.

Solution

STEP 1 **Make** an input-output table.

x	0	1	2	3	4
y	0	3	6	9	12

STEP 2 **Plot** a point for each ordered pair (x, y).

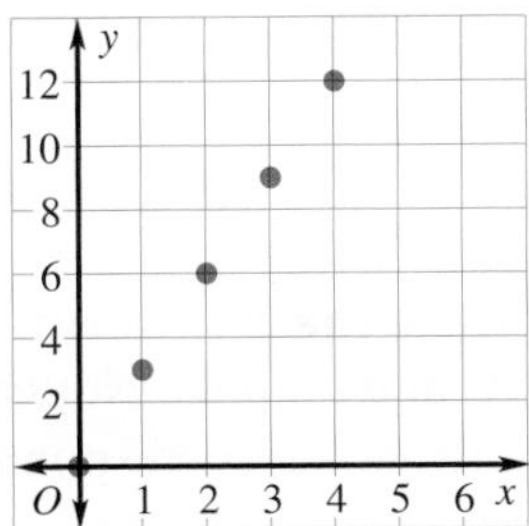

Guided Practice for Example 1

Graph the function.

1. $y = \frac{1}{2}x + 3$

Domain: 0, 2, 4, 6, and 8

2. $y = 4x - 4$

Domain: 1, 2, 3, 4, and 5

3. $y = -\frac{3}{4}x + 6$

Domain: 0, 4, 8, 12, and 16

4. $y = -2x + 7$

Domain: 1, 2, 3, 4, and 5

5. $y = \frac{1}{3}x - 3$

Domain: 0, 3, 6, 9, and 12

Georgia Performance Standards

MM1A1d Investigate and explain the characteristics of a function: domain, range, zeros, intercepts, intervals of increase and decrease, maximum and minimum values, and end behavior. 

Example 2 Write a function rule for a graph

Write a rule for the function represented by the graph. Identify the domain and the range of the function.

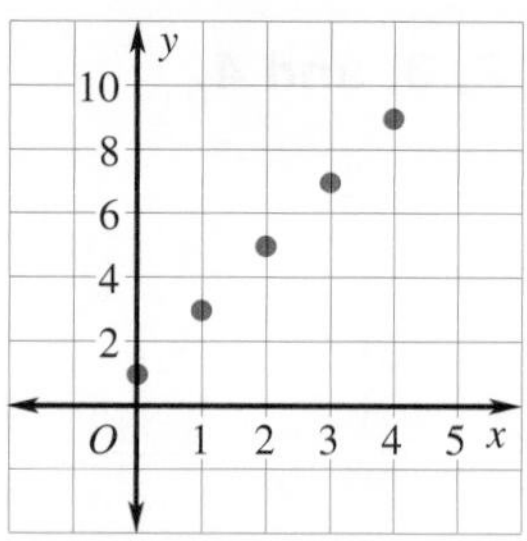

Solution

STEP 1 **Make** a table for the graph.

x	0	1	2	3	4
y	1	3	5	7	9

STEP 2 **Find** a relationship between the inputs and outputs. Notice from the table that each output value is 1 more than twice the corresponding input value.

STEP 3 **Write** a function rule that describes the relationship: $y = 2x + 1$.

A rule for the function is $y = 2x + 1$. The domain of the function is 0, 1, 2, 3, and 4. The range is 1, 3, 5, 7, and 9.

Guided Practice for Example 2

Write a rule for the function represented by the graph. Identify the domain and the range of the function.

6. 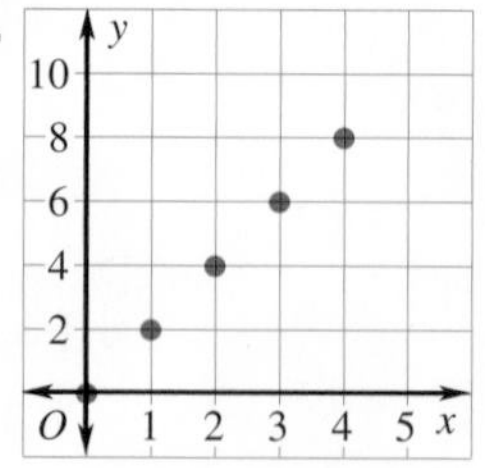

7. 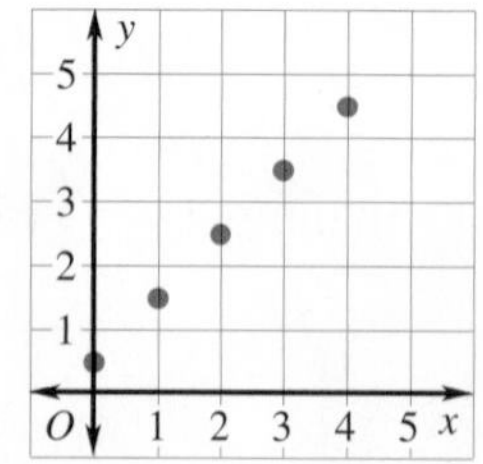

8. 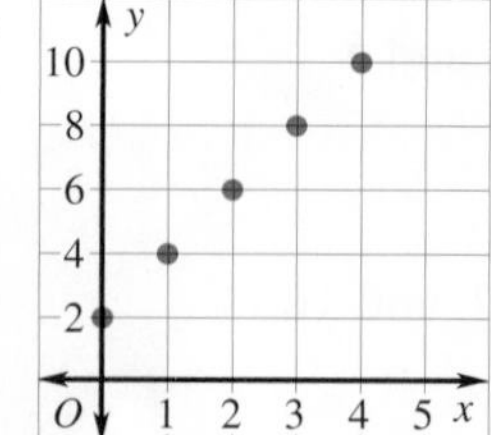

9. 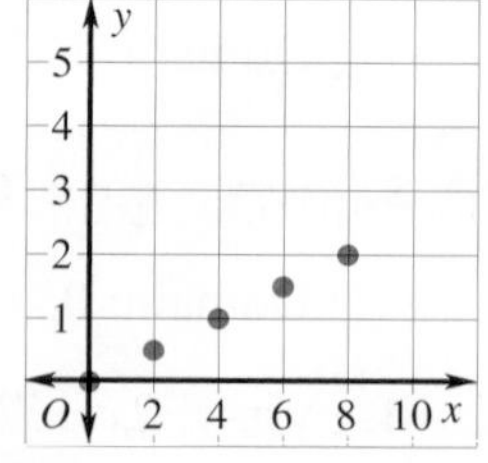

LESSON 1.3 **Exercise Set A**

MM1A1d Investigate and explain the characteristics of a function: domain, range, zeros, intercepts, intervals of increase and decrease, maximum and minimum values, and end behavior.

Write the ordered pairs that can be formed from the table.

1.

Input	Output
0	3
1	5
2	7
3	9
4	11

2.

Input	Output
2	4
4	7
6	10
8	13
10	16

3.

Input	Output
3	2
6	2
9	4
12	4
15	6

Identify the ordered pairs in the graph. Then identify the domain and range.

4.

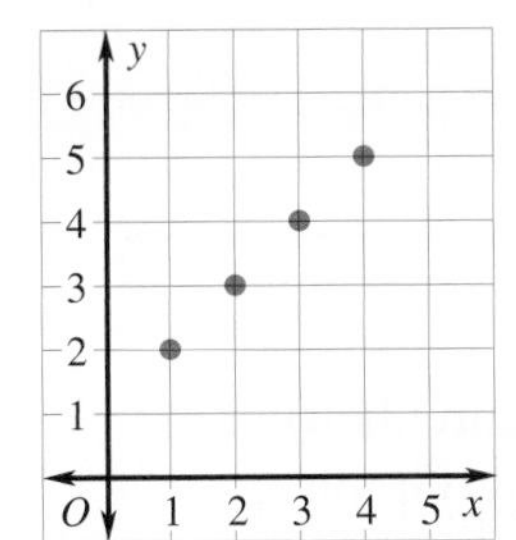

5.

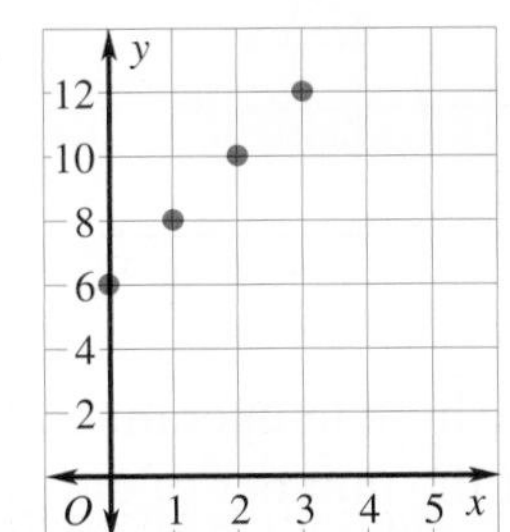

6.

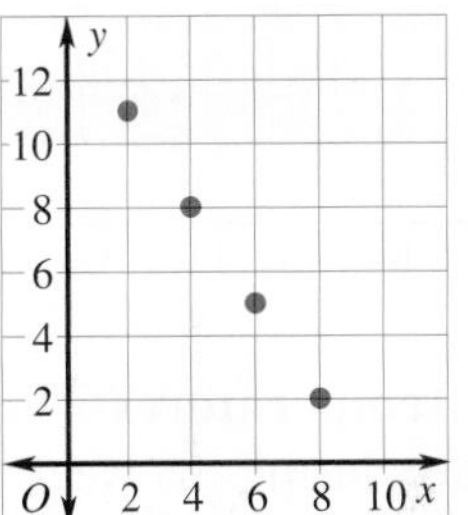

Make an input-output table for the function.

7. $y = 3x + 2$

Domain: 0, 1, 2, 3

8. $y = 4x - 1$

Domain: 1, 2, 3, 4

Graph the ordered pairs.

9. (3, 4), (4, 7), (5, 10), (6, 13), (7, 16)

10. (2, 5), (6, 7), (4, 6), (12, 10), (10, 9)

Graph the function.

11. $y = 6 - x$

Domain: 6, 5, 4, 3, 2

12. $y = \frac{1}{3}x$

Domain: 6, 9, 12, 15, 18

13. $y = 4x - 3$

Domain: 1, 2, 3, 4, 5

14. $y = 1.2x$

Domain: 1, 2, 3, 4, 5

Exercise Set A *(continued)*

Write a rule for the function represented by the graph. Identify the domain and range of the function.

15.

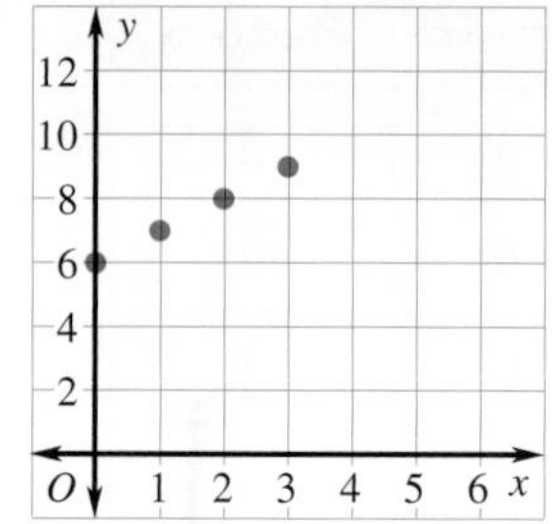

16.

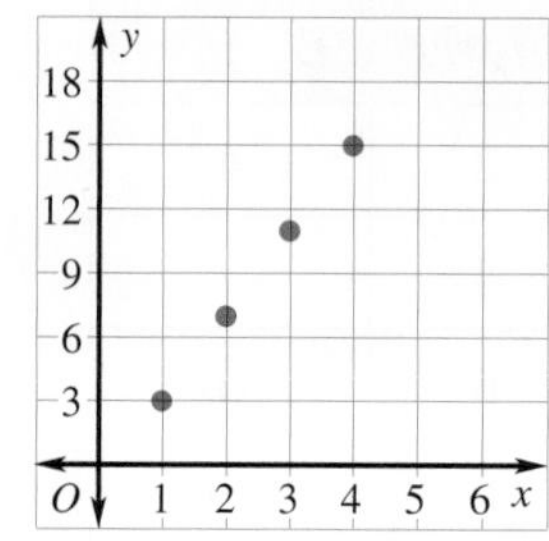

17.

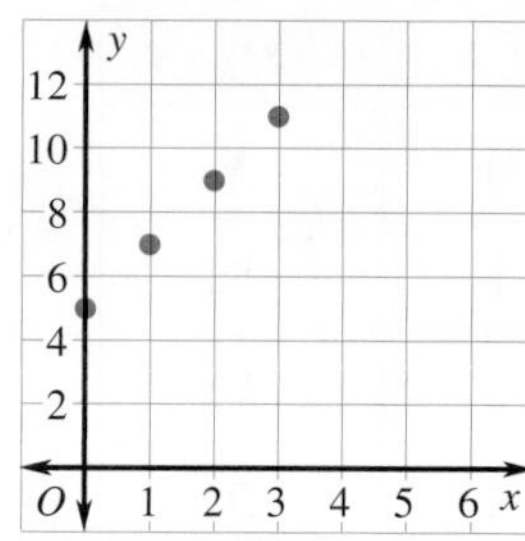

18.

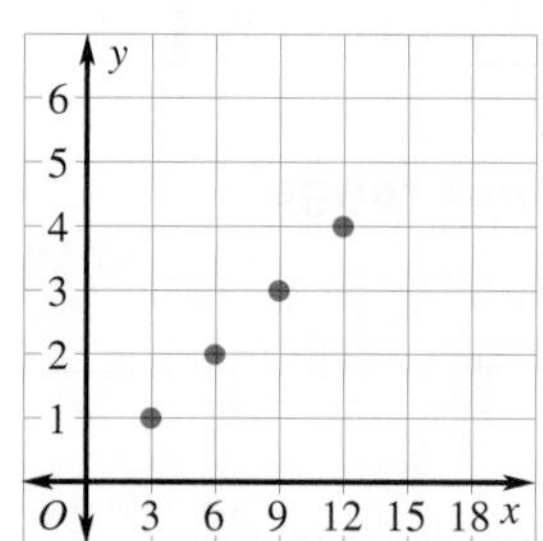

19.

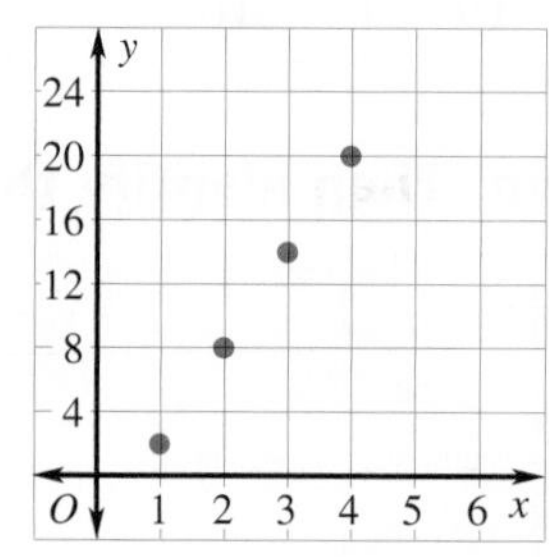

20.

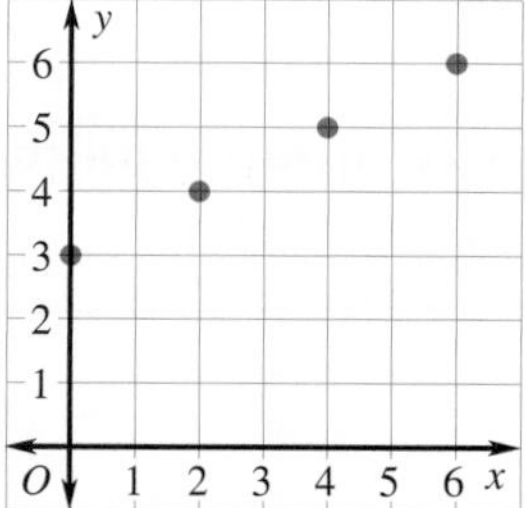

21. High Temperatures The table shows the high temperature H (in degrees Fahrenheit) in a city during the week as a function of the number of days d since Monday. Graph the function. *Describe* how the high temperatures change as the week progresses.

Number of days since Monday, *d*	0	1	2	3	4	5
High temperature (degrees Fahrenheit), *H*	24	34	41	39	37	39

22. Metal Screws The table shows the number of threads per inch on a screw as a function of screw size.

Screw size number, *x*	0	1	2	3	4	5	6
Number of threads per inch, *y*	80	72	64	56	48	44	40

a. Graph the function.

b. *Describe* how the number of threads per inch changes as the screw size increases.

c. Would it be reasonable to expect a #8 screw to have 32 threads per inch? *Explain.*

LESSON 1.3

Exercise Set B

MM1A1d Investigate and explain the characteristics of a function: domain, range, zeros, intercepts, intervals of increase and decrease, maximum and minimum values, and end behavior.

Write the ordered pairs that can be formed from the table.

1.

Input	Output
4	8
6	12
8	16
10	20
12	24

2.

Input	Output
−2	−7
7	0
9	2
13	6
19	12

3.

Input	Output
−3	−15
3	−9
9	−3
15	3
21	9

Identify the ordered pairs in the graph. Then identify the domain and range.

4.

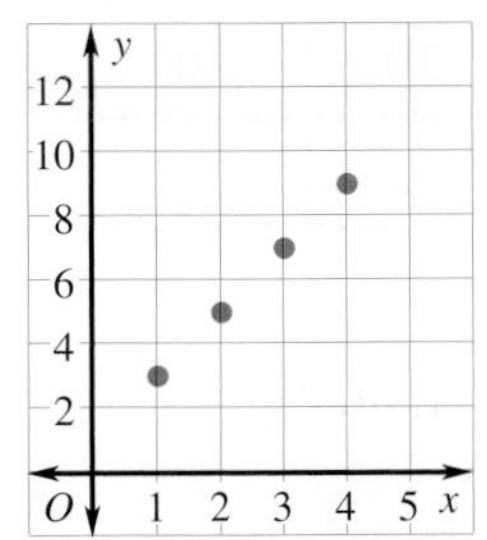

5.

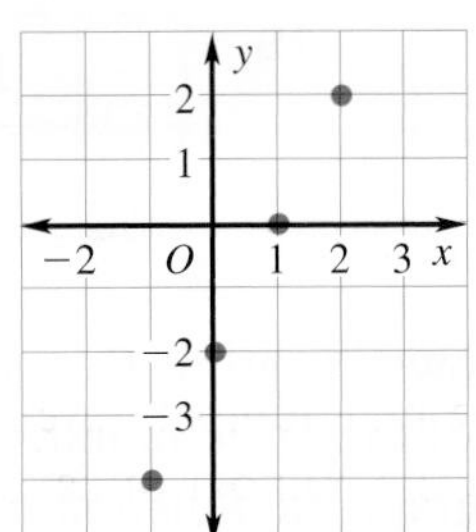

6.

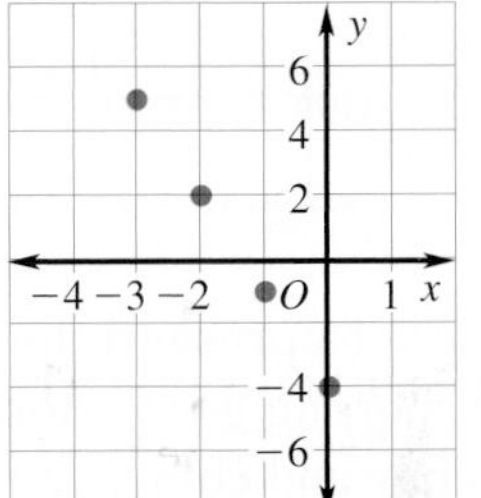

Make an input-output table for the function.

7. $y = \frac{2}{3}x - 4$

Domain: 6, 9, 12, 15

8. $y = 8 - 3x$

Domain: −1, 0, 1, 2

Graph the ordered pairs.

9. (1, 2.5), (3, 4), (5, 6.5), (7, 8), (9, 10.5)

10. (0.25, 1), (0.5, 4), (0.75, 7), (1, 10)

Graph the function.

11. $y = 8x + 1$

Domain: 0.5, 1, 1.5, 2, 2.5

12. $y = \frac{1}{2}x - 3$

Domain: 6, 7, 8, 9, 10

13. $y = 10 - 2x$

Domain: 1, 2, 3, 4, 5

14. $y = 4.5x + 2$

Domain: 1, 2, 3, 4, 5

UNIT 1

Exercise Set B *(continued)*

Write a rule for the function represented by the graph. Identify the domain and range of the function.

15. 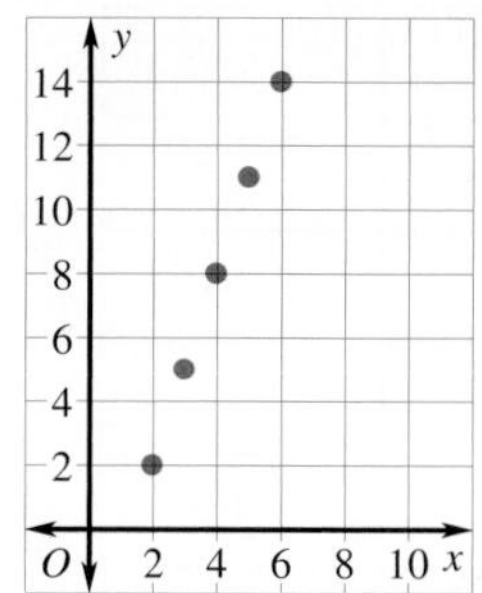

16. 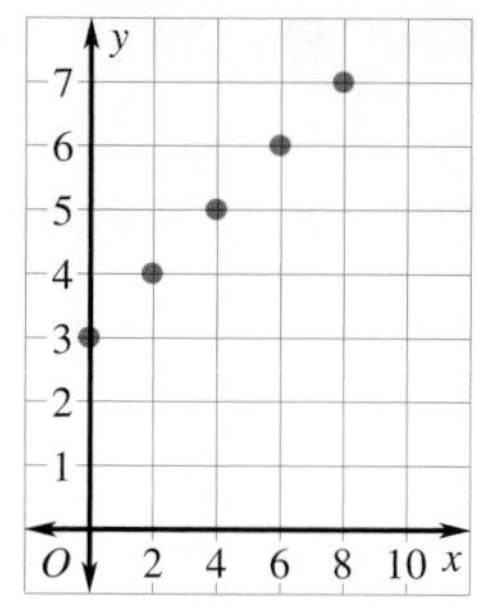

17. 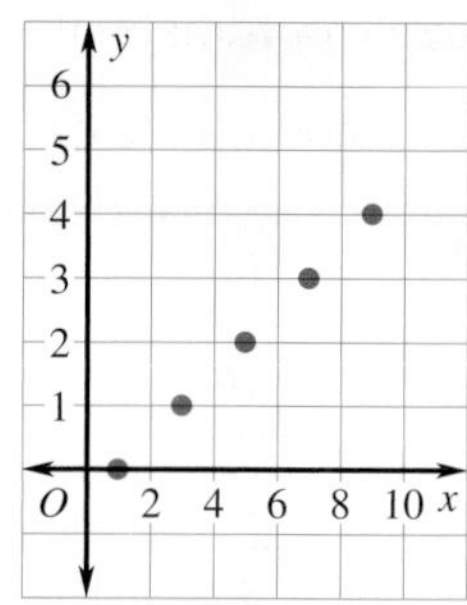

Write a rule for the function represented by the table. Identify the domain and range of the function.

18.

x	0	1	2	3
y	0	4	8	12

19.

x	10	20	30	40
y	1	2	3	4

20. Multiple Representations The table shows the profit P (in dollars) of a small sporting goods store as a function of time t (in months) since January. First copy and complete the table. Then graph the function represented by the first and third rows.

Months since January, t	1	2	3	4	5	6
Profit (dollars), P	3200	2500	2800	3000	4100	7400
Profit (thousands of dollars), P	?	?	?	?	?	?

21. Wind Chill Temperatures The table shows the wind chill temperature w (in degrees Fahrenheit), or how cold it feels to you depending on the wind speed, as a function of the actual temperature t (in degrees Fahrenheit).

Actual temperature (°F), t	40	35	30	25	20
Wind chill temperature (°F) for 10mi/h wind, w	34	27	21	15	9

a. Graph the function represented by the table.

b. *Describe* how the wind chill temperature changes as the actual temperature decreases.

LESSON 1.4

Graph Using Intercepts

Georgia Performance Standards: MM1A1b, MM1A1d

Goal Graph a linear equation using intercepts.

Vocabulary

The x-coordinate of a point where a graph crosses the x-axis is an ***x*-intercept.**

The y-coordinate of a point where a graph crosses the y-axis is a ***y*-intercept.**

Example 1 Find the intercepts of a graph of an equation

Find the *x*-intercept and the *y*-intercept of the graph of $7x - 3y = 21$.

Solution

To find the x-intercept, substitute 0 for y and solve for x.

$7x - 3y = 21$ Write original equation.

$7x - 3(0) = 21$ Substitute 0 for y.

$x = \frac{21}{7} = 3$ Solve for x.

To find the y-intercept, substitute 0 for x and solve for y.

$7x - 3y = 21$ Write original equation.

$7(0) - 3y = 21$ Substitute 0 for x.

$y = \frac{21}{-3} = -7$ Solve for y.

The x-intercept is 3. The y-intercept is -7.

Example 2 Use a graph to find the intercepts

Identify the *x*-intercept and *y*-intercept of the graph.

Solution

To find the x-intercept, look to see where the graph crosses the x-axis. The x-intercept is -2. To find the y-intercept, look to see where the graph crosses the y-axis. The y-intercept is 1.

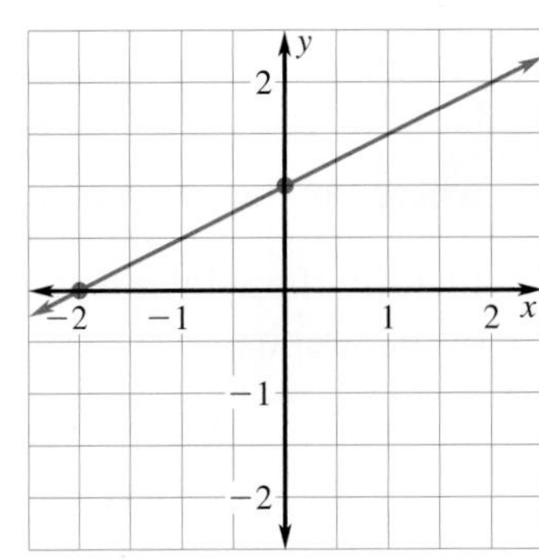

UNIT 1

Georgia Performance Standards

MM1A1b Graph the basic functions $f(x) = x^n$, where $n = 1$ to 3, $f(x) = \sqrt{x}$, $f(x) = |x|$, and $f(x) = \frac{1}{x}$.

MM1A1d Investigate and explain the characteristics of a function: domain, range, zeros, intercepts, intervals of increase and decrease, maximum and minimum values, and end behavior.

Example 3 Use intercepts to graph an equation

Graph $3x + 2y = 6$. Label the points where the line crosses the axes.

Solution

STEP 1 **Find** the intercepts.

$3x + 2y = 6$	$3x + 2y = 6$
$3x + 2(0) = 6$	$3(0) + 2y = 6$
$x = 2$ ← x-intercept	$y = 3$ ← y-intercept

STEP 2 **Plot** the points that correspond to the intercepts. The x-intercept is 2, so plot and label the point (2, 0). The y-intercept is 3, so plot and label the point (0, 3).

STEP 3 **Connect** the points by drawing a line through them.

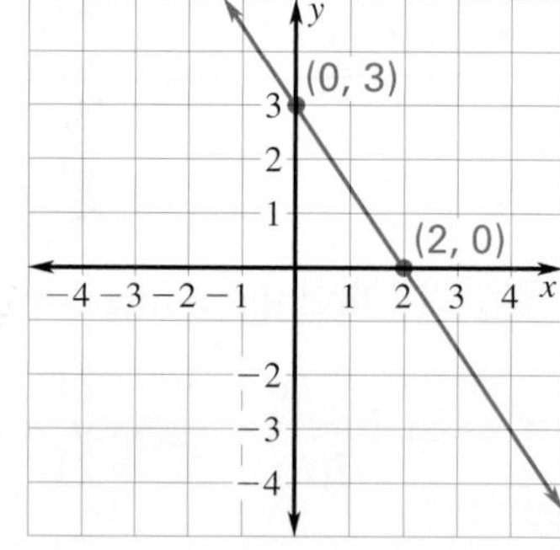

CHECK You can check the graph of the equation by using a third point. When $x = 4$, $y = -3$, so the ordered pair $(4, -3)$ is a third solution of the equation. You can see that $(4, -3)$ lies on the graph, so the graph is correct.

Guided Practice for Examples 1, 2, and 3

Find the x-intercept and the y-intercept of the graph of the equation.

1. $-4x + 3y = 24$ **2.** $5x - y = 15$ **3.** $y = \frac{1}{5}x - 3$

4. Graph $x - \frac{1}{2}y = 1$. Label the points where the line crosses the axes.

5. Identify the x-intercept and y-intercept of the graph.

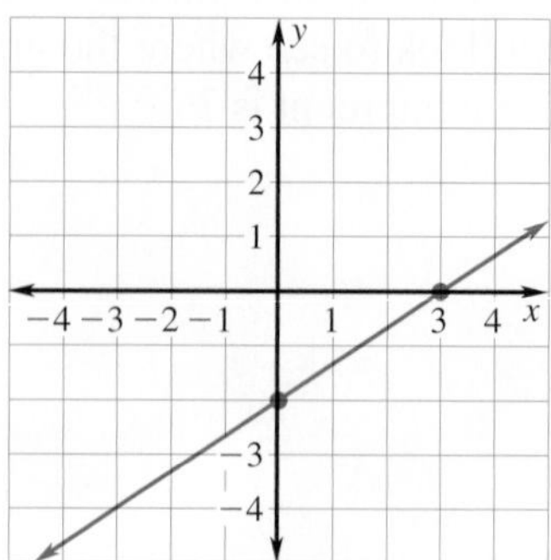

LESSON 1.4 **Exercise Set A**

MM1A1b Graph the basic functions $f(x) = x^n$, where $n = 1$ to 3, $f(x) = \sqrt{x}$, $f(x) = |x|$, and $f(x) = \frac{1}{x}$.

MM1A1d Investigate and explain the characteristics of a function: domain, range, zeros, intercepts, intervals of increase and decrease, maximum and minimum values, and end behavior.

Identify the *x*-intercept and the *y*-intercept of the graph.

1. 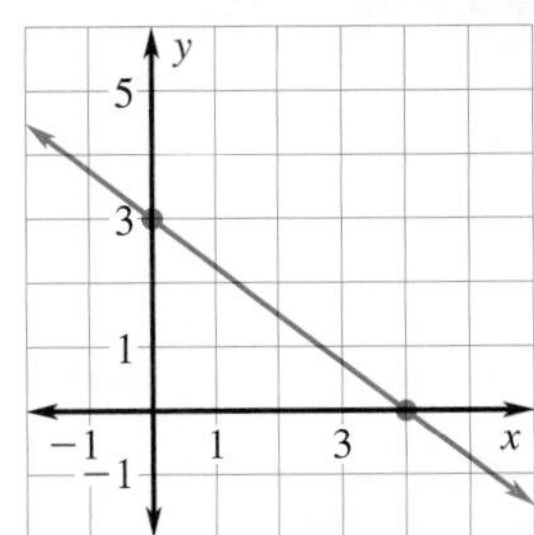

2. 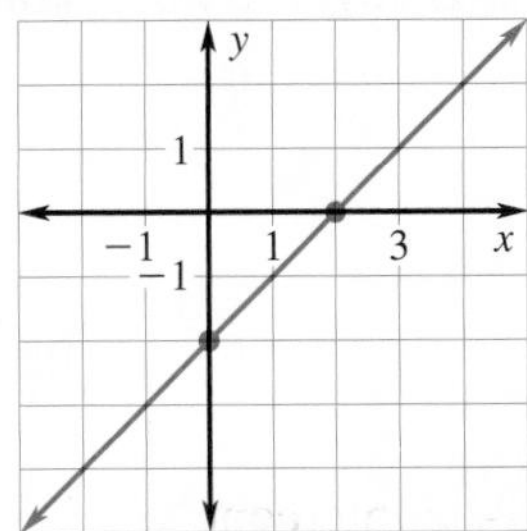

3. 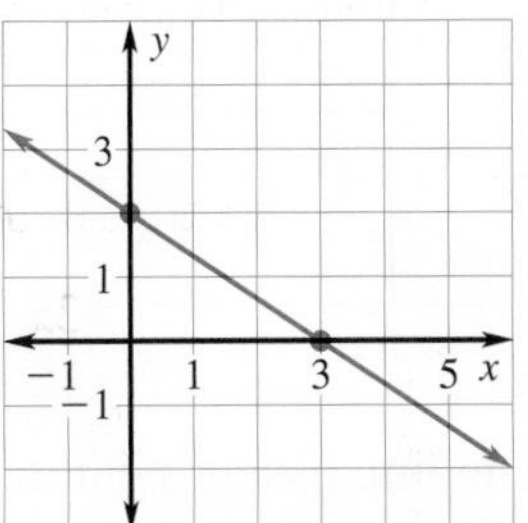

Find the *x*-intercept and the *y*-intercept of the graph of the equation.

4. $x + y = 1$

5. $x - y = -5$

6. $6x - 3y = -3$

7. $5x + 10y = 30$

8. $9y - 5x = 20$

9. $8x - 2y = 16$

10. $7x + 8y = 18$

11. $2y - 12x = -6$

12. $2x - 0.5y = 8$

Draw the line that has the given intercepts.

13. *x*-intercept: 5
y-intercept: 4

14. *x*-intercept: -1
y-intercept: 6

15. *x*-intercept: 2
y-intercept: -3

Graph the equation. Label the points where the line crosses the axes.

16. $y = -x - 4$

17. $y = 6 + 3x$

18. $y = 8x - 7$

19. $y = 1 - 3x$

20. $7x - 7y = 42$

21. $3y + 2x = -5$

22. $4x - 9y = 16$

23. $y = 0.5x - 2$

24. $y = x$

Match the equation with its intercepts.

25. $7y = 28 - 4x$

26. $7x = 4y + 28$

27. $4y = 7x + 28$

A. *x*-intercept: 4
y-intercept: -7

B. *x*-intercept: -4
y-intercept: 7

C. *x*-intercept: 7
y-intercept: 4

UNIT 1

Exercise Set A *(continued)*

28. **Error Analysis** *Describe* and correct the error in finding the intercepts of the line shown.

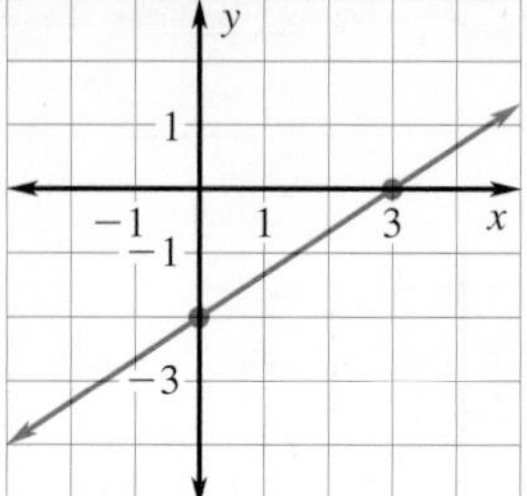

The line has an x-intercept of -2 and a y-intercept of 3.

29. **Rabbit Hutch** The cage that you keep your rabbit in has a perimeter of 118 inches. Let x be the cage's width (in inches) and let y be its length (in inches).

a. Write an equation for the perimeter.

b. Find the intercepts of the graph of the equation you wrote. Then graph the equation.

30. **Home and Garden Show** Admission to a home and garden show costs \$7 per person during the week and \$9 per person on the weekend. During one week of the show, a total of \$142,506 was paid in admissions. This situation can be represented by the equation $7x + 9y = 142{,}506$ where x is the number of tickets sold during the week and y is the number of tickets sold on the weekend.

a. Find the intercepts of the graph of the equation. Graph the equation.

b. Give three possibilities for the number of each kind of ticket that could have been sold for the week.

31. **Multiple Representations** A man burns 10 calories per minute mountain biking and 7.5 calories per minute in-line skating. His goal is to burn approximately 420 calories daily. This situation can be represented by the equation $10x + 7.5y = 420$ where x is the number of minutes spent mountain biking and y is the number of minutes spent in-line skating.

a. **Graphing an Equation** Find the intercepts of the graph of the equation. Graph the equation.

b. **Interpreting Intercepts** What do the intercepts mean in this situation?

c. **Finding Solutions** What are three possible numbers of minutes of biking and skating the man could do to reach his goal?

LESSON 1.4 **Exercise Set B**

MM1A1b Graph the basic functions $f(x) = x^n$, where $n = 1$ to 3, $f(x) = \sqrt{x}$, $f(x) = |x|$, and $f(x) = \frac{1}{x}$.

MM1A1d Investigate and explain the characteristics of a function: domain, range, zeros, intercepts, intervals of increase and decrease, maximum and minimum values, and end behavior.

Identify the *x*-intercept and the *y*-intercept of the graph.

1.

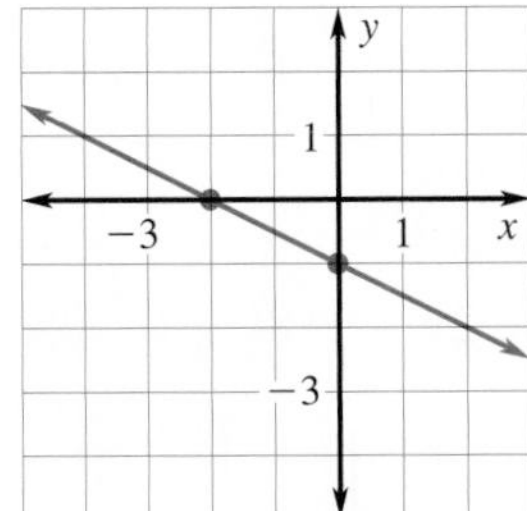

2.

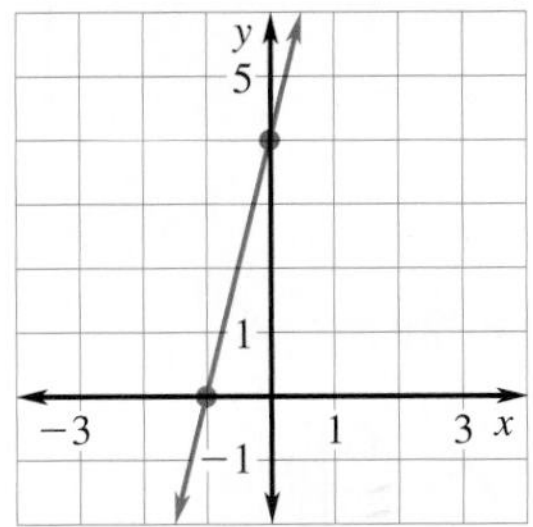

3.

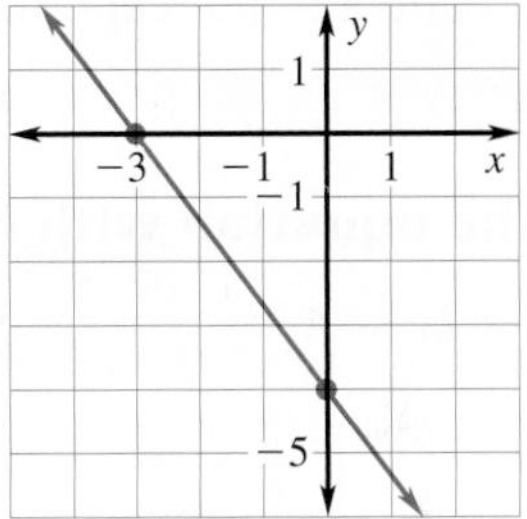

Find the *x*-intercept and the *y*-intercept of the graph of the equation.

4. $6x + 8y = 24$

5. $7x - 5y = -35$

6. $4x - 9y = 18$

7. $0.5x + 4y = -1$

8. $0.2y - 0.3x = 0.6$

9. $y = 7x - 15$

10. $y = -4x + 10$

11. $y = -2.4x - 9$

12. $y = \frac{5}{3}x + 6$

Draw the line that has the given intercepts.

13. *x*-intercept: 10
y-intercept: -1

14. *x*-intercept: -7
y-intercept: 4

15. *x*-intercept: 11
y-intercept: -9

16. *x*-intercept: -3
y-intercept: 3

17. *x*-intercept: 8
y-intercept: -8

18. *x*-intercept: 5
y-intercept: -2

Graph the equation. Label the points where the line crosses the axes.

19. $y = 8 + 2x$

20. $y = 5x - 2$

21. $6y + 3x = 18$

22. $4y - 6x = 48$

23. $10x - 70y = 210$

24. $2y + 9x = -15$

25. $5x - 8y = 36$

26. $y = 0.4x - 1.2$

27. $y = 0.5x + 7$

Exercise Set B *(continued)*

28. **Error Analysis** *Describe* and correct the error in finding the intercepts of the line shown.

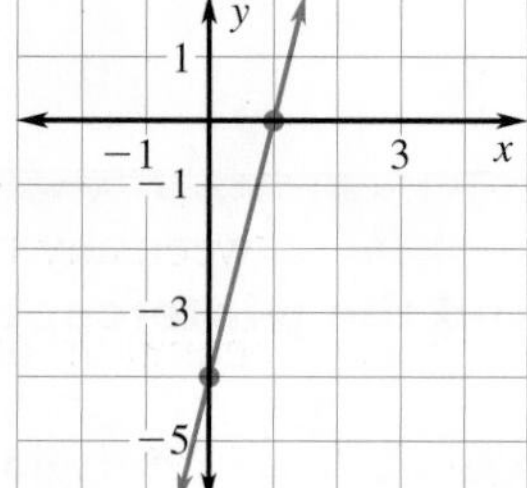

The line has an x-intercept of -4 and a y-intercept of 1.

Match the equation with its graph.

29. $8x - 2y = 4$

30. $8x - 2y = -4$

31. $8x - 2y = -8$

A.

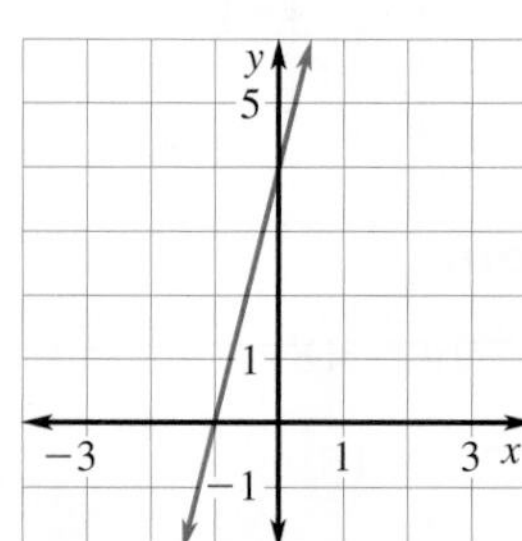

B.

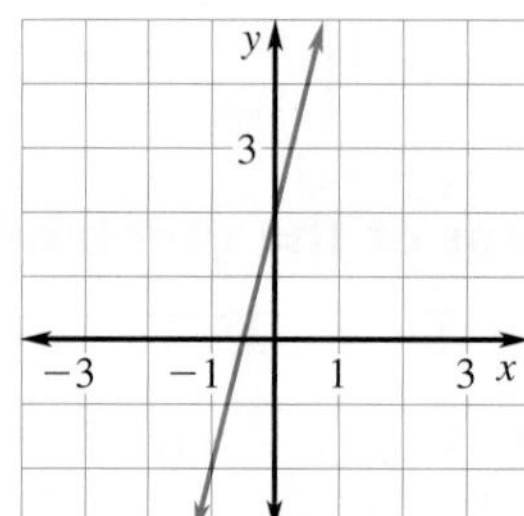

C.

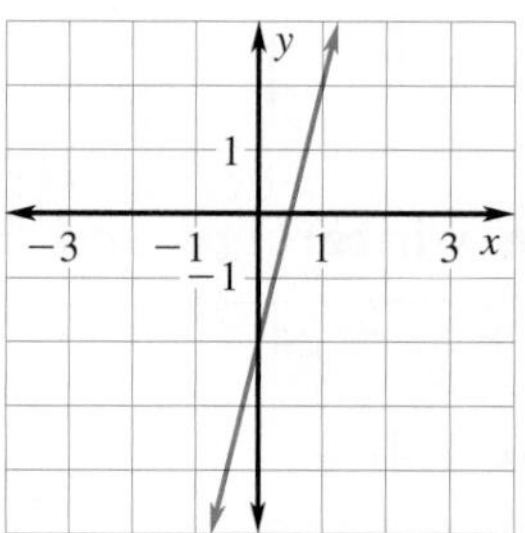

32. **Multiple Representations** You earn \$16 an hour mowing lawns and \$10 an hour washing windows. You want to make \$500 in one week. This situation can be represented by the equation $16x + 10y = 500$ where x is the number of hours you mow lawns and y is the number of hours you wash windows.

a. **Graphing an Equation** Find the intercepts of the graph of the equation. Graph the equation.

b. **Interpreting Intercepts** What do the intercepts mean in this situation?

c. **Finding Solutions** What are three possible numbers of hours you could work at each job?

d. **Calculating a Value** If you work 30 hours washing windows, how many hours do you have to mow lawns?

33. **Fruit Baskets** A small mail-order company that sells fruit baskets currently has 400 orders for fruit baskets. The person who assigns workers to tasks is trying to figure out how many workers need to be assigned to assembling fruit baskets in order to get them out on time. To do this, the person needs to know how many fruit baskets must be produced in one hour. The number B of fruit baskets left to assemble can be modeled by the function $B = 400 - nh$ where n is the number of fruit baskets that can be assembled in one hour and h is the number of hours the company has to produce the fruit baskets.

a. Graph the function if the baskets have to be assembled in 48 hours. Then identify the domain and range of this function. How many baskets per hour have to be assembled?

b. Suppose 220 baskets are made in the first 24 hours. How does this affect the graph? How many baskets per hour have to be assembled to finish the job?

LESSON 1.5

Find Slope and Rate of Change

Georgia Performance Standards: MM1A1g

Goal Find the slope of a line and interpret slope as a rate of change.

Vocabulary

The **slope** of a nonvertical line is the ratio of the vertical change (the *rise*) to the horizontal change (the *run*) between any two points on the line.

A **rate of change** compares a change in one quantity to a change in another quantity.

Example 1 Find a positive slope

Find the slope of the line shown.

Solution

Let $(x_1, y_1) = (-2, 0)$ and $(x_2, y_2) = (3, 3)$.

$m = \dfrac{y_2 - y_1}{x_2 - x_1}$ Write formula for slope.

$= \dfrac{3 - 0}{3 - (-2)}$ Substitute.

$= \dfrac{3}{5}$ Simplify.

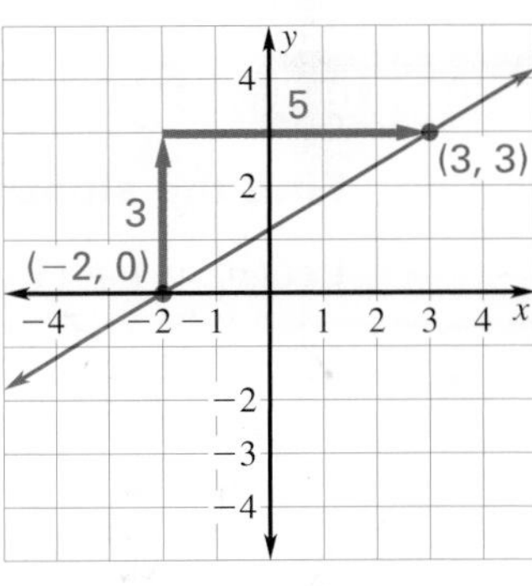

Example 2 Find a negative slope

Find the slope of the line shown.

Solution

Let $(x_1, y_1) = (4, -2)$ and $(x_2, y_2) = (-2, 6)$.

$m = \dfrac{y_2 - y_1}{x_2 - x_1}$ Write formula for slope.

$= \dfrac{6 - (-2)}{-2 - 4}$ Substitute.

$= \dfrac{8}{-6} = -\dfrac{4}{3}$ Simplify.

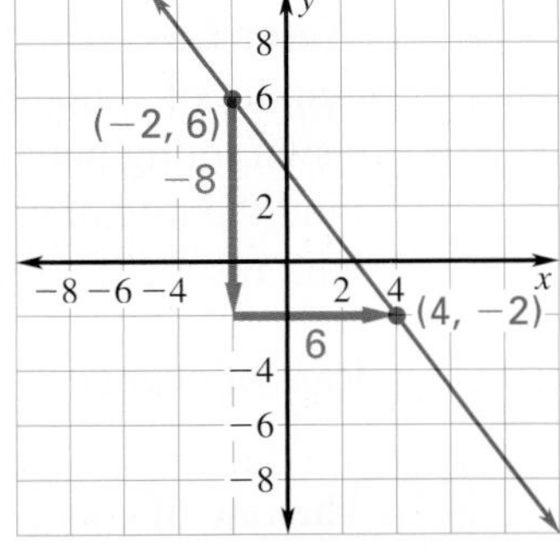

The line falls from left to right. The slope is negative.

Guided Practice for Examples 1 and 2

Find the slope of the line that passes through the points.

1. $(-4, -1)$ and $(5, 9)$ **2.** $(-2, 5)$ and $(-7, 8)$

UNIT 1

Georgia Performance Standards

MM1A1g Explore rates of change, comparing constant rates of change (i.e., slope) versus variable rates of change. Compare rates of change of linear, quadratic, square root, and other function families.

Example 3 Find the slope of a horizontal line

Find the slope of the line shown.

Let $(x_1, y_1) = (-4, -2)$ and $(x_2, y_2) = (2, -2)$.

$m = \dfrac{y_2 - y_1}{x_2 - x_1}$ Write formula for slope.

$= \dfrac{-2 - (-2)}{2 - (-4)}$ Substitute.

$= \dfrac{0}{6} = 0$ Simplify.

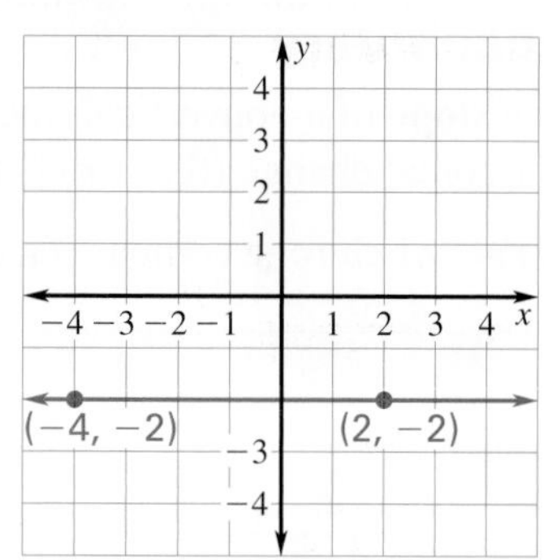

Example 4 Find the slope of a vertical line

Find the slope of the line shown.

Let $(x_1, y_1) = (1, 4)$ and $(x_2, y_2) = (1, -3)$.

$m = \dfrac{y_2 - y_1}{x_2 - x_1}$ Write formula for slope.

$= \dfrac{-3 - 4}{1 - 1}$ Substitute.

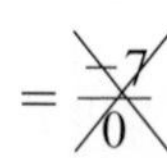

$= \dfrac{-7}{0}$ Division by zero is undefined.

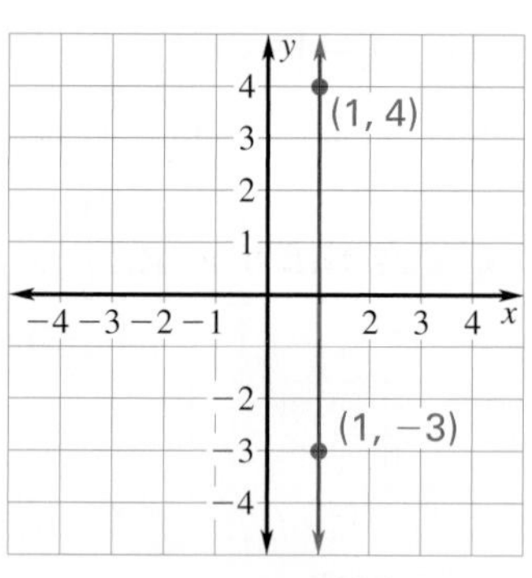

Example 5 Find a rate of change

Water Loss The table shows the amount of water evaporating from a swimming pool on a hot day. Find the rate of change in gallons with respect to time.

Time (hours)	2	6	12
Gallons evaporated	4.5	13.5	27

$$\text{Rate of change} = \frac{\text{change in gallons}}{\text{change in time}} = \frac{13.5 - 4.5}{6 - 2} = \frac{9}{4}$$

The rate of change is $\frac{9}{4}$ gallons per hour, or 2.25 gallons per hour.

Guided Practice for Examples 3, 4, and 5

Find the slope of the line that passes through the points.

3. $(-8, 0)$ and $(3, 0)$

4. $(5, -8)$ and $(5, 4)$

5. Find the rate of change in calories burned with respect to time.

Time (minutes)	40	60	80
Calories burned	500	750	1000

LESSON 1.5 **Exercise Set A**

MM1A1g Explore rates of change, comparing constant rates of change (i.e., slope) versus variable rates of change. Compare rates of change of linear, quadratic, square root, and other function families.

Tell whether the slope of the line is *positive, negative, zero,* or *undefined.*

1.
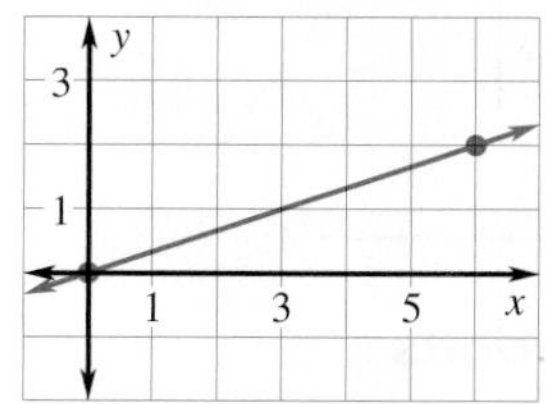

2.
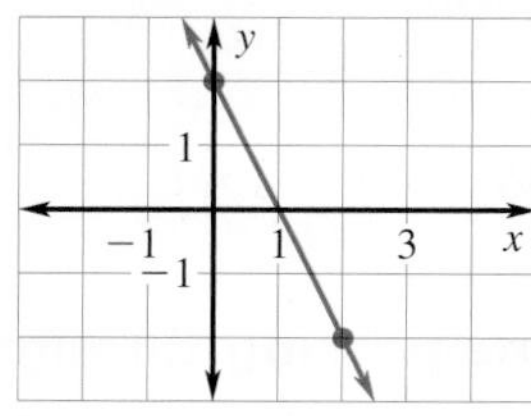

3.
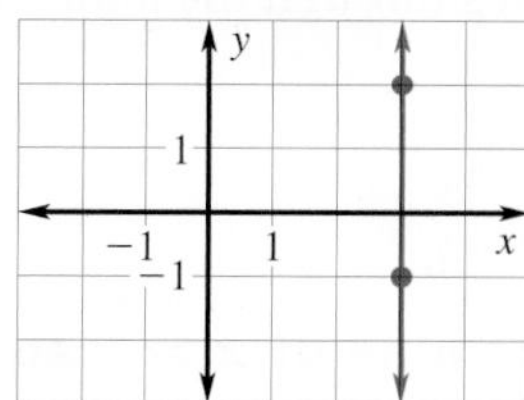

Plot the points and draw a line through them. Without calculating, tell whether the slope of the line is *positive, negative, zero,* or *undefined.*

4. $(1, -4)$ and $(5, -8)$
5. $(-3, 6)$ and $(-3, 0)$
6. $(-3, 3)$ and $(7, -1)$
7. $(0, -2)$ and $(9, -5)$
8. $(7, 1)$ and $(-2, 1)$
9. $(-3, -1)$ and $(6, -2)$
10. $(-4, -5)$ and $(-3, -2)$
11. $(-7, 1)$ and $(-7, -8)$
12. $(2, -10)$ and $(12, 10)$

Find the slope of the line that passes through the points.

13.
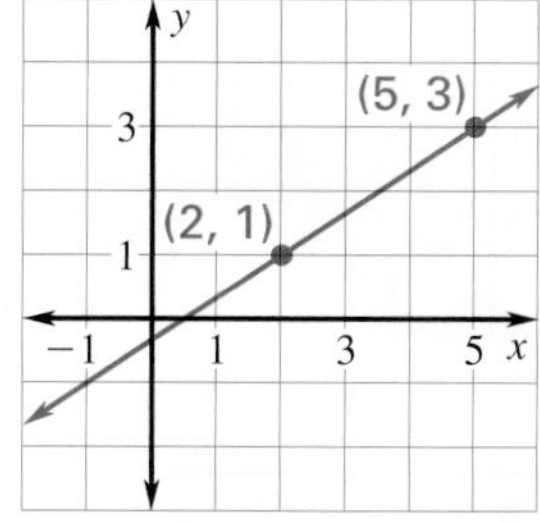

14.
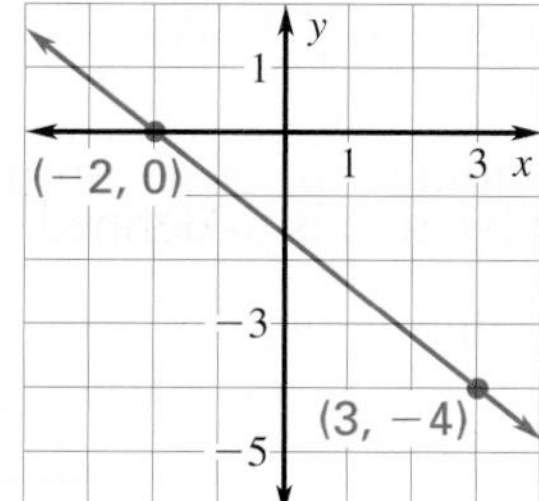

15.
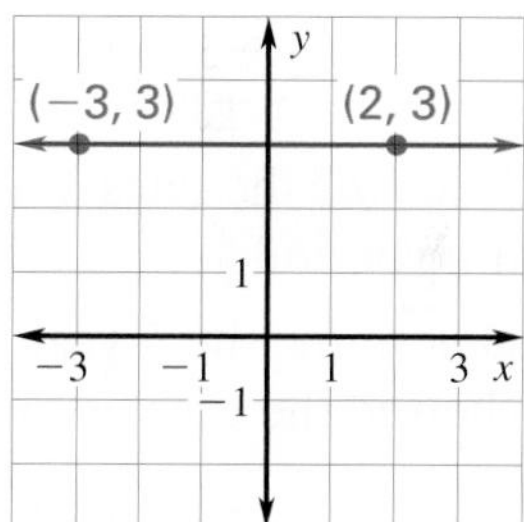

16.
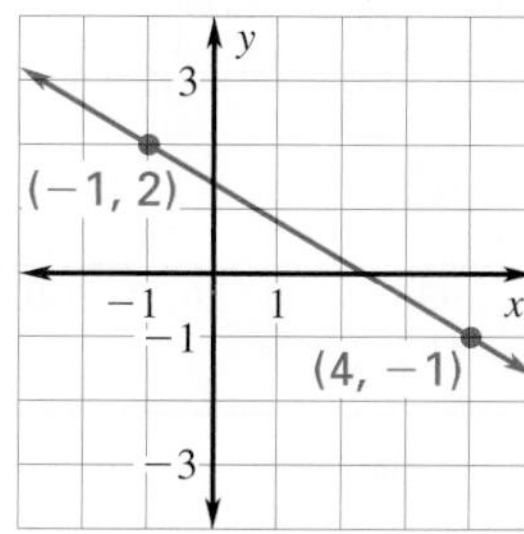

17.
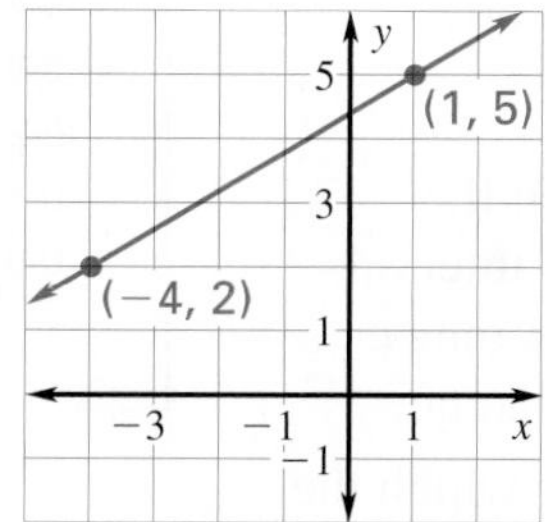

18.
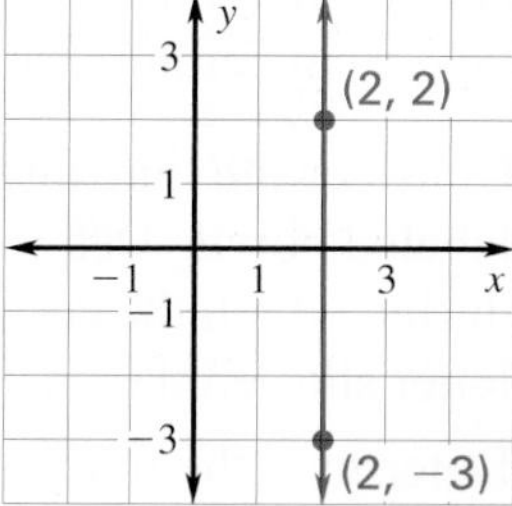

Find the slope of the line that passes through the points.

19. $(1, 2)$ and $(7, 7)$
20. $(3, 4)$ and $(-5, 0)$
21. $(5, -2)$ and $(5, 8)$
22. $(3, 1)$ and $(-5, 3)$
23. $(-7, 1)$ and $(1, 5)$
24. $(2, -5)$ and $(5, -2)$
25. $(3, 0)$ and $(8, 0)$
26. $(-6, -6)$ and $(-2, -2)$
27. $(-5, -4)$ and $(1, -2)$

UNIT 1

Exercise Set A *(continued)*

28. **Error Analysis** *Describe* and correct the error in calculating the slope of the line that passes through the points (3, 2) and (1, 4).

> The slope of the line through (3, 2) and (1, 4) is
>
> $$m = \frac{4-2}{3-1} = \frac{2}{2} = 1.$$

Find the value of *x* or *y* so that the line passing through the two points has the given slope.

29. $(-3, y), (-9, -2); m = 1$

30. $(-1, 4), (x, 3); m = \frac{1}{5}$

31. $(8, 1), (1, y); m = -1$

32. $(x, -7), (1, 2); m = 3$

33. $(9, y), (3, 2); m = \frac{2}{3}$

34. $(7, 5), (x, 2); m = \frac{3}{4}$

35. **Trolley Bus** The table shows the number of trolley buses in operation in the United States during certain years.

Year	1980	1985	1990	1995	2000
Number of buses	823	676	832	885	951

a. *Describe* the rates of change in the number of buses during the time period.

b. Determine the 5-year time intervals during which the number of trolley buses showed the greatest positive and least positive rates of change.

36. **Postage Rate** The graph shows the cost (in dollars) to mail a letter that weighs one ounce during certain years.

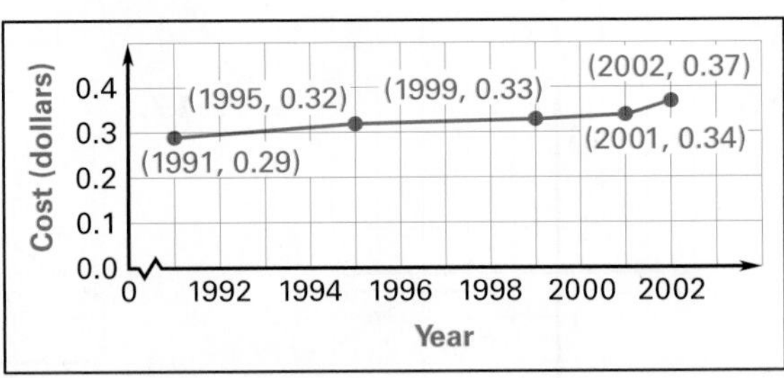

a. Consider the time intervals between the labeled points. Determine the time interval during which the cost to mail a one-ounce letter showed the greatest rate of change.

b. Determine the time interval during which the cost to mail a one-ounce letter showed the least rate of change.

37. **Heart Rate** The graph shows the heart rate of a person during 30 minutes of exercise. Give a verbal description of the workout.

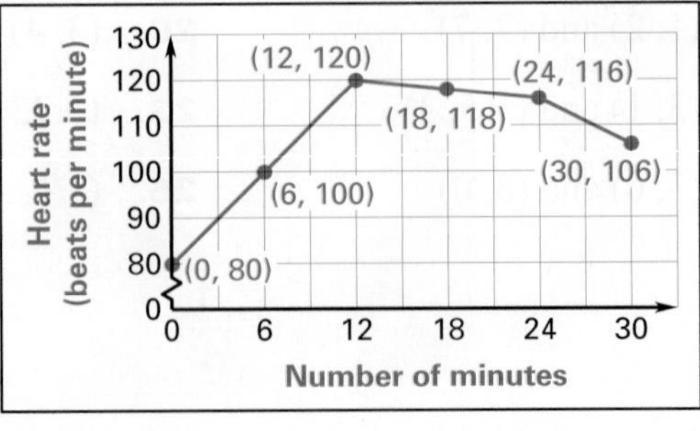

LESSON 1.5 **Exercise Set B**

MM1A1g Explore rates of change, comparing constant rates of change (i.e., slope) versus variable rates of change. Compare rates of change of linear, quadratic, square root, and other function families.

Tell whether the slope of the line is *positive, negative, zero,* or *undefined.*

1. 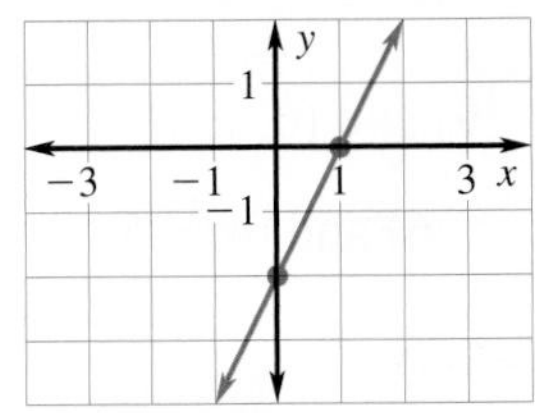

2. 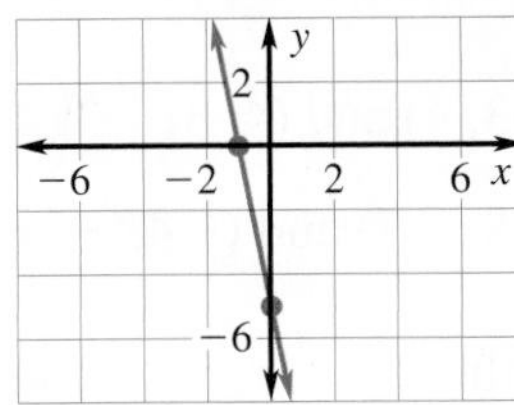

3. 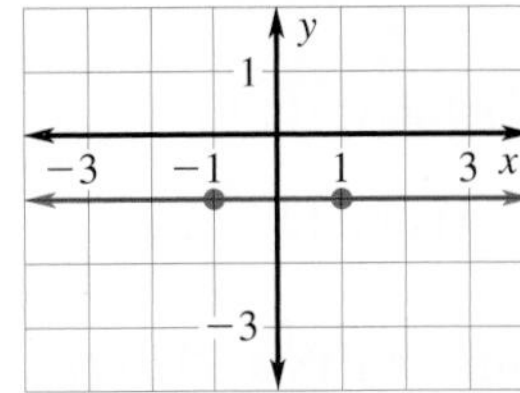

Plot the points and draw a line through them. Without calculating, tell whether the slope of the line is *positive, negative, zero,* or *undefined.*

4. $(2, -5)$ and $(6, -9)$

5. $(-4, 5)$ and $(-4, -2)$

6. $(-6, -2)$ and $(-1, -8)$

7. $(5, 3)$ and $(-4, 3)$

8. $(-7, 2)$ and $(3, -2)$

9. $(6, -4)$ and $(-5, -8)$

Find the slope of the line that passes through the points.

10. 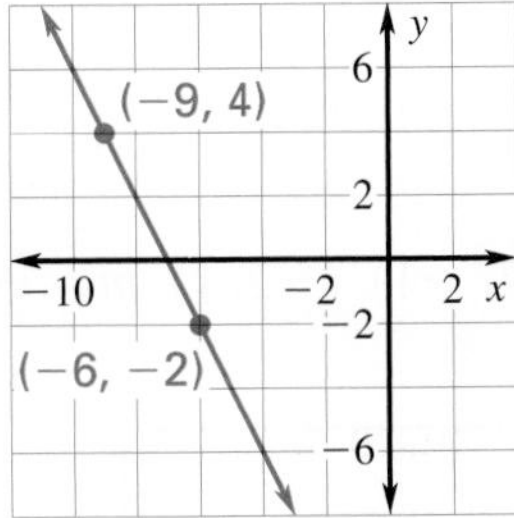

11. 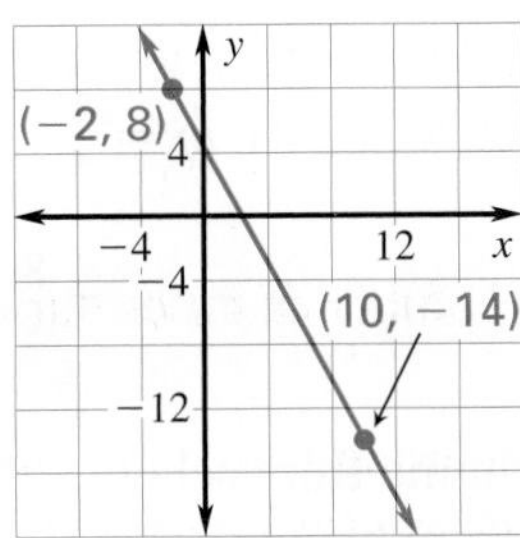

12. 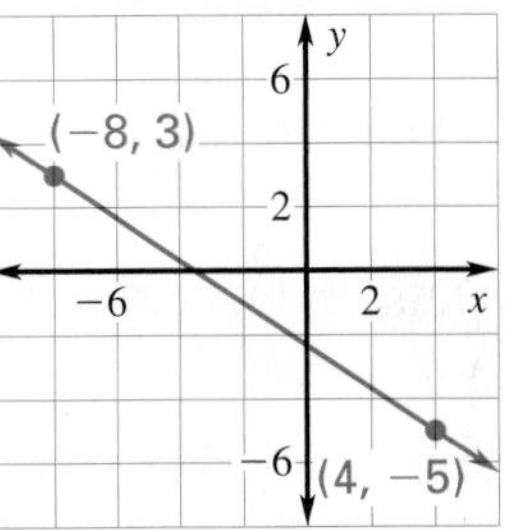

13. 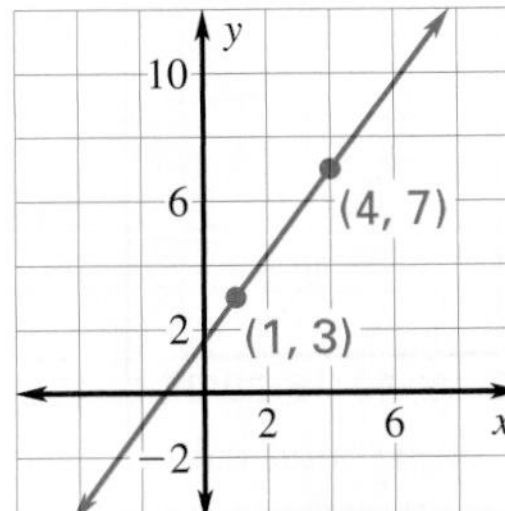

14. 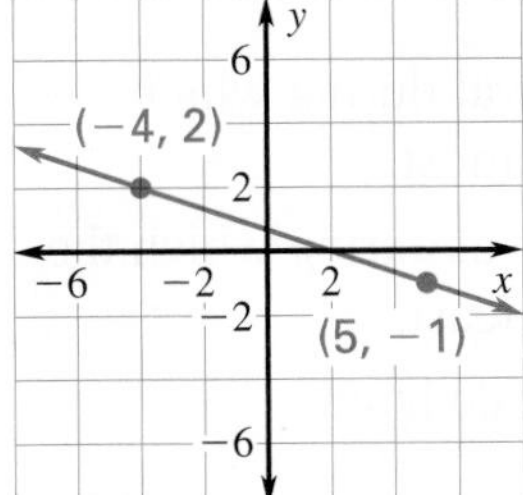

15. 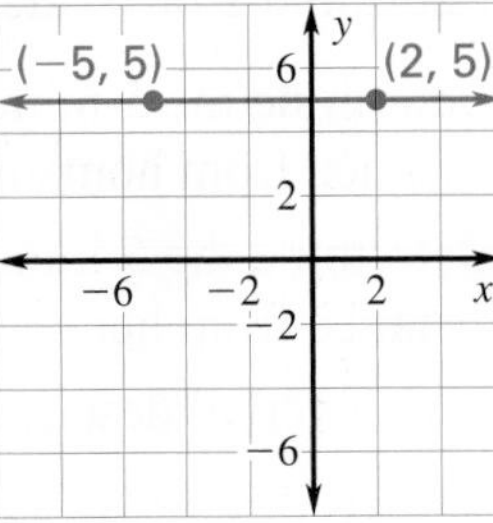

16. 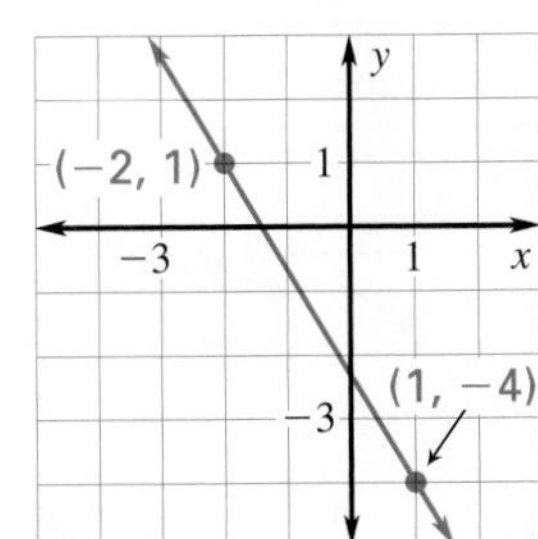

17. 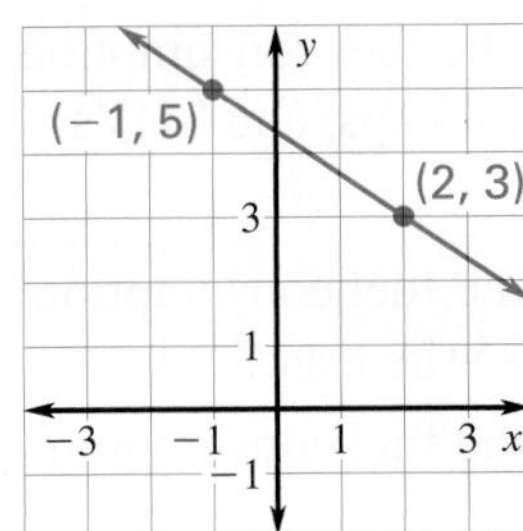

18. 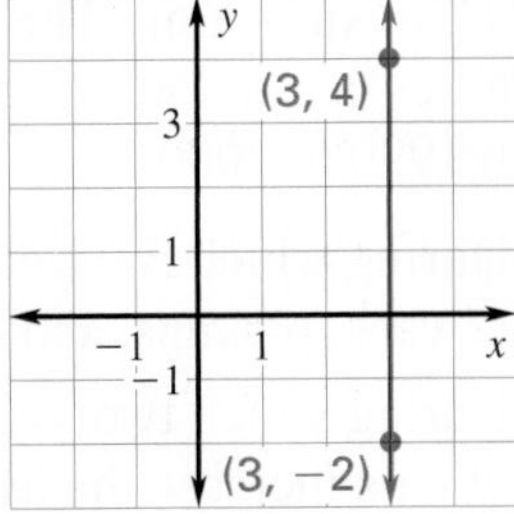

UNIT 1

Exercise Set B *(continued)*

Find the slope of the line that passes through the points.

19. (3, 4) and (8, 7)

20. (5, 5) and (−2, 1)

21. (6, −1) and $\left(6, \frac{1}{2}\right)$

22. (4, 2) and (−6, 6)

23. (−3, 4) and (4, 8)

24. (1, −9) and (6, −5)

25. (2, −5) and (5, −5)

26. (−8, −7) and (−4, −2)

27. (−2, −6) and (4, −5)

28. **Error Analysis** *Describe* and correct the error in calculating the slope of the line that passes through the points (6, 5) and (2, 7).

The slope of the line through (6, 5) and (2, 7) is

$$m = \frac{7-5}{6-2} = \frac{2}{4} = \frac{1}{2}.$$

Find the value of *x* or *y* so that the line passing through the two points has the given slope.

29. (−3, *y*), (−9, −2); $m = 1$

30. (−2, 8), (*x*, 4); $m = \frac{4}{5}$

31. (7, 5), (1, *y*); $m = -\frac{2}{3}$

32. (*x*, 8), (2, −1); $m = -3$

33. (−1, 5), (−6, *y*); $m = \frac{8}{5}$

34. (−7, −1), (−2, *y*); $m = -\frac{3}{5}$

35. **Biking** Every day, you ride your bike home from school. The graph shows the distance you are from home during your 20-minute bike ride.

a. Determine the 5-minute time interval during which the distance from home decreased the most.

b. Determine the 5-minute time interval during which the distance from home decreased the least.

c. Give a verbal description of your ride home.

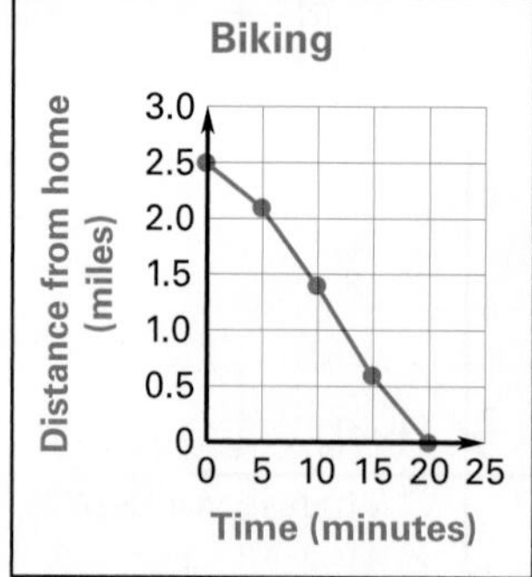

36. **Fuel Consumption** The graph shows the fuel consumption (in miles per gallon) of cars and vans, pickups, and SUVs from 1990 to 2000.

a. During which two-year period did the fuel consumption of vans, pickups, and SUVs decrease the least?

b. During which two-year period did the fuel consumption of cars increase the least?

c. How did the fuel consumption for the types of vehicles change during the 10-year period? *Explain* your reasoning.

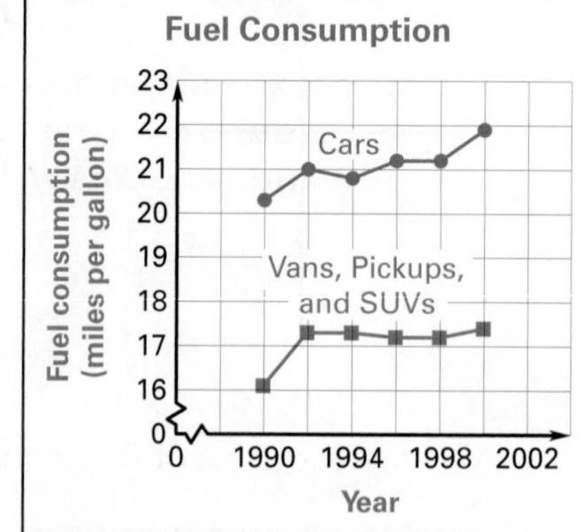

UNIT 1

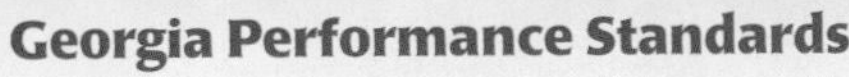

Georgia Performance Standards

MM1A1d Investigate and explain the characteristics of a function: domain, range, zeros, intercepts, intervals of increase and decrease, maximum and minimum values, and end behavior.

Investigating Math Activity

Slope and y-Intercept

Use before Lesson 1.6

Question

How can you use the equation of a line to find its slope and *y*-intercept?

Explore

Find the slopes and the *y*-intercepts of lines.

STEP 1 **Find y when x = 0** Copy the table below. Let $x_1 = 0$ and find y_1 for each equation. Use your answers to complete the second and fifth columns in the table.

STEP 2 **Find y when x = 2** Let $x_2 = 2$ and find y_2 for each equation. Use your answers to complete the third column in the table.

STEP 3 **Compute the slope** Use the slope formula and the ordered pairs you found in the second and third columns to complete the fourth column.

Line	$(0, y_1)$	$(2, y_2)$	Slope	*y*-intercept
$y = 4x + 3$	(0, 3)	(2, 11)	$\frac{11-3}{2-0} = 4$	3
$y = -2x + 3$	(0, ?)	(2, ?)	?	?
$y = \frac{1}{2}x + 4$	(0, ?)	(2, ?)	?	?
$y = -4x - 3$	(0, ?)	(2, ?)	?	?
$y = -\frac{1}{4}x - 3$	(0, ?)	(2, ?)	?	?

Draw Conclusions

1. *Compare* the slope of each line with the equation of the line. What do you notice?
2. *Compare* the *y*-intercept of each line with the equation of the line. What do you notice?

Predict the slope and the *y*-intercept of the line with the given equation. Then check your predictions by finding the slope and *y*-intercept as you did in the table above.

3. $y = -3x + 2$
4. $y = -\frac{2}{3}x + 2$
5. $y = \frac{4}{3}x - 1$

6. **Reasoning** Use the procedure you followed to complete the table above to show the *y*-intercept of the graph of $y = mx + b$ is b and the slope of the graph is m.

UNIT 1

LESSON 1.6

Graph Using Slope-Intercept Form

Georgia Performance Standards: MM1A1b, MM1A1d

Goal Graph linear equations using slope-intercept form.

Vocabulary

A linear equation of the form $y = mx + b$ is written in **slope-intercept form**, where m is the slope and b is the y-intercept of the equation's graph.

Two lines in the same plane are **parallel** if they do not intersect. Parallel lines have the same slope.

Two lines in the same plane are **perpendicular** if they intersect to form a right angle. Perpendicular lines have slopes that are negative reciprocals.

Example 1 Identify the slope and y-intercept

Identify the slope and y-intercept of the line with the given equation.

a. $y = \frac{1}{4}x - 2$

b. $-2x + 3y = 9$

Solution

a. The equation is in the form $y = mx + b$. So, the slope of the line is $\frac{1}{4}$, and the y-intercept is -2.

b. Rewrite the equation in slope-intercept form by solving for y.

$-2x + 3y = 9$ Write original equation.

$3y = 2x + 9$ Add $2x$ to each side.

$y = \frac{2}{3}x + 3$ Divide each side by 3.

The line has a slope of $\frac{2}{3}$ and a y-intercept of 3.

Guided Practice for Example 1

Identify the slope and y-intercept of the line with the given equation.

1. $y = -3x + 7$

2. $y = 4x - 10$

3. $y = -x$

4. $y = \frac{1}{3}x + 4$

5. $y = -0.8x - 2.1$

6. $y = 5 - 7x$

7. $15x - 5y = 10$

8. $-x - 6y = 18$

9. $2x - 9y = 6$

UNIT 1

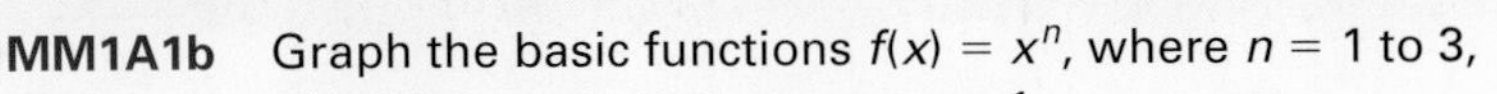

Georgia Performance Standards

MM1A1b Graph the basic functions $f(x) = x^n$, where $n = 1$ to 3, $f(x) = \sqrt{x}$, $f(x) = |x|$, and $f(x) = \frac{1}{x}$. 

MM1A1d Investigate and explain the characteristics of a function: domain, range, zeros, intercepts, intervals of increase and decrease, maximum and minimum values, and end behavior.

Example 2 Graph an equation using slope-intercept form

Graph the equation $4x + y = 3$.

Solution

STEP 1 **Rewrite** the equation in slope-intercept form.

$y = -4x + 3$

STEP 2 **Identify** the slope and the y-intercept.
$m = -4$ and $b = 3$

STEP 3 **Plot** the point that corresponds to the y-intercept, (0, 3).

STEP 4 **Use** the slope to locate a second point on the line. Draw a line through the two points.

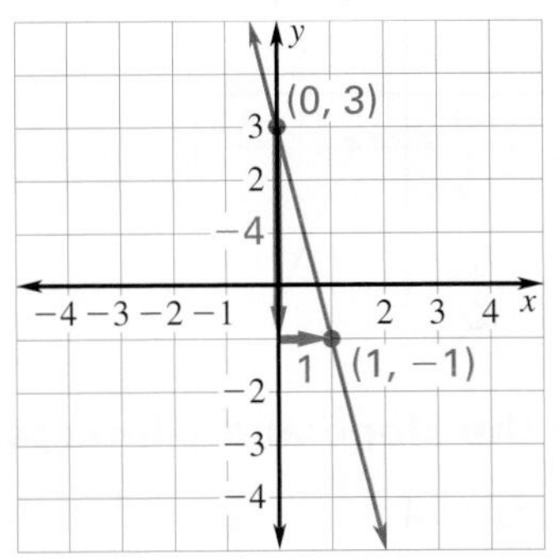

Guided Practice for Example 2

Graph the equation.

10. $y = \frac{3}{4}x - 1$

11. $y = -x$

Example 3 Identify parallel and perpendicular lines

Determine which of the lines are parallel or perpendicular: line *a* through (−4, 1) and (−6, 7); line *b* through (−7, −5) and (1, 11); line *c* through (2, 5) and (4, 9); line *d* through (4, 3) and (10, 5).

Solution

Find the slope of each line.

Line *a*: $m = \frac{7 - 1}{-6 - (-4)} = \frac{6}{-2} = -3$

Line *b*: $m = \frac{11 - (-5)}{1 - (-7)} = \frac{16}{8} = 2$

Line *c*: $m = \frac{9 - 5}{4 - 2} = \frac{4}{2} = 2$

Line *d*: $m = \frac{5 - 3}{10 - 4} = \frac{2}{6} = \frac{1}{3}$

Line b and line c have the same slope, so they are parallel. Line a and line d have slopes that are negative reciprocals, so they are perpendicular.

Guided Practice for Example 3

12. Determine which of the lines are parallel or perpendicular: line a through (5, 3) and (8, 5); line b through (−2, 9) and (1, 11); line c through (12, 8) and (8, 2); line d through (4, 6) and (7, 4).

UNIT 1

LESSON 1.6

Exercise Set A

MM1A1b Graph the basic functions $f(x) = x^n$, where $n = 1$ to 3, $f(x) = \sqrt{x}$, $f(x) = |x|$, and $f(x) = \frac{1}{x}$.

MM1A1d Investigate and explain the characteristics of a function: domain, range, zeros, intercepts, intervals of increase and decrease, maximum and minimum values, and end behavior.

Identify the slope and *y*-intercept of the line whose graph is shown.

1.

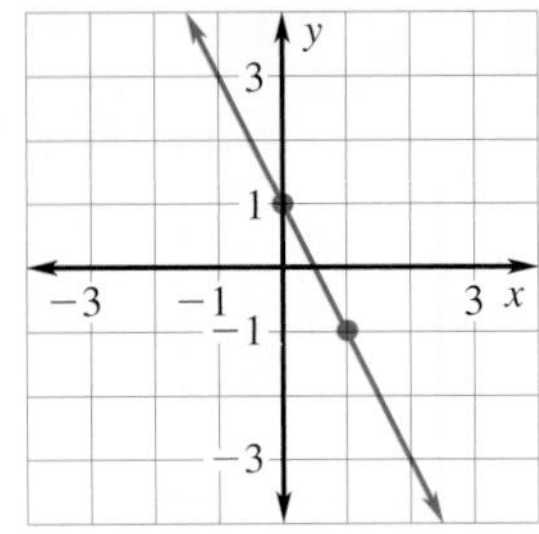

2.

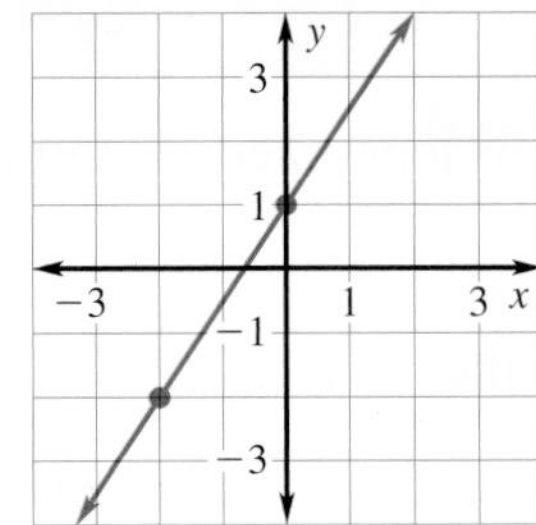

3.

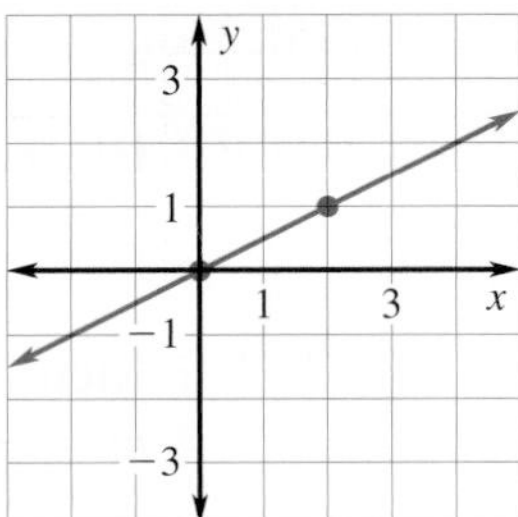

Identify the slope and *y*-intercept of the line with the given equation.

4. $y = 5x - 4$

5. $y = 10 - 4x$

6. $9x + y = 8$

7. $12x + 3y = 9$

8. $6x - 2y = 2$

9. $2x + 5y = 10$

10. $9x - 3y = -1$

11. $4y + 6x = 2$

12. $8y - 2x = 5$

13. $5x + 5y = 3$

14. $-4y = 16$

15. $6x = 12$

Match the equation with its graph.

16. $3x + 4y = 12$

17. $3x + 4y = -12$

18. $3x - 4y = 12$

A.

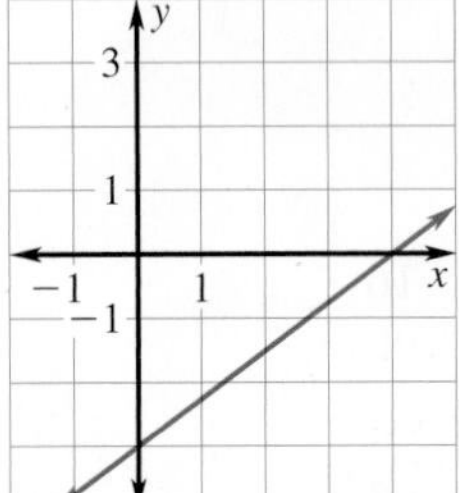

B.

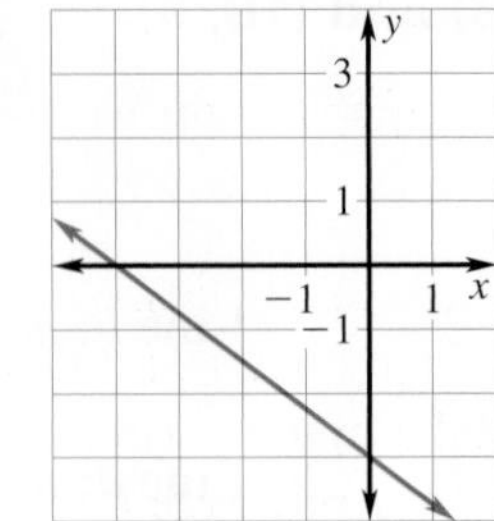

C.

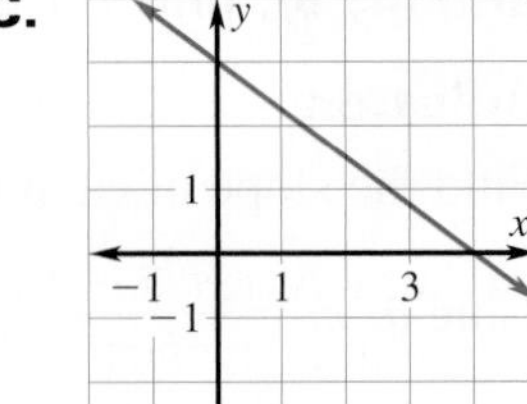

Graph the equation.

19. $y = -7x + 2$

20. $y = 5x + 4$

21. $y = -x + 9$

22. $y = \frac{1}{5}x$

23. $y = -\frac{2}{3}x + 1$

24. $y = \frac{4}{3}x - 5$

UNIT 1

Exercise Set A *(continued)*

Determine which lines are parallel.

25.

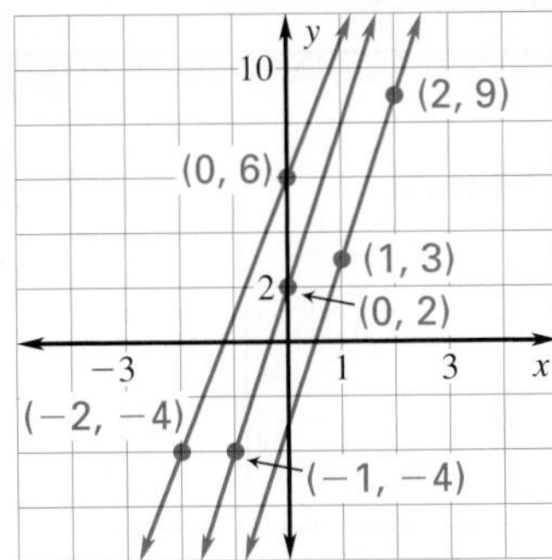

26.

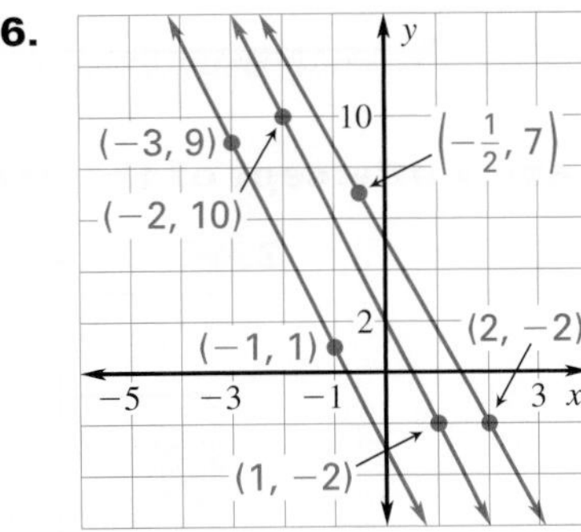

Tell whether the graphs of the two equations are *parallel lines, perpendicular lines,* or *neither.*

27. $y = 8x - 3,\ 8x + y = 3$

28. $2x + y = 5,\ -6 + 2x = y$

29. $2x + y = 5,\ y = 0.5x - 3$

30. $y = -0.6x + 2,\ 5y + 3x = 8$

31. $8x + 3y = 9,\ 8y - 4 = 3x$

32. $10x + 2y = 7,\ 5x - y = 6$

33. **Squirrels** A family of squirrels takes up residence in the roof of your house. You call a company to get rid of the squirrels. The company traps the squirrels and then releases them in a wooded area. The company charges \$30 to drop off the traps and then charges \$15 for each squirrel it traps. The total cost C (in dollars) is given by the equation $C = 30 + 15s$ where s is the number of squirrels that are taken away.

a. Graph the equation.

b. Suppose the company raises its fee to \$18 to take away each squirrel so that the total cost for s squirrels is given by the equation $C = 30 + 18s$. Graph the equation in the same coordinate plane as the equation in part (a).

c. How much more does it cost for the company to trap 4 squirrels after the fee is raised?

34. **Water Usage** A new toilet model has two different flush settings in order to conserve water. One setting uses 1.6 gallons of water per flush and the other setting uses 0.8 gallon of water per flush. The total amount w (in gallons) of water used in the first setting is given by the equation $w = 1.6f$ where f is the number of times the toilet is flushed. The total amount of water used in the second setting is given by the equation $w = 0.8f$.

a. Graph both equations in the same coordinate plane. What do the slopes and the w-intercepts mean in this situation?

b. How much more water is used by the first setting if the toilet is flushed 10 times?

LESSON 1.6

Exercise Set B

MM1A1b Graph the basic functions $f(x) = x^n$, where $n = 1$ to 3, $f(x) = \sqrt{x}$, $f(x) = |x|$, and $f(x) = \frac{1}{x}$.

MM1A1d Investigate and explain the characteristics of a function: domain, range, zeros, intercepts, intervals of increase and decrease, maximum and minimum values, and end behavior.

Identify the slope and *y*-intercept of the line whose graph is shown.

1. 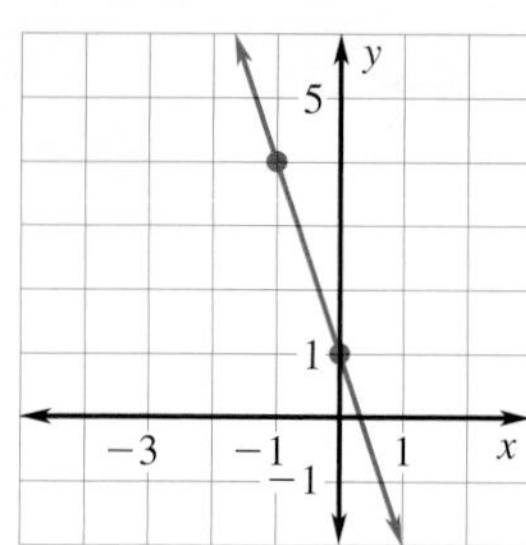

2. 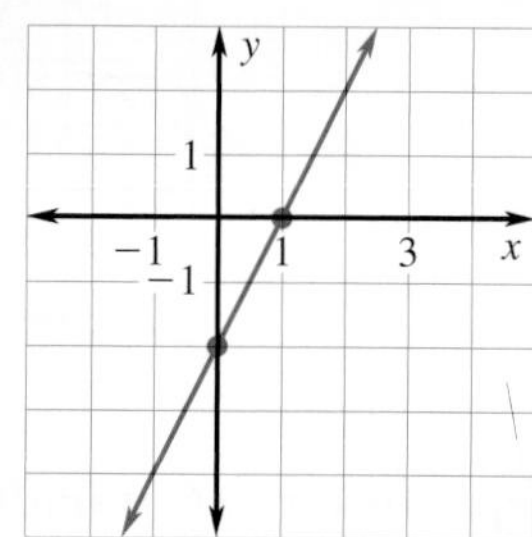

3. 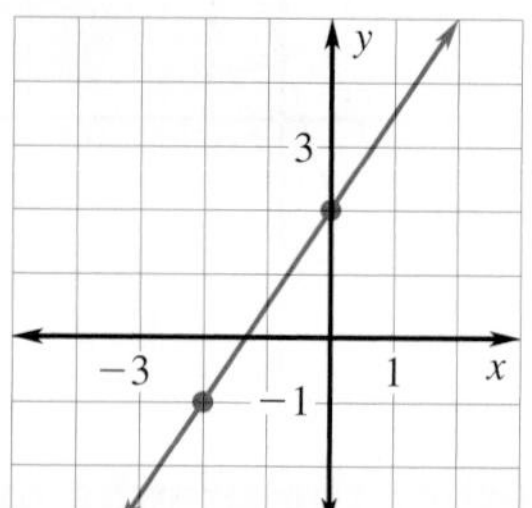

Identify the slope and *y*-intercept of the line with the given equation.

4. $y = \frac{2}{3}x - 4$
5. $y = 19 - 6x$
6. $6x + 2y = 14$
7. $3x + 2y = 8$
8. $4x - 5y = 15$
9. $6y - 8x = 18$
10. $8x - 10y = 14$
11. $4x - 9y = 18$
12. $5y - 3x = 12$
13. $2x - 5y = 10$
14. $-12x - 4y = -2$
15. $-x - 10y = -20$

Graph the equation.

16. $y = \frac{5}{3}x$
17. $y = \frac{3}{2}x - 2$
18. $y = -\frac{3}{4}x + 6$
19. $7x - y = 3$
20. $6x + 2y = 5$
21. $4x - 3y = -6$
22. $0.5x - 0.2y = 1$
23. $8y - 2x = 4$
24. $-6x - 4y = 8$

25. **Error Analysis** *Describe* and correct the error in graphing the equation $y = 3x - 1$.

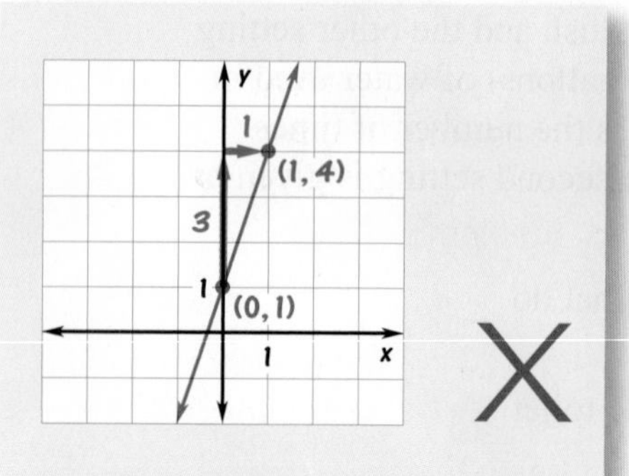

Exercise Set B *(continued)*

Determine which lines are parallel.

26.

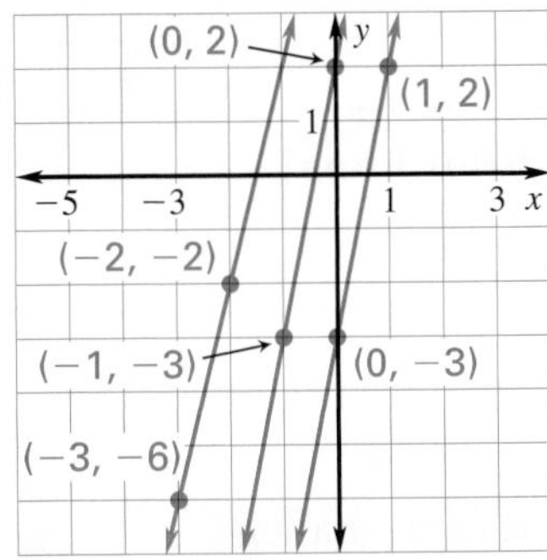

27.

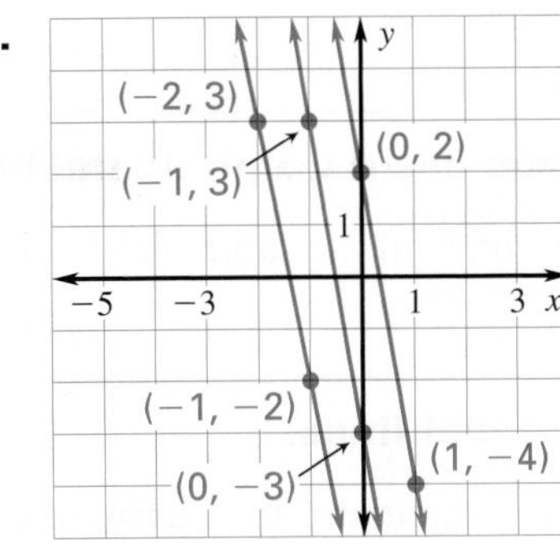

Tell whether the graphs of the two equations are *parallel lines, perpendicular lines,* or *neither.*

28. $x - 3y = 6, y = -\frac{1}{3}x$

29. $4x - 8y = 8, y = 0.5x - 1$

30. $2x - y = 7, 4y = -2x - 4$

31. $y + 3x = 8, 6x = 2y + 4$

Find the value of *k* so that the lines through the given points are parallel.

32. Line 1: $(-5, -2)$ and $(0, 0)$
Line 2: $(1, 6)$ and $(k, 7)$

33. Line 1: $(-2, -7)$ and $(3, 8)$
Line 2: $(-3, -6)$ and $(2, k)$

34. Line 1: $(-2, 8)$ and $(-4, -6)$
Line 2: $(-5, k)$ and $(0, -3)$

35. Line 1: $(-2, k)$ and $(4, -5)$
Line 2: $(-2, 3)$ and $(8, -2)$

36. Power Tools You are considering buying a variable-speed drill. One model you are considering has two different speeds. The number of revolutions r of the drill bit in m minutes using the slower speed is given by the equation $r = 300m$. The number of revolutions using the faster speed is given by the equation $r = 1200m$.

a. Graph both equations in the same coordinate plane. What do the r-intercepts mean in this situation?

b. How many more revolutions in 3 minutes does the faster speed on the drill make than the slower speed?

37. Plumber A plumber charges \$50 to come to your house to diagnose a problem and then charges \$30 an hour for labor if you decide to have the plumber repair the problem. The total cost C (in dollars) is given by the equation $C = 50 + 30t$ where t is the time (in hours) the plumber takes to repair the problem.

a. Graph the equation.

b. Suppose the plumber raises the charge for labor to \$32 per hour so that the total cost for a repair that takes t hours is given by the equation $C = 50 + 32t$. Graph the equation in the same coordinate plane as the equation in part (a).

c. How much more does it cost for a repair if it takes the plumber 3 hours to complete the job? What do you notice about the difference in the costs? *Explain.*

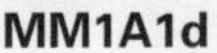

Georgia Performance Standards

MM1A1d Investigate and explain the characteristics of a function: domain, range, zeros, intercepts, intervals of increase and decrease, maximum and minimum values, and end behavior.

Technology Activity
Identifying Parallel Lines

Use after Lesson 1.6

Question

How can you use a graphing calculator to identify parallel lines?

Two different lines in the same plane are *parallel* if they do not intersect.

Example

Identify parallel lines.

Use a graphing calculator to determine which of the following lines are parallel.

Line a: $-3x + 2y = -4$ Line b: $-4x + 2y = 6$ Line c: $-2x + y = -1$

STEP 1 Rewrite equations

Write each equation in slope-intercept form.

Line a: $-3x + 2y = -4$
$$2y = 3x - 4$$
$$y = \frac{3}{2}x - 2$$

Line b: $-4x + 2y = 6$
$$2y = 4x + 6$$
$$y = 2x + 3$$

Line c: $-2x + y = -1$
$$y = 2x - 1$$

STEP 2 Enter equations

Enter the equations into the Y= screen.

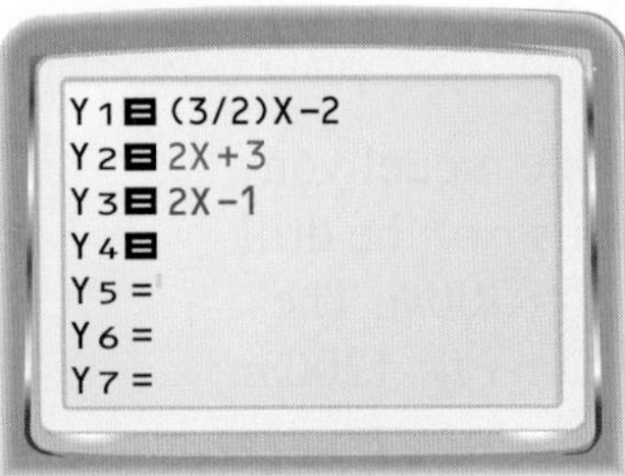

STEP 3 Graph equations

Graph the equations in the standard viewing window.

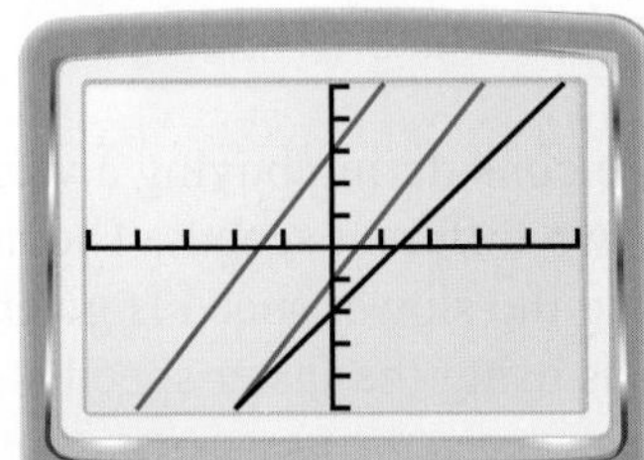

STEP 4 Analyze graphs

You can see from the graph that lines a and c intersect. Use the *intersect* feature in the calc menu to determine whether lines a and b intersect and whether lines b and c intersect. The calculator will give you an error if the lines do not intersect. Using this method, you will find that lines b and c do not intersect. So, lines b and c are parallel.

Practice

Use a graphing calculator to determine whether the graphs of the two equations are parallel lines.

1. $y = -x + 5$
$y + x = -2$

2. $y + 6x + 7 = 0$
$2y = 12x + 4$

3. $-15 = 2x - 3y$
$9y + 9 = 6x$

4. What do you notice about the equations of the lines that are parallel?

UNIT 1

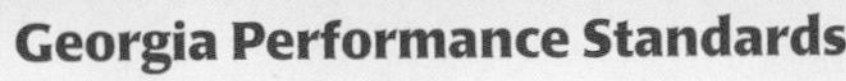

Georgia Performance Standards

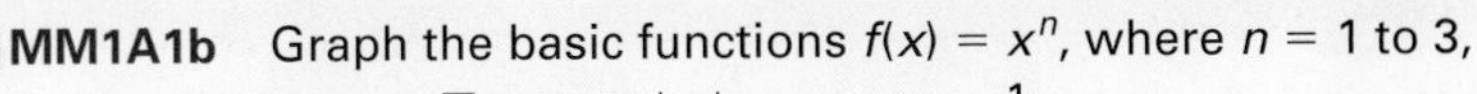

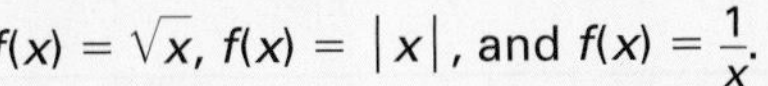

MM1A1b Graph the basic functions $f(x) = x^n$, where $n = 1$ to 3, $f(x) = \sqrt{x}$, $f(x) = |x|$, and $f(x) = \frac{1}{x}$.

MM1A1c Graph transformations of basic functions including vertical shifts, stretches, and shrinks, as well as reflections across the x- and y-axes.

Investigating Math Activity

Families of Linear Functions

Use before Lesson 1.7

Materials desk, textbooks, graph paper, meter stick or meter ruler

Question

What are some relationships that exist between members of a family of linear functions?

Explore

Graph families of linear functions.

In this activity, you will work in a small group. You will use a linear equation $y = mx + b$ to model the height y from the floor to the top of a stack of x books that are m centimeters thick sitting on a desk b centimeters high.

STEP 1 Measure and record

Measure the thickness of your algebra textbook. Measure the height of the top of your desk to the floor. Record your measurements.

STEP 2 Write and graph model

Write a model for the height y from the top of a stack of x algebra textbooks the same size as yours sitting on your desk. Then graph your model.

STEP 3 Measure and record

Measure the thickness of your English textbook.

STEP 4 Write and graph model

Repeat Step 2 using your English textbook, graphing your model in the same coordinate plane.

STEP 5 Repeat

Repeat Steps 3 and 4 using another textbook.

Draw Conclusions

1. **Writing** Functions that have characteristics in common can be thought of as a *family of functions*. List all the characteristics that the functions have in common. List all of the characteristics that their graphs have in common.

2. Suppose in the Explore that you used the same algebra textbook, but you used a table with a height of 65 centimeters, a desk with a height of 72 centimeters, and the floor. Graph these models in the same coordinate plane. What characteristics do these functions share? What characteristics do their graphs share?

3. What characteristics are shared by the family of functions in which $m = 1$?

UNIT 1

LESSON 1.7

Graph Linear Functions

Georgia Performance Standards: MM1A1a, MM1A1b, MM1A1c

Goal Use function notation.

Vocabulary

You have seen linear functions written in the form $y = mx + b$. By naming a function f, you can write it using **function notation:** $f(x) = mx + b$.

A **family of functions** is a group of functions with similar characteristics.

The most basic linear function in the family of all linear functions is called the **parent linear function** and has the following form: $f(x) = x$.

Example 1 Standardized Test Practice

What is the value of the function $f(x) = -2x - 7$ when $x = -2$?

Ⓐ -11 Ⓑ -3 Ⓒ 3 Ⓓ 11

Solution

$f(x) = -2x - 7$ Write original function.

$f(-2) = -2(-2) - 7$ Substitute -2 for x.

$= -3$ Simplify.

The correct answer is B.

Guided Practice for Example 1

Evaluate the function for the given value of *x*.

1. $f(x) = 0.3x - 1.2;\ 7$

2. $g(x) = -\frac{2}{5}x + \frac{1}{10};\ 4$

Example 2 Find an *x*-value

For the function $f(x) = -3x + 2$, find the value of x so that $f(x) = -13$.

Solution

$f(x) = -3x + 2$ Write original function.

$-13 = -3x + 2$ Substitute -13 for $f(x)$.

$5 = x$ Solve for x.

When $x = 5, f(x) = -13$.

Georgia Performance Standards

MM1A1a	Represent functions using function notation.	☑
MM1A1b	Graph the basic functions $f(x) = x^n$, where $n = 1$ to 3, $f(x) = \sqrt{x}$, $f(x) = \lvert x \rvert$, and $f(x) = \frac{1}{x}$.	☑
MM1A1c	Graph transformations of basic functions including vertical shifts, stretches, and shrinks, as well as reflections across the *x*- and *y*-axes.	☑

Guided Practice for Example 2

Find the value of *x* so that the function has the given value.

3. $g(x) = -\frac{1}{2}x - 3;\ 4$

4. $h(x) = 5x - 3;\ -13$

Example 3 Compare graphs with the graph of $f(x) = x$

Graph the function. Compare the graph with the graph of $f(x) = x$.

a. $g(x) = x + 1$

b. $n(x) = x - 2$

Solution

a. Because the graphs of *g* and *f* have the same slope, $m = 1$, the lines are parallel. Also, the *y*-intercept of the graph of *g* is 1 more than the *y*-intercept of the graph of *f*. The graph of *g* is a vertical shift of 1 unit up of the graph of *f*.

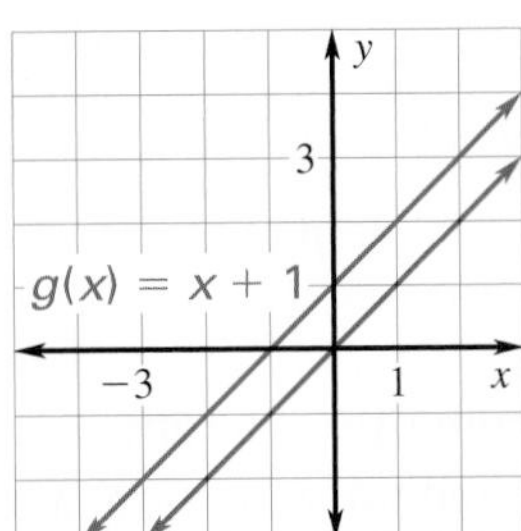

b. Because the graphs of *n* and *f* have the same slope, $m = 1$, the lines are parallel. Also, the *y*-intercept of the graph of *n* is 2 less than the *y*-intercept of the graph of *f*. The graph of *n* is a vertical shift of 2 units down of the graph of *f*.

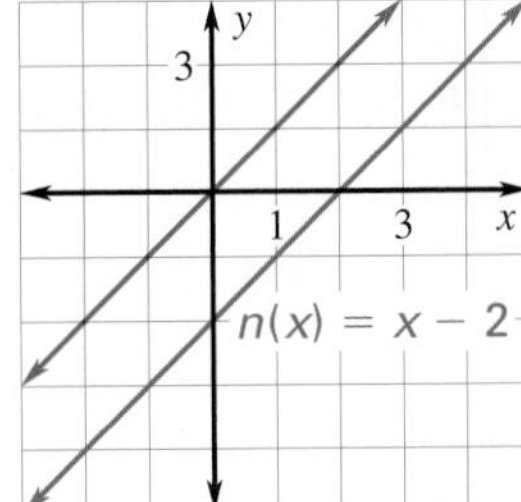

Example 4 Compare graphs with the graph of $f(x) = x$

Graph the function. Compare the graph with the graph of $f(x) = x$.

a. $h(x) = 2x$ **b.** $n(x) = \frac{1}{3}x$

Solution

a. The graph of h is $2f(x)$ which means each value of y is multiplied by 2. The graph of h is a vertical stretch of the graph of f using a scale factor of 2.

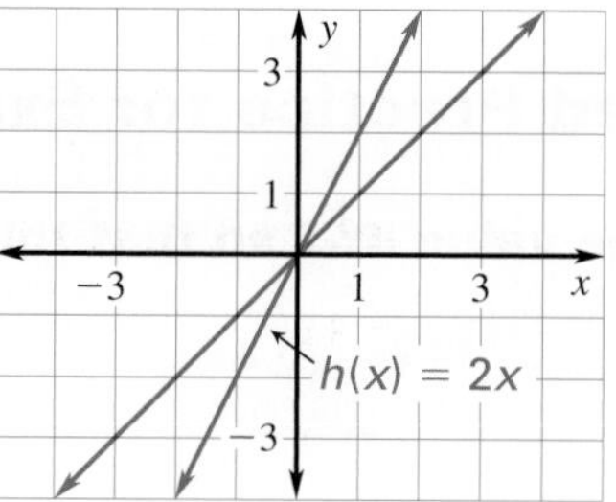

b. The graph of n is $\frac{1}{3}f(x)$ which means each value of y is multiplied by $\frac{1}{3}$. The graph of n is a vertical shrink of the graph of f using a scale factor of $\frac{1}{3}$.

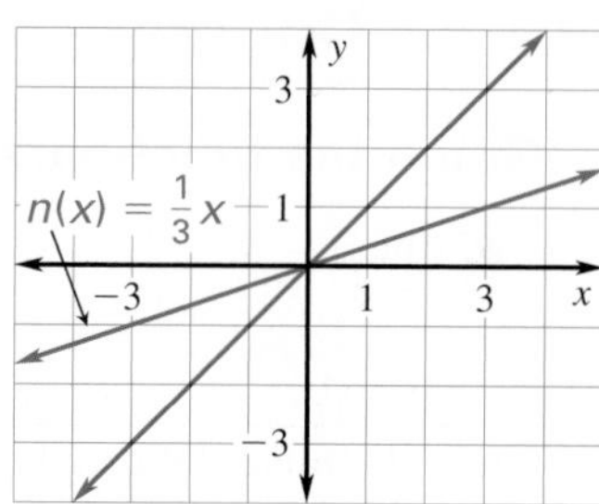

Example 5 Compare graphs

Graph the functions. Compare the graphs.

a. $g(x) = x + 2, h(x) = -x + 2$ **b.** $p(x) = x - 3, q(x) = -x + 3$

Solution

a. The graph of h is a reflection of the graph of g in the y-axis.

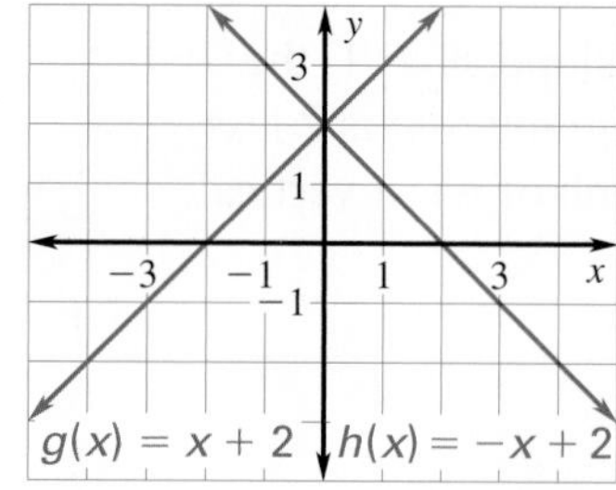

b. The graph of q is a reflection of the graph of p in the x-axis.

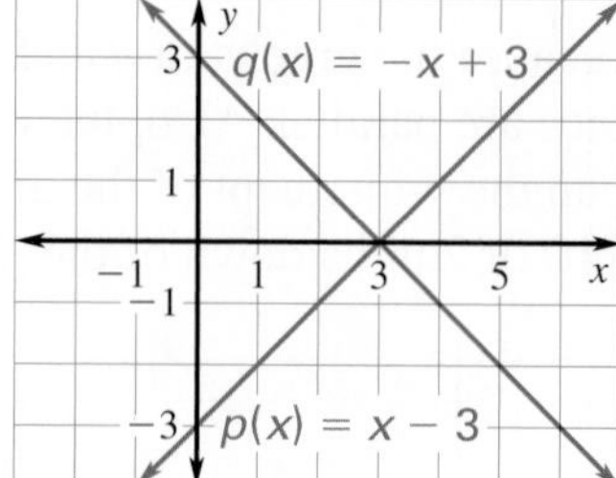

Guided Practice for Examples 3, 4, and 5

Graph the functions. *Compare* the graphs.

5. $f(x) = x, g(x) = x - 3$

6. $h(x) = x, n(x) = 4x$

7. $p(x) = x + 5, q(x) = -x - 5$

LESSON 1.7

Exercise Set A

MM1A1a Represent functions using function notation.

MM1A1b Graph the basic functions $f(x) = x^n$, where $n = 1$ to 3, $f(x) = \sqrt{x}$, $f(x) = |x|$, and $f(x) = \frac{1}{x}$.

MM1A1c Graph transformations of basic functions including vertical shifts, stretches, and shrinks, as well as reflections across the x- and y-axes.

Evaluate the function when $x = -3$, 0, and 2.

1. $f(x) = 15x + 4$

2. $g(x) = -9x + 1$

3. $p(x) = -7x - 5$

4. $h(x) = 3.25x$

5. $m(x) = -4.4x$

6. $f(x) = 6.1x - 3.3$

7. $s(x) = \frac{4}{5}x - 2$

8. $d(x) = -\frac{5}{3}x + 4$

9. $h(x) = \frac{3}{8}x - 6$

10. $f(x) = -2.5x + 7$

11. $h(x) = 4.2x - 3$

12. $g(x) = 6.1x - 2.2$

Find the value of x so that the function has the given value.

13. $f(x) = 4x - 2; 18$

14. $n(x) = 7x + 4; 39$

15. $q(x) = 6 - 5x; 21$

16. $g(x) = -3x + 8; 14$

17. $h(x) = 9x - 13; 23$

18. $r(x) = 12x - 30; 30$

19. $s(x) = -4x - 9; 3$

20. $c(x) = 8.5x - 3; 82$

21. $p(x) = -2.4x + 6; 18$

22. $d(x) = 3.3x - 1.1; 31.9$

***Compare* the graph of $g(x)$ to the graph of $f(x) = x$.**

23.

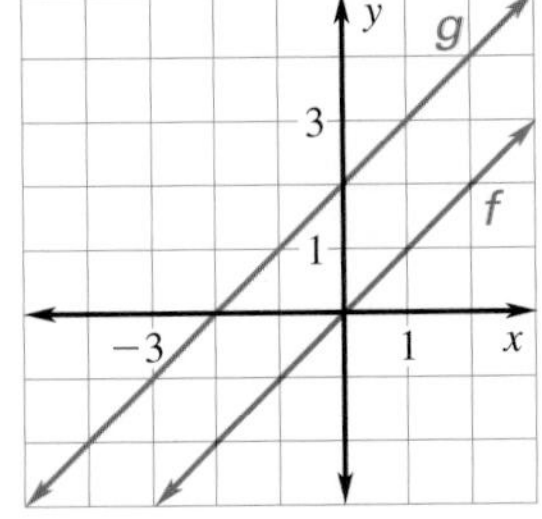

24.

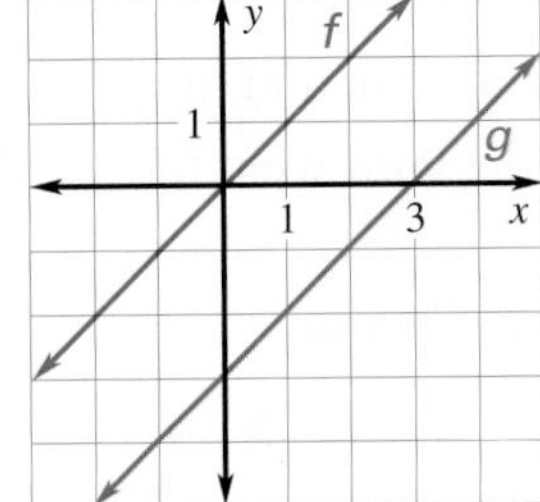

25.

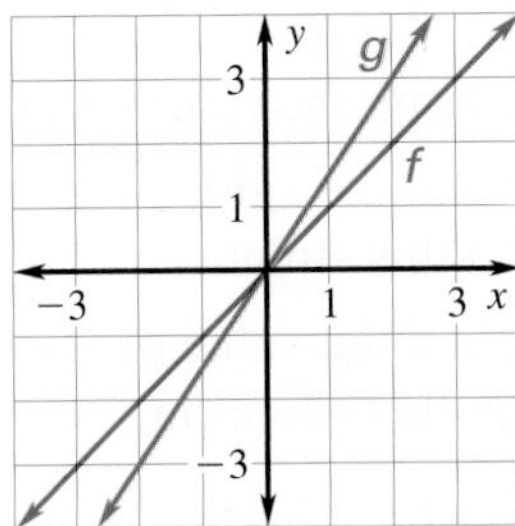

Graph the function. *Compare* your graph to the graph of $f(x) = x$.

26. $h(x) = x - 4$

27. $g(x) = x + 7$

28. $n(x) = 5x$

29. $d(x) = 8x$

30. $p(x) = \frac{1}{3}x$

31. $n(x) = -2x$

32. $p(x) = -\frac{1}{4}x$

33. $d(x) = x - 1.5$

34. $g(x) = x + 4.5$

Exercise Set A *(continued)*

35. Error Analysis *Describe* and correct the error in comparing the graph of g with the graph of f.

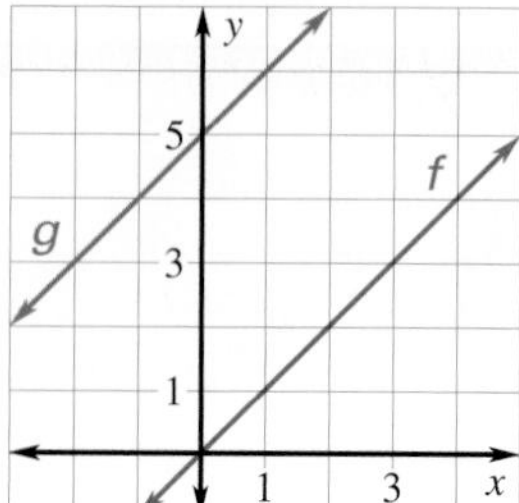

The graph of g is a vertical shift of 5 units down of the graph of f.

Match the function with the description of its graph in relation to the graph of $f(x) = x$.

36. $g(x) = 4x$

37. $g(x) = x + 4$

38. $g(x) = x - 4$

A. vertical shift of 4 units up of the graph of f

B. vertical shift of 4 units down of the graph of f

C. vertical stretch of the graph of f using a scale factor of 4

Graph the functions. *Compare* the graphs.

39. $g(x) = x - 1$, $h(x) = -x + 1$

40. $p(x) = x + 4$, $q(x) = -x + 4$

41. Video Games The number of hours people in the United States spent playing video games each year from 1998 to 2001 can be modeled by the function $f(x) = 11.9x + 46.4$ where x is the number of years since 1998.

a. Graph the function and identify its domain and range.

b. Find the value of $f(x)$ when $x = 2$. *Explain* what the solution means in this situation.

c. Find the value of x so that $f(x) = 60$. *Explain* what the solution means in this situation.

42. Pool Membership A pool membership during the summer costs $7 per week. The total cost of a membership is given by $f(x) = 7x$. The pool also rents out lockers for $2 per week. The total cost of a membership and a rental is given by $g(x) = 9x$.

a. Graph both functions. How is the graph of f related to the graph of g?

b. What is the difference between a 12-week membership if you get a locker and if you don't? *Explain* how you got your answer.

LESSON 1.7

Exercise Set B

MM1A1a Represent functions using function notation.

MM1A1b Graph the basic functions $f(x) = x^n$, where $n = 1$ to 3, $f(x) = \sqrt{x}$, $f(x) = |x|$, and $f(x) = \frac{1}{x}$.

MM1A1c Graph transformations of basic functions including vertical shifts, stretches, and shrinks, as well as reflections across the x- and y-axes.

Evaluate the function when $x = -3, 2,$ and 4.5.

1. $f(x) = 5.2x - 4$

2. $g(x) = -6x + 2.2$

3. $p(x) = -3.2x - 7.1$

4. $h(x) = 8.5 - 10x$

5. $n(x) = 5x + 12.7$

6. $f(x) = -2.8x + 14.3$

7. $s(x) = \frac{7}{3}x - 2$

8. $d(x) = \frac{9}{2}x + \frac{3}{4}$

9. $h(x) = \frac{5}{4} - \frac{1}{2}x$

10. $f(x) = -7.2x + 6$

11. $g(x) = 2.25x - 3$

12. $h(x) = 4.3x - 2.1$

Find the value of x so that the function has the given value.

13. $f(x) = 8x + 9; -7$

14. $d(x) = 11x - 15; 40$

15. $p(x) = 14 - 4x; 26$

16. $h(x) = 13x - 4; -43$

17. $q(x) = 6x + 4; 13$

18. $g(x) = 9 - 7x; 44$

19. $f(x) = -5x + 13; -14$

20. $n(x) = 12x - 17; 19$

21. $s(x) = 20x - 34; -134$

22. $f(x) = -6.5x + 7.4; -70.6$

23. $g(x) = 10.2x - 8.1; -39.6$

24. $h(x) = 6.75x - 2.5; 58.25$

Compare **the graph of $g(x)$ to the graph of $f(x) = x$.**

25.

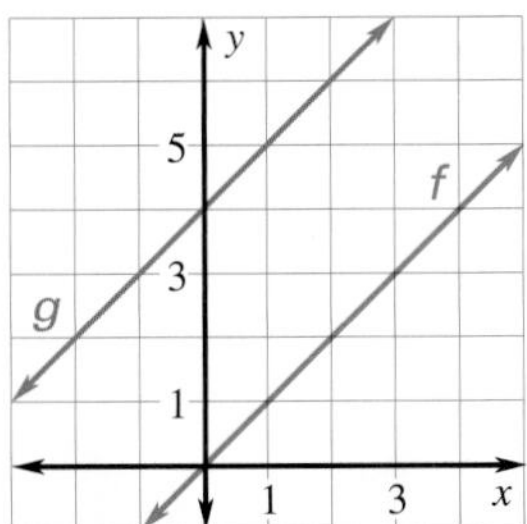

26.

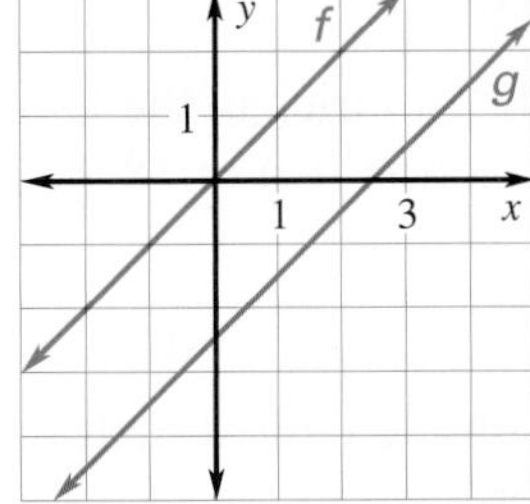

27.

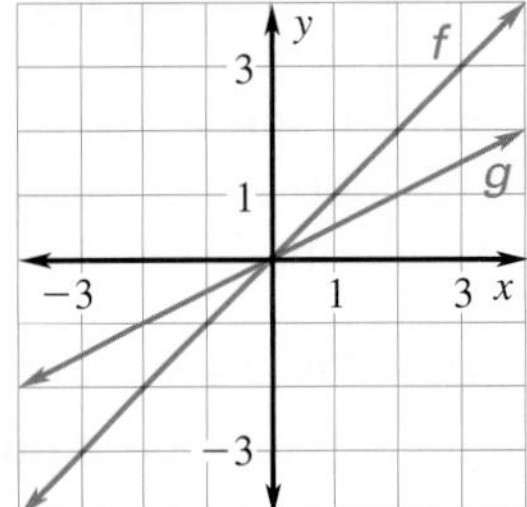

Graph the function. *Compare* your graph to the graph of $f(x) = x$.

28. $d(x) = x + 9$

29. $h(x) = x - 10$

30. $q(x) = 5x$

31. $g(x) = \frac{1}{4}x$

32. $p(x) = \frac{3}{2}x$

33. $h(x) = -\frac{2}{3}x$

34. $d(x) = x - 7.5$

35. $g(x) = x + 8.5$

36. $p(x) = 2.5x$

Exercise Set B *(continued)*

37. **Error Analysis** *Describe* and correct the error in comparing the graph of g with the graph of f.

> The graph of g is a vertical shift of 5 units down of the graph of f. 

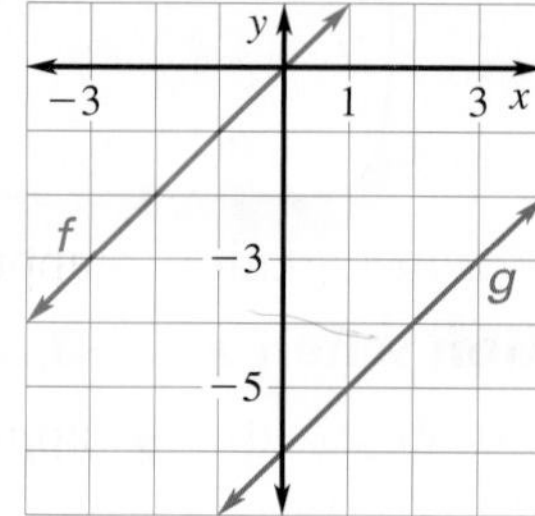

Match the function with the description of its graph.

38. $g(x) = 7x$

39. $g(x) = x + 7$

40. $g(x) = x - 7$

A. vertical shift of 7 units up of the graph of f

B. vertical shift of 7 units down of the graph of f

C. vertical stretch of the graph of f using a scale factor of 7

Graph the functions. *Compare* the graphs.

41. $g(x) = x - 4$, $h(x) = -x - 4$

42. $p(x) = x + 3$, $q(x) = -x - 3$

43. **Internet Usage** The number of hours people in the United States spent using the Internet each year from 1998 to 2001 can be modeled by the function $f(x) = 26.4x + 54.4$ where x is the number of years since 1998.

a. Graph the function and identify its domain and range.

b. Find the number of hours that people spent on the Internet in 2000. *Explain* how you found your answer.

c. When did people spend about 120 hours per year on the Internet? *Explain* how you found your answer.

44. **Public Libraries** The number of public libraries in the United States from 1980 to 2000 can be modeled by the function $f(x) = 38.9x + 8685.8$ where x is the number of years since 1980.

a. Graph the function and identify its domain and range.

b. Find the number of public libraries in the United States in 1996. *Explain* how you found your answer.

c. When were there 9000 public libraries in the United States? *Explain* how you found your answer.

45. **Gym Membership** You join a gym that charges a \$75 initial sign up fee and \$35 a month for a membership. The total cost of the membership can be modeled by $f(x) = 35x + 75$ where x is the number of months of the membership. After some time, you decide to rent a locker that costs \$50 for the entire year. A function for the total cost of the membership with the locker rental is $g(x) = 35x + 125$. Graph both functions. How is the graph of g related to the graph of f?

LESSON 1.8

Predict with Linear Models

Georgia Performance Standards: MM1A1d

Goal Make predictions using best-fitting lines.

Vocabulary

The line that most closely follows a trend in data is called the **best-fitting line**.

Using a line or its equation to approximate a value between two known values is called **linear interpolation.**

Using a line or its equation to approximate a value outside the range of known values is called **linear extrapolation.**

A **zero of a function** $y = f(x)$ is an x-value for which $f(x) = 0$ (or $y = 0$).

Example 1 Interpolate using an equation

Nesting Eagles The table shows the number of pairs of nesting Bald Eagles at a national wildlife reserve from 1998 to 2002.

Year	1998	2000	2001	2002
Pairs of Nesting Eagles	5	12	18	25

a. Make a scatter plot of the data.

b. Find an equation that models the number of pairs of nesting Bald Eagles as a function of the number of years since 1998.

c. Approximate the number of nesting eagle pairs in 1999.

Solution

a. Enter the data into lists on a graphing calculator. Make a scatter plot, letting the number of years since 1998 be the x-values (0, 2, 3, 4) and the number of nesting eagle pairs be the y-values.

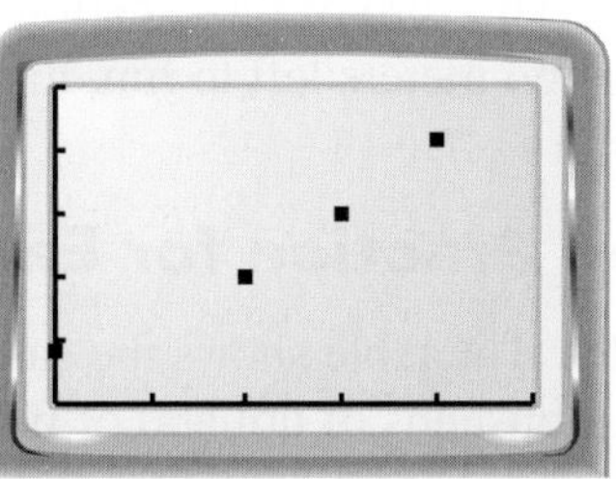

b. Use a calculator to find the best-fitting line. The equation of the best-fitting line is approximately $y = 5x + 4$.

c. Graph the best-fitting line. Use the trace feature and the arrow keys to find the value of the equation when $x = 1$.

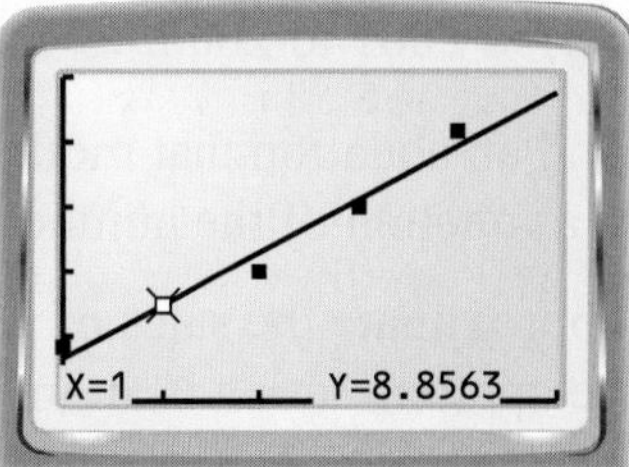

There were about 9 nesting pairs in 1999.

UNIT 1

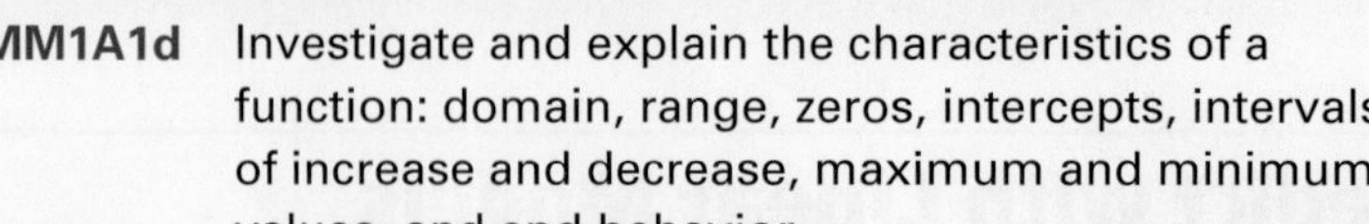

Georgia Performance Standards

MM1A1d Investigate and explain the characteristics of a function: domain, range, zeros, intercepts, intervals of increase and decrease, maximum and minimum values, and end behavior.

Example 2 Extrapolate using an equation

Nesting Eagles Look back at Example 1.

a. Use the equation from Example 1 to approximate the number of nesting Bald Eagle pairs in 2003 and 2005.

b. In 2003 there were actually 31 pairs of nesting eagles. In 2005 there were actually 34 pairs. Describe the accuracy of the extrapolations made in part (a).

Solution

a. Evaluate the equation of the best-fitting line from Example 1 for $x = 5$ and $x = 7$. The model predicts about 29 pairs in 2003 and about 39 pairs for 2005.

b. The difference between the predicted number of pairs and the actual number of pairs are 2 and 5, respectively. The difference in actual and predicted numbers increased from 2003 to 2005. So, the equation of the best-fitting line gives a less accurate prediction for years farther from the given data.

Example 3 Find the zero of a function

Race You can run a 100 meter race at an average rate of 4.8 meters per second. The distance d you have left to run after t seconds is given by the function $d = -4.8t + 100$. Find the zero of the function to the nearest tenth. Explain what the zero means in this situation.

Solution

$d = -4.8t + 100$ Write the equation.

$0 = -4.8t + 100$ Substitute 0 for d.

$t \approx 20.8$ Solve for t.

The zero of the function is about 20.8. According to the model, you have no meters left to run, meaning you will finish the race in about 20.8 seconds.

Guided Practice for Examples 1, 2, and 3

1. Sales The table shows the sales (in thousands of dollars) of pet care items at one pet store during the period 2001 to 2006.

Year	2001	2003	2005	2006
Dollar amount spent (thousands)	21	25	32	37

a. Find an equation that models the sales (in thousands of dollars) of pet care items as a function of the number of years since 2001.

b. Approximate the sales of pet care items for the years 2004 and 2007. Tell whether the approximation is an interpolation or an extrapolation.

c. Which of the approximations from part (b) would you expect to be more accurate? *Explain* your reasoning.

d. Find the zero of the function. *Explain* what the zero means in this situation.

LESSON 1.8 **Exercise Set A**

MM1A1d Investigate and explain the characteristics of a function: domain, range, zeros, intercepts, intervals of increase and decrease, maximum and minimum values, and end behavior.

Find the equation of the best-fitting line. Approximate the value of y for $x = 1$.

1.
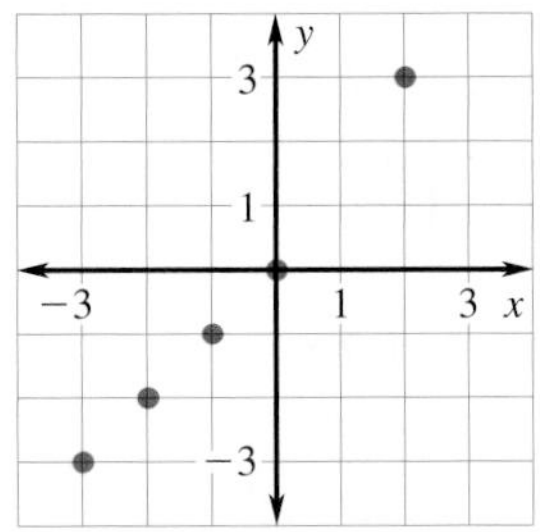

2.
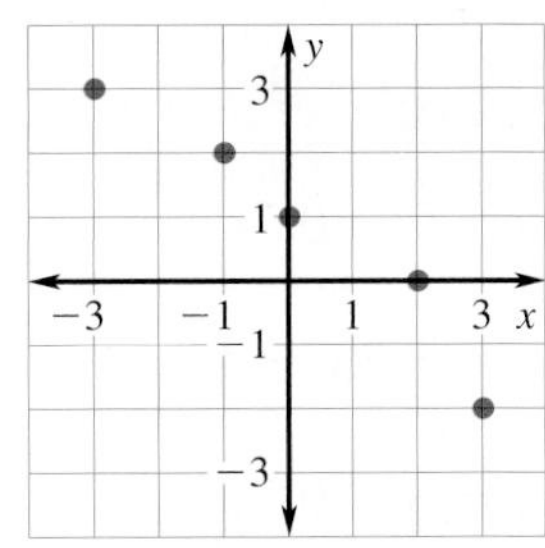

3.
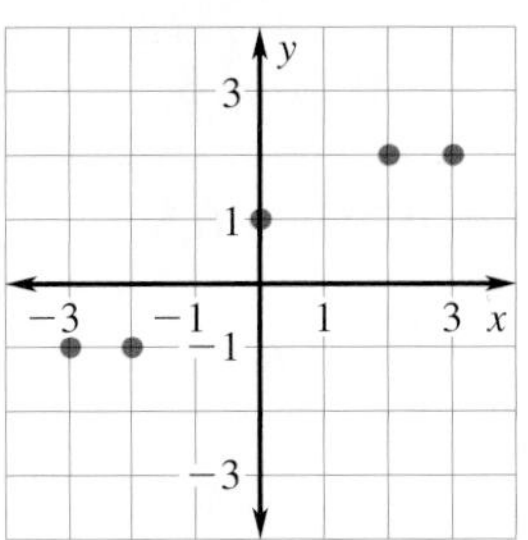

Make a scatter plot of the data. Find the equation of the best-fitting line. Approximate the value of y for $x = 3$.

4.

x	−1	0	1	2	4
y	3	3	1	0	−3

5.

x	−1	0	1	2	4
y	−1	1	2	1	5

6.

x	−2	−1	0	1	2
y	−3	−1	1	3	2

7.

x	−2	−1	0	1	2
y	4	4	3	1	−1

Make a scatter plot of the data. Find the equation of the best-fitting line. Approximate the value of y for $x = 5$.

8.

x	−1	0	1	2	3
y	5	3	2	0	−2

9.

x	−5	−3	−1	1	2
y	−4	−2	−1	1	0

10.

x	−2	−1	0	1	2
y	−4	−2	−1	−1	1

11.

x	−1	0	1	2	3
y	−2	0	1	3	5

12.

x	−3	−1	1	2	3
y	4	1	0	−1	−3

13.

x	−4	−2	0	1	3
y	3	3	1	0	−2

Exercise Set A *(continued)*

Find the zero of the function.

14. $f(x) = 16x - 4$

15. $f(x) = 2 - 4x$

16. $f(x) = 0.5x + 5$

17. $f(x) = -0.1x - 3$

18. $f(x) = \frac{3}{4}x - 3$

19. $f(x) = -\frac{2}{5}x + 4$

20. $f(x) = 0.25x + 0.5$

21. $f(x) = 9 - 0.7x$

22. $f(x) = 1.2x + 10$

23. $f(x) = \frac{1}{2}x - 6$

24. $f(x) = -\frac{2}{5}x - 4$

25. $f(x) = -0.8x + 15$

26. $f(x) = 1.25x - 5$

27. $f(x) = 6 - 0.2x$

28. $f(x) = 2.5x - 3$

29. **Profit** The table shows the monthly profit of a small company.

Month	January	February	March	April	May
Profit (dollars)	1200	1250	1400	1380	1450

a. Make a scatter plot of the data. Let x represent the number of months since January and let y represent the profit.

b. Find an equation that models the profit (in dollars) as a function of the number of months since January.

c. Approximate the profit in August.

30. **Multiple Representations** The table shows several planet diameters and escape velocities. The escape velocity is the velocity at which an object has to travel in order to escape the effect of a planet's gravity.

Planet	Mercury	Uranus	Earth	Mars	Venus
Diameter (km)	4879	51,118	12,756	6794	12,104
Escape velocity (km/sec)	4.3	21.3	11.186	5.03	10.36

a. **Drawing a Graph** Make a scatter plot of the data. Let x represent the diameter of the planet and let y represent the escape velocity.

b. **Writing an Equation** Find an equation that models the escape velocity (in kilometers per second) as a function of the diameter (in kilometers).

c. **Approximating a Value** Approximate the escape velocity of Neptune, which has a diameter of 49,528 kilometers.

LESSON 1.8

Exercise Set B

MM1A1d Investigate and explain the characteristics of a function: domain, range, zeros, intercepts, intervals of increase and decrease, maximum and minimum values, and end behavior.

Find the equation of the best-fitting line. Approximate the value of *y* for *x* = 1.

1. 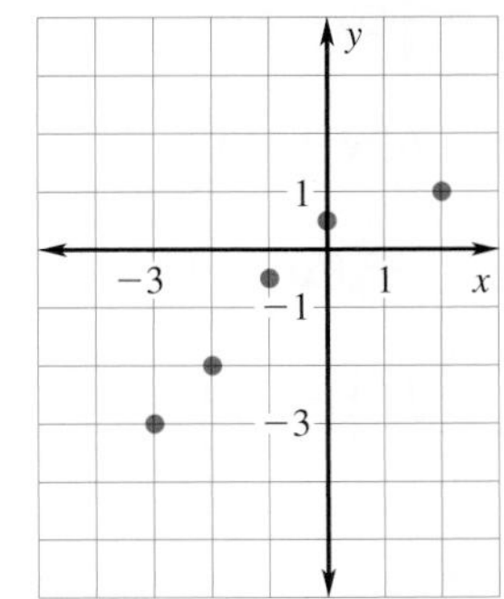

2. 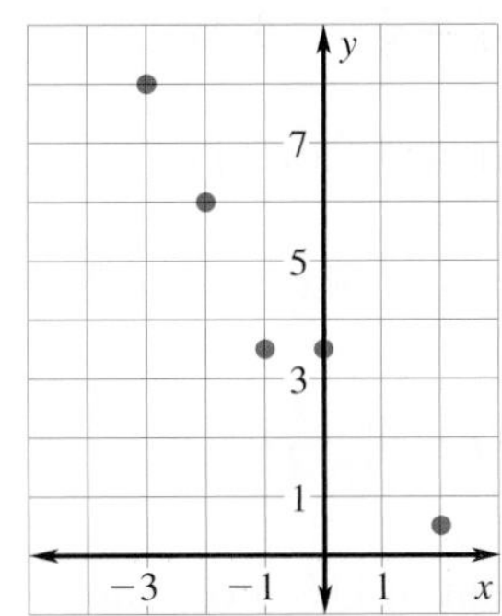

3. 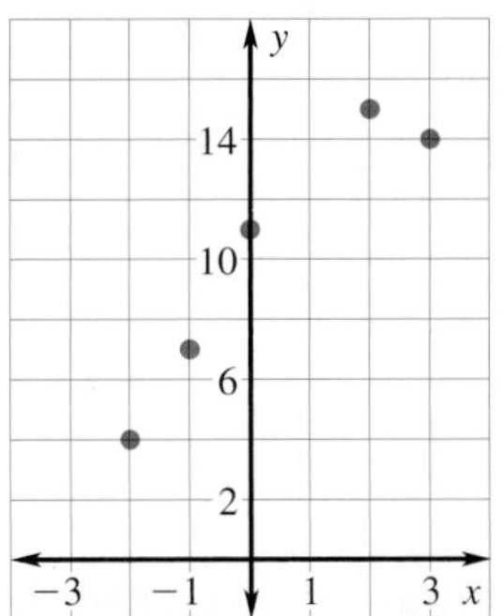

Make a scatter plot of the data. Find the equation of the best-fitting line. Approximate the value of *y* for *x* = −2.

4.

x	−5	−3	−1	1	2
y	1	0	−2	−2	−3

5.

x	−4	−3	−1	1	2
y	−4	−3.2	−2.5	−2	−1

6.

x	−3	−1	0	2	3
y	−2.5	−1.5	−1	1	2.4

7.

x	−5	−3	0	1	3
y	3	1.6	−0.7	−1.8	−2.1

Make a scatter plot of the data. Find the equation of the best-fitting line. Approximate the value of *y* for *x* = 1.25.

8.

x	−3	−2	−1	0	1
y	3	1.5	0.25	−1	−3

9.

x	−3	−2	−1	0	1
y	−1	0	0.25	0.75	2

10.

x	−4	−3	−2	−1	0
y	6	4	3	3	1

11.

x	−3	−2	−1	0	1
y	−3	−1	0	2	4

12.

x	−4	−3	−2	0	1
y	−3	−1.5	−1	0.5	2

13.

x	−5	−4	−2	−1	0
y	2	0	−0.5	−0.5	−2

Exercise Set B *(continued)*

Find the zero of the function.

14. $f(x) = 4.8x + 1.2$

15. $f(x) = 2.5x - 0.5$

16. $f(x) = 1.5x - 0.3$

17. $f(x) = -0.4x - 0.36$

18. $f(x) = 52 - 1.3x$

19. $f(x) = \frac{3}{4}(x - 8)$

20. $f(x) = -3(x + 4)$

21. $f(x) = 4(2x - 1)$

22. $f(x) = 6(3x + 5) - 4$

23. $f(x) = 4(3x - 3) + 2$

24. $f(x) = \frac{1}{2}(4x - 3) + 1$

25. $f(x) = -\frac{2}{3}(6x - 3) + 2$

26. $f(x) = -3\left(\frac{3}{4}x + 5\right)$

27. $f(x) = 4\left(-\frac{1}{2}x + 5\right)$

28. $f(x) = \frac{1}{2}\left(\frac{4}{3}x - 6\right)$

29. **Computers** The table shows the percent of U.S. households with computers from 1995 to 2000.

Year	1995	1996	1997	1998	1999	2000
Percent with computers	31.7	35.5	39.2	42.6	48.2	53.0

a. Make a scatter plot of the data where x represents the number of years since 1995 and y represents the percent of households with computers.

b. Find an equation that models the percent of households as a function of the number of years since 1995.

c. Predict how many households will have computers in 2009.

d. Find the zero of the function. *Explain* what the zero means in this situation.

30. **Multiple Representations** The table shows the sales (in millions of dollars) of corded telephones in the United States from 1990 to 2002.

Year	1990	1999	2000	2001	2002
Sales (millions of dollars)	765	688	678	666	660

a. **Drawing a Graph** Make a scatter plot of the data where x represents the number of years since 1990 and y represents the sales (in millions of dollars).

b. **Writing an Equation** Find an equation that models the sales as a function of the number of years since 1990.

c. **Analyzing a Model** How well do you think your model fits the data? *Explain* your reasoning.

d. **Estimating a Value** Use your model to estimate the sales in 1995.

e. **Analyzing a Model** The actual sales in 1995 were 668 million dollars. How well does this fit with your answer to part (d)? Do you think your model is still a good model? *Explain.*

LESSON 1.9

Graph Absolute Value Functions

Georgia Performance Standards: MM1A1a, MM1A1b, MM1A1c

Goal Graph absolute value functions.

Vocabulary

The **absolute value** of a number a is the distance between a and 0 on a number line. The symbol $|a|$ represents the absolute value of a.

Absolute value functions are transformations of the parent function $f(x) = |x|$.

Graph of Parent Function for Absolute Value Functions

x	−2	−1	0	1	2
$f(x) = \|x\|$	2	1	0	1	2

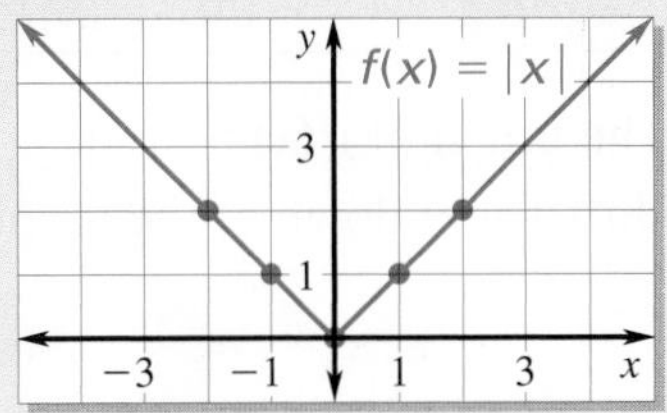

Comparing Graphs of Absolute Value Functions with the Graph of $f(x) = |x|$

$g(x) = \|x - h\|$	$g(x) = \|x\| + k$	$g(x) = a\|x\|$
The graph of g is a horizontal shift of the graph of $f(x) = \|x\|$. The shift is h units right if $h > 0$ and $\|h\|$ units left if $h < 0$. The graph of $h(x) = \|x + h\|$ is a reflection in the y-axis of the graph of g.	The graph of g is a vertical shift of the graph of $f(x) = \|x\|$. The shift is k units up if $k > 0$ and $\|k\|$ units down if $k < 0$.	If $\|a\| > 1$, the graph of g is a vertical stretch of the graph of $f(x) = \|x\|$. If $0 < \|a\| < 1$, the graph of g is a vertical shrink of the graph of $f(x) = \|x\|$. The graph of $h(x) = -a\|x\|$ is a reflection in the x-axis of the graph of g.

Example 1 Graph $g(x) = |x - h|$ and $g(x) = |x| + k$

Graph each function. Compare the graph with the graph of $f(x) = |x|$.

a. $g(x) = |x - 2|$ **b.** $g(x) = |x| - 1$

Make a table of values. Graph the function. Compare the graphs of g and f.

a.

x	0	1	2	3	4
$g(x)$	2	1	0	1	2

The graph of $g(x) = |x - 2|$ is a horizontal shift 2 units right of the graph of $f(x) = |x|$.

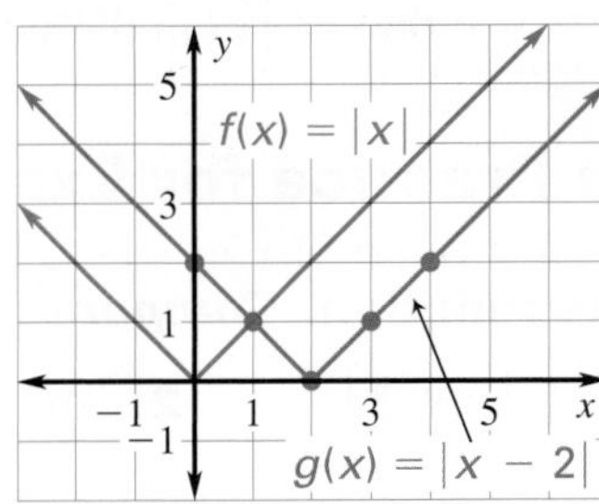

UNIT 1

Georgia Performance Standards

MM1A1a Represent functions using function notation. ☑

MM1A1b Graph the basic functions $f(x) = x^n$, where $n = 1$ to 3, $f(x) = \sqrt{x}$, $f(x) = |x|$, and $f(x) = \frac{1}{x}$. ☑

MM1A1c Graph transformations of basic functions including vertical shifts, stretches, and shrinks, as well as reflections across the x- and y-axes. ☑

Example 1 Graph $g(x) = |x - h|$ and $g(x) = |x| + k$ *(continued)*

b.

x	−2	−1	0	1	2
$g(x)$	1	0	−1	0	1

The graph of $g(x) = |x| - 1$ is a vertical shift 1 unit down of the graph of $f(x) = |x|$.

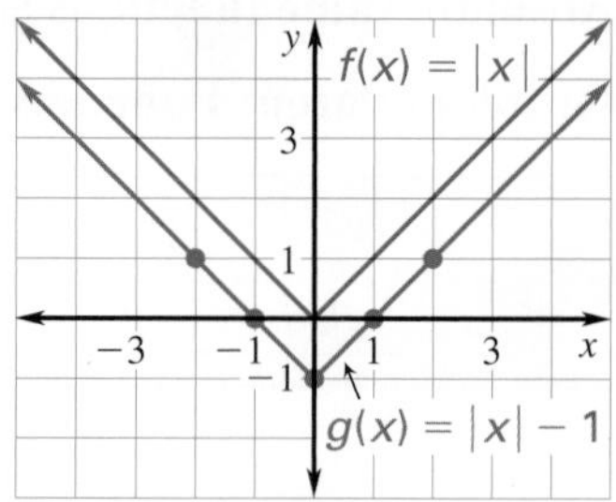

Example 2 Graph $g(x) = a|x|$

Graph each function. Compare the graph with the graph of $f(x) = |x|$.

a. $g(x) = 3|x|$

b. $g(x) = -0.5|x|$

Solution

Make a table of values. Graph the function. Compare the graphs of g and f.

a.

x	−2	−1	0	1	2
$g(x)$	6	3	0	3	6

The graph of $g(x) = 3|x|$ is a vertical stretch of the graph of $f(x) = |x|$ using a scale factor of 3.

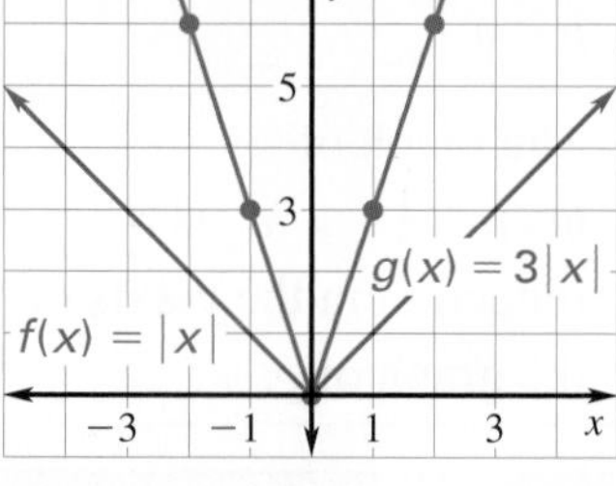

b.

x	−4	−2	0	2	4
$g(x)$	−2	−1	0	−1	−2

The graph of $g(x) = -0.5|x|$ is a vertical shrink of the graph of $f(x) = |x|$ using a scale factor of 0.5 and a reflection of the graph of $f(x) = |x|$ in the x-axis.

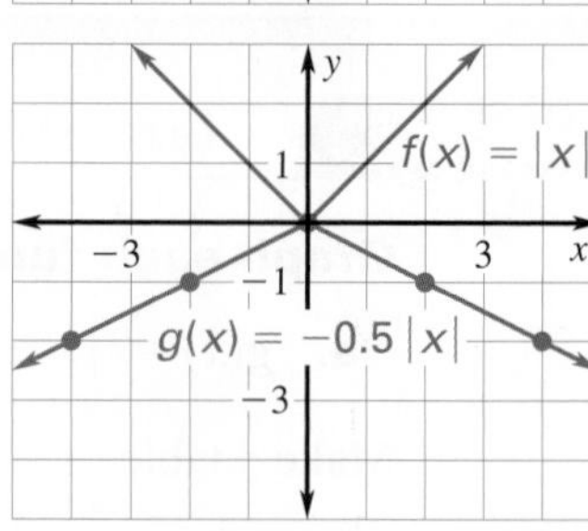

Guided Practice for Examples 1 and 2

Graph the function. *Compare* the graph with the graph of $f(x) = |x|$.

1. $g(x) = |x + 3|$ **2.** $g(x) = |x| + 5$ **3.** $g(x) = 2|x|$

UNIT 1

LESSON 1.9

Exercise Set A

MM1A1a Represent functions using function notation.

MM1A1b Graph the basic functions $f(x) = x^n$, where $n = 1$ to 3, $f(x) = \sqrt{x}$, $f(x) = |x|$, and $f(x) = \frac{1}{x}$.

MM1A1c Graph transformations of basic functions including vertical shifts, stretches, and shrinks, as well as reflections across the x- and y-axes.

Match the function with its graph.

1. $f(x) = 2|x|$
2. $f(x) = -2|x|$
3. $f(x) = \frac{1}{2}|x|$

A.

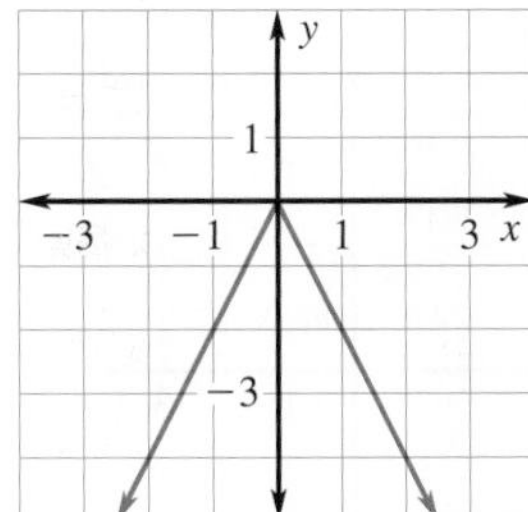

B.

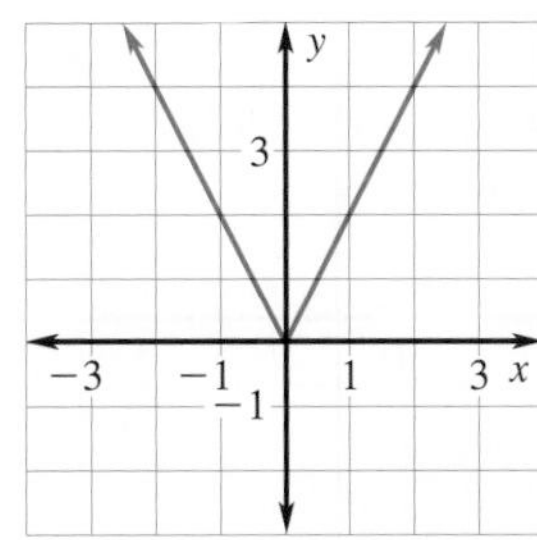

C.

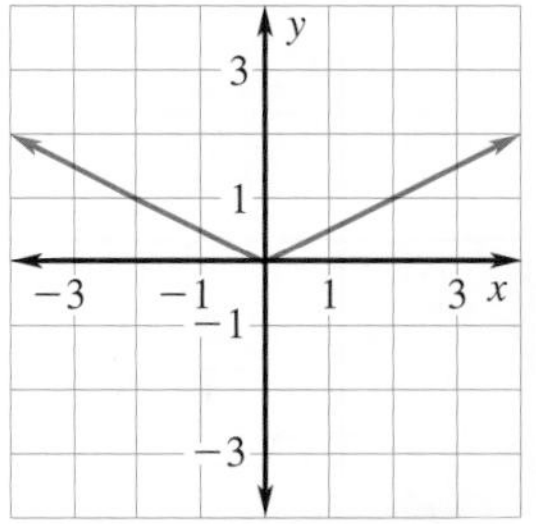

Match the function with its graph.

4. $f(x) = |x - 4|$
5. $f(x) = |x| - 4$
6. $f(x) = |x + 4|$

A.

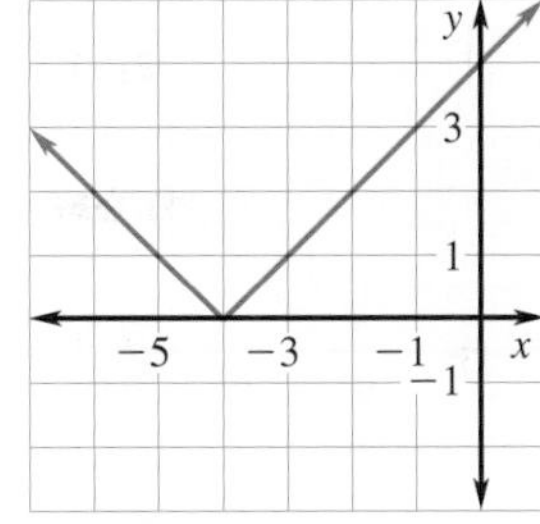

B.

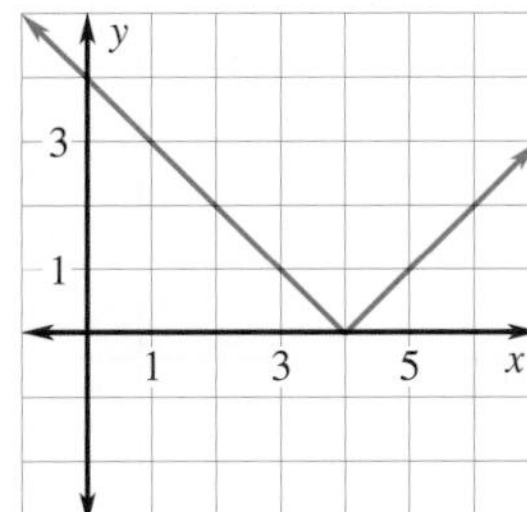

C.

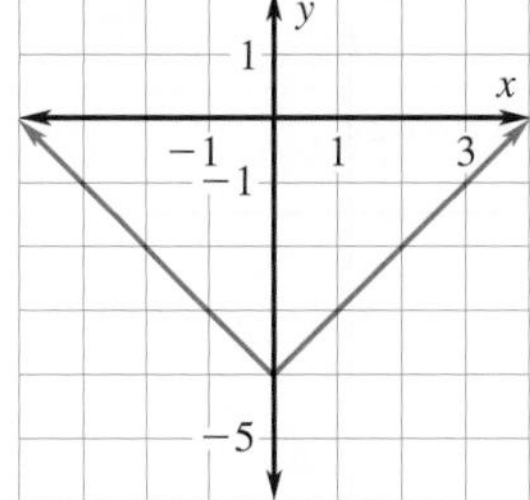

Graph the function. *Compare* the graph with the graph of $f(x) = |x|$.

7. $g(x) = |x - 1|$
8. $g(x) = |x| + 3$
9. $g(x) = \frac{1}{3}|x|$
10. $g(x) = |x - 6|$
11. $g(x) = 4|x|$
12. $g(x) = -\frac{1}{4}|x|$
13. $g(x) = -|x - 5|$
14. $g(x) = |x| + 6$
15. $g(x) = 5|x|$

16. **Multiple Representations** Consider the function $g(x) = |x - 3|$.

    a. **Graphing a Function** Make a table of values and then graph the function.

    b. **Comparing Graphs** *Compare* the graph of g to the graph of $f(x) = |x + 3|$.

    c. **Analyzing a Function** Write a rule for the function whose graph is a reflection of the graph of g in the x-axis.

UNIT 1

LESSON 1.9 **Exercise Set B**

MM1A1a Represent functions using function notation.

MM1A1b Graph the basic functions $f(x) = x^n$, where $n = 1$ to 3, $f(x) = \sqrt{x}$, $f(x) = |x|$, and $f(x) = \frac{1}{x}$.

MM1A1c Graph transformations of basic functions including vertical shifts, stretches, and shrinks, as well as reflections across the x- and y-axes.

Match the function with its graph.

1. $f(x) = 3|x|$ **2.** $f(x) = -3|x|$ **3.** $f(x) = \frac{1}{3}|x|$

A.

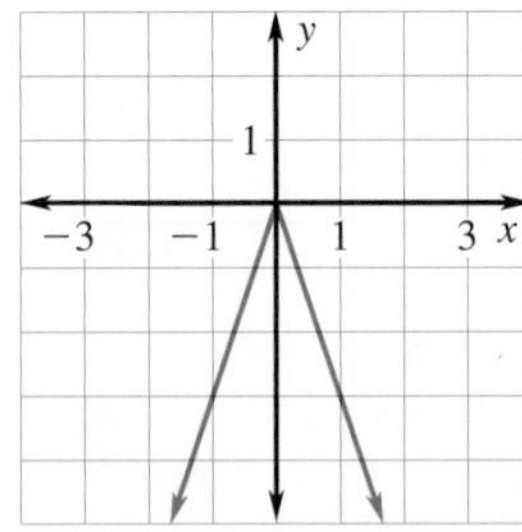

B.

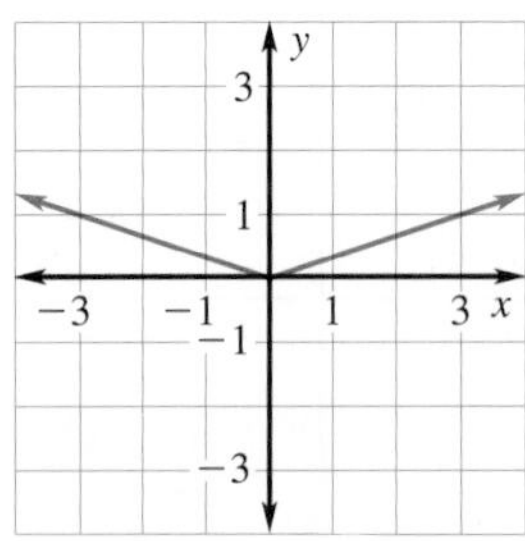

C.

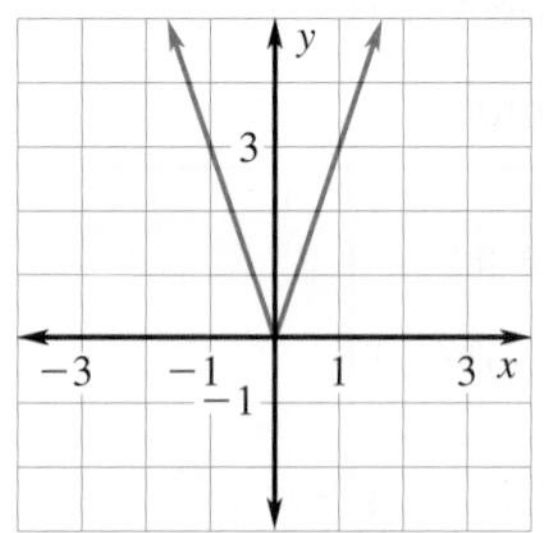

Match the function with its graph.

4. $f(x) = |x - 7|$ **5.** $f(x) = |x| - 7$ **6.** $f(x) = |x + 7|$

A.

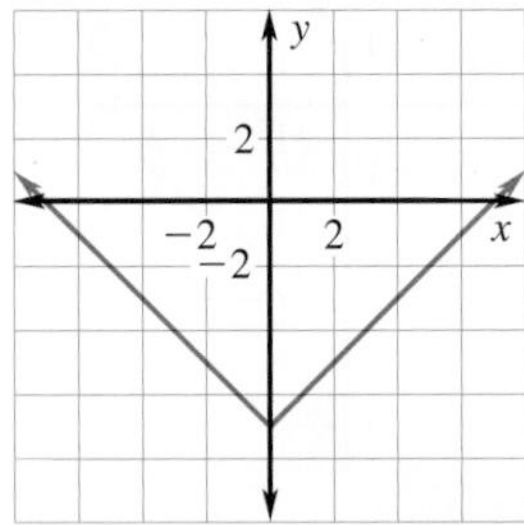

B.

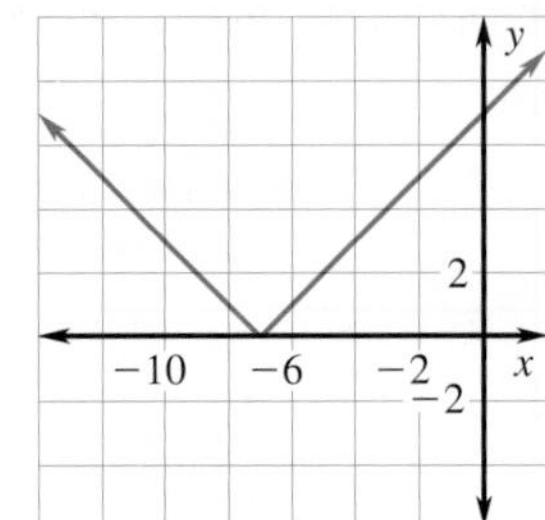

C.

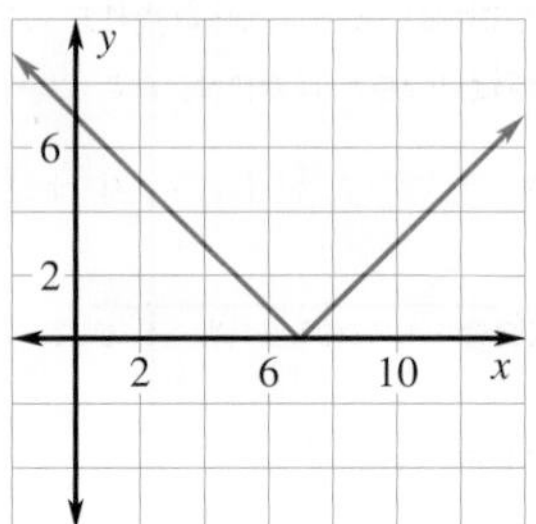

Graph the function. *Compare* the graph with the graph of $f(x) = |x|$.

7. $g(x) = |x + 5|$ **8.** $g(x) = |x| - 6$ **9.** $g(x) = -4|x|$

10. $g(x) = |x - 8|$ **11.** $g(x) = 8|x|$ **12.** $g(x) = -0.25|x|$

13. $g(x) = -|x - 6|$ **14.** $g(x) = |x| + \frac{1}{2}$ **15.** $g(x) = 3|x| - 4$

16. Multiple Representations Consider the function $g(x) = |x - 2| + 1$.

a. Comparing Graphs *Compare* the graph of g to the graph of $f(x) = |x|$.

b. Analyzing a Function How could $g(x)$ be written so that it opens down?

c. Analyzing a Function How could $g(x)$ be written so that it is 2 units to the left and 1 unit down of the graph of $f(x) = |x|$?

UNIT 1

TEST | for Unit 1

Identify what you know and what you need to find out. Then solve the problem.

1. You are responsible for buying the hamburger rolls for an upcoming picnic. Each bag of rolls cost \$1.30 and contains 8 rolls. You need to buy a total of 64 rolls. How much money will it cost for the rolls?

Graph the function.

2. $y = 4x + 1$; domain: 0, 1, 2, 3
3. $y = \frac{1}{2}x - 1$; domain: 4, 8, 12, 16

Draw the line that has the given intercepts.

4. x-intercept: -4; y-intercept: 6
5. x-intercept: 2; y-intercept: -5

Find the slope of the line that passes through the points.

6. $(0, 1), (5, 6)$
7. $(4, 1), (7, 5)$
8. $(-3, -1), (2, -1)$

Graph the equation.

9. $y = -2x + 7$
10. $y = 3x - 8$
11. $y = -4x - 1$
12. $5x - 4y = 0$
13. $x - 4y = 12$
14. $-3x + 6y = -24$

Tell whether the graphs of the two equations are *parallel lines, perpendicular lines,* or *neither.*

15. $y = -3x - 1, 6y = 4 + 2x$
16. $10y + 20 = 6x, 5y = 3x + 35$

Graph the function. *Compare* the graph to the graph of $f(x) = x$.

17. $g(x) = x + 1$
18. $g(x) = x - 4$
19. $g(x) = -2x$

Graph the function. *Compare* the graph with the graph of $f(x) = |x|$.

20. $g(x) = |x - 3|$
21. $g(x) = 0.6|x|$
22. $g(x) = |x| + 1$

Find the zero of the function.

23. $f(x) = 16x - 4$
24. $f(x) = \frac{3}{4}x - 3$
25. $g(x) = -6 - 0.2x$

Make a scatter plot of the data. Find the equation of the best-fitting line.

26.

x	−1	0	1	2	3
y	3	3	1	0	−3

27.

x	−1	0	1	2	3
y	−2	0	1	3	5

UNIT 1

28. Nutrition The table shows the number of grams of protein and the number of calories from protein in four different foods.

Number of grams of protein, p	6	8	12	15
Number of calories from protein, c	24	32	48	60

a. Use the table to write a rule for the foods' number of calories from protein as a function of their number of grams of protein.

b. Another food has 17 grams of protein. Predict the number of calories from protein.

29. Agriculture The table shows the federal outlays for agriculture (in billions of dollars) from 2000 through 2004.

Year	Federal Outlay (in billions)
2000	36.5
2001	26.3
2002	22.0
2003	22.5
2004	15.4

a. Find an equation that models federal outlays (in billions of dollars) as a function of the number of years since 2000.

b. At approximately what rate did the federal outlays change from 2000 to 2004?

c. Find the zero of the function. *Explain* what the zero means in this situation.

30. Business Curtis is renting a T-shirt printing machine for a week. A small printing machine costs \$200 per week to rent. He plans to sell T-shirts for \$8 each. The profit P (in dollars) Curtis makes after selling n T-shirts is given by $P = 8n - 200$.

a. Graph the equation.

b. If Curtis decided to rent a larger printing machine for \$350, the profit is given by $P = 8n - 350$. Graph this equation on the same coordinate plane you used in part (a).

c. Curtis can print 100 T-shirts with the small printing machine and 150 T-shirts with the larger printing machine. If Curtis is able to sell all of the T-shirts, which machine should Curtis rent?

Performance Task

Cell Phone

You have a cell phone plan that charges you \$33 a month and 5 cents for each minute that you use. The monthly bill g (in dollars) can be written as the function $g(x) = 0.05x + 33$ where x is the number of minutes used.

a. What is the slope of the graph of the function?

b. What is the y-intercept of the graph of the function?

c. Graph the function with domain 0, 100, 200, and 300.

d. *Compare* the graph to the graph of $f(x) = x$.

e. What will your monthly bill be if you use 500 minutes?

f. If your monthly bill came to \$99, how many minutes did you use?

UNIT 2

Algebra: Polynomials and Quadratic Functions

Georgia Performance Standards

MM1A2c Add, subtract, multiply, and divide polynomials.

Investigating Math Activity
Addition of Polynomials

Use before Lesson 2.1

Materials algebra tiles

Question

How can you model the addition of polynomials with algebra tiles?

Explore

Add $2x^2 + 5x - 3$ and $x^2 - 3x + 1$.

Algebra tiles can be used to model polynomials.

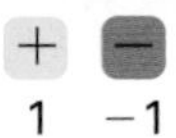

These 1-by-1 square tiles have an area of 1 square unit.

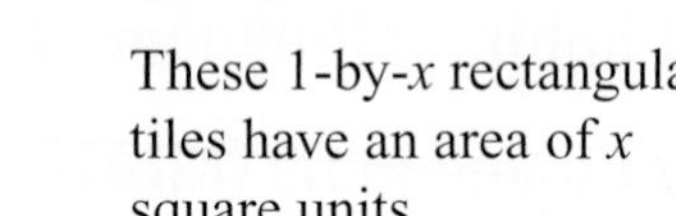

These 1-by-x rectangular tiles have an area of x square units.

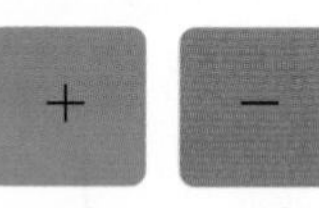

These x-by-x rectangular tiles have an area of x^2 square units.

STEP 1 Model polynomials

Use algebra tiles to model $(2x^2 + 5x - 3) + (x^2 - 3x + 1)$.

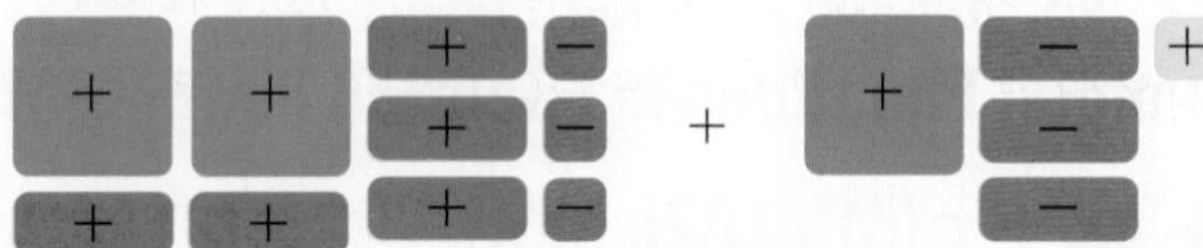

STEP 2 Combine like terms

To add the polynomials, combine like terms. Group the x^2-tiles, the x-tiles, and the 1-tiles.

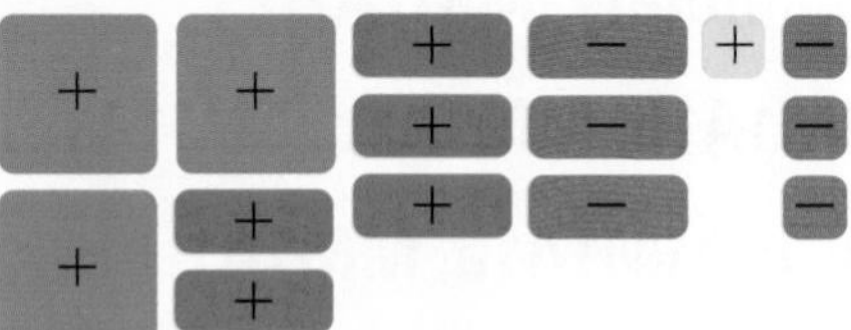

STEP 3 Form zero pairs

Rearrange the tiles to form zero pairs. Remove the zero pairs. The sum is $3x^2 + 2x - 2$.

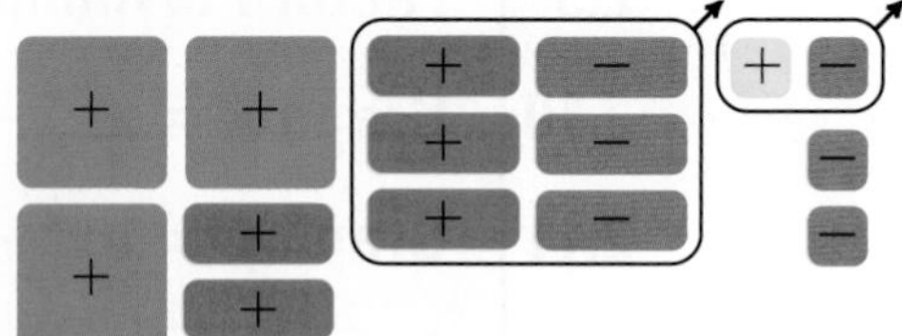

Draw Conclusions

In Exercises 1 and 2, use algebra tiles to find the sum. Sketch your solution.

1. $(-x^2 + 2x - 1) + (4x^2 + 3x - 2)$

2. $(5x^2 - x + 4) + (-3x^2 + 4x - 6)$

3. **Writing** *Describe* how to use algebra tiles to model subtraction of polynomials.

Use algebra tiles to find the difference.

4. $(x^2 + 2x + 1) - (x^2 + 4)$

5. $(-x^2 - 2x + 4) - (2x^2 - 5x + 1)$

UNIT 2

LESSON 2.1

Add and Subtract Polynomials

Georgia Performance Standards: MM1A2c

Goal Add and subtract polynomials.

Vocabulary

A **monomial** is a number, a variable, or the product of a number and one or more variables with whole number exponents.

The **degree of a monomial** is the sum of the exponents of the variables in the monomial. The degree of a nonzero constant term is 0.

A **polynomial** is a monomial or a sum of monomials, each called a *term* of the polynomial.

The **degree of a polynomial** is the greatest degree of its terms.

When a polynomial is written so that the exponents of a variable decrease from left to right, the coefficient of the first term is called the **leading coefficient.**

A polynomial with two terms is called a **binomial.**

A polynomial with three terms is called a **trinomial.**

UNIT 2

Example 1 Rewrite a polynomial

Write $12x^3 - 15x + 13x^5$ so that the exponents decrease from left to right. Identify the degree and the leading coefficient of the polynomial.

Solution

Consider the degree of each of the polynomial's terms.

Degree is 3. Degree is 1. Degree is 5.

$$12x^3 - 15x + 13x^5$$

The polynomial can be rewritten as $13x^5 + 12x^3 - 15x$. The greatest degree is 5, so the degree of the polynomial is 5, and the leading coefficient is 13.

Guided Practice for Example 1

Write the polynomial so that the exponents decrease from left to right. Identify the degree and the leading coefficient of the polynomial.

1. $9 - 2x^2$

2. $16 + 3y^3 + 2y$

3. $6z^3 + 7z^2 - 3z^5$

4. $4a + 5a^4 - 8a^2$

5. $2b^2 - 10 - b^3$

6. $-11c + 14c^4 + 18c^6$

Georgia Performance Standards

MM1A2c Add, subtract, multiply, and divide polynomials.

Example 2 Add polynomials

Find the sum.

a. $(3x^4 - 2x^3 + 5x^2) + (7x^2 + 9x^3 - 2x)$

b. $(7x^2 - 3x + 6) + (9x^2 + 6x - 11)$

Solution

a. Vertical format: Align like terms in vertical columns.

$$\begin{array}{rrrrr} 3x^4 & - 2x^3 & + 5x^2 & & \\ + & 9x^3 & + 7x^2 & - 2x \\ \hline 3x^4 & + 7x^3 & + 12x^2 & - 2x \end{array}$$

b. Horizontal format: Group like terms and simplify.

$$\begin{aligned}(7x^2 - 3x + 6) + (9x^2 + 6x - 11) &= (7x^2 + 9x^2) + (-3x + 6x) + (6 - 11) \\ &= 16x^2 + 3x - 5\end{aligned}$$

Example 3 Subtract polynomials

Find the difference.

a. $(3x^2 - 9x) - (2x^2 - 5x + 6)$ **b.** $(11x^2 + 6x - 1) - (2x^2 - 7x + 5)$

Solution

a. Vertical format: Align like terms in vertical columns.

$$\begin{array}{r} 3x^2 - 9x \\ -\ (2x^2 - 5x + 6) \\ \hline \end{array} \longrightarrow \begin{array}{r} 3x^2 - 9x \\ -\ 2x^2 + 5x - 6 \\ \hline x^2 - 4x - 6 \end{array}$$

b. Horizontal format: Group like terms and simplify.

$$\begin{aligned}(11x^2 + 6x - 1) - (2x^2 - 7x + 5) &= 11x^2 + 6x - 1 - 2x^2 + 7x - 5 \\ &= (11x^2 - 2x^2) + (6x + 7x) + (-1 - 5) \\ &= 9x^2 + 13x - 6\end{aligned}$$

Guided Practice for Examples 2 and 3

Find the sum or difference.

7. $(2a^2 + 7) + (7a^2 + 4a - 3)$

8. $(9b^2 - b + 8) + (4b^2 - b - 3)$

9. $(7c^3 - 6c + 4) - (9c^3 - 5c^2 - c)$

10. $(d^2 - 15d + 10) - (-12d^2 + 8d - 1)$

LESSON 2.1

Exercise Set A

MM1A2c Add, subtract, multiply, and divide polynomials.

Write the polynomial so that the exponents decrease from left to right. Identify the degree and leading coefficient of the polynomial.

1. $4n^5$

2. $4x - 2x^2 + 3$

3. $6y^3 - 2y^2 + 4y^4 - 5$

Tell whether the expression is a polynomial. If it is a polynomial, find its degree and classify it by the number of its terms. Otherwise, tell why it is not a polynomial.

4. 10^x

5. $-6n^2 - n^3 + 4$

6. $w^{-3} + 5$

Find the sum or difference.

7. $(3z^2 + z - 4) + (2z^2 + 2z - 3)$

8. $(8c^2 - 4c + 1) + (-3c^2 + c + 5)$

9. $(2x^2 + 5x - 1) + (x^2 - 5x + 7)$

10. $(10b^2 - 3b + 2) - (4b^2 + 5b + 1)$

11. $(-4m^2 + 3m - 1) - (m + 2)$

12. $(3m + 4) - (2m^2 - 6m + 5)$

Write a polynomial that represents the perimeter of the figure.

13.

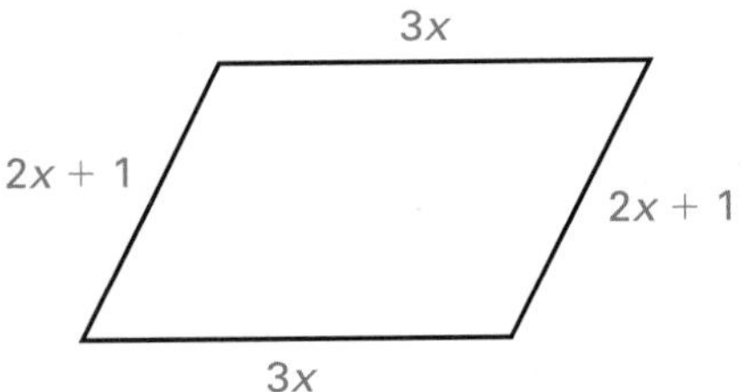

14.

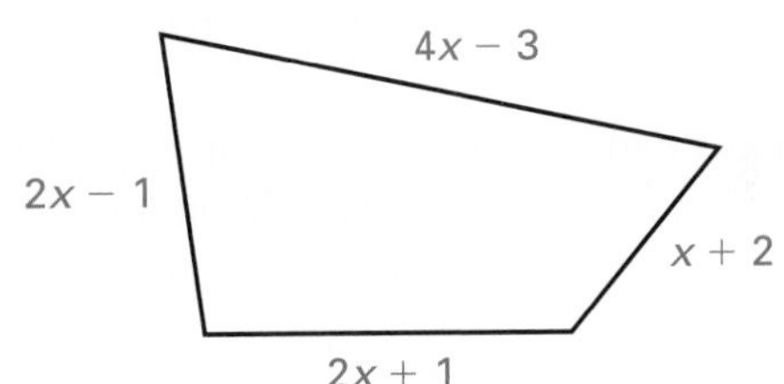

15. Floor Plan The first floor of a home has the floor plan shown. Find the area of the first floor.

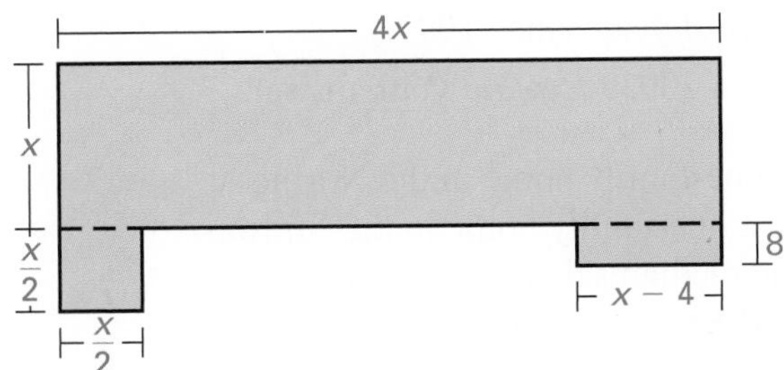

16. Profit For 1995 through 2005, the revenue R (in dollars) and the cost C (in dollars) of producing a product can be modeled by

$$R = \frac{1}{4}t^2 + \frac{21}{4}t + 400 \quad \text{and} \quad C = \frac{1}{12}t^2 + \frac{13}{4}t + 200$$

where t is the number of years since 1995. Write an equation for the profit earned from 1995 through 2005. (*Hint:* Profit = Revenue − Cost)

LESSON 2.1 **Exercise Set B**

MM1A2c Add, subtract, multiply, and divide polynomials.

Tell whether the expression is a polynomial. If it is a polynomial, find its degree and classify it by the number of its terms. Otherwise, tell why it is not a polynomial.

1. -8

2. $x^2 - 5x + x^{-1}$

3. $-3b^2 - 5 + \frac{1}{2}b$

Find the sum or difference.

4. $(3m^3 + 2m + 1) + (4m^2 - 3m + 1)$

5. $(-4y^2 + y + 5) + (4 - 3y - y^2)$

6. $(-4c + c^3 + 8) + (c^2 - 5c - 3)$

7. $(-3z + 6) - (4z^2 - 7z - 8)$

8. $(14x^4 - 3x^2 + 2) - (3x^3 + 4x^2 + 5)$

9. $(5 - x^4 - 2x^3) - (-6x^2 + 5x + 5)$

10. Find the sum $f(x) + g(x)$ and the difference $f(x) - g(x)$ for the functions $f(x) = -5x^2 + 2x - 1$ and $g(x) = 6x^3 + 2x^2 - 5$.

Find the sum or difference.

11. $(10a^2b^2 - 7a^2b) + (-4a^3b^2 + 5a^2b^2 - 3a^2b + 5)$

12. $(6m^2n - 5mn^2 - 8n + 2m) - (6n^2m + 3m^2n)$

13. Mineral Production For 1997 through 2003, the amount P of peat produced (in thousand metric tons) and the amount L of perlite produced (in thousand metric tons) in the United States can be modeled by

$$P = 3.09t^4 - 36.74t^3 + 121.38t^2 - 77.65t + 663.57 \text{ and}$$
$$L = 1.84t^4 - 20.04t^3 + 56.27t^2 - 48.77t + 703.94$$

where t is the number of years since 1997.

a. Write an equation that gives the total number T of thousand metric tons of peat and perlite produced as a function of the number of years since 1997.

b. Was more peat and perlite produced in 1997 or in 2003? *Explain* your answer.

14. Home Sales In 1997, the median sale price for a one-family home in the Northeast was about \$187,443 and the median sale price for a one-family home in the Midwest was about \$151,629. From 1997 through 2003, the median sale price for a one-family home in the Northeast increased by about \$13,857 per year and the median sale price for a one-family home in the Midwest increased by about \$5457 per year.

a. Write two equations that model the median sale prices of a one-family home in the Northeast and Midwest as functions of the number of years since 1997.

b. How much more did a home in the Northeast cost than a home in the Midwest in 1997 and 2003? What was the change in the sale price of each area from 1997 to 2003?

Georgia Performance Standards

MM1A2c Add, subtract, multiply, and divide polynomials

MM1A2g Use area and volume models for polynomial arithmetic.

Investigating Math Activity

Multiplication with Algebra Tiles

Use before Lesson 2.2

Materials algebra tiles

Question

How can you multiply binomials using algebra tiles?

Explore

Find the product $(x + 2)(2x + 3)$.

STEP 1 Model the rectangle's dimensions

Model each binomial with algebra tiles. Arrange the first binomial vertically and the second horizontally, as shown. These polynomials model the length and width of a rectangle.

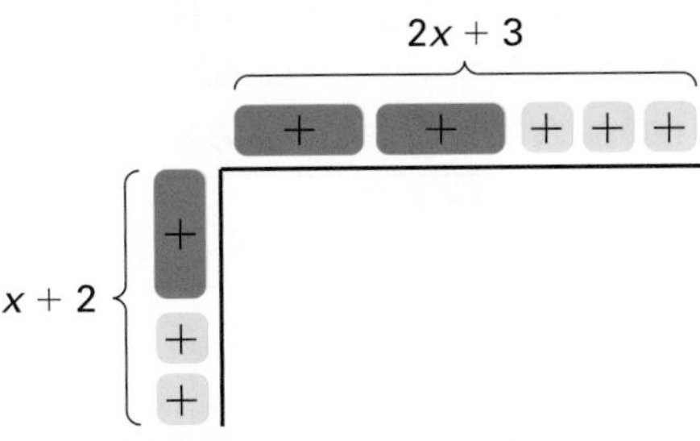

STEP 2 Fill in the area

Fill in the rectangle with the appropriate algebra tiles.

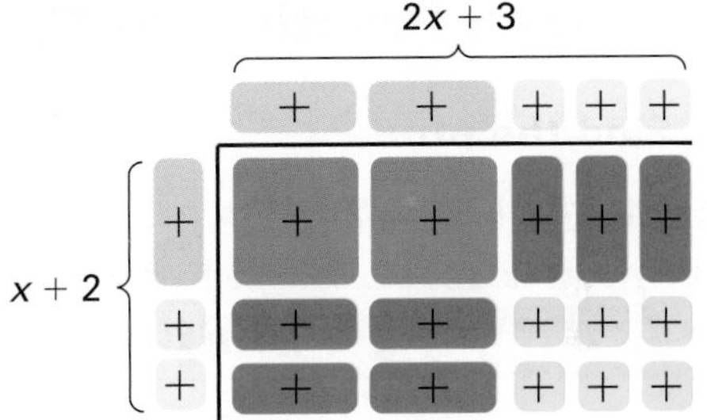

STEP 3 Find the product

The rectangle you created represents the polynomial $2x^2 + 7x + 6$.
So, $(x + 2)(2x + 3) = 2x^2 + 7x + 6$.

Draw Conclusions

Use algebra tiles to find the product. Include a drawing of your model.

1. $(x + 2)(x + 3)$
2. $(x + 3)(x + 6)$
3. $(2x + 1)(x + 3)$
4. $(3x + 1)(x + 2)$
5. $(3x + 1)(2x + 1)$
6. $(4x + 1)(2x + 3)$
7. **Reasoning** Find the product $x(2x + 3)$ and the product $2(2x + 3)$. What is the sum of these two products? What do your answers suggest you can do to find the product $(x + 2)(2x + 3)$?

UNIT 2

LESSON 2.2

Multiply Polynomials

Georgia Performance Standards: MM1A2c, MM1A2g

Goal Multiply polynomials.

Vocabulary

An **area model for polynomial arithmetic** is a way to visually represent multiplying two polynomials using geometry.

A **volume model for polynomial arithmetic** is a way to visually represent multiplying three polynomials using geometry.

Example 1 Multiply a monomial and a polynomial

Find the product $5x^4(2x^3 - 3x^2 + x - 6)$.

$5x^4(2x^3 - 3x^2 + x - 6)$	Write product.
$= 5x^4(2x^3) - 5x^4(3x^2) + 5x^4(x) - 5x^4(6)$	Distributive property
$= 10x^7 - 15x^6 + 5x^5 - 30x^4$	Product of powers property

Guided Practice for Example 1

Find the product.

1. $3x^2(7x^2 - 2x + 3)$

2. $4x^5(3x^3 - 2x^2 - 8x + 9)$

Example 2 Multiply polynomials using an area model

Write a polynomial for the area of the model shown.

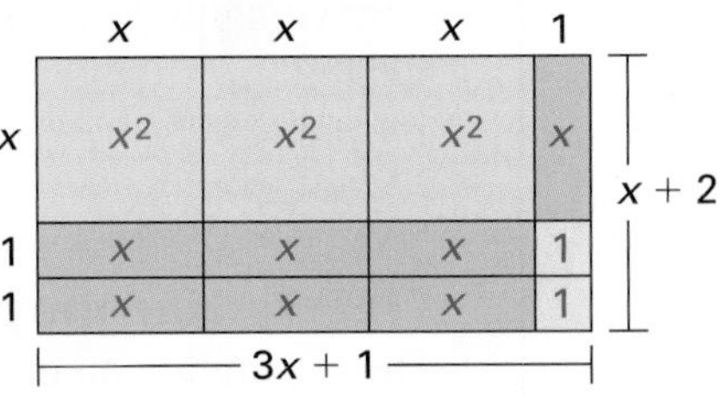

You know that the area of a rectangle is the product of its length and width. In the model, let $3x + 1$ represent the length and let $x + 2$ represent the width. To find the total area of the model, add the areas of each rectangular part.

$$A = \ell \cdot w = (3x + 1)(x + 2) = x^2 + x^2 + x^2 + x + x + x + x + x + x + x + 1 + 1$$
$$= 3x^2 + 7x + 2$$

Example 3 Multiply polynomials horizontally

Find the product $(9x^2 - x + 6)(5x - 2)$.

$(9x^2 - x + 6)(5x - 2)$	Write product.
$= 9x^2(5x - 2) - x(5x - 2) + 6(5x - 2)$	Distributive property
$= 45x^3 - 18x^2 - 5x^2 + 2x + 30x - 12$	Distributive property
$= 45x^3 - 23x^2 + 32x - 12$	Combine like terms.

UNIT 2

Georgia Performance Standards

MM1A2c Add, subtract, multiply, and divide polynomials. ☑

MM1A2g Use area and volume models for polynomial arithmetic. ☑

Example 4 Multiply binomials

Find the product $(2x - 1)(7x + 6)$.

$(2x - 1)(7x + 6)$	Write product.
$= (2x)(7x) + (2x)(6) + (-1)(7x) + (-1)(6)$	Write products of terms.
$= 14x^2 + 12x + (-7x) + (-6)$	Multiply.
$= 14x^2 + 5x - 6$	Combine like terms.

Guided Practice for Examples 2, 3, and 4

3. The dimensions of a rectangle are $y + 9$ and $2y + 3$. Draw an area model. Then write an expression for the area of the rectangle.

Find the product.

4. $(m^2 + 6m + 4)(3m - 1)$

5. $(2n + 7)(3n + 4)$

6. $(2p^2 - p + 6)(p + 7)$

7. $(8s - 7)(9s - 7)$

Example 5 Multiply polynomials using a volume model

Write a polynomial for the volume of the rectangular prism shown.

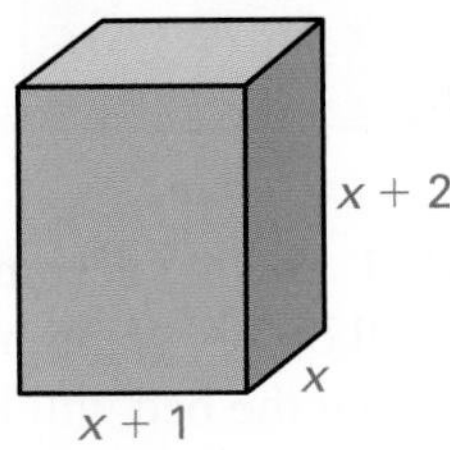

You know that the volume of a rectangular prism is the product of its length, width, and height. In the figure shown, let x represent the length, $x + 1$ represent the width, and $x + 2$ represent the height.

Volume = length • width • height	Formula for volume of a rectangular prism
$= x(x + 1)(x + 2)$	Substitute for length, width, and height.
$= x[(x)(x) + (x)(2) + (1)(x) + (1)(2)]$	Write products of terms.
$= x(x^2 + 2x + x + 2)$	Multiply.
$= x(x^2 + 3x + 2)$	Combine like terms.
$= x(x^2) + x(3x) + x(2)$	Distributive property
$= x^3 + 3x^2 + 2x$	Product of powers property

Guided Practice for Example 5

8. The dimensions of a rectangle are x, $x + 8$, and $x + 4$. Write an expression for the volume of the prism.

LESSON 2.2 **Exercise Set A**

MM1A2c Add, subtract, multiply, and divide polynomials.

MM1A2g Use area and volume models for polynomial arithmetic.

Find the product.

1. $x^2(6x^2 - 3x - 1)$
2. $-5a^3(4a^4 - 3a + 1)$
3. $4d^2(-2d^3 + 5d^2 - 6d + 2)$
4. $(3x + 1)(2x - 5)$
5. $(2y + 3)(y - 5)$
6. $(6a - 3)(4a - 1)$
7. $(b - 8)(5b - 2)$
8. $(8m + 7)(2m + 3)$
9. $(-p + 2)(3p^2 + 1)$
10. $(2z - 7)(-z + 3)$
11. $(-3d + 10)(2d - 1)$
12. $(n + 1)(n^2 + 4n + 5)$
13. $(w - 3)(w^2 + 8w + 1)$
14. $(2s + 5)(s^2 + 3s - 1)$
15. $(x^2 - 4xy + y^2)(5xy)$

Simplify the expression.

16. $a(3a + 1) + (a + 1)(a - 1)$
17. $(x + 2)(x + 5) - x(4x - 1)$
18. $(m + 7)(m - 3) + (m - 4)(m + 5)$

Write a polynomial for the area of the model.

19.

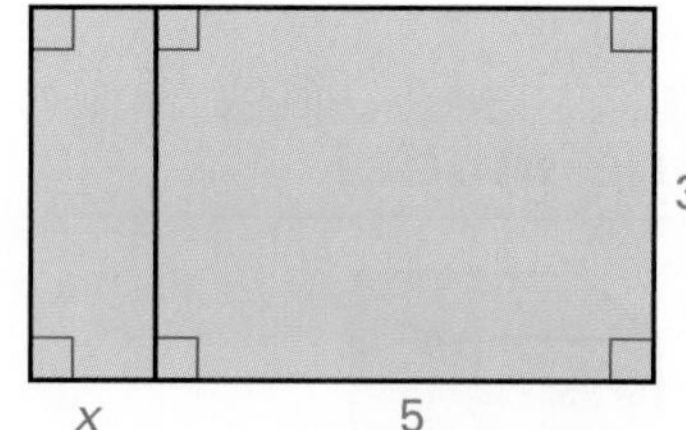

20.

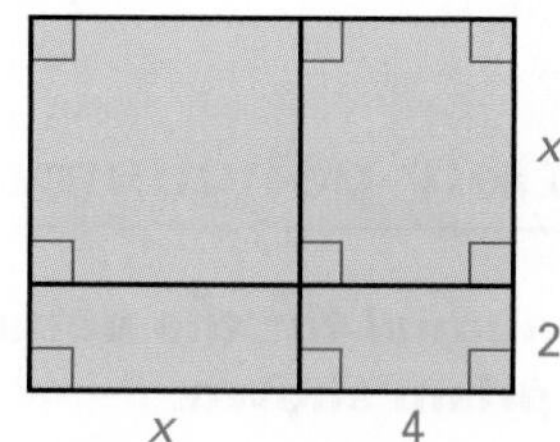

21. **Flower Bed** You are designing a rectangular flower bed that you will border using brick pavers. The width of the border around the bed will be the same on every side, as shown.

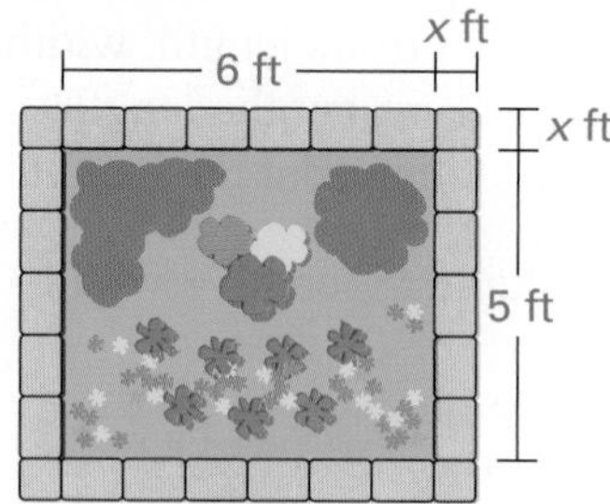

   a. Write a polynomial that represents the total area of the flower bed and the border.
   b. Find the total area of the flower bed and border when the width of the border is 1.5 feet.

22. **Shipping** A box used for shipping is shown at the right.

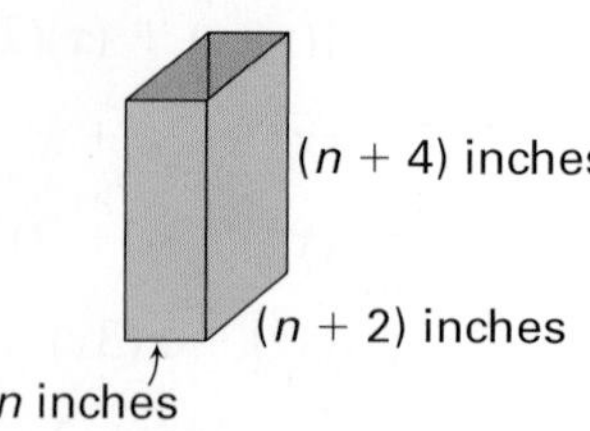

   a. Write a polynomial that represents the area of the base of the box.
   b. Write a polynomial that represents the volume of the box.
   c. What is the volume if the length of the shortest side is 8 inches?

UNIT 2

LESSON 2.2

Exercise Set B

MM1A2c Add, subtract, multiply, and divide polynomials.

MM1A2g Use area and volume models for polynomial arithmetic.

Find the product.

1. $-8y^3(2y^4 - 5y^2 + 3)$
2. $(b + 3)(3b^2 - 2b + 1)$
3. $(6w - 3)(4 - 3w)$
4. $(9m^3 + 1)(4m^2 - 1)$
5. $(2x^2 + 5x - 2)(x + 3)$
6. $(8n^2 - 1)(3n^2 - 4n + 5)$
7. $(3p^4 - 5)(2p^2 + 4)$
8. $(-8r^3 + 2)(6r^2 - 1)$
9. $(-5z^2 - 3)(-2z^2 + 9)$
10. $xy(x^2 + 2y)$
11. $-3x(2xy + 5y)$
12. $y^2(x^2y + y^2x)$
13. $(x - y)(5x + 6y)$
14. $(xy^2 + 70)(3x + 2y)$
15. $(x^2 - 4xy + y^2)(5xy)$

Simplify the expression.

16. $(7n + 1)(3n + 5) + (4n - 2)(3n + 1)$
17. $5w^2(3w^3 - 2w + 1) + w^4(w^2 - 2w + 3)$

Write a polynomial for the area of the model.

18.

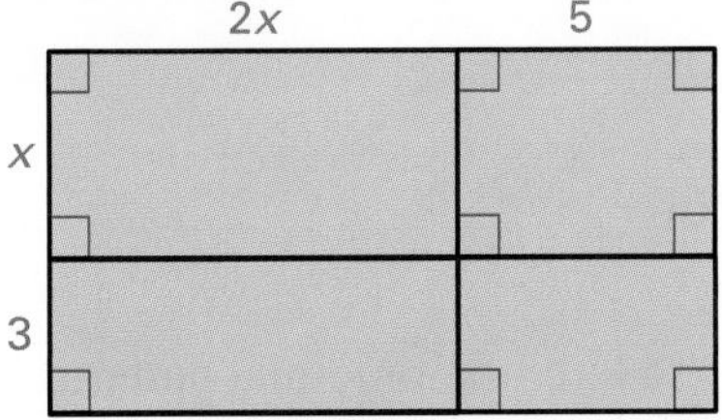

19.

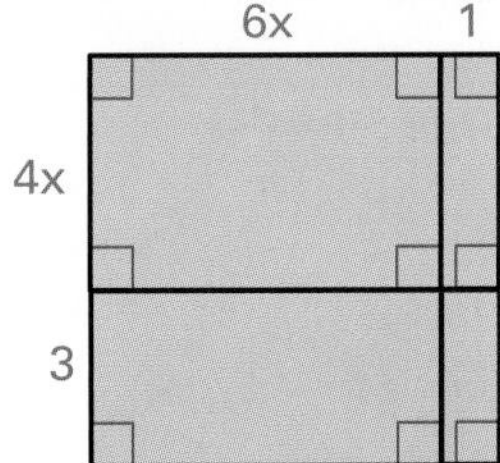

20. **Gifts** An open gift box is shown at the right.

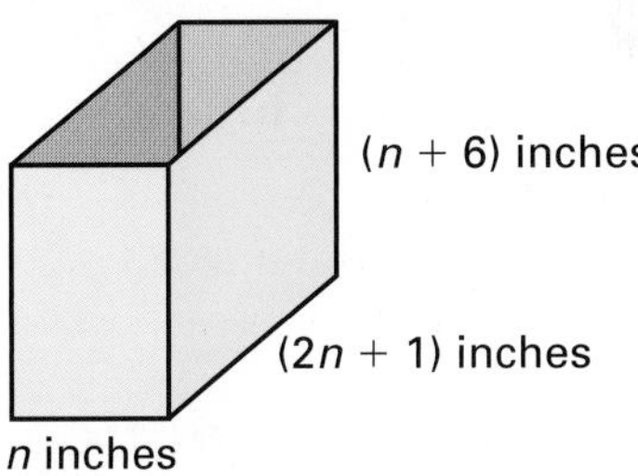

   a. Write a polynomial that represents the area of the base of the box.
   b. Write a polynomial that represents the volume of the box.
   c. Write a polynomial for the area of the base if the length and width increase by 4.

21. **Sporting Goods Equipment** During the period 1990–2002, the amount of money E (in millions of dollars) spent on sporting goods equipment in the U.S. and the percent P (in decimal form) of this amount that is spent on exercise equipment can be modeled by

$$E = -5.56t^4 + 149.93t^3 - 1314.65t^2 + 4396.75t + 14{,}439.09$$
$$\text{and } P = -0.00002t^4 - 0.0005t^3 + 0.0028t^2 + 0.001t + 0.126$$

where t is the number of years since 1990.

   a. Find the values of E and P for $t = 0$. What does the product $E \cdot P$ mean for $t = 0$ in the context of this problem?
   b. Write an equation that models the amount spent on exercise equipment as a function of the number of years since 1990.
   c. How much money was spent in the U.S. on exercise equipment in 1990?

UNIT 2

LESSON 2.3

Find Special Products of Polynomials

Georgia Performance Standards: MM1A2c

Goal Use special product patterns to multiply polynomials.

Square of a Binomial Pattern

Algebra	Example
$(a + b)^2 = a^2 + 2ab + b^2$	$(x + 3)^2 = x^2 + 6x + 9$
$(a - b)^2 = a^2 - 2ab + b^2$	$(3x - 2)^2 = 9x^2 - 12x + 4$

Example 1 Use the square of a binomial pattern

Find the product.

a. $(7x + 2)^2$

b. $(6x - 5y)^2$

Solution

a. $(7x + 2)^2 = (7x)^2 + 2(7x)(2) + 2^2$ — Square of a binomial pattern

$= 49x^2 + 28x + 4$ — Simplify.

b. $(6x - 5y)^2 = (6x)^2 - 2(6x)(5y) + (5y)^2$ — Square of a binomial pattern

$= 36x^2 - 60xy + 25y^2$ — Simplify.

Guided Practice for Example 1

Find the product.

1. $(y + 9)^2$

2. $(3z + 7)^2$

3. $(2w - 3)^2$

4. $(10r - 3s)^2$

Sum and Difference Pattern

Algebra	Example
$(a + b)(a - b) = a^2 - b^2$	$(x + 5)(x - 5) = x^2 - 25$

UNIT 2

Georgia Performance Standards

MM1A2c Add, subtract, multiply, and divide polynomials.

Example 2 Use the sum and difference pattern

Find the product.

a. $(m + 9)(m - 9)$ **b.** $(4n - 3)(4n + 3)$

Solution

a. $(m + 9)(m - 9) = m^2 - 9^2$ Sum and difference pattern

$= m^2 - 81$ Simplify.

b. $(4n - 3)(4n + 3) = (4n)^2 - 3^2$ Sum and difference pattern

$= 16n^2 - 9$ Simplify.

Guided Practice for Example 2

Find the product.

5. $(g + 11)(g - 11)$

6. $(7f - 1)(7f + 1)$

7. $(2h + 9)(2h - 9)$

8. $(6k - 8)(6k + 8)$

Example 3 Use special products and mental math

Use special products to find the product of 37 • 43.

Solution

Notice that 37 is 3 less than 40 while 43 is 3 more than 40.

$37 \cdot 43 = (40 - 3)(40 + 3)$ Write as product of difference and sum.

$= 40^2 - 3^2$ Sum and difference pattern

$= 1600 - 9$ Evaluate powers.

$= 1591$ Simplify.

Guided Practice for Example 3

Describe **how you can use special products to find the product.**

9. 55^2

10. $31 \cdot 49$

UNIT 2

LESSON 2.3 **Exercise Set A**

MM1A2c Add, subtract, multiply, and divide polynomials.

Find the product of the square of the binomial.

1. $(x - 9)^2$
2. $(m + 11)^2$
3. $(5s + 2)^2$
4. $(3m + 7)^2$
5. $(4p - 5)^2$
6. $(7a - 6)^2$
7. $(10z - 3)^2$
8. $(2x + y)^2$
9. $(3y - x)^2$

Find the product of the sum and difference.

10. $(a - 9)(a + 9)$
11. $(z - 20)(z + 20)$
12. $(5r + 1)(5r - 1)$
13. $(6m + 10)(6m - 10)$
14. $(7p - 2)(7p + 2)$
15. $(9c - 1)(9c + 1)$
16. $(4x + 3)(4x - 3)$
17. $(4 - w)(4 + w)$
18. $(5 - 2y)(5 + 2y)$

Describe **how you can use mental math to find the product.**

19. $15 \cdot 25$
20. $43 \cdot 57$
21. 18^2

Perform the indicated operation using the functions $f(x) = 4x + 0.5$ and $g(x) = 4x - 0.5$.

22. $f(x) \cdot g(x)$
23. $(f(x))^2$
24. $(g(x))^2$

25. **Error Analysis** *Describe* and correct the error in multiplying $(s - 5)^2$.

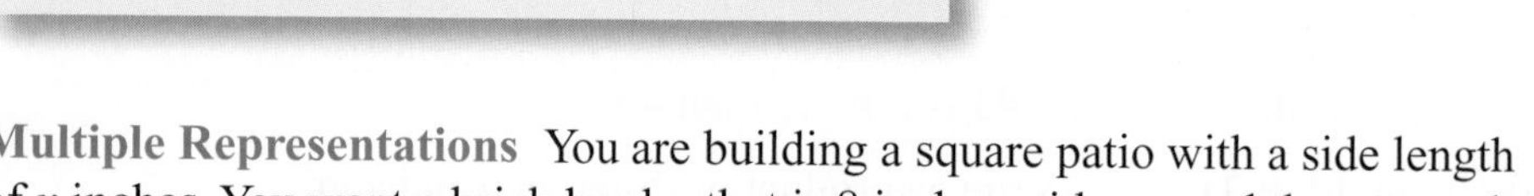

$$(s - 5)^2 = s^2 - 2(s)(-5) + (-5)^2$$
$$= s^2 + 10s + 25$$

26. **Multiple Representations** You are building a square patio with a side length of x inches. You want a brick border that is 8 inches wide around the outer edge of the patio.
    a. **Drawing a Model** Draw an area model.
    b. **Writing an Expression** Use the square of a binomial pattern to write an expression for the total area of the patio including the brick border.
    c. **Evaluating an Expression** Find the total area of the patio including the brick border if the side length of the patio is 96 inches.

LESSON 2.3 **Exercise Set B**

MM1A2c Add, subtract, multiply, and divide polynomials.

Find the product.

1. $(8x - 5)^2$
2. $(4p + 4)^2$
3. $(10m - 11)^2$
4. $(11s - 10)^2$
5. $(20b - 15)^2$
6. $(m + 4n)^2$
7. $(r - 8s)^2$
8. $(10a + 3b)^2$
9. $(2x - 4y)^2$
10. $(8p - 3)(8p + 3)$
11. $(11t + 4)(11t - 4)$
12. $(7n - 5)(7n + 5)$
13. $(9z + 12)(9z - 12)$
14. $(15 - w)(15 + w)$
15. $(6 - 5p)(6 + 5p)$
16. $(20 - 3m)(20 + 3m)$
17. $(10a - 5b)(10a + 5b)$
18. $(4x - 3y)(4x + 3y)$

Describe **how you can use mental math to find the product.**

19. $36 \cdot 44$
20. 23^2
21. 49^2

Perform the indicated operation using the functions $f(x) = 9x - 0.5$ and $g(x) = 9x + 0.5$.

22. $f(x) \cdot g(x)$
23. $(f(x) + g(x))^2$
24. $(f(x) - g(x))^2$

25. Write two binomials that have the product $x^2 - 144$. *Explain* how you found your answer.

26. Write a pattern for the cube of a binomial $(a - b)^3$. *Justify* your answer.

27. **Total Profit** For 1995 through 2005, the number N (in thousands) of units produced by a manufacturing company can be modeled by $N = 1.4t + 2.1$ and the profit P (in dollars per unit) can be modeled by $P = 1.4t - 2.1$ where t is the number of years since 1995.
    a. Write a polynomial that models the company total profit T (in thousands of dollars) in terms of the number of years since 1995.
    b. What was the company's total profit in 2002?
    c. In which years from 1995 through 2005 were the company's total profits negative?

28. **Fencing** You use 120 feet of fencing to form a square with a side length of 30 feet. You want to change the dimensions of the enclosed region. For every 1 foot you increase the width, you must decrease the length by 1 foot. Write a polynomial that gives the area of the rectangle after you increase the width by x feet and decrease the length by x feet. *Explain* why any change in dimensions results in an area less than that of the original square.

LESSON 2.4

Use the Binomial Theorem

Georgia Performance Standards: MM1A2d

Goal Use the Binomial Theorem to expand binomials.

Vocabulary

Binomial Theorem and Pascal's Triangle

The numbers in **Pascal's triangle** can be used to find coefficients in binomial expansions $(a + b)^n$ where n is a postive integer.

Binomial expansion	Pascal's Triangle	
$(a + b)^0 = \mathbf{1}$	1	$n = 0$ (0th row)
$(a + b)^1 = \mathbf{1}a + \mathbf{1}b$	1 1	$n = 1$ (1st row)
$(a + b)^2 = \mathbf{1}a^2 + \mathbf{2}ab + \mathbf{1}b^2$	1 2 1	$n = 2$ (2nd row)
$(a + b)^3 = \mathbf{1}a^3 + \mathbf{3}a^2b + \mathbf{3}ab^2 + \mathbf{1}b^3$	1 3 3 1	$n = 3$ (3rd row)
$(a + b)^4 = \mathbf{1}a^4 + \mathbf{4}a^3b + \mathbf{6}a^2b^2 + \mathbf{4}ab^3 + \mathbf{1}b^4$	1 4 6 4 1	$n = 4$ (4th row)

The first and last numbers in each row are 1. Beginning with the 2nd row, every other number is formed by adding the two numbers immediately above the number.

UNIT 2

Example 1 Use Pascal's triangle

Use the fourth row of Pascal's triangle to find the numbers in the fifth row of Pascal's triangle.

Solution

Write the fifth row of Pascal's triangle by adding numbers from the fourth row.

$n = 4$ (4th row) 1 4 6 4 1

$n = 5$ (5th row) 1 5 10 10 5 1

The first and last numbers are 1, so the numbers in the fifth row of Pascal's triangle are 1, 5, 10, 10, 5, and 1.

Guided Practice for Example 1

1. Find the numbers in the sixth row of Pascal's triangle.
2. Find the numbers in the seventh row of Pascal's triangle.

Georgia Performance Standards

MM1A2d Expand binomials using the Binomial Theorem.

Example 2 Expand a power of a binomial sum

Use the Binomial Theorem and Pascal's triangle to write the binomial expansion of $(x + 2)^3$.

Solution

The binomial coefficients from the third row of Pascal's Triangle are 1, 3, 3, and 1. So, the expansion is as follows.

$$(x + 2)^3 = (1)(x^3) + (3)(x^2)(2) + (3)(x)(2^2) + (1)(2^3)$$
$$= x^3 + 6x^2 + 12x + 8$$

Guided Practice for Example 2

Use the Binomial Theorem and Pascal's triangle to write the binomial expansion.

3. $(x + 5)^3$

4. $(x + 1)^4$

5. $(3 + y)^5$

UNIT 2

Example 3 Expand a power of a binomial difference

Use the Binomial Theorem and Pascal's triangle to write the binomial expansion of $(x - 3)^4$.

Solution

The binomial coefficients from the fourth row of Pascal's Triangle are 1, 4, 6, 4, and 1. So, the expansion is as follows.

$$(x - 3)^4 = [x + (-3)]^4$$
$$= (1)(x^4) + (4)(x^3)(-3) + (6)(x^2)(-3)^2 + (4)(x)(-3)^3 + (1)(-3)^4$$
$$= x^4 - 12x^3 + 54x^2 - 108x + 81$$

Guided Practice for Example 3

Use the Binomial Theorem and Pascal's triangle to write the binomial expansion.

6. $(x - 1)^2$

7. $(x - 2)^3$

8. $(4 - y)^4$

Example 4 Expand a power of a binomial sum

Use the Binomial Theorem and Pascal's triangle to write the binomial expansion of $(2x + 3)^4$.

Solution

The binomial coefficients from the fourth row of Pascal's Triangle are 1, 4, 6, 4, and 1. So, the expansion is as follows.

$$(2x + 3)^4 = (1)(2x)^4 + (4)(2x)^3(3) + (6)(2x)^2(3^2) + (4)(2x)(3^3) + (1)(3^4)$$
$$= 16x^4 + 96x^3 + 216x^2 + 216x + 81$$

Guided Practice for Example 4

Use the Binomial Theorem and Pascal's triangle to write the binomial expansion.

9. $(2x - 1)^3$

10. $(a + 3b)^4$

11. $(5 - 2y)^3$

UNIT 2

Example 5 Find a coefficient in an expansion

Find the coefficient of x^2 in the expansion of $(3x + 2)^5$.

Solution

From Example 1, you know that the binomial coefficients from the fifth row of Pascal's triangle are 1, 5, 10, 10, 5, and 1. From the Binomial Theorem, you know the expansion has the following form.

$$(3x + 2)^5 = (1)(3x)^5 + (5)(3x)^4(2) + (10)(3x)^3(2^2) + (10)(3x)^2(2^3) + (5)(3x)(2^4) + (1)(2^5)$$

The coefficient of the x^2-term is $(10)(3^2)(2^3) = 720$.

Guided Practice for Example 5

12. Find the coefficient of x^3 in the expansion of $(4x - 1)^5$.

13. Find the coefficient of x^4 in the expansion of $(2x + 3)^6$.

14. Find the coefficient of x^2 in the expansion of $(5 - x)^6$.

15. Find the coefficient of x in the expansion of $(3 - x)^5$.

LESSON 2.4 **Exercise Set A**

MM1A2d Expand binomials using the Binomial Theorem.

1. Find the numbers in the eighth row of Pascal's triangle.
2. Find the numbers in the ninth row of Pascal's triangle.

Use the Binomial Theorem and Pascal's triangle to write the binomial expansion.

3. $(x + 1)^2$
4. $(a + 3)^3$
5. $(p + 5)^4$
6. $(2 + y)^4$
7. $(1 + b)^6$
8. $(4 + q)^3$
9. $(x + 4)^2$
10. $(c - 2)^4$
11. $(z - 1)^5$
12. $(1 - g)^3$
13. $(5 - r)^4$
14. $(3 - b)^6$
15. $(2x + 1)^3$
16. $(3x - 1)^4$
17. $(2 + 5y)^3$
18. $(2x - 3)^4$
19. $(a + 4b)^5$
20. $(6x + y)^4$
21. Find the coefficient of x^2 in the expansion of $(x - 7)^4$.
22. Find the coefficient of x^3 in the expansion of $(2x + 5)^5$.
23. Find the coefficient of x^4 in the expansion of $(3x - 4)^6$.
24. **Error Analysis** *Describe* and correct the error in writing the binomial expansion.

$(x - 4)^3 = x^3 + 12x^2 + 48x + 64$

25. How many terms are in the expansion of $(x + y)^n$?
26. Use the diagram shown.

1	Row 0
1 1	Row 1
1 2 1	Row 2
1 3 3 1	Row 3
1 4 6 4 1	Row 4
1 5 10 10 5 1	

a. What is the sum of the numbers in each of rows 0 through 4 of Pascal's triangle?
b. What is the sum in row n?

UNIT 2

LESSON 2.4 **Exercise Set B**

MM1A2d Expand binomials using the Binomial Theorem.

Use the Binomial Theorem and Pascal's triangle to write the binomial expansion.

1. $(x + 4)^3$
2. $(k + 8)^4$
3. $(w + 1)^6$
4. $(7 + y)^5$
5. $(5 + b)^6$
6. $(1 + m)^7$
7. $(x - 1)^6$
8. $(g - 6)^4$
9. $(4 - b)^6$
10. $(m - n)^5$
11. $(4 - 3y)^3$
12. $(2x - 1)^5$
13. $(4x + 2)^3$
14. $(10x - 1)^4$
15. $(5 + 3y)^3$
16. $(u - 2v)^4$
17. $(3c + d)^6$
18. $(4p - q)^6$
19. $(x^2 + 2)^4$
20. $(w^3 - 3)^4$
21. $(2s^4 + 5)^5$

22. Find the coefficient of x in the expansion of $(x + 9)^4$.

23. Find the coefficient of x^2 in the expansion of $(3x - 5)^5$.

24. Find the coefficient of x^4 in the expansion of $(5x - 6)^6$.

25. **Error Analysis** *Describe* and correct the error in writing the binomial expansion.

$$(x + 3)^3 = x^3 + 3x^2 + 3x + 27 \quad X$$

26. How are the expansions of $(x + y)^n$ and $(x - y)^n$ alike? How do they differ?

27. Use the diagram shown to describe the pattern formed by the sums of the numbers along the diagonal segments of Pascal's triangle.

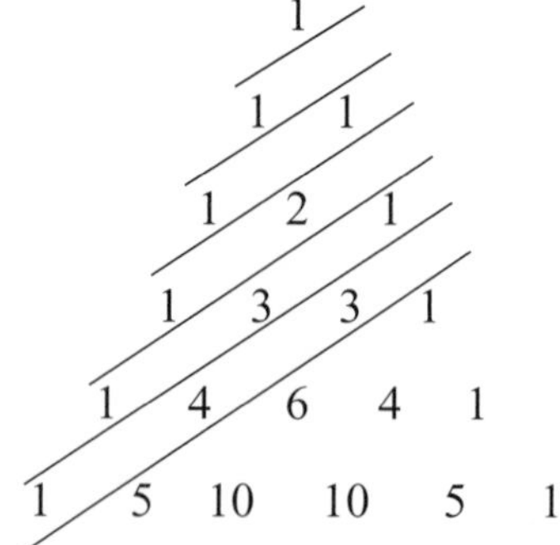

UNIT 2

LESSON 2.5

Solve Polynomial Equations in Factored Form

Georgia Performance Standards: MM1A2f

Goal Solve polynomial equations.

Vocabulary

The zero-product property is used to solve an equation when one side is zero and the other side is a product of polynomial factors. The solutions of such an equation are also called **roots.**

The height of a projectile can be described by the **vertical motion model:** $h = -16t^2 + vt + s$, where t is the time (in seconds) the object has been in the air, v is the initial vertical velocity (in feet per second), and s is the initial height (in feet).

Example 1 Use the zero-product property

Solve $(x - 3)(x + 6) = 0$.

Solution

$(x - 3)(x + 6) = 0$	Write original equation.
$x - 3 = 0$ *or* $x + 6 = 0$	Zero-product property
$x = 3$ *or* $x = -6$	Solve for x.

The solutions of the equation are 3 and -6.

CHECK Substitute each root into the original equation to check.

$(3 - 3)(3 + 6) \stackrel{?}{=} 0$	$(-6 - 3)(-6 + 6) \stackrel{?}{=} 0$
$0 \cdot 9 \stackrel{?}{=} 0$	$-9 \cdot 0 \stackrel{?}{=} 0$
$0 = 0$ ✓	$0 = 0$ ✓

Guided Practice for Example 1

Solve the equation.

1. $(m - 7)(m - 9) = 0$

2. $(5n + 10)(4n + 12) = 0$

Example 2 Solve an equation by factoring

Solve $6x^2 + 12x = 0$.

$6x^2 + 12x = 0$	Write original equation.
$6x(x + 2) = 0$	Factor left side.
$6x = 0$ *or* $x + 2 = 0$	Zero-product property
$x = 0$ *or* $x = -2$	Solve for x.

The solutions of the equation are 0 and -2.

Georgia Performance Standards

MM1A2f Factor expressions by greatest common factor, grouping, trial and error, and special products.

Example 3 Solve an equation by factoring

Solve $9y^2 = 21y$.

$9y^2 = 21y$	Write original equation.
$9y^2 - 21y = 0$	Subtract $21y$ from each side.
$3y(3y - 7) = 0$	Factor left side.
$3y = 0$ *or* $3y - 7 = 0$	Zero-product property
$y = 0$ *or* $y = \frac{7}{3}$	Solve for y.

The solutions of the equation are 0 and $\frac{7}{3}$.

Guided Practice for Examples 2 and 3

Solve the equation.

3. $q^2 + 16q = 0$ **4.** $4k^2 - 8k = 0$ **5.** $12h^2 = 36h$

UNIT 2

Example 4 Solve a multi-step problem

Jump Rope A child jumping rope leaves the ground at an initial vertical velocity of 8 feet per second. After how many seconds does the child land on the ground?

Solution

STEP 1 **Write** a model for the height above the ground.

$h = -16t^2 + vt + s$	Vertical motion model
$h = -16t^2 + 8t + 0$	Substitute 8 for v and 0 for s.
$h = -16t^2 + 8t$	Simplify.

STEP 2 **Substitute** 0 for h. When the child lands, the child's height above the ground is 0 feet. Solve for t.

$0 = -16t^2 + 8t$	Substitute 0 for h.
$0 = 8t(-2t + 1)$	Factor right side.
$8t = 0$ *or* $-2t + 1 = 0$	Zero-product property
$t = 0$ *or* $t = \frac{1}{2}$	Solve for t.

The child lands on the ground $\frac{1}{2}$ second after the child jumps.

Guided Practice for Example 4

6. In Example 4, suppose the initial vertical velocity is 10 feet per second. After how many seconds will the child land on the ground?

LESSON 2.5 **Exercise Set A**

MM1A2f Factor expressions by greatest common factor, grouping, trial and error, and special products.

Solve the equation.

1. $(x + 14)(x - 3) = 0$

2. $(m - 12)(m + 5) = 0$

3. $(p + 15)(p + 24) = 0$

4. $(n - 8)(n - 9) = 0$

5. $(d + 8)\left(d - \frac{1}{2}\right) = 0$

6. $\left(c + \frac{3}{4}\right)(c - 6) = 0$

7. $(2z - 8)(z + 5) = 0$

8. $(y - 3)(5y + 10) = 0$

9. $(6b - 4)(b - 8) = 0$

10. $(8x + 4)(6x - 3) = 0$

11. $(3x + 9)(6x - 3) = 0$

12. $(4x + 5)(4x - 5) = 0$

Factor out the greatest common monomial factor.

13. $10x - 10y$

14. $8x^2 + 20y$

15. $18a^2 - 6b$

16. $4x^2 - 4x$

17. $r^2 + 2rs$

18. $2m^2 + 6mn$

19. $5p^2q + 10q$

20. $9a^5 + a^3$

21. $6w^3 - 14w^2$

Solve the equation.

22. $m^2 - 10m = 0$

23. $b^2 + 14b = 0$

24. $5w^2 - 5w = 0$

25. $24k^2 + 24k = 0$

26. $8r^2 - 24r = 0$

27. $9p^2 + 18p = 0$

28. $6n^2 - 15n = 0$

29. $-8y^2 - 10y = 0$

30. $-10b^2 + 25b = 0$

31. $8c^2 = 4c$

32. $30r^2 = -15r$

33. $-24y^2 = 9y$

34. Diving Board A diver jumps from a diving board that is 24 feet above the water. The height of the diver is given by

$$h = -16(t - 1.5)(t + 1)$$

where the height h is measured in feet, and the time t is measured in seconds. When will the diver hit the water? Can you see a quick way to find the answer? *Explain.*

35. Dog To catch a frisbee, a dog leaps into the air with an initial vertical velocity of 14 feet per second.

a. Write a model for the height of the dog above the ground.

b. After how many seconds does the dog land on the ground?

36. Desktop Areas You have two components to the desktop where you do your homework that fit together into an L-shape. The two components have the same area.

a. Write an equation that relates the areas of the desktop components.

b. Find the value of w.

c. What is the combined area of the desktop components?

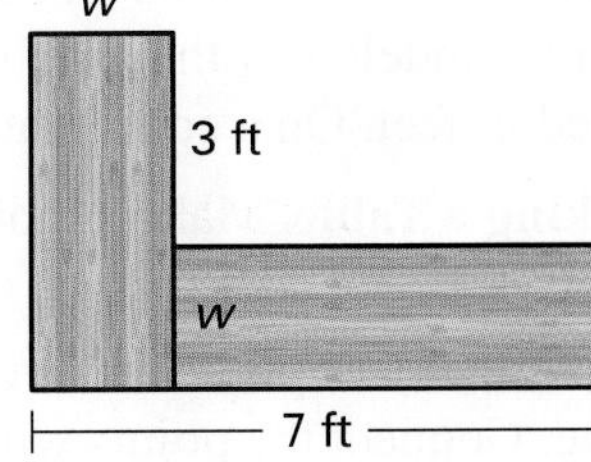

UNIT 2

LESSON 2.5 **Exercise Set B**

MM1A2f Factor expressions by greatest common factor, grouping, trial and error, and special products.

Solve the equation.

1. $(x + 3)\left(x - \frac{2}{5}\right) = 0$
2. $\left(m - \frac{5}{2}\right)\left(m + \frac{3}{2}\right) = 0$
3. $(4b + 16)(b - 6) = 0$
4. $(7a - 14)(a + 8) = 0$
5. $(2y + 3)(y - 9) = 0$
6. $(5z - 8)(3z + 2) = 0$
7. $(9w - 2)(7w - 3) = 0$
8. $(8 - 2c)(5c + 1) = 0$
9. $(9 - 8r)(10 - 4r) = 0$

Factor out the greatest common monomial factor.

10. $9x^2 - 21y$
11. $4m^3 + 24m$
12. $10p^2q - 5pq^2$
13. $6x^3y + 9y^2$
14. $35a^2b^2 - 5ab$
15. $12m^2n - 8mn^2$
16. $w^4 - 2w^3 + w$
17. $-3p^4 + 15p^2 + 6p$
18. $8r^5 - 20r^4 - 12r^2$

Solve the equation.

19. $12a^2 - 9a = 0$
20. $18x^2 + 12x = 0$
21. $6z^2 - 8z = 0$
22. $20p^2 = -24p$
23. $-28m^2 = 14m$
24. $-30r^2 = -25r$
25. $100m^2 = -6m$
26. $15y - 50y^2 = 0$
27. $26w + 34w^2 = 0$

28. **Error Analysis** *Describe* and correct the error in solving $(z - 24)(z + 9) = 0$.

$(z - 24)(z + 9) = 0$

$z = -24$ or $z = 9$ ✗

Find the zeros of the function.

29. $f(x) = -28x^2 + 7x$
30. $f(x) = -9x^2 + 4x$
31. $f(x) = 5x^2 - 3x$

32. **Fish** A fish jumps out of the water while swimming. The height h (in feet) of the fish can be modeled by $h = -16t^2 + 3.5t$ where t is the time (in seconds) since the fish jumped out of the water.
    a. Find the zeros of the function. *Explain* what the zeros mean in this situation.
    b. What is a reasonable domain for the function? *Explain* your answer.

33. **Multiple Representations** An arch frames the entrance to a garden. The shape of the arch is modeled by the graph of the equation $y = -3x^2 + 12x$ where x and y are measured in feet. On a coordinate plane, the ground is represented by the x-axis.
    a. **Making a Table** Make a table of values that shows the height of the arch for $x = 0, 1, 2, 3,$ and 4 feet.
    b. **Drawing a Graph** Plot the ordered pairs in the table as points in a coordinate plane. Connect the points with a smooth curve that represents the arch.
    c. **Interpreting a Graph** How wide is the base of the arch?

UNIT 2

LESSON 2.6

Factor $x^2 + bx + c$

Georgia Performance Standards: MM1A2f, MM1A3a, MM1A3c

Goal Factor trinomials of the form $x^2 + bx + c$.

Use the following information to factor trinomials of the form $x^2 + bx + c$:
$x^2 + bx + c = (x + p)(x + q)$ provided $p + q = b$ and $pq = c$.

Example 1 Factor when b and c are positive

Factor $x^2 + 10x + 24$.

Solution

Find two positive factors of 24 whose sum is 10. Make an organized list.

Factors of 24	Sum of factors	
24, 1	$24 + 1 = 25$	✗
12, 2	$12 + 2 = 14$	✗
6, 4	$6 + 4 = 10$	← correct sum
8, 3	$8 + 3 = 11$	✗

The factors 6 and 4 have a sum of 10, so they are the correct values of p and q.

$x^2 + 10x + 24 = (x + 6)(x + 4)$

CHECK $(x + 6)(x + 4) = x^2 + 4x + 6x + 24$ Multiply binomials.

$= x^2 + 10x + 24$ ✓ Simplify.

Example 2 Factor when b is negative and c is positive

Factor $w^2 - 10w + 9$.

Solution

Because b is negative and c is positive, p and q must be negative.

Factors of 9	Sum of factors	
$-9, -1$	$-9 + (-1) = -10$	← correct sum
$-3, -3$	$-3 + (-3) = -6$	✗

The factors -9 and -1 have a sum of -10, so they are the correct values of p and q.

$w^2 - 10w + 9 = (w - 9)(w - 1)$

UNIT 2

Georgia Performance Standards

MM1A2f Factor expressions by greatest common factor, grouping, trial and error, and special products.

MM1A3a Solve quadratic equations in the form $ax^2 + bx + c = 0$, where $a = 1$, by using factorization and finding square roots where applicable.

MM1A3c Use a variety of techniques, including technology, tables, and graphs to solve equations resulting from the investigation of $x^2 + bx + c = 0$.

Example 3 Factor when *b* is positive and *c* is negative

Factor $k^2 + 6k - 7$.

Solution

Because c is negative, p and q must have different signs.

Factors of 7	Sum of factors	
$-7, 1$	$-7 + 1 = -6$	✗
$7, -1$	$7 + (-1) = 6$	← correct sum

The factors 7 and -1 have a sum of 6, so they are the correct values of p and q.

$k^2 + 6k - 7 = (k + 7)(k - 1)$

UNIT 2

Guided Practice for Examples 1, 2, and 3

Factor the trinomial.

1. $x^2 + 10x + 16$ **2.** $y^2 + 6y + 5$ **3.** $z^2 - 7z + 12$

4. $x^2 + 10x - 11$ **5.** $y^2 + 2y - 63$ **6.** $z^2 + 5z - 36$

Example 4 Solve a polynomial equation

Solve the equation $h^2 - 4h = 21$.

Solution

$h^2 - 4h = 21$ Write original equation.

$h^2 - 4h - 21 = 0$ Subtract 21 from each side.

$(h + 3)(h - 7) = 0$ Factor left side.

$h + 3 = 0$ *or* $h - 7 = 0$ Zero-product property

$h = -3$ *or* $h = 7$ Solve for h.

The solutions of the equation are -3 and 7.

Guided Practice for Example 4

7. Solve the equation $x^2 + 30 = 11x$.

LESSON 2.6 **Exercise Set A**

MM1A2f Factor expressions by greatest common factor, grouping, trial and error, and special products.

MM1A3a Solve quadratic equations in the form $ax^2 + bx + c = 0$, where $a = 1$, by using factorization and finding square roots where applicable.

MM1A3c Use a variety of techniques, including technology, tables, and graphs to solve equations resulting from the investigation of $x^2 + bx + c = 0$.

Factor the trinomial.

1. $x^2 + 8x + 7$ **2.** $b^2 - 7b + 10$ **3.** $w^2 - 12w - 13$

4. $p^2 + 10p + 25$ **5.** $m^2 - 10m + 24$ **6.** $y^2 - 5y - 24$

7. $a^2 + 13a + 36$ **8.** $n^2 + 2n - 48$ **9.** $z^2 - 14z + 40$

Solve the equation.

10. $y^2 + 17y + 72 = 0$ **11.** $a^2 - 9a - 36 = 0$ **12.** $w^2 - 13w + 42 = 0$

13. $m^2 - 5m - 14 = 0$ **14.** $x^2 + 11x + 24 = 0$ **15.** $n^2 - 12n + 27 = 0$

16. $d^2 + 5d - 50 = 0$ **17.** $p^2 + 16p + 48 = 0$ **18.** $z^2 - z - 30 = 0$

Find the zeros of the polynomial function.

19. $f(x) = x^2 - 5x - 36$ **20.** $g(x) = x^2 + 8x - 20$ **21.** $h(x) = x^2 - 11x + 24$

22. $f(x) = x^2 + 11x + 28$ **23.** $g(x) = x^2 + 11x - 12$ **24.** $h(x) = x^2 + 3x - 18$

Solve the equation.

25. $x(x + 17) = -60$ **26.** $s^2 - 3(s + 2) = 4$ **27.** $w(w + 8) = -15$

28. Patio Area A community center is building a patio area along two sides of its pool. The pool is rectangular with a width of 50 feet and a length of 100 feet. The patio area will have the same width on each side of the pool.

a. Write a polynomial that represents the combined area of the pool and the patio area.

b. The combined area of the pool and patio area should be 8400 square feet. How wide should the patio area be?

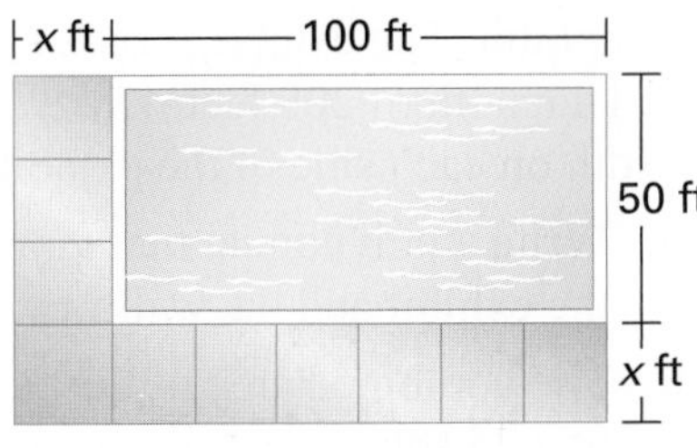

29. Area Rug You create your own area rug from a square piece of remnant carpeting. You cut 4 inches from the length and 3 inches from the width. The area of the resulting area rug is 1056 square inches.

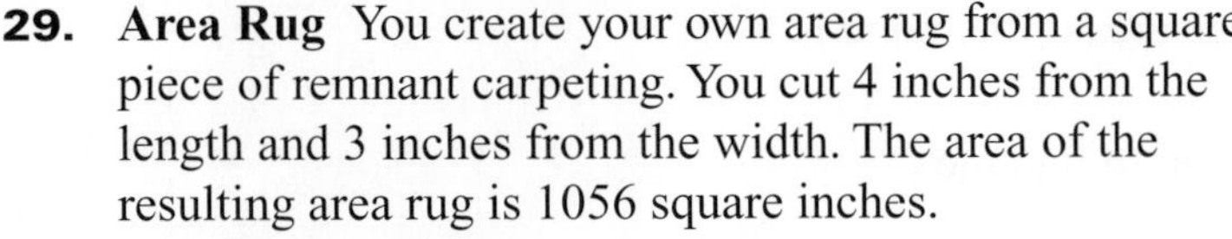

a. Write a polynomial that represents the area of your area rug.

b. What was the perimeter of the original piece of remnant carpeting?

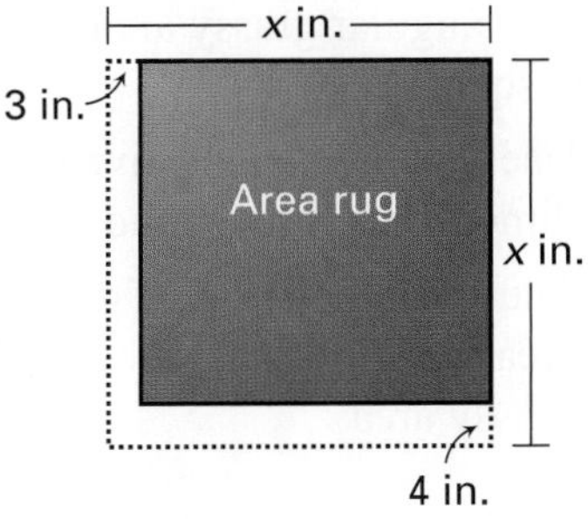

UNIT 2

LESSON 2.6 **Exercise Set B**

MM1A2f Factor expressions by greatest common factor, grouping, trial and error, and special products.

MM1A3a Solve quadratic equations in the form $ax^2 + bx + c = 0$, where $a = 1$, by using factorization and finding square roots where applicable.

MM1A3c Use a variety of techniques, including technology, tables, and graphs to solve equations resulting from the investigation of $x^2 + bx + c = 0$.

Factor the trinomial.

1. $x^2 - x - 56$
2. $m^2 + 14m + 48$
3. $y^2 - 15y + 54$
4. $p^2 + 12p + 20$
5. $w^2 - 14w + 45$
6. $x^2 + 2x - 24$

Solve the equation.

7. $n^2 - 11n - 60 = 0$
8. $z^2 + 22z + 121 = 0$
9. $c^2 - 24c + 144 = 0$
10. $x^2 + 5x - 500 = 0$
11. $b^2 + b - 132 = 0$
12. $m^2 + 17m + 72 = 0$
13. $r^2 - 4r - 60 = 0$
14. $p^2 - 6p - 72 = 0$
15. $y^2 - 16y + 64 = 0$

Find the zeros of the polynomial function.

16. $f(x) = x^2 + 30x + 225$
17. $h(x) = x^2 - 5x - 150$
18. $g(x) = x^2 - 13x + 30$
19. $g(x) = x^2 - 10x - 600$
20. $f(x) = x^2 + 16x + 28$
21. $f(x) = x^2 + 13x + 40$

Solve the equation.

22. $x^2 + 2\left(\frac{1}{2}x - 10\right) = 0$
23. $x^2 - 10(x + 2) = 4$
24. $c(c - 11) = -18$

25. Zoo Exhibit A zoo is building a walkway along two sides of an exhibit. The exhibit is rectangular with a width of 400 feet and a length of 200 feet. The walkway will have the same width on each side of the exhibit.

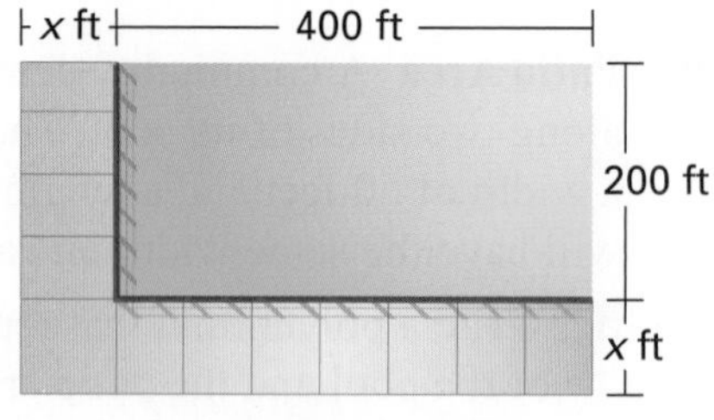

a. Write a polynomial that represents the combined area of the exhibit and the walkway.

b. The combined area of the exhibit and walkway should be 95,625 square feet. How wide should the walkway be?

26. Fish Pond A rectangular fish pond is positioned in the center of a rectangular grassy area, as shown. The area of the pond is 2000 square feet.

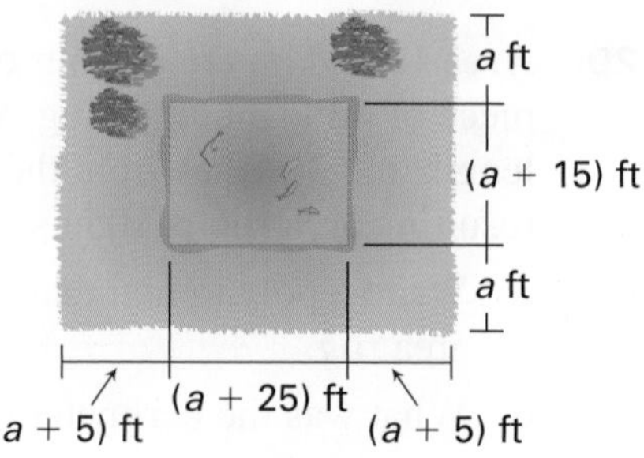

a. Use the dimensions given in the diagram to find the dimensions of the pond.

b. The combined area of the pond and the surrounding grassy area is 9900 square feet. Find the length and width of the grassy area.

UNIT 2

LESSON 2.7

Factor $ax^2 + bx + c$

Georgia Performance Standards: MM1A2f

Goal Factor trinomials of the form $ax^2 + bx + c$.

Example 1 Factor when *b* is negative and *c* is positive

Factor $5n^2 - 12n + 7$.

Solution

Because b is negative and c is positive, both factors of c must be negative. Make a table to organize your work.

You must consider the order of the factors of 7, because the x-terms of the possible factorization are different.

Factors of 5	Factors of 7	Possible factorization	Middle term when multiplied	
1, 5	$-1, -7$	$(n - 1)(5n - 7)$	$-5n - 7n = -12n$	← correct
1, 5	$-7, -1$	$(n - 7)(5n - 1)$	$-n - 35n = -36n$	✗

$5n^2 - 12n + 7 = (n - 1)(5n - 7)$

Example 2 Factor when *b* is negative and *c* is negative

Factor $3m^2 - 5m - 22$.

Solution

Because c is negative, the factors of c must have different signs.

Factors of 3	Factors of 22	Possible factorization	Middle term when multiplied	
1, 3	$1, -22$	$(m + 1)(3m - 22)$	$3m - 22m = -19m$	✗
1, 3	$-1, 22$	$(m - 1)(3m + 22)$	$22m - 3m = 19m$	✗
1, 3	$2, -11$	$(m + 2)(3m - 11)$	$-11m + 6m = -5m$	← correct
1, 3	$-11, 2$	$(m - 11)(3m + 2)$	$2m - 33m = -31m$	✗

$3m^2 - 5m - 22 = (m + 2)(3m - 11)$

Guided Practice for Examples 1 and 2

Factor the trinomial.

1. $7a^2 - 50a + 7$ **2.** $4b^2 - 8b - 5$ **3.** $6c^2 + 5c - 14$

UNIT 2

Georgia Performance Standards

MM1A2f Factor expressions by greatest common factor, grouping, trial and error, and special products.

Example 3 Factor when *a* is negative

Factor $-2x^2 + 11x - 12$.

Solution

STEP 1 **Factor** -1 from each term of the trinomial.

$$-2x^2 + 11x - 12 = -(2x^2 - 11x + 12)$$

STEP 2 **Factor the trinomial** $2x^2 - 11x + 12$. Because b is negative and c is positive, both factors of c must be negative. Use a table to organize information about the factors of a and c.

Factors of 2	Factors of 12	Possible factorization	Middle term when multiplied	
1, 2	$-1, -12$	$(x - 1)(2x - 12)$	$-12x - 2x = -14x$	✗
1, 2	$-12, -1$	$(x - 12)(2x - 1)$	$-x - 24x = -25x$	✗
1, 2	$-2, -6$	$(x - 2)(2x - 6)$	$-6x - 4x = -10x$	✗
1, 2	$-6, -2$	$(x - 6)(2x - 2)$	$-2x - 12x = -14x$	✗
1, 2	$-3, -4$	$(x - 3)(2x - 4)$	$-4x - 6x = -10x$	✗
1, 2	$-4, -3$	$(x - 4)(2x - 3)$	$-3x - 8x = -11x$	← correct

$$-2x^2 + 11x - 12 = -(x - 4)(2x - 3)$$

Guided Practice for Example 3

Factor the trinomial.

4. $-3r^2 - 7r - 4$

5. $-3s^2 + 8s + 16$

6. $-8t^2 + 6t - 1$

7. $-2x^2 + 9x - 9$

8. $-12y^2 + 5y + 2$

9. $-3z^2 - 10z - 8$

LESSON 2.7

Exercise Set A

MM1A2f Factor expressions by greatest common factor, grouping, trial and error, and special products.

Factor the trinomial.

1. $-x^2 - 3x + 28$ **2.** $-p^2 + 8p - 12$ **3.** $-m^2 - 13m - 40$

4. $2y^2 + 15y + 7$ **5.** $3a^2 - 13a + 4$ **6.** $5d^2 - 18d - 8$

7. $6c^2 + 7c + 2$ **8.** $10n^2 - 26n + 12$ **9.** $12w^2 + 8w - 15$

10. $-2b^2 - 5b + 12$ **11.** $-3r^2 - 17r - 10$ **12.** $-4s^2 + 6s + 4$

Solve the equation.

13. $-x^2 + x + 20 = 0$ **14.** $-m^2 - 10m - 16 = 0$ **15.** $-p^2 + 13p - 42 = 0$

16. $2c^2 - 11c + 5 = 0$ **17.** $2y^2 + y - 10 = 0$ **18.** $16r^2 + 18r + 5 = 0$

19. $3w^2 + 19w + 6 = 0$ **20.** $12n^2 - 11n + 2 = 0$ **21.** $15a^2 - 2a - 8 = 0$

22. $-2x^2 - 9x - 4 = 0$ **23.** $-3s^2 - s + 10 = 0$ **24.** $8d^2 - 6d - 5 = 0$

25. **Error Analysis** *Describe* and correct the error in solving $6x^2 + x = 5$.

$6x^2 + x = 5$ $x = 5$ or $6x + 1 = 5$

$x(6x + 1) = 5$ $x = 5$ or $x = \frac{2}{3}$

Find the zeros of the polynomial function.

26. $f(x) = -x^2 + 6x + 27$ **27.** $f(x) = 6x^2 + 45x - 24$ **28.** $f(x) = -3x^2 - 14x + 24$

29. $f(x) = -2x^2 + 2x + 4$ **30.** $f(x) = 3x^2 - 17x + 20$ **31.** $f(x) = 8x^2 + 53x - 21$

32. $f(x) = 4x^2 + 29x + 30$ **33.** $f(x) = -2x^2 - 17x + 30$ **34.** $f(x) = 10x^2 + 5x - 5$

35. **Wall Mirror** You plan on making a wall hanging that contains two small mirrors as shown.

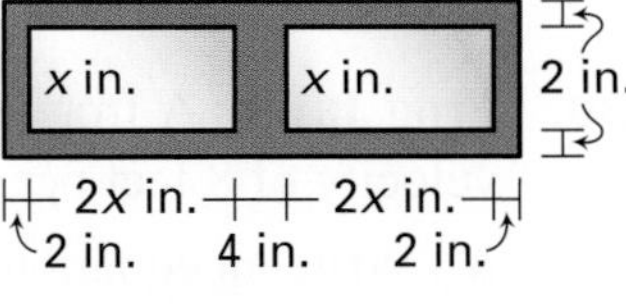

a. Write a polynomial that represents the area of the wall hanging.

b. The area of the wall hanging will be 480 square inches. Find the length and width of the mirrors you will use.

36. **Multiple Representations** An African cat called a serval leaps from the ground in an attempt to catch a bird. The serval's initial vertical velocity is 28 feet per second.

a. **Writing an Equation** Write an equation that gives the serval's height h (in feet) as a function of the time t (in seconds) since it left the ground.

b. **Making a Table** Use the equation from part (a) to make a table that shows the height of the serval for $t = 0, 0.25, 0.5, 0.75, 1, 1.25, 1.5$ and 1.75 seconds.

c. **Drawing a Graph** Plot the ordered pairs in the table as points in a coordinate plane. Connect the points with a smooth curve. After how many seconds does the serval first reach a height of 10 feet? *Justify* your answer using the equation from part (a).

LESSON 2.7 **Exercise Set B**

MM1A2f Factor expressions by greatest common factor, grouping, trial and error, and special products.

Factor the trinomial.

1. $-x^2 - 11x + 180$
2. $-2m^2 + 19m - 24$
3. $-3p^2 + 26p + 40$
4. $8r^2 + 26r + 15$
5. $14b^2 + 38b - 12$
6. $10y^2 - 36y + 18$

Solve the equation.

7. $-32x^2 - 28x + 15 = 0$
8. $-8n^2 - 16n - 6 = 0$
9. $-15s^2 + 4s + 4 = 0$
10. $-6p^2 - 17p - 5 = 0$
11. $63m^2 - 31m - 10 = 0$
12. $40r^2 - 42r + 9 = 0$
13. $16a^2 - 2a - 3 = 0$
14. $-15d^2 - 2d + 8 = 0$
15. $-6y^2 + 32y - 10 = 0$

Find the zeros of the polynomial function.

16. $f(x) = -16x^2 + 50x - 25$
17. $h(x) = -20x^2 + 44x - 21$
18. $h(x) = 20x^2 + 18x - 44$
19. $g(x) = -36x^2 - 30x - 6$
20. $f(x) = 12x^2 + 8x - 15$
21. $g(x) = 21x^2 + 14x - 7$

Multiply each side of the equation by an appropriate power of 10 to obtain integer coefficients. Then solve the equation.

22. $0.2x^2 - 0.3x - 3.5 = 0$
23. $r^2 + 0.6r - 0.4 = 0$
24. $0.8m^2 + m - 0.3 = 0$
25. $-0.5x^2 + 1.2x = 0.4$
26. $1.2(p^2 + 1) = 2.5p$
27. $-0.36n^2 + 0.6n - 0.25 = 0$

28. **Baseball** A baseball player releases a baseball at a height of 7 feet with an initial vertical velocity of 54 feet per second. How long will it take the ball to reach the ground?

29. **Rocket Launch** A miniature rocket is launched off a roof 20 feet above the ground with an initial vertical velocity of 22 feet per second. How much time will elapse before the rocket reaches the ground?

30. **Frog Jump** A frog jumps from the ground into the air with an initial vertical velocity of 8 feet per second.
    - **a.** Write an equation that gives the frog's height (in feet) as a function of the time (in seconds) since it left the ground.
    - **b.** After how many seconds is the frog 12 inches above the ground?
    - **c.** Does the frog go any higher than 12 inches? *Explain* your reasoning using your answer from part (b).
    - **d.** Suppose the frog now jumps from 4 feet above the ground with the same initial vertical velocity. Write an equation that gives the frog's height (in feet) as a function of the time (in seconds) since it left the ground.
    - **e.** Should the frog reach the ground in the same time in both jumps? *Explain* why or why not.

LESSON 2.8

Factor Special Products

Georgia Performance Standards: MM1A2f

Goal Factor special products.

Difference of Two Squares Pattern

Algebra	**Example**
$a^2 - b^2 = (a + b)(a - b)$	$9x^2 - 4 = (3x)^2 - 2^2 = (3x + 2)(3x - 2)$

Example 1 Factor the difference of two squares

Factor the polynomial.

a. $r^2 - 81 = r^2 - 9^2$ — Write as $a^2 - b^2$.

$= (r - 9)(r + 9)$ — Difference of two squares pattern

b. $9s^2 - 4t^2 = (3s)^2 - (2t)^2$ — Write as $a^2 - b^2$.

$= (3s - 2t)(3s + 2t)$ — Difference of two squares pattern

c. $80 - 125q^2 = 5(16 - 25q^2)$ — Factor out common factor.

$= 5[4^2 - (5q)^2]$ — Write $16 - 25q^2$ as $a^2 - b^2$.

$= 5(2 - 5q)(2 + 5q)$ — Difference of two squares pattern

UNIT 2

Perfect Square Trinomial Pattern

Algebra	**Example**
$a^2 + 2ab + b^2 = (a + b)^2$	$x^2 + 6x + 9 = x^2 + 2(x)(3) + 3^2 = (x + 3)^2$
$a^2 - 2ab + b^2 = (a - b)^2$	$x^2 - 12x + 36 = x^2 - 2(x)(6) + 6^2 = (x - 6)^2$

Example 2 Factor perfect square trinomials

Factor the polynomial.

a. $x^2 + 14x + 49 = x^2 + 2(x)(7) + 7^2$ — Write as $a^2 + 2ab + b^2$.

$= (x + 7)^2$ — Perfect square trinomial pattern

b. $x^2 - 16x + 64 = x^2 - 2(x)(8) + 8^2$ — Write as $a^2 - 2ab + b^2$.

$= (x - 8)^2$ — Perfect square trinomial pattern

Georgia Performance Standards

MM1A2f Factor expressions by greatest common factor, grouping, trial and error, and special products.

Example 3 Factor perfect square trinomials

Factor the polynomial.

a. $144y^2 + 120y + 25 = (12y)^2 + 2(12y)(5) + 5^2$ Write as $a^2 + 2ab + b^2$.

$= (12y + 5)^2$ Perfect square trinomial pattern

b. $150z^2 - 60z + 6 = 6(25z^2 - 10z + 1)$ Factor out common factor.

$= 6[(5z)^2 - 2(5z)(1) + 1^2]$ Write $25z^2 - 10z + 1$ as $a^2 - 2ab + b^2$.

$= 6(5z - 1)^2$ Perfect square trinomial pattern

c. $9x^2 - 12xy + 4y^2 = (3x)^2 - 2(3x)(2y) + (2y)^2$ Write as $a^2 - 2ab + b^2$.

$= (3x - 2y)^2$ Perfect square trinomial pattern

Guided Practice for Examples 1, 2, and 3

Factor the polynomial.

1. $m^2 - 121$ **2.** $9n^2 - 64$ **3.** $3y^2 - 147z^2$

4. $m^2 - \frac{1}{2}m + \frac{1}{16}$ **5.** $16r^2 + 40rs + 25s^2$ **6.** $36x^2 - 36xy + 9y^2$

UNIT 2

Example 4 Solve a polynomial equation

Solve the equation $q^2 - 100 = 0$.

Solution

$q^2 - 100 = 0$ Write original equation.

$q^2 - 10^2 = 0$ Write left side as $a^2 - b^2$.

$(q + 10)(q - 10) = 0$ Difference of two squares pattern

$q + 10 = 0$ *or* $q - 10 = 0$ Zero-product property

$q = -10$ *or* $q = 10$ Solve for q.

The solutions of the equation are -10 and 10.

Guided Practice for Example 4

Solve the equation.

7. $r^2 - 10r + 25 = 0$ **8.** $16m^2 - 81 = 0$

LESSON 2.8 **Exercise Set A**

MM1A2f Factor expressions by greatest common factor, grouping, trial and error, and special products.

Factor the polynomial.

1. $x^2 - 36$

2. $25p^2 - 144$

3. $4b^2 - 100$

4. $36m^2 - 81$

5. $-2x^2 + 32$

6. $-4r^2 + 100s^2$

7. $y^2 + 24y + 144$

8. $9c^2 + 24c + 16$

9. $25w^2 - 20w + 4$

10. $16n^2 - 56n + 49$

11. $-18a^2 - 12a - 2$

12. $20z^2 - 140z + 245$

13. $x^2 - 18xy + 81y^2$

14. $9x^2 - 30xy + 25y^2$

15. $16x^2 + 80xy + 100y^2$

Solve the equation.

16. $x^2 + 14x + 49 = 0$

17. $8w^2 = 50$

18. $64p^2 - 16p + 1 = 0$

19. $8a^2 - 72 = 0$

20. $3m^2 + 30m + 75 = 0$

21. $-4y^2 + 32y - 64 = 0$

22. $-5x^2 + 125 = 0$

23. $-7r^2 + 140r - 700 = 0$

24. $24w^2 - 24w + 6 = 0$

25. $18n^2 + 60n + 50 = 0$

26. $\frac{25}{2}x^2 + 15x + \frac{9}{2} = 0$

27. $4x^2 = \frac{9}{16}$

Find the value of *x* in the geometric shape.

28. Area $= 144\pi$ cm^2

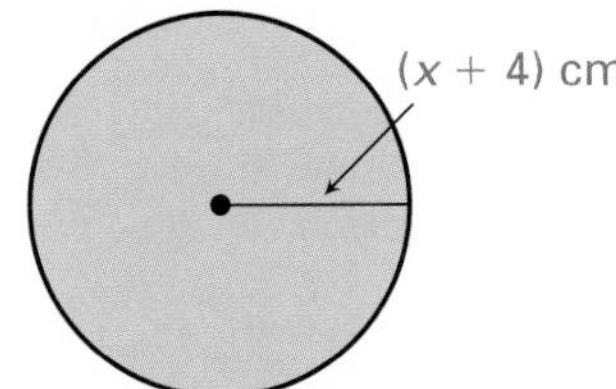

29. 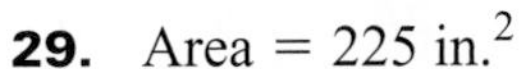 Area $= 225$ in.^{2}

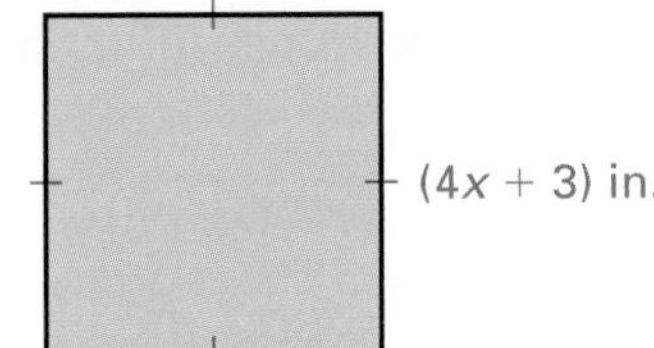

30. Measuring Tape A measuring tape drops from a roof that is 16 feet above the ground. After how many seconds does the measuring tape land on the ground?

31. Multiple Representations A curved ladder that children can climb on can be modeled by the equation

$$y = -\frac{1}{20}x^2 + x$$

where x and y are measured in feet.

a. Making a Table Make a table of values that shows the height of the ladder for $x = 0, 5, 10, 15,$ and 20 feet from the left end.

b. Interpreting an Equation For what additional values of x does the equation make sense? *Explain.*

c. Drawing a Graph Plot the ordered pairs in the table from part (a) as points in a coordinate plane. Connect the points with a smooth curve.

d. Interpreting a Graph At approximately what distance from the left end does the ladder reach a height of 5 feet? Check your answer algebraically.

LESSON 2.8 **Exercise Set B**

MM1A2f Factor expressions by greatest common factor, grouping, trial and error, and special products.

Factor the polynomial.

1. $25x^2 - 81$
2. $225p^2 - 100$
3. $121w^2 - 625$
4. $36m^2 - 64$
5. $\frac{9}{16}r^2 - \frac{1}{16}$
6. $81x^2 - 49y^2$
7. $-3y^2 - 48y - 192$
8. $4n^2 - 40n + 100$
9. $12z^2 + 12z + 3$
10. $24a^2 - 120ab + 150b^2$
11. $-18s^2 - 48st - 32t^2$
12. $5z^2 + 2z + \frac{1}{5}$
13. **Error Analysis** *Describe* and correct the error in factoring the polynomial $y^2 - 10y + 25$.

$$y^2 - 10y + 25 = y^2 - 2(y \cdot 5) + 5^2$$
$$= (y - 5)(y + 5)$$

Solve the equation.

14. $25m^2 - 64 = 0$
15. $2p^2 + 36p + 162 = 0$
16. $-16r^2 + 196 = 0$
17. $3w^2 - 60w + 300 = 0$
18. $36x^2 - 132x + 121 = 0$
19. $225a^2 - 120a + 16 = 0$
20. $-75y^2 - 90y - 27 = 0$
21. $196n^2 - 224n + 64 = 0$
22. $160z^2 = 640$
23. $0.9r^2 - 4.8r + 6.4 = 0$
24. $\frac{25}{2}b^2 + 5b + \frac{1}{2} = 0$
25. $-96d^2 + 144d - 54 = 0$

Determine the value(s) of *k* that make the expression a perfect square trinomial.

26. $81x^2 + kx + 25$
27. $100x^2 + kx + 49$
28. $25x^2 - 60x + k$
29. $kx^2 + 72x + 81$
30. $4x^2 - 12x + k$
31. $49x^2 + kxy + 4y^2$
32. **Squirrel** A squirrel jumps straight up with an initial vertical velocity of 16 feet per second. How many times does the squirrel reach a height of 4 feet? *Explain* your answer.
33. **Multiple Representations** A foot bridge that spans a small creek can be modeled by the equation

$$y = -\frac{3}{800}x^2 + \frac{3}{10}x$$

where x and y are measured in feet.

   a. **Making a Table** Make a table of values that shows the height of the bridge for $x = 0, 20, 40, 60$, and 80 feet from the left end.
   b. **Interpreting an Equation** For what additional values of x does the equation make sense? *Explain.*
   c. **Drawing a Graph** Plot the ordered pairs in the table from part (a) as points in a coordinate plane. Connect the points with a smooth curve.
   d. **Interpreting a Graph** At approximately what distance from the left end does the bridge reach a height of 6 feet? Check your answer algebraically.

UNIT 2

LESSON 2.9

Factor Polynomials Completely

Georgia Performance Standards: MM1A2f

Goal Factor polynomials completely.

Vocabulary

Factoring a common monomial from pairs of terms, then looking for a common binomial factor is called **factor by grouping.**

A polynomial that cannot be written as the product of polynomials with integer coefficients is called unfactorable. A factorable polynomial with integer coefficients is **factored completely** if it is written as a product of unfactorable polynomials with integer coefficients.

Example 1 Factor out common binomial

Factor the expression.

a. $5x^2(x - 2) - 3(x - 2)$ **b.** $7y(5 - y) + 3(y - 5)$

Solution

a. $5x^2(x - 2) - 3(x - 2) = (x - 2)(5x^2 - 3)$

b. The binomials $5 - y$ and $y - 5$ are opposites. Factor -1 from $5 - y$ to obtain a common binomial factor.

$7y(5 - y) + 3(y - 5) = -7y(y - 5) + 3(y - 5)$ Factor -1 from $(5 - y)$.

$= (y - 5)(-7y + 3)$ Distributive property

Example 2 Factor by grouping

Factor the polynomial.

a. $m^3 + 7m^2 - 2m - 14$ **b.** $n^3 + 30 + 6n^2 + 5n$

Solution

a. $m^3 + 7m^2 - 2m - 14 = (m^3 + 7m^2) + (-2m - 14)$ Group terms.

$= m^2(m + 7) - 2(m + 7)$ Factor each group.

$= (m + 7)(m^2 - 2)$ Distributive property

b. $n^3 + 30 + 6n^2 + 5n = n^3 + 6n^2 + 5n + 30$ Rearrange terms.

$= (n^3 + 6n^2) + (5n + 30)$ Group terms.

$= n^2(n + 6) + 5(n + 6)$ Factor each group.

$= (n + 6)(n^2 + 5)$ Distributive property

Georgia Performance Standards

MM1A2f Factor expressions by greatest common factor, grouping, trial and error, and special products.

Example 3 Factor completely

Factor the polynomial completely.

a. $5x^3 - 55x^2 + 90x$ **b.** $48y^4 - 3y^2$

Solution

a. $5x^3 - 55x^2 + 90x = 5x(x^2 - 11x + 18)$ Factor out $5x$.

$= 5x(x - 2)(x - 9)$ Find two negative factors of 18 that have a sum of -11.

b. $48y^4 - 3y^2 = 3y^2(16y^2 - 1)$ Factor out $3y^2$.

$= 3y^2(4y - 1)(4y + 1)$ Difference of two squares pattern

Guided Practice for Examples 1, 2, and 3

Factor the expression.

1. $11x(x - 8) + 3(x - 8)$

2. $9x^3 + 9x^2 - 7x - 7$

3. $10x^3 + 21y - 35x^2 - 6xy$

4. $4x^3 - 36x$

5. $2y^3 - 16y^2 + 32y$

6. $m^3 - 3m^2 - 40m$

UNIT 2

Example 4 Solve a polynomial equation

Solve the equation $7x^3 + 14x^2 = 105x$.

Solution

$7x^3 + 14x^2 = 105x$ Write original equation.

$7x^3 + 14x^2 - 105x = 0$ Subtract $105x$ from each side.

$7x(x^2 + 2x - 15) = 0$ Factor out $7x$.

$7x(x + 5)(x - 3) = 0$ Factor the trinomial.

$7x = 0$ *or* $x + 5 = 0$ *or* $x - 3 = 0$ Zero-product property

$x = 0$ *or* $x = -5$ *or* $x = 3$ Solve for x.

The solutions of the equation are 0, -5, and 3.

Guided Practice for Example 4

Solve the equation.

7. $2c^3 + 8c^2 - 42c = 0$ **8.** $4x^3 + 48x^2 + 144x = 0$ **9.** $5r^3 + 15r = 20r^2$

LESSON 2.9 **Exercise Set A**

MM1A2f Factor expressions by greatest common factor, grouping, trial and error, and special products.

Factor the expression.

1. $4x(x + 5) - 3(x + 5)$
2. $12(a - 3) - 2a(a - 3)$
3. $w^2(w + 8) - 5(w + 8)$
4. $2b^2(b + 6) + 3(b + 6)$
5. $y(15 + x) - (x + 15)$
6. $3x(4 + y) - 6(4 + y)$

Factor the polynomial by grouping.

7. $x^3 + x^2 + 5x + 5$
8. $y^3 - 14y^2 + y - 14$
9. $m^3 - 6m^2 + 2m - 12$
10. $p^3 + 9p^2 + 4p + 36$
11. $t^3 + 12t^2 - 2t - 24$
12. $3n^3 - 3n^2 + n - 1$

Factor the polynomial completely.

13. $7x^3 + 28x^2$
14. $4m^3 - 16m$
15. $-16p^3 - 2p$
16. $48r^3 - 30r^2$
17. $15y - 60y^2$
18. $18xy - 24x^2$
19. $5m^2 + 20m + 40$
20. $6x^2 + 6x - 120$
21. $4z^3 - 4z^2 - 8z$
22. $9x^3 + 36x^2 + 36$
23. $x^3 + x^2 + 5x + 5$
24. $d^3 + 4d^2 + 5d + 20$

Solve the equation.

25. $3x^2 + 18x + 24 = 0$
26. $10x^2 = 250$
27. $4m^2 - 28m + 49 = 0$
28. $12x^2 + 18x + 6 = 0$
29. $18x^2 - 48x + 32 = 0$
30. $-18x^2 - 60x - 50 = 0$

31. **Countertop** A countertop will have a hole drilled in it to hold a cylindrical container that will function as a utensil holder. The area of the entire countertop is given by $5x^2 + 12x + 7$. The area of the hole is given by $x^2 + 2x + 1$. Write an expression for the area in factored form of the countertop that is left after the hole is drilled.

32. **Film Canister** A film canister in the shape of a cylinder has a height of 8 centimeters and a volume of 32π cubic centimeters.
    a. Write an equation for the volume of the film canister.
    b. What is the radius of the film canister?

33. **Badminton** You hit a badminton birdie upward with a racket from a height of 2 feet with an initial vertical velocity of 8 feet per second.
    a. Write an equation that models this situation.
    b. How high is the birdie at 0.1 second?
    c. How long will it take the birdie to reach the ground?

UNIT 2

LESSON 2.9 **Exercise Set B**

MM1A2f Factor expressions by greatest common factor, grouping, trial and error, and special products.

Factor the polynomial completely.

1. $13a - 26a^2$
2. $30xy - 45x^2$
3. $-2m^2 - 16m - 14$
4. $14p^2 - 35p + 21$
5. $r^3 + 10r^2 + 25r$
6. $5b^4 + 40b^3 + 80b^2$
7. $4n^5 + 4n^4 - 120n^3$
8. $7c^3 - 28c^2 + 28c$
9. $-10t^2 - 5t + 75$
10. $x^2 + 9x - xy - 9y$
11. $x^3 + 5x^2 - 8x - 40$
12. $9x^2 - 64y^2$
13. $3x^5y - 243x^3y$
14. $8r^3s^4 - 72rs^4$
15. $25x^3y - 100x^2y$

Solve the equation.

16. $5x^3 + 20x^2 + 15x = 0$
17. $-19x^2 + 76 = 0$
18. $-18p^3 - 21p^2 + 15p = 0$
19. $48p^2 - 675 = 0$
20. $14x^3 - 68x^2 - 10x = 0$
21. $-3n^4 - 36n^3 - 108n^2 = 0$
22. $20t^4 + 28t^3 = 24t^2$
23. $64t = 12t^2 + 45$
24. $900x^2 = 625$
25. $16m^4 - 81m^2 = 0$
26. $16x + 280 = 8x^2$
27. $2r^2 + 392 = 56r$
28. $75a^3 + 90a^2 + 27a = 0$
29. $2p^2 = 12p + 54$
30. $81x^3 = 100x$

31. Use factoring by grouping to show that a trinomial of the form $a^2 - 2ab + b^2$ can be factored as $(a - b)^2$. *Justify* your steps.

32. **Work Bench** You are drilling holes into your work bench that will hold caddies for some of your gardening equipment. The area of the entire work bench before the holes are drilled is given by $24x^2 + 5x$. The area of one hole is given by $3x^2 + x + 3$. Write an expression for the area in factored form of the work bench that is left after the holes are drilled.

33. **Poster Tube** A poster tube in the shape of a cylinder has a height of 2 feet and a volume of $\frac{1}{2}\pi$ cubic feet.

    a. Write an equation for the volume of the poster tube.

    b. What is the radius of the poster tube?

34. **Moon** On the moon, the vertical motion model is given by

$$h = -\frac{16}{6}t^2 + vt + s$$

where h is the height (in feet), v is the initial velocity (in feet per second), t is the time (in seconds), and s is the initial height (in feet). On the moon, an astronaut tosses a baseball from a height of 64 feet with an initial upward velocity of $23\frac{2}{3}$ feet per second. How long does it take the ball to reach the ground?

UNIT 2

Georgia Performance Standards

MM1A1b Graph the basic functions $f(x) = x^n$, where $n = 1$ to 3, $f(x) = \sqrt{x}$, $f(x) = |x|$, and $f(x) = \frac{1}{x}$.

Investigating Math Activity

Graphing $y = ax^2 + c$

Use before Lesson 2.10

Materials graph paper or graphing calculator

Question

How do the coefficients of a and c affect the shape of the graph of the quadratic function $y = ax^2 + c$?

Explore 1

Graph $y = ax^2$.

STEP 1 **Graph $y = x^2$**

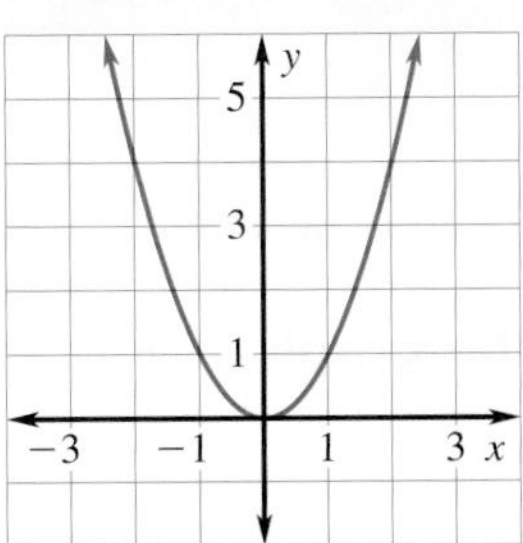

STEP 2 **Graph $y = 2x^2$**

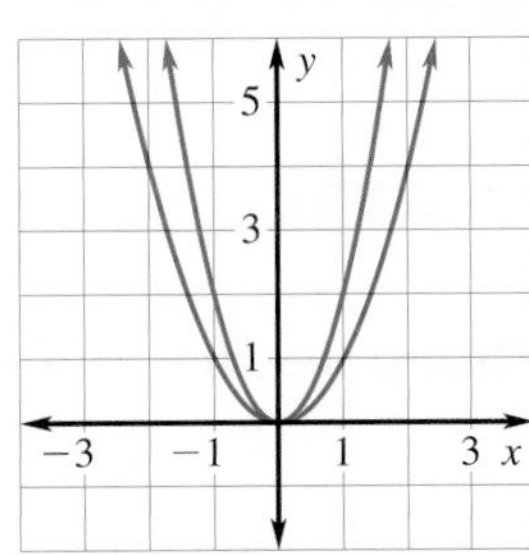

STEP 3 Graph $y = ax^2$ using -2, -0.5, and 0.5 as values of a. Compare each graph to the graph of $y = x^2$. Describe how the value of a affects the graph of $y = ax^2$.

Explore 2

Graph $y = x^2$.

STEP 1 **Graph $y = x^2$**

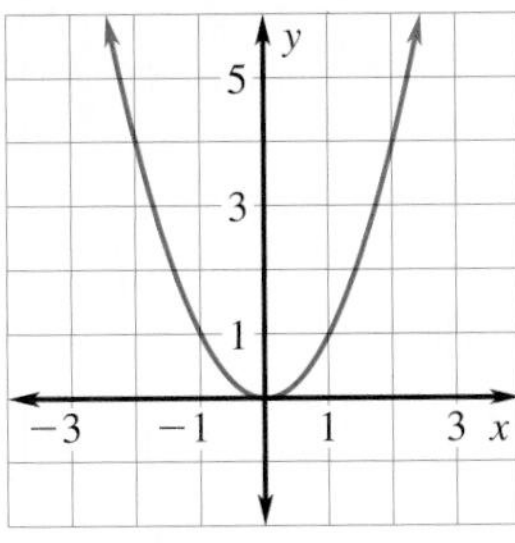

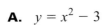

STEP 2 **Graph $y = x^2 + 2$**

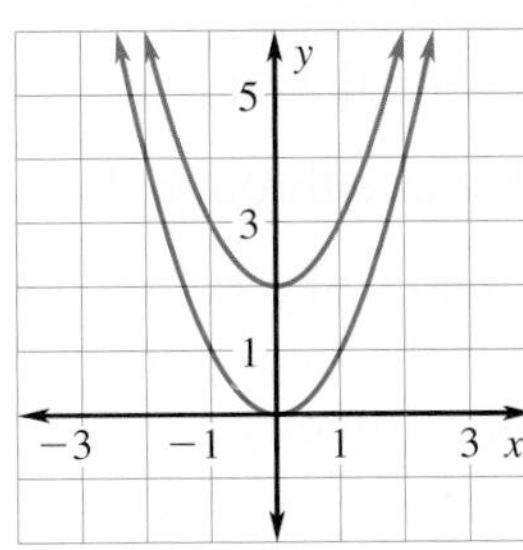

STEP 3 Graph $y = x^2 + c$ using -2, 1, and 3 as values of c. Compare each graph to the graph of $y = x^2$. Describe how the value of c affects the graph of $y = x^2 + c$.

Draw Conclusions

1. **Reasoning** Which of the quadratic functions could be shown by the graph at the right? *Explain* your reasoning.

   A. $y = x^2 - 3$ **B.** $y = x^2 + 3$

   C. $y = 3x^2$ **D.** $y = \frac{1}{3}x^2$

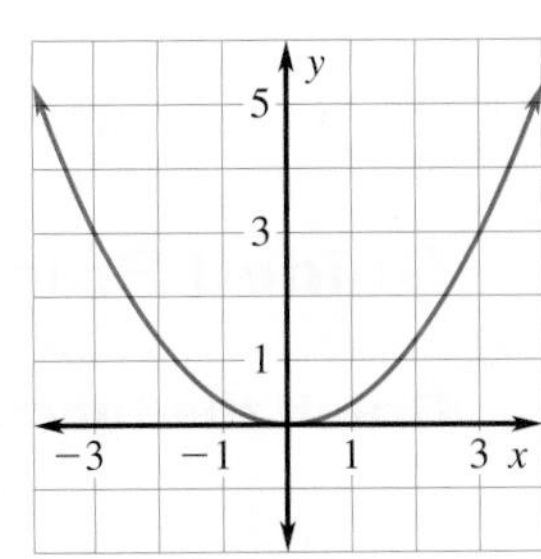

2. Use the values of a and c to sketch the graph of $y = -x^2 + 3$.

UNIT 2

LESSON 2.10

Graph $y = ax^2 + c$

Georgia Performance Standards: MM1A1b, MM1A1c, MM1A1e

Goal Graph the simple quadratic functions.

Vocabulary

A **quadratic function** is a nonlinear function that can be written in the **standard form** $y = ax^2 + bx + c$ where $a \neq 0$.

Every quadratic function has a U-shaped graph called a **parabola.**

The most basic quadratic function in the family of quadratic functions, called the **parent quadratic function,** is $y = x^2$.

The lowest or highest point on a parabola is the **vertex.**

The line that passes through the vertex and divides the parabola into two symmetric parts is called the **axis of symmetry.**

Example 1 Graph $y = ax^2$

Graph $y = -6x^2$. Compare the graph with the graph of $y = x^2$.

Solution

STEP 1 **Make** a table of values for $y = -6x^2$.

x	-2	-1	0	1	2
y	-24	-6	0	-6	-24

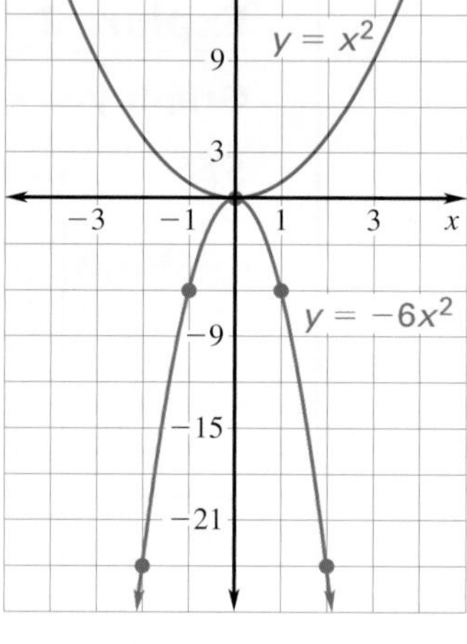

STEP 2 **Plot** the points from the table.

STEP 3 **Draw** a smooth curve through the points.

STEP 4 **Compare** the graphs of $y = -6x^2$ and $y = x^2$. Both graphs have the same vertex, (0, 0), and the same axis of symmetry, $x = 0$. However, the graph of $y = -6x^2$ is narrower than the graph of $y = x^2$ and it opens down. This is because the graph of $y = -6x^2$ is a vertical stretch (by a factor of 6) of the graph of $y = x^2$ and a reflection in the x-axis of the graph of $y = x^2$.

Guided Practice for Example 1

Graph the function. *Compare* the graph with the graph of $y = x^2$.

1. $y = -8x^2$

2. $y = \frac{1}{7}x^2$

3. $y = -\frac{1}{3}x^2$

UNIT 2

Georgia Performance Standards

MM1A1b Graph the basic functions $f(x) = x^n$, where $n = 1$ to 3, $f(x) = \sqrt{x}$, $f(x) = |x|$, and $f(x) = \frac{1}{x}$.

MM1A1c Graph transformations of basic functions including vertical shifts, stretches, and shrinks, as well as reflections across the x- and y-axes.

MM1A1e Relate to a given context the characteristics of a function, and use graphs and tables to investigate its behavior.

Example 2 Graph $y = ax^2 + c$

Graph $y = 0.5x^2 - 1$. Compare the graph with the graph of $y = x^2$.

STEP 1 **Make** a table of values for $y = 0.5x^2 - 1$.

x	−2	−1	0	1	2
y	1	−0.5	−1	−0.5	1

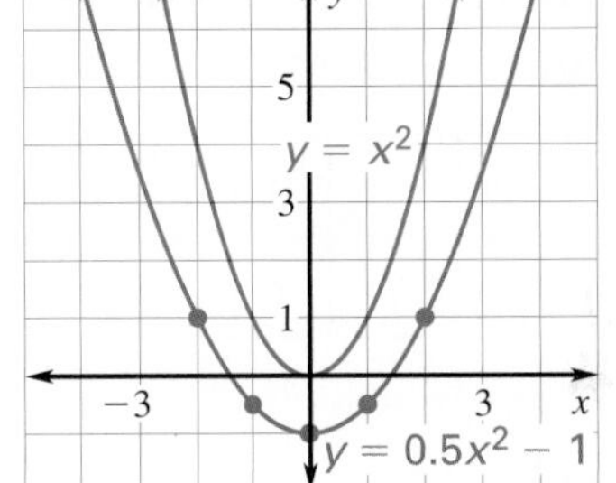

STEP 2 **Plot** the points from the table.

STEP 3 **Draw** a smooth curve through the points.

STEP 4 **Compare** the graphs of $y = 0.5x^2 - 1$ and $y = x^2$. Both graphs open up and have the same axis of symmetry, $x = 0$. However, the graph of $y = 0.5x^2 - 1$ is wider and has a different vertex than the graph of $y = x^2$. This is because the graph of $y = 0.5x^2 - 1$ is a vertical shrink and a vertical translation of the graph of $y = x^2$.

Example 3 Use a graph

Solar Energy A solar trough has a reflective parabolic surface that is used to collect solar energy to help produce electricity. The graph of the function $y = 0.15x^2$ models the cross section of the reflective surface where x and y are measured in meters. Use the graph to find the domain and range of the function in this situation.

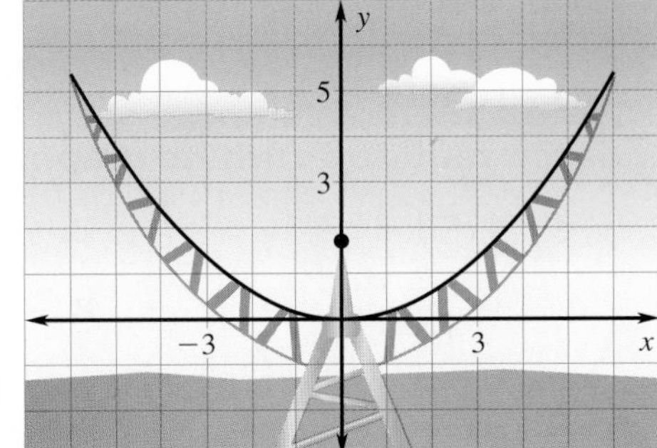

STEP 1 **Find** the domain. In the graph, the reflective surface extends 6 meters on either side of the origin. So, the domain is $-6 \le x \le 6$.

STEP 2 **Find** the range using the fact that the lowest point on the reflective surface is (0, 0) and the highest points occur at $x = \pm 6$.

$y = 0.15(6)^2 = 5.4$, so the range is $0 \le y \le 5.4$.

Guided Practice for Examples 2 and 3

Graph the function. *Compare* the graph with the graph of $y = x^2$.

4. $y = x^2 - 3$ **5.** $y = \frac{1}{4}x^2 + 2$ **6.** $y = -\frac{1}{2}x^2 - 1$

7. In Example 3, suppose the reflective surface extends just 4 meters on either side of the origin. Find the domain and range of the function in this situation.

LESSON 2.10 **Exercise Set A**

MM1A1b Graph the basic functions $f(x) = x^n$, where $n = 1$ to 3, $f(x) = \sqrt{x}$, $f(x) = |x|$, and $f(x) = \frac{1}{x}$.

MM1A1c Graph transformations of basic functions including vertical shifts, stretches, and shrinks, as well as reflections across the *x*- and *y*-axes.

MM1A1e Relate to a given context the characteristics of a function, and use graphs and tables to investigate its behavior.

Use the quadratic function to complete the table of values.

1. $y = 9x^2$

x	−2	−1	0	1	2
y	?	?	?	?	?

2. $y = -5x^2$

x	−2	−1	0	1	2
y	?	?	?	?	?

3. $y = \frac{5}{2}x^2 + 1$

x	−4	−2	0	2	4
y	?	?	?	?	?

4. $y = -\frac{1}{8}x^2 - 2$

x	−16	−8	0	8	16
y	?	?	?	?	?

5. $y = -4x^2 + 3$

x	−2	−1	0	1	2
y	?	?	?	?	?

6. $y = 6x^2 - 5$

x	−2	−1	0	1	2
y	?	?	?	?	?

Match the function with its graph.

7. $y = -4x^2 + 3$

8. $y = \frac{1}{4}x^2 - 3$

9. $y = 4x^2 + 3$

A.

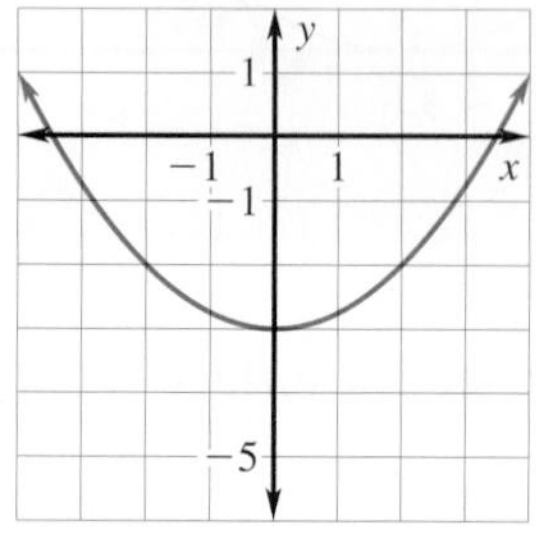

B.

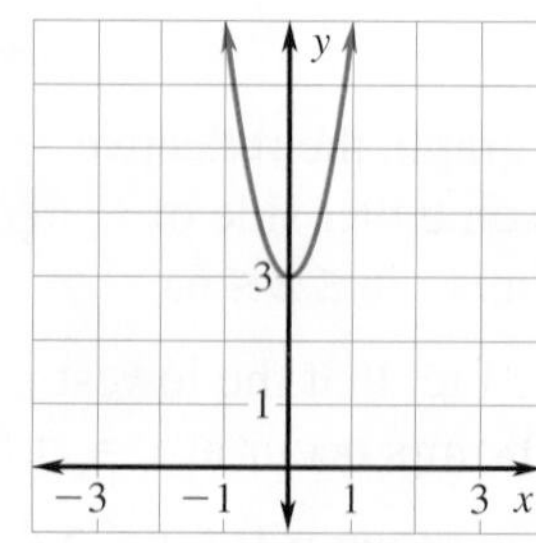

C.

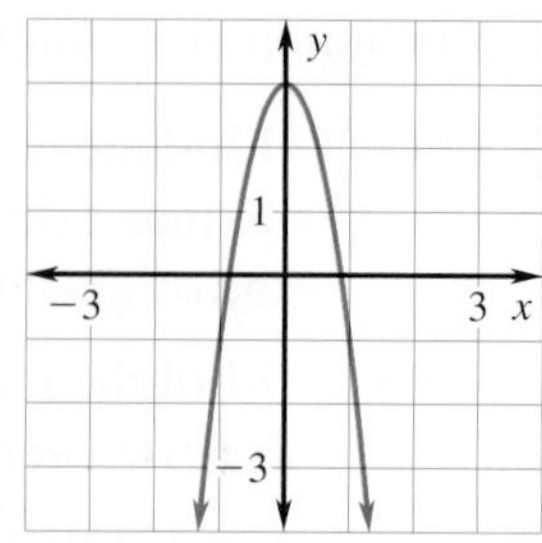

Describe **how you can use the graph of $y = x^2$ to graph the given function.**

10. $y = x^2 - 8$

11. $y = -x^2 + 4$

12. $y = 2x^2 + 3$

13. $y = -5x^2 + 1$

14. $y = \frac{1}{2}x^2 - 2$

15. $y = -\frac{3}{4}x^2 + 5$

Exercise Set A *(continued)*

Graph the function and identify its domain and range. *Compare* the graph with the graph of $y = x^2$.

16. $y = x^2 + 9$ **17.** $y = -\frac{1}{5}x^2$ **18.** $y = -\frac{3}{2}x^2$

19. $y = x^2 - 3.5$ **20.** $y = 2x^2 - 9$ **21.** $y = -5x^2 + 2$

22. $y = x^2 - \frac{9}{4}$ **23.** $y = \frac{3}{4}x^2 + 2$ **24.** $y = -\frac{1}{5}x^2 + 3$

25. Error Analysis *Describe* and correct the error in drawing and comparing the graphs of $y = x^2$ and $y = x^2 - 3$.

> Both graphs open up and have the same axis of symmetry. However, the vertex of the graph of $y = x^2 - 3$, (0, 3), is 3 units above the vertex of the graph of $y = x^2$, (0, 0). X

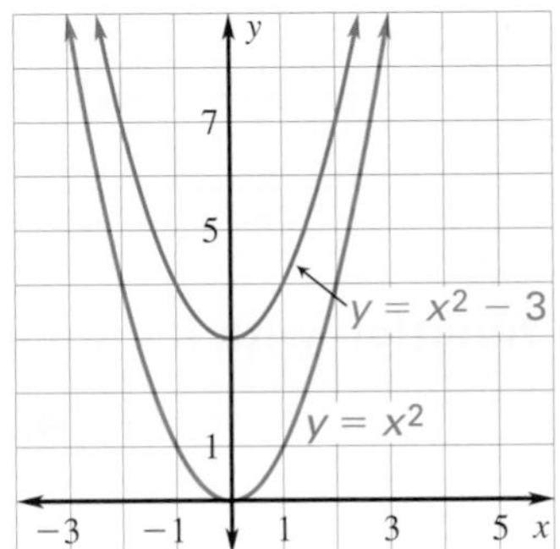

26. Serving Plate The top view of a freeform serving plate you made in a ceramics class is shown in the graph. One edge of the plate can be modeled by the graph of the function

$$y = -\frac{5}{81}x^2 + 20$$

where x and y are measured in inches.

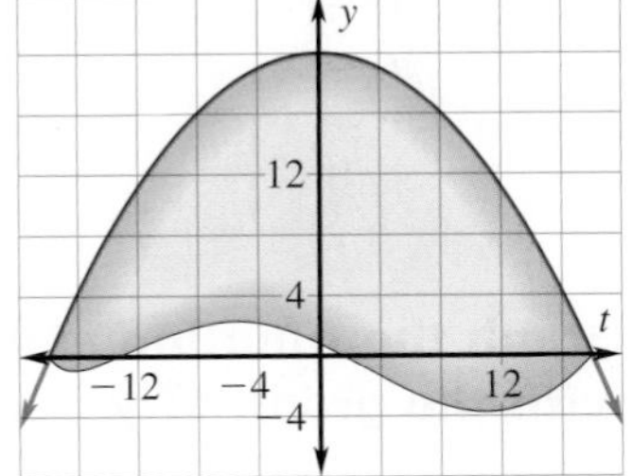

a. Find the domain of the function in this situation.

b. Find the range of the function in this situation.

27. Roof Shingle A roof shingle is dropped from a rooftop that is 100 feet above the ground. The height y (in feet) of the dropped roof shingle is given by the function

$$y = -16t^2 + 100$$

where t is the time (in seconds) since the shingle is dropped.

a. Graph the function.

b. Identify the domain and range of the function in this situation.

c. Use the graph to estimate the shingle's height at 1 second.

d. Verify your answer from part (c) algebraically.

e. Use the graph to estimate when the shingle is at a height of 50 feet.

LESSON 2.10 **Exercise Set B**

MM1A1b Graph the basic functions $f(x) = x^n$, where $n = 1$ to 3, $f(x) = \sqrt{x}$, $f(x) = |x|$, and $f(x) = \frac{1}{x}$.

MM1A1c Graph transformations of basic functions including vertical shifts, stretches, and shrinks, as well as reflections across the x- and y-axes.

MM1A1e Relate to a given context the characteristics of a function, and use graphs and tables to investigate its behavior.

Use the quadratic function to complete the table of values.

1. $y = 10x^2 - 4$

x	−2	−1	0	1	2
y	?	?	?	?	?

2. $y = -1.5x^2 + 3$

x	−2	−1	0	1	2
y	?	?	?	?	?

Match the function with its graph.

3. $y = 4x^2 + 3$

4. $y = \frac{1}{4}x^2 - 3$

5. $y = -4x^2 + 3$

A.

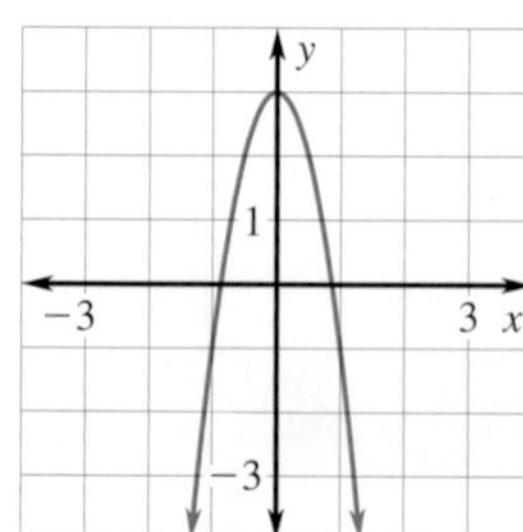

B.

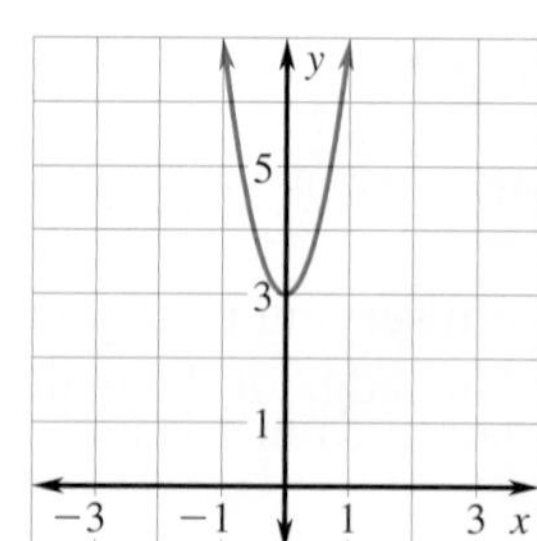

C.

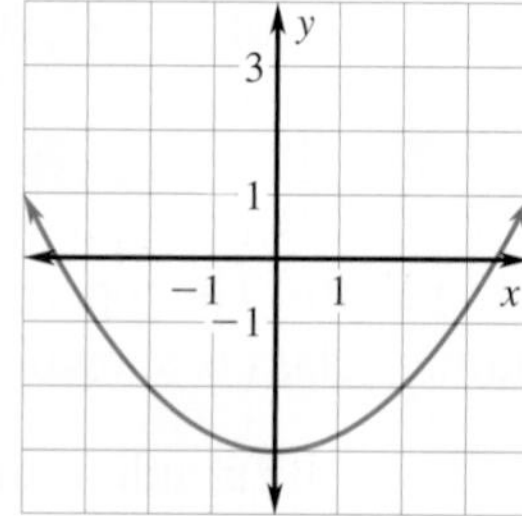

Graph the function and identify its domain and range. *Compare* the graph with the graph of $y = x^2$.

6. $y = \frac{1}{6}x^2 + 2$

7. $y = -4x^2 - 3$

8. $y = 9x^2 - \frac{7}{2}$

9. $y = \frac{3}{5}x^2 + \frac{1}{5}$

10. $y = -\frac{1}{2}x^2 + 4$

11. $y = 6x^2 + \frac{3}{4}$

12. $y = 4x^2 - \frac{2}{3}$

13. $y = -2x^2 - \frac{1}{2}$

14. $y = -5x^2 + 15$

15. $y = 4x^2 - 9$

16. $y = -\frac{3}{4}x^2 + 7$

17. $y = 5x^2 + \frac{1}{3}$

UNIT 2

Exercise Set B *(continued)*

Tell how you can obtain the graph of *g* from the graph of *f* by using transformations.

18. $f(x) = x^2 + 6$

$g(x) = x^2 - 2$

19. $f(x) = 2x^2 + 14$

$g(x) = 2x^2 + 9$

20. $f(x) = -\frac{1}{2}x^2 - 3$

$g(x) = -\frac{1}{2}x^2 - 7$

21. $f(x) = 3x^2 - 5$

$g(x) = 3x^2 + 11$

22. $f(x) = 3x^2$

$g(x) = 9x^2$

23. $f(x) = 8x^2$

$g(x) = 4x^2$

Write a function of the form $y = ax^2 + c$ whose graph passes through the two given points. Then graph the function.

24. (0, 6), (2, 10)

25. (0, 1), (−1, 0)

26. (0, −4), (−3, 5)

27. Nylon Rope The breaking weight w (in pounds) of a nylon rope can be modeled by the function $w = 22{,}210d^2$ where d is the diameter (in inches) of the rope.

a. Graph the function.

b. Use the graph to estimate the diameter of a nylon rope that has a breaking weight of 50,000 pounds.

UNIT 2

28. Multiple Representations Two acorns drop from an oak tree. Acorn A falls 45 feet, while acorn B falls 32 feet.

a. Writing an Equation For each acorn, write an equation that gives the height h (in feet) of the acorn as a function of the time t (in seconds) it has fallen.

b. Making a Table Complete the table for each equation from part (a). Estimate how long it takes each acorn to hit the ground.

Time, t	0	0.4	0.8	1.2	1.4	1.8
Height, h	?	?	?	?	?	?

c. Drawing a Graph Graph each equation from part (a). *Describe* how the graphs of the two equations are related.

29. Foam Ball A foam ball is dropped from a deck that is 20 feet above the ground.

a. The distance y (in feet) that the ball falls is given by the function $y = 16t^2$ where t is the time (in seconds) since the ball was dropped. Graph the function.

b. The height y (in feet) of the dropped ball is given by the function $y = -16t^2 + 20$ where t is the time (in seconds) since the ball was dropped. Graph the function.

c. How are the graphs from part (a) and part (b) related? *Explain* how you can use each graph to find the number of seconds after which the ball has dropped 8 feet.

LESSON 2.11

Graph $y = ax^2 + bx + c$

Georgia Performance Standards: MM1A1a, MM1A1c, MM1A1d

Goal Graph general quadratic functions.

Vocabulary

For $y = ax^2 + bx + c$, the y-coordinate of the vertex is the **minimum value** of the function if $a > 0$ and the **maximum value** of the function if $a < 0$.

Example 1 Find the axis of symmetry and the vertex

Consider the function $y = 3x^2 - 18x + 11$.

a. Find the axis of symmetry of the graph of the function.

b. Find the vertex of the graph of the function.

Solution

a. For the function $y = 3x^2 - 18x + 11$, $a = 3$ and $b = -18$.

$x = -\frac{b}{2a} = -\frac{(-18)}{2(3)} = 3$ Substitute 3 for a and -18 for b. Then simplify.

The axis of symmetry is $x = 3$.

b. The x-coordinate of the vertex is $-\frac{b}{2a}$, or 3. To find the y-coordinate, substitute 3 for x in the function and find y.

$y = 3(3)^2 - 18(3) + 11 = -16$ Substitute 3 for x. Then simplify.

The vertex is $(3, -16)$.

Example 2 Find the minimum or maximum value

Tell whether the function $f(x) = x^2 + 14x - 3$ has a *minimum value* or a *maximum value*. Then find the minimum or maximum value.

Solution

Because $a = 1$ and $1 > 0$, the parabola opens up, and the function has a minimum value. To find the minimum value, find the vertex.

$x = -\frac{b}{2a} = -\frac{14}{2(1)} = -7$ The x-coordinate is $-\frac{b}{2a}$.

$f(-7) = (-7)^2 + 14(-7) - 3 = -52$ Substitute -7 for x. Then simplify.

The minimum value of the function is $f(-7) = -52$.

Georgia Performance Standards

MM1A1a Represent functions using function notation. 

MM1A1c Graph transformations of basic functions including vertical shifts, stretches, and shrinks, as well as reflections across the x- and y-axes. 

MM1A1d Investigate and explain the characteristics of a function: domain, range, zeros, intercepts, intervals of increase and decrease, maximum and minimum values, and end behavior.

Guided Practice for Examples 1 and 2

Find the axis of symmetry and the vertex of the graph of the function.

1. $y = 5x^2 + 20x + 9$

2. $y = \frac{1}{3}x^2 - 4x - 19$

3. Tell whether the function $f(x) = \frac{1}{2}x^2 - 8x + 13$ has a *minimum value* or a *maximum value*. Then find the minimum value or maximum value.

Example 3 Graph $y = ax^2 + bx + c$

Graph $y = \frac{1}{5}x^2 - 2x + 3$.

Solution

STEP 1 **Determine** whether the parabola opens up or down. Because $a > 0$, the parabola opens up.

STEP 2 **Find** and draw the axis of symmetry:

$$x = -\frac{b}{2a} = -\frac{(-2)}{2\left(\frac{1}{5}\right)} = 5.$$

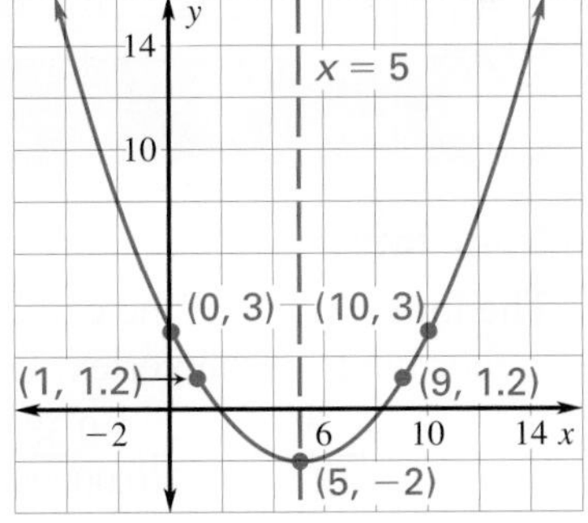

STEP 3 **Find** and plot the vertex.

The x-coordinate of the vertex is $-\frac{b}{2a}$, or 5. To find the y-coordinate, substitute 5 for x in the function and simplify.

$$y = \frac{1}{5}(5)^2 - 2(5) + 3 = -2, \text{ so the vertex is } (5, -2).$$

STEP 4 **Plot** two points. Choose two x-values less than the x-coordinate of the vertex. Then find the corresponding y-values.

x	0	1
y	3	1.2

STEP 5 **Reflect** the points plotted in Step 4 in the axis of symmetry.

STEP 6 **Draw** a parabola through the plotted points.

Guided Practice for Example 3

4. Graph the function $f(x) = x^2 - 4x + 7$. Label the vertex and axis of symmetry.

Example 4 Compare graphs

Compare the graphs of $f(x) = x^2 + 6x + 9$ and $g(x) = x^2 - 6x + 9$.

Solution

Consider the y-axis as a mirror. The graph $g(x) = x^2 - 6x + 9$ is the mirror image of the graph of $f(x) = x^2 + 6x + 9$. So, the graph of $g(x)$ is a reflection in the y-axis of the graph of $f(x)$.

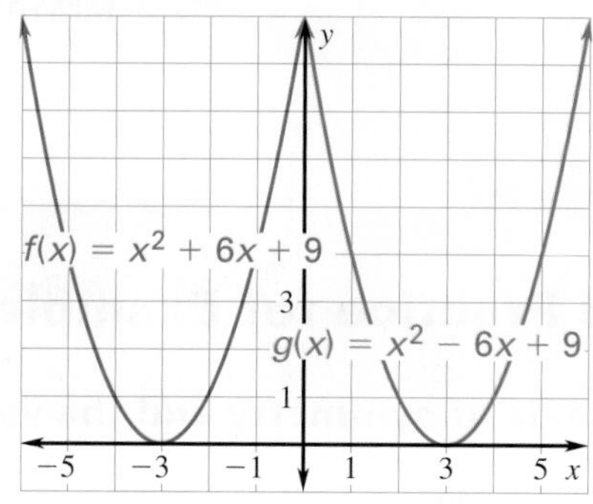

Example 5 Find the minimum value of a function

Suspension Bridges The suspension cables between the two towers of a bridge form a parabola that can be modeled by the graph of $y = 0.000095x^2 - 0.38x + 545$ where x and y are measured in feet. What is the height of the cable above the water at its lowest point?

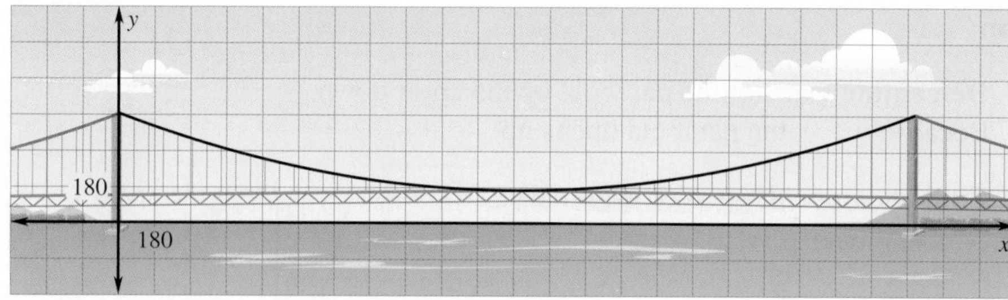

Solution

The lowest point of the cable is at the vertex of the parabola. Find the x-coordinate of the vertex. Use $a = 0.000095$ and $b = -0.38$.

$$x = -\frac{b}{2a} = -\frac{-0.38}{2(0.000095)} = 2000 \qquad \text{Use a calculator.}$$

Substitute 2000 for x in the equation to find the y-coordinate of the vertex.

$$y = 0.000095(2000)^2 - 0.37(2000) + 545 = 185$$

The cable is 185 feet above the water at its lowest point.

Guided Practice for Examples 4 and 5

5. *Compare* the graphs of $f(x) = x^2 - 4x + 4$ and $g(x) = x^2 + 4x + 4$.

6. **Telephone Poles** The cables between two telephone poles can be modeled by the graph of the equation $y = 0.0024x^2 - 0.1x + 24$ where x and y are measured in feet. To the nearest foot, what is the height of the cable above the ground at its lowest point?

UNIT 2

LESSON 2.11 **Exercise Set A**

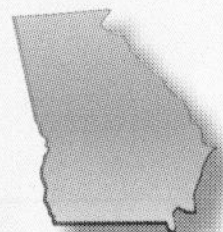

MM1A1a	Represent functions using function notation.
MM1A1c	Graph transformations of basic functions including vertical shifts, stretches, and shrinks, as well as reflections across the *x*- and *y*-axes.
MM1A1d	Investigate and explain the characteristics of a function: domain, range, zeros, intercepts, intervals of increase and decrease, maximum and minimum values, and end behavior.

Identify the values of *a*, *b*, and *c* in the quadratic function.

1. $y = 6x^2 + 3x + 5$

2. $y = \frac{3}{2}x^2 - x + 8$

3. $y = 7x^2 - 3x - 1$

4. $y = -2x^2 + 9x$

5. $y = \frac{3}{4}x^2 - 10$

6. $y = -8x^2 + 3x - 7$

Tell whether the graph opens *upward* or *downward*. Then find the axis of symmetry and vertex of the graph of the function.

7. $y = x^2 - 5$

8. $y = -x^2 + 9$

9. $y = -2x^2 + 6x + 7$

10. $y = 3x^2 - 12x + 1$

11. $y = 3x^2 + 6x - 2$

12. $y = -2x^2 + 7x - 21$

13. $y = \frac{1}{2}x^2 + 5x - 4$

14. $y = -\frac{1}{4}x^2 - 24$

15. $y = -3x^2 + 9x - 8$

16. $y = 3x^2 - 2x + 3$

17. $y = -2x^2 + 7x + 1$

18. $y = 3x^2 + 2x - 5$

Find the vertex of the graph of the function. Make a table of values using *x*-values to the left and right of the vertex.

19. $y = x^2 - 10x + 3$

x	?	?	?	?	?
y	?	?	?	?	?

20. $y = -x^2 + 6x - 2$

x	?	?	?	?	?
y	?	?	?	?	?

21. $y = \frac{1}{2}x^2 - x + 7$

x	?	?	?	?	?
y	?	?	?	?	?

22. $y = \frac{1}{3}x^2 - 2x + 3$

x	?	?	?	?	?
y	?	?	?	?	?

Graph the function. Label the vertex and axis of symmetry.

23. $y = -x^2 - 10$

24. $y = 2x^2 + 3$

25. $y = -2x^2 + 2x + 1$

26. $y = 5x^2 + 2x$

27. $y = -2x^2 + x - 4$

28. $y = x^2 - 8x + 5$

29. $y = -\frac{1}{2}x^2 - 8x + 3$

30. $y = \frac{1}{4}x^2 + 3x - 1$

31. $y = -\frac{3}{4}x^2 - 2x + 2$

UNIT 2

Exercise Set A *(continued)*

32. **Error Analysis** *Describe* and correct the error in finding the axis of symmetry of the graph of $y = 3x^2 + 18x - 1$.

> $x = \frac{b}{2a} = \frac{18}{2(3)} = 3$
>
> The axis of symmetry is $x = 3$.

Tell whether the function has a *minimum value* or a *maximum value*. Then find the minimum or maximum value.

33. $f(x) = 8x^2 - 40$

34. $f(x) = -5x^2 + 10x - 2$

35. $f(x) = 8x^2 - 4x + 4$

***Compare* the graphs of *f*(*x*) and *g*(*x*).**

36.

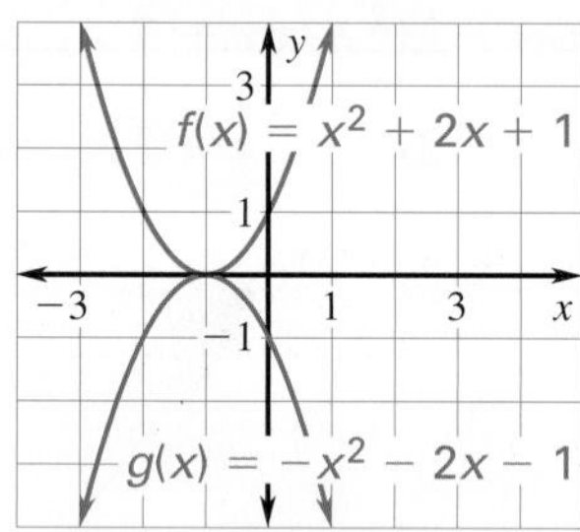

37.

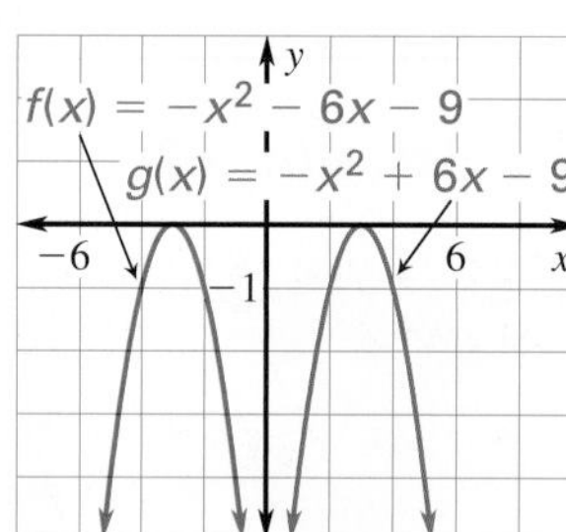

38.

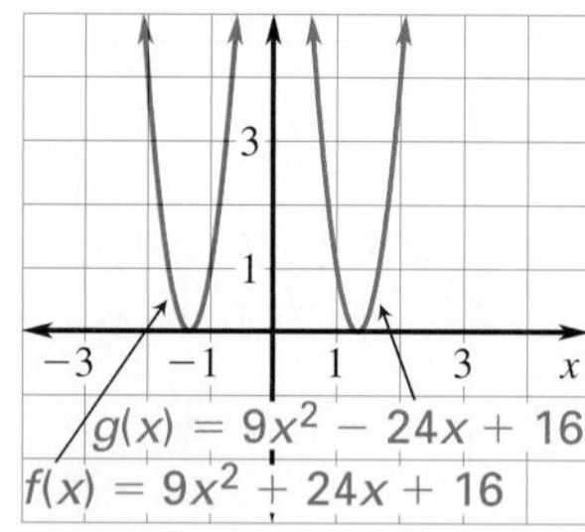

39. **Storage Building** The storage building shown can be modeled by the graph of the function $y = -0.12x^2 + 2.4x$ where x and y are measured in feet. What is the height h at the highest point of the building as shown in the diagram?

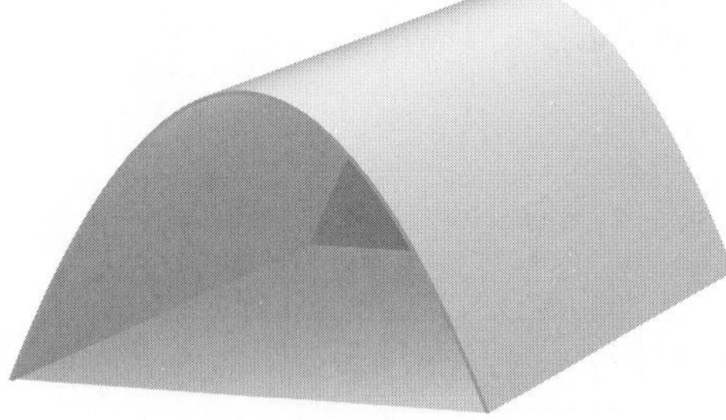

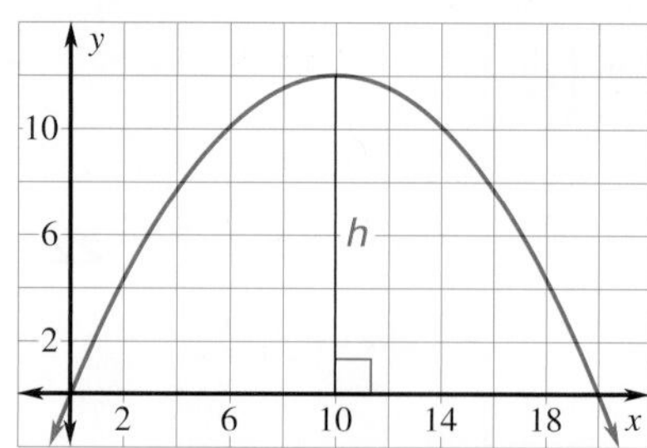

40. **Velvet Rope** A parabola is formed by a piece of velvet rope found around a museum display as shown. This parabola can be modeled by the graph of the function $y = \frac{4}{225}x^2 - \frac{16}{15}x + 40$ where x and y are measured in inches and y represents the number of inches the parabola is above the ground. How far above the ground is the lowest point on the rope?

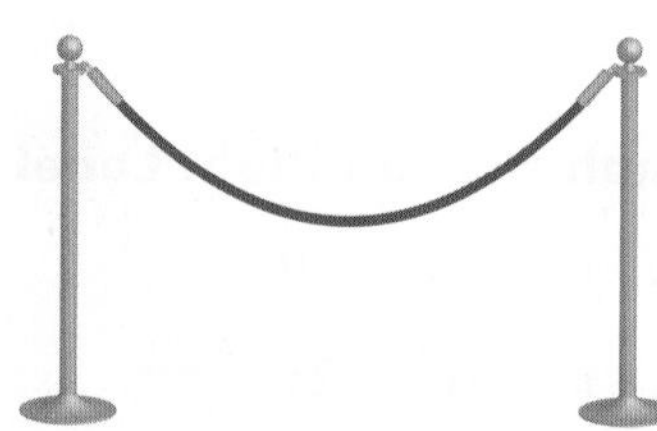

LESSON 2.11 **Exercise Set B**

MM1A1a	Represent functions using function notation.
MM1A1c	Graph transformations of basic functions including vertical shifts, stretches, and shrinks, as well as reflections across the *x*- and *y*-axes.
MM1A1d	Investigate and explain the characteristics of a function: domain, range, zeros, intercepts, intervals of increase and decrease, maximum and minimum values, and end behavior.

Tell whether the graph opens *upward* or *downward*. Then find the axis of symmetry and vertex of the graph of the function.

1. $y = -3x^2 + 3x + 5$

2. $y = \frac{5}{2}x^2 - 2x + 1$

3. $y = 8x^2 - 2x + 3$

4. $y = -9x^2 + 9x$

5. $y = \frac{2}{3}x^2 - 9$

6. $y = -5x^2 + 2x - 3$

7. $y = \frac{1}{8}x^2 - 2x$

8. $y = -\frac{1}{5}x^2 + 7$

9. $y = -6x^2 + 12x + 5$

10. $y = 4x^2 - 12x + 8$

11. $y = 5x^2 + 10x - 3$

12. $y = -6x^2 + 8x - 10$

Find the vertex of the graph of the function. Make a table of values using *x*-values to the left and right of the vertex.

13. $y = \frac{1}{4}x^2 - 2x + 5$

x	?	?	?	?	?
y	?	?	?	?	?

14. $y = -\frac{5}{2}x^2 + 10x - 1$

x	?	?	?	?	?
y	?	?	?	?	?

Graph the function. Label the vertex and axis of symmetry.

15. $y = -x^2 - 15$

16. $y = 6x^2 + 8$

17. $y = -4x^2 + 4x + 3$

18. $y = -x^2 + 20$

19. $y = 7x^2 - 14x + 6$

20. $y = -3x^2 + 18x - 4$

21. $y = -\frac{7}{2}x^2 + 21x - 5$

22. $y = \frac{1}{4}x^2 - 2x + 10$

23. $y = 6x^2 - 12x + 13$

24. $y = \frac{5}{3}x^2 - 15x + 2$

25. $y = \frac{7}{4}x^2 + 35x - 4$

26. $y = -\frac{2}{5}x^2 - 20x + 5$

Tell whether the function has a *minimum value* or a *maximum value*. Then find the minimum or maximum value.

27. $f(x) = 9x^2 - 36$

28. $f(x) = -\frac{3}{4}x^2 + 18x - 7$

29. $f(x) = \frac{5}{4}x^2 - 10x + 3$

30. $f(x) = -2x^2 + 8x - 15$

31. $f(x) = x^2 + 5x - 3$

32. $f(x) = -3x^2 - x + 9$

33. $f(x) = \frac{1}{3}x^2 - 3x + 8$

34. $f(x) = -\frac{2}{5}x^2 + 4$

35. $f(x) = \frac{3}{4}x^2 + 9x + 16$

Exercise Set B *(continued)*

Graph the functions in the same coordinate plane. *Describe* how the graphs are related.

36. $f(x) = x^2 - 10x + 25$
$g(x) = -x^2 + 10x - 25$

37. $f(x) = 4x^2 + 12x + 9$
$g(x) = 4x^2 - 12x + 9$

38. $f(x) = -x^2 + 3x - 5$
$g(x) = -x^2 - 3x - 5$

39. $f(x) = -2x^2 + x - 6$
$g(x) = 2x^2 - x + 6$

40. Follow the steps below to justify the equation for the axis of symmetry for the graph of $y = ax^2 + bx + c$. Because the graph of $y = ax^2 + bx + c$ is a vertical translation of the graph of $y = ax^2 + bx$, the two graphs have the same axis of symmetry. Use the function $y = ax^2 + bx$ in place of $y = ax^2 + bx + c$.

a. Find the x-intercepts of the graph of $y = ax^2 + bx$. (You can do this by finding the zeros of the function $y = ax^2 + bx$ using factoring.)

b. Because a parabola is symmetric about its axis of symmetry, the axis of symmetry passes through a point halfway between the x-intercepts of the parabola. Find the x-coordinate of this point. What is an equation of the vertical line through this point?

UNIT 2

41. Lamps A lighting company offers two models of small lamps, both of which contain a reflector in the shape of a parabola. The shape of the reflector in lamp A can be modeled by the function $y = -0.16x^2 + 25$ and the shape of the reflector in lamp B can be modeled by the function $y = -0.2x^2 + 20$ where x and y are measured in centimeters.

a. Find the maximum value of each function, which gives the height of the reflector.

b. How much taller is the reflector for lamp A than the reflector for lamp B?

42. Fund Raising Students are selling packages of flower bulbs to raise money for a class trip. Last year, when the students charged \$4 per package, they sold 120 packages. The students want to increase the cost per package. They estimate that they will lose 10 sales for each \$1 increase in the cost per package. The sales revenue R (in dollars) generated by selling the packages is given by the function $R = (4 + n)(120 - 10n)$ where n is the number of \$1 increases.

a. Write the function in standard form.

b. Find the maximum value of the function.

c. At what price should the packages be sold to generate the most sales revenue. *Explain* your reasoning.

43. Window An artist designs a window in a house to be in the shape of a parabola as shown. The top part of the window can be modeled by the function $y = -1.875x^2 + 7.5x$ and the bottom part of the window can be modeled by the function $y = 1.5$ where x represents the width of the window (in feet) and y represents the height of the window (in feet) above the ground. How tall is the window? *Explain* how you got your answer.

Georgia Performance Standards

MM1A1d Investigate and explain the characteristics of a function: domain, range, zeros, intercepts, intervals of increase and decrease, maximum and minimum values, and end behavior. 

MM1A1e Relate to a given context the characteristics of a function, and use graphs and tables to investigate its behavior. 

LESSON 2.11

Problem Solving Workshop

Problem You throw a basketball whose path can be modeled by the graph of $y = -16x^2 + 19x + 6$ where x is the time (in seconds) and y is the height (in feet) of the basketball. What is the maximum height of the basketball?

STEP 1 **Read and Understand**

What do you know? The equation that models the path of a basketball

What do you want to find out? The maximum height of the basketball

STEP 2 **Make a Plan** Use what you know to find the vertex of the parabola.

STEP 3 **Solve the Problem** The highest point of the basketball is at the vertex of the parabola. Find the x-coordinate of the vertex. Use $a = -16$ and $b = 19$.

$$x = -\frac{b}{2a} = -\frac{19}{2(-16)} \approx 0.59 \qquad \text{Use a calculator.}$$

Substitute 0.59 for x in the equation to find the y-coordinate of the vertex.

$$y \approx -16(0.59)^2 + 19(0.59) + 6 \approx 11.64$$

The basketball reaches a maximum height of about 11.64 feet.

STEP 4 **Look Back** By graphing the function, it appears that the maximum occurs after about 0.6 second and at a height between 11 and 12 feet. The answer seems reasonable.

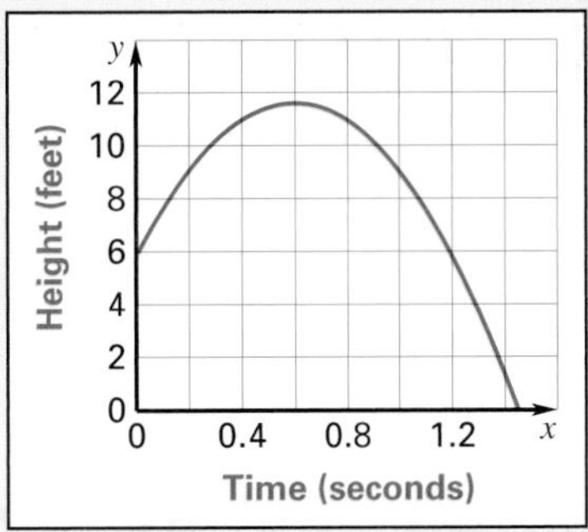

Practice

1. **Bridges** The cables between the two towers of the Golden Gate Bridge in California form a parabola that can be modeled by the graph of $y = 0.00012x^2 - 0.505x + 746$ where x and y are measured in feet. What is the height of the cable above the water at its lowest point?
2. **Baseball** You hit a baseball whose path can be modeled by the graph of $y = -16x^2 + 40x + 3$ where x is the time (in seconds) since the ball was hit and y is the height (in feet) of the baseball. What is the maximum height of the baseball?
3. **Tunnel** The shape of a tunnel for cars can be modeled by the graph of the equation $y = -0.5x^2 + 4x$ where x and y are measured in feet. On a coordinate plane, the ground is represented by the x-axis. How wide is the tunnel at its base?
4. **Sprinkler** A sprinkler ejects water at an angle of 35° with the ground. The path of the water can be modeled by the equation $y = -0.06x^2 + 0.7x + 0.5$ where x and y are measured in feet. What is the maximum height of the water?

UNIT 2

LESSON 2.12

Solve Quadratic Equations by Graphing

Georgia Performance Standards: MM1A1d, MM1A3c

Goal Solve quadratic equations by graphing.

Vocabulary

A **quadratic equation** is an equation that can be written in the **standard form** $ax^2 + bx + c = 0$ **where** $a \neq 0$.

Example 1 Solve a quadratic equation having two solutions

Solve $x^2 + 5x = 14$ by graphing.

Solution

STEP 1 **Write** the equation in standard form.

$x^2 + 5x = 14$ Write original equation.

$x^2 + 5x - 14 = 0$ Subtract 14 from each side.

STEP 2 **Graph** the function $y = x^2 + 5x - 14$.

The x-intercepts are -7 and 2.

The solutions of the equation $x^2 + 5x = 14$ are -7 and 2.

CHECK You can check -7 and 2 in the original equation.

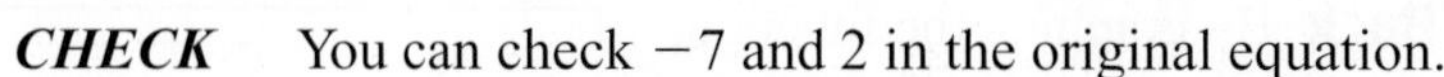

$x^2 + 5x = 14$	$x^2 + 5x = 14$	Write original equation.
$(-7)^2 + 5(-7) \stackrel{?}{=} 14$	$(2)^2 + 5(2) \stackrel{?}{=} 14$	Substitute for x.
$14 = 14$ ✓	$14 = 14$ ✓	Simplify. Each solution checks.

Example 2 Solve a quadratic equation having one solution

Solve $x^2 + 25 = 10x$ by graphing.

Solution

STEP 1 **Write** the equation in standard form.

$x^2 + 25 = 10x$ Write original equation.

$x^2 - 10x + 25 = 0$ Subtract $10x$ from each side.

STEP 2 **Graph** the function $y = x^2 - 10x + 25$.

The x-intercept is 5.

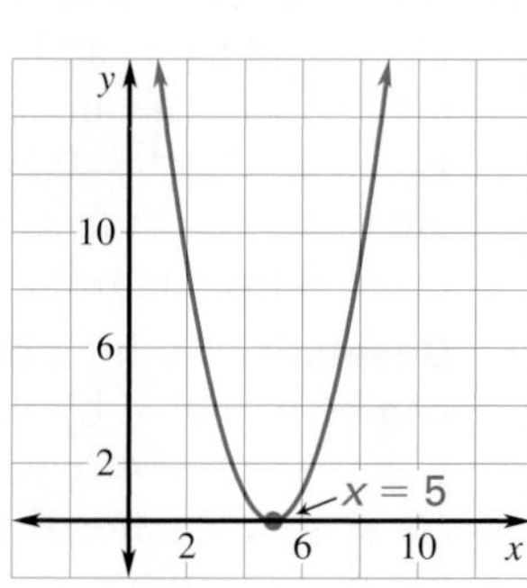

The solution of the equation $x^2 + 25 = 10x$ is 5.

UNIT 2

Georgia Performance Standards

MM1A1d Investigate and explain the characteristics of a function: domain, range, zeros, intercepts, intervals of increase and decrease, maximum and minimum values, and end behavior. 

MM1A3c Use a variety of techniques, including technology, tables, and graphs to solve equations resulting from the investigation of $x^2 + bx + c = 0$. 

Example 3 Solve a quadratic equation having no solution

Solve $x^2 + 11 = 5x$ by graphing.

Solution

STEP 1 **Write** the equation in standard form.

$x^2 + 11 = 5x$ Write original equation.

$x^2 - 5x + 11 = 0$ Subtract $5x$ from each side.

STEP 2 **Graph** the function $y = x^2 - 5x + 11$.

The graph has no x-intercepts.

The equation $x^2 + 11 = 5x$ has no solution.

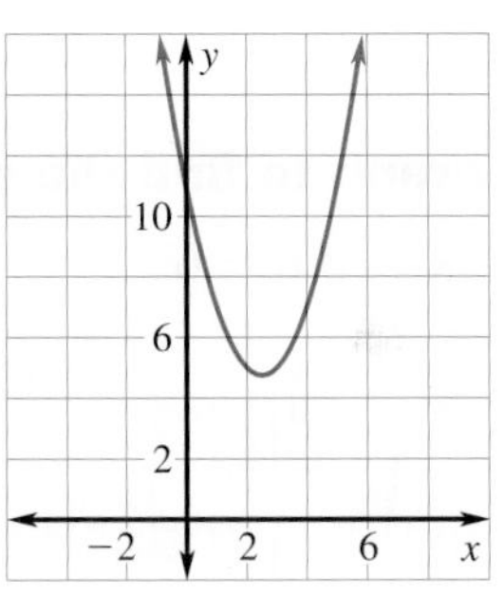

Guided Practice for Examples 1, 2, and 3

Solve the equation by graphing.

1. $x^2 = 2x + 15$ **2.** $x^2 + 4 = -4x$ **3.** $x^2 + x = -4$

Example 4 Find the zeros of a quadratic function

Find the zeros of $f(x) = x^2 - 10x + 24$.

Solution

Graph the function $f(x) = x^2 - 10x + 24$.

The x-intercepts are 4 and 6.

The zeros of the function are 4 and 6.

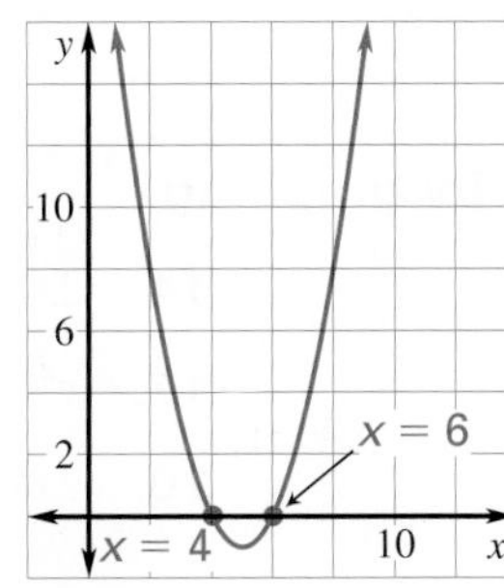

Guided Practice for Example 4

Find the zeros of the function.

4. $f(x) = x^2 - 4$ **5.** $f(x) = x^2 + x - 12$

LESSON 2.12

Exercise Set A

MM1A1d Investigate and explain the characteristics of a function: domain, range, zeros, intercepts, intervals of increase and decrease, maximum and minimum values, and end behavior.

MM1A3c Use a variety of techniques, including technology, tables, and graphs to solve equations resulting from the investigation of $x^2 + bx + c = 0$.

Determine whether the given value is a solution of the equation.

1. $x^2 - 2x + 15 = 0; 3$

2. $x^2 - 4x - 12 = 0; 2$

3. $-x^2 - 5x - 6 = 0; 3$

4. $x^2 + 3x - 4 = 0; 1$

5. $2x^2 + 9x - 5 = 0; -2$

6. $3x^2 - 5x - 2 = 0; 2$

Use the graph to find the solutions of the given equation.

7. $x^2 + 8x + 16 = 0$

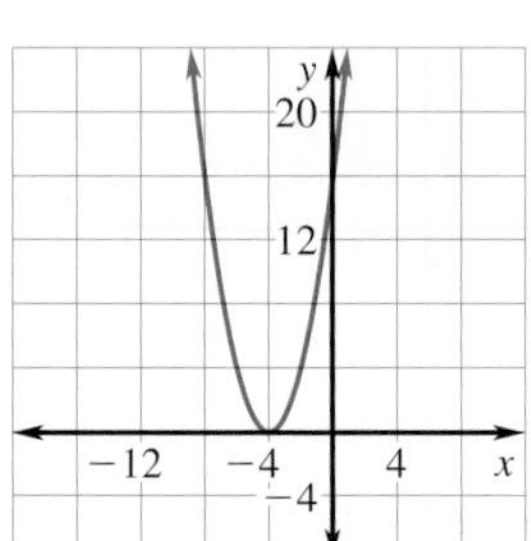

8. $-x^2 + 36 = 0$

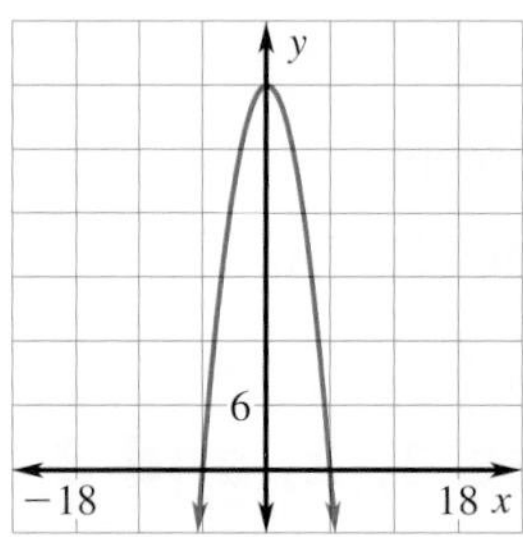

9. $x^2 + 5x - 24 = 0$

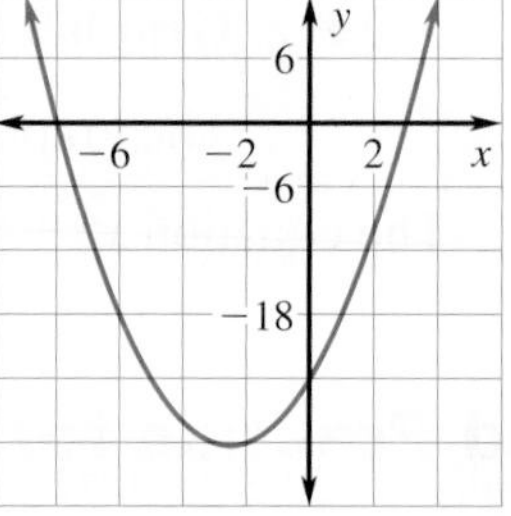

10. $x^2 + 11x + 30 = 0$

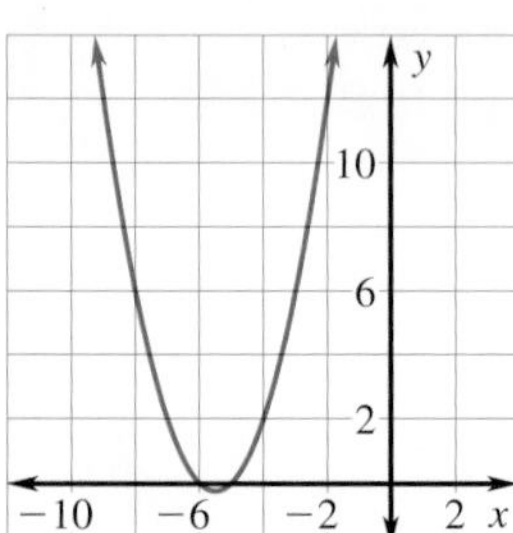

11. $x^2 - 25 = 0$

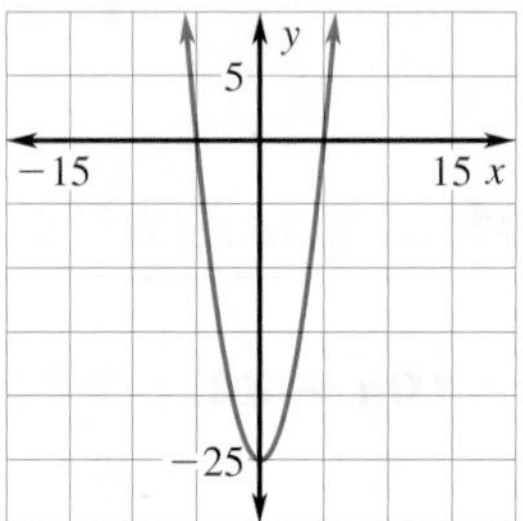

12. $x^2 + 7 = 0$

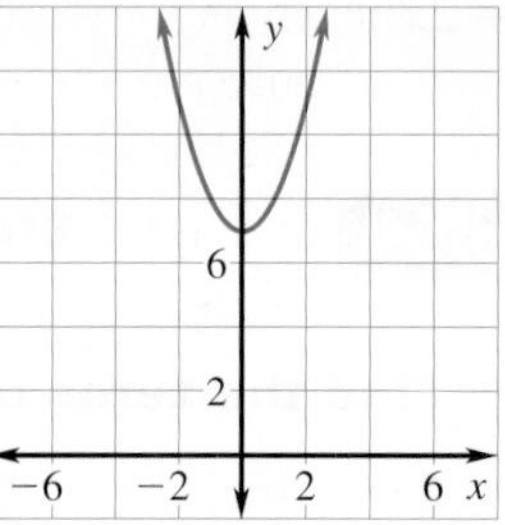

Solve the equation by graphing.

13. $-x^2 - 6x = 0$

14. $2x^2 = 2$

15. $x^2 - 7x + 10 = 0$

16. $x^2 = 10x$

17. $x^2 - 6x + 9 = 0$

18. $-x^2 + 9x = 18$

19. $x^2 - 6x + 8 = 0$

20. $2x^2 - x = -3$

21. $4x^2 - 5 = -8x$

Find the zeros of the function by graphing.

22. $f(x) = -x^2 - 5x - 10$

23. $f(x) = x^2 + 12x + 36$

24. $f(x) = 2x^2 + 24x$

25. $f(x) = x^2 - 49$

26. $f(x) = -x^2 + 1$

27. $f(x) = 3x^2 + 12x$

UNIT 2

Exercise Set A *(continued)*

In Exercises 28–33, (a) graph the function, then (b) use the graph to approximate the zeros of the function to the nearest integer.

28. $f(x) = x^2 + 2x - 1$

29. $f(x) = -x^2 - 4x + 2$

30. $f(x) = x^2 - 6x + 3$

31. $f(x) = x^2 - 2x - 9$

32. $f(x) = -x^2 + 5x + 5$

33. $f(x) = -x^2 + 9x - 3$

34. **Kickball** The height y (in feet) of a soccer ball after it is kicked can be modeled by the graph of the equation

$$y = -0.03x^2 + 1.5x$$

where x is the horizontal distance (in feet) that the ball travels. the ball is not touched, and it lands on the ground. Find the distance that the ball was kicked.

35. **Aircraft** An aircraft hanger is a large building where planes are stored. The opening of one airport hanger is a parabolic arch that can be modeled by the graph of the equation

$$y = -0.009x^2 + 1.9x$$

where x and y are measured in feet. Graph the function. Use the graph to determine how wide, to the nearest tenth of a foot, the hanger is at its base.

36. **Stunt Double** A movie stunt double jumps from the top of a building 50 feet above the ground onto a pad on the ground below. The stunt double jumps with an initial vertical velocity of 10 feet per second.

a. Write and graph a function that models the height h (in feet) of the stunt double t seconds after she jumps.

b. How long does it take the stunt double to reach the ground?

37. **Multiple Representations** You throw a wad of used paper towards a wastebasket from a height of about 1.3 feet above the floor with an initial vertical velocity of 3 feet per second.

a. **Writing a Function** Write a function that models the height h (in feet) of the paper t seconds after it is thrown.

b. **Drawing a Graph** Graph the function from part (a).

c. **Interpreting a Graph** If you miss the wastebasket and the paper hits the floor, how long does it take for the ball of paper to reach the floor?

d. **Interpreting a Graph** If the ball of paper hits the rim of the wastebasket one-half foot above the ground, how long was the ball in the air?

UNIT 2

LESSON 2.12 **Exercise Set B**

MM1A1d Investigate and explain the characteristics of a function: domain, range, zeros, intercepts, intervals of increase and decrease, maximum and minimum values, and end behavior.

MM1A3c Use a variety of techniques, including technology, tables, and graphs to solve equations resulting from the investigation of $x^2 + bx + c = 0$.

Solve the equation by graphing.

1. $x^2 = 4$

2. $x^2 + 3x = 4$

3. $-x^2 - 14x - 49 = 0$

4. $-x^2 + 6x + 16 = 0$

5. $x^2 + 10x + 25 = 0$

6. $x^2 + 8x + 15 = 0$

7. $x^2 + 2 = 0$

8. $x^2 = 4x + 12$

9. $-x^2 + 25 = 0$

10. $x^2 + 81 = -18x$

11. $-x^2 + 12x = 36$

12. $x^2 = 2x - 3$

13. $\frac{1}{4}x^2 - 16 = 0$

14. $-\frac{1}{2}x^2 + 2x = 6$

15. $-\frac{1}{4}x^2 + 6 = -\frac{1}{2}x$

Find the zeros of the function by graphing.

16. $f(x) = x^2 + 3x - 18$

17. $f(x) = -x^2 - 9x + 10$

18. $f(x) = x^2 - 9x - 36$

19. $f(x) = 2x^2 - 8x - 10$

20. $f(x) = -3x^2 - 6x + 24$

21. $f(x) = 4x^2 - 4x - 8$

In Exercises 22–27, (a) graph the function, then (b) use the graph to approximate the zeros of the function to the nearest integer.

22. $f(x) = -2x^2 + 5x + 1$

23. $f(x) = 3x^2 - 5$

24. $f(x) = 4x^2 - 3x - 4$

25. $f(x) = 2x^2 + x - 4$

26. $f(x) = -3x^2 + 5x - 3$

27. $f(x) = 6x^2 + 48x + 30$

28. **Error Analysis** The graph of the function related to the equation $0 = x^2 - 6x + 9$ is shown. *Describe* and correct the error in solving the equation.

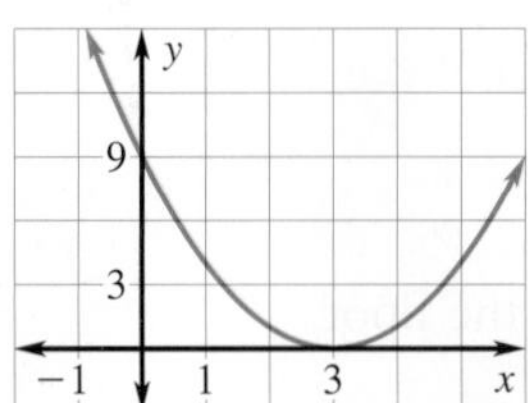

The only solution of the equation $0 = x^2 - 6x + 9$ is 9.

UNIT 2

Exercise Set B *(continued)*

Use the given surface area *S* of the cylinder to find the radius *r* to the nearest tenth. (Use 3.14 for π.)

29. $S = 301\text{ in.}^2$

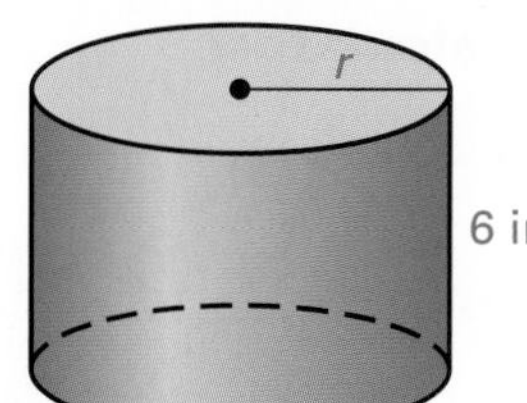

30. $S = 58\text{ ft}^2$

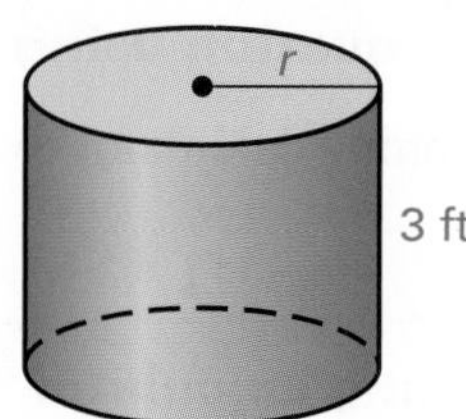

31. $S = 1356\text{ cm}^2$

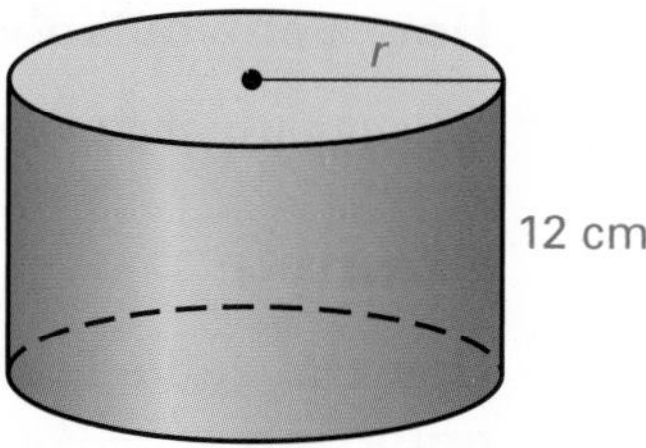

32. Multiple Representations A cat jumps down to the floor from a countertop 30 inches above the floor. It jumps with an initial vertical velocity of 5 feet per second.

a. **Writing a Function** Write a function that models the height h (in feet) of the cat t seconds after it jumps. *Explain* how you got your model.

b. **Drawing a Graph** Graph the function from part (a).

c. **Interpreting a Graph** How far above the ground is the cat after one half of a second?

d. **Interpreting a Graph** How long does it take the cat to reach the ground?

33. **Basketball** A basketball player throws a ball towards a hoop at a height of 6 feet with an initial vertical velocity of 50 feet per second.

a. Write and graph a function that models the height h (in feet) of the ball t seconds after it is thrown.

b. If the player misses the hoop completely and the ball lands on the ground, how long was the ball in the air?

c. If an opposing player catches the ball at a height of 5 feet, how long was the ball in the air? *Explain* your reasoning.

34. **Fountain** An arc of water sprayed from the nozzle of a fountain can be modeled by the graph of $y = -0.64x^2 + 8x$ where x is the horizontal distance (in feet) and y is the vertical distance (in feet) from the nozzle. The diameter of the circle formed by the arcs on the surface of the water is called the display diameter. Find the display diameter of the fountain. *Explain* your reasoning.

35. **Fire Hose** A stream of water from a fire hose can be modeled by the graph of $y = -0.002x^2 + 0.45x + 3$ where x and y are measured in feet. A firefighter is holding the hose 3 feet above the ground, 130 feet from a building. Will the stream of water pass through a window that is 4 feet tall if the top of the window is 27 feet above the ground? *Explain.*

Georgia Performance Standards

MM1A3c Use a variety of techniques, including technology, tables, and graphs to solve equations resulting from the investigation of $x^2 + bx + c = 0$. 

Technology Activity

Using Tables to Solve Quadratic Equations

Use after Lesson 2.12

Question

How can you solve a quadratic equation using a graphing calculator?

You can use the *table* feature of a graphing calculator to solve quadratic equations.

Example

Use the *table* feature of a graphing calculator to solve the equation $x^2 - 3x - 4 = 0$.

Solution

STEP 1 **Enter expression**

Enter the left side of the equation as $y_1 = x^2 - 3x - 4$.

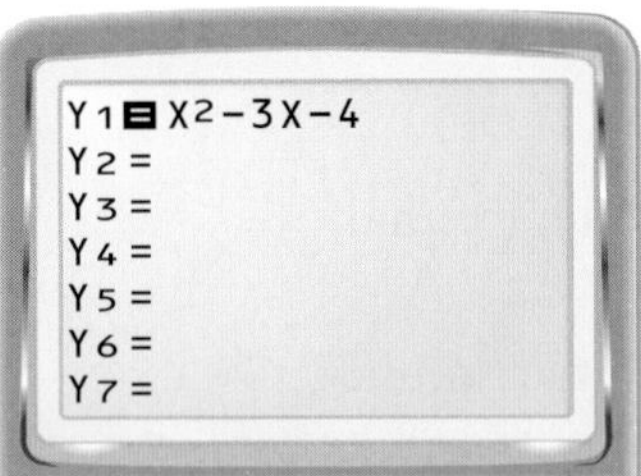

STEP 2 **Make a table**

Set the table so that the x-values start at -5 and increase in increments of 1.

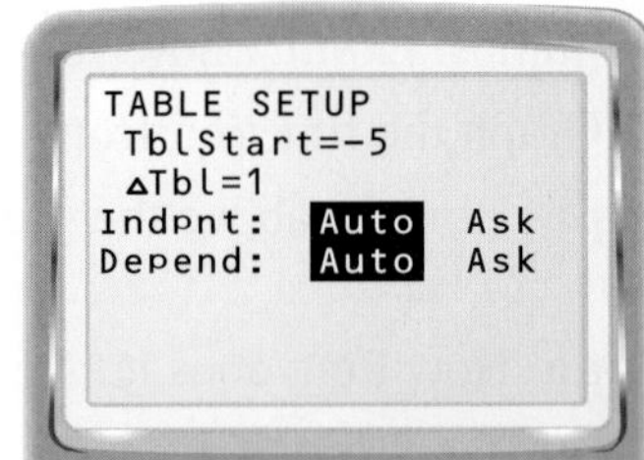

STEP 3 **Identify solutions**

Display the table. Scroll through the table until you find the x-values for which y_1 is 0.

You can see that y_1 is 0 when $x = -1$ and when $x = 4$. So, the solutions of $x^2 - 3x - 4 = 0$ are -1 and 4.

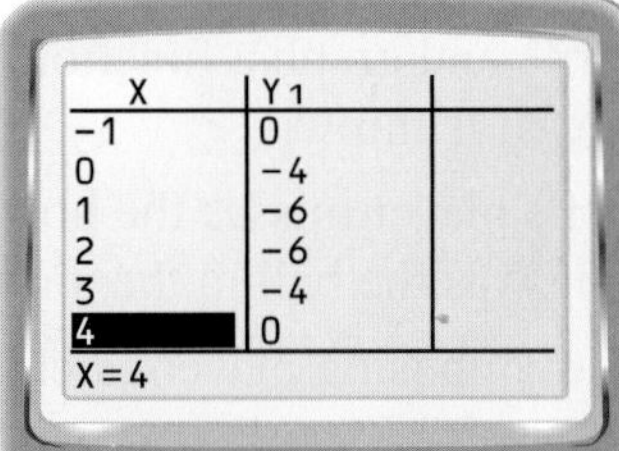

Practice

Use the *table* feature of a graphing calculator to solve the equation.

1. $x^2 + 5x + 6 = 0$ **2.** $x^2 - 11x + 28 = 0$ **3.** $x^2 + 3x - 10 = 0$

4. $x^2 + 6x = 27$ **5.** $x^2 + 2x = 80$ **6.** $x^2 - 16x = -55$

7. **Reasoning** Consider the equation $8x^2 + 2x - 1 = 0$.

a. Attempt to solve the equation using the *table* feature of a graphing calculator with x-values that increase in increments of 1. Between what two integers do each of the solutions lie? How do you know?

b. Use a smaller step value to find the exact solutions of the equation.

LESSON 2.13

Use Square Roots to Solve Quadratic Equations

Georgia Performance Standards: MM1A3a

Goal Solve a quadratic equation by finding square roots.

Vocabulary

If $b^2 = a$ then b is a **square root** of a. All positive real numbers have two **square roots,** a positive square root (or *principle* square root) and a negative square root.

A square root is written with the radical symbol $\sqrt{\ }$. The number or expression inside the radical symbol is the **radicand.**

The square of an integer is called a **perfect square.**

Example 1 Solve quadratic equations

Solve the equation.

a. $x^2 - 7 = 9$ **b.** $z^2 + 13 = 5$

Solution

a.

$x^2 - 7 = 9$	Write original equation.
$x^2 = 16$	Add 7 to each side.
$x = \pm\sqrt{16}$	Take square roots of each side.
$= \pm 4$	Simplify.

The solutions are -4 and 4.

b.

$z^2 + 13 = 5$	Write original equation.
$z^2 = -8$	Subtract 13 from each side.

Negative real numbers do not have real square roots. So, there is no solution.

Example 2 Take square root of a fraction

Solve $9m^2 = 169$.

$9m^2 = 169$	Write original equation.
$m^2 = \frac{169}{9}$	Divide each side by 9.
$m = \pm\sqrt{\frac{169}{9}}$	Take square roots of each side.
$m = \pm\frac{13}{3}$	Simplify.

The solutions are $-\frac{13}{3}$ and $\frac{13}{3}$.

UNIT 2

Georgia Performance Standards

MM1A3a Solve quadratic equations in the form $ax^2 + bx + c = 0$, where $a = 1$, by using factorization and finding square roots where applicable.

Example 3 Approximate solutions of a quadratic equation

Solve $2x^2 + 5 = 15$. Round the solutions to the nearest hundredth.

Solution

$2x^2 + 5 = 15$	Write original equation.
$2x^2 = 10$	Subtract 5 from each side.
$x^2 = 5$	Divide each side by 2.
$x = \pm\sqrt{5}$	Take square roots of each side.
$x \approx \pm 2.24$	Use a calculator. Round to the nearest hundredth.

The solutions are about -2.24 and about 2.24.

Guided Practice for Examples 1, 2, and 3

Solve the equation.

1. $w^2 - 9 = 0$ **2.** $4r^2 - 7 = 9$ **3.** $5s^2 + 13 = 9$

4. $36x^2 = 121$ **5.** $16m^2 + 81 = 81$ **6.** $4q^2 - 225 = 0$

Solve the equation. Round the solutions to the nearest hundredth.

7. $7x^2 - 8 = 13$ **8.** $-6y^2 + 15 = -15$ **9.** $4z^2 + 7 = 12$

Example 4 Solve a quadratic equation

Solve $3(x + 3)^2 = 39$. Round the solutions to the nearest hundredth.

Solution

$3(x + 3)^2 = 39$	Write original equation.
$(x + 3)^2 = 13$	Divide each side by 3.
$x + 3 = \pm\sqrt{13}$	Take square roots of each side.
$x = -3 \pm \sqrt{13}$	Subtract 3 from each side.

The solutions are $-3 + \sqrt{13} \approx 0.61$ and $-3 - \sqrt{13} \approx -6.61$.

Guided Practice for Example 4

Solve the equation. Round the solutions to the nearest hundredth, if necessary.

10. $5(x - 1)^2 = 40$ **11.** $2(y + 4)^2 = 18$ **12.** $4(z - 5)^2 = 32$

LESSON 2.13

Exercise Set A

MM1A3a Solve quadratic equations in the form $ax^2 + bx + c = 0$, where $a = 1$, by using factorization and finding square roots where applicable.

Solve the equation.

1. $6x^2 - 24 = 0$
2. $8x^2 - 128 = 0$
3. $x^2 - 13 = 23$
4. $3x^2 - 60 = 87$
5. $2x^2 - 33 = 17$
6. $5x^2 - 200 = 205$
7. $4x^2 - 125 = -25$
8. $7x^2 - 50 = 13$
9. $\frac{1}{2}x^2 - \frac{1}{2} = 0$

Solve the equation. Round the solutions to the nearest hundredth.

10. $x^2 + 15 = 23$
11. $x^2 - 16 = -13$
12. $12 - x^2 = 17$
13. $3x^2 - 8 = 7$
14. $9 - x^2 = 9$
15. $4 + 5x^2 = 34$
16. $48 = 14 + 2x^2$
17. $8x^2 = 50$
18. $3x^2 + 23 = 18$
19. $(x - 3)^2 = 5$
20. $(x + 2)^2 = 10$
21. $3(x - 4)^2 = 18$

Use the given area *A* of the circle to find the radius *r* or the diameter *d* of the circle. Round the answer to the nearest hundredth, if necessary.

22. $A = 169\pi$ m^2

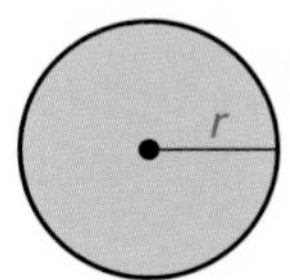

23. $A = 38\pi$ in.^{2}

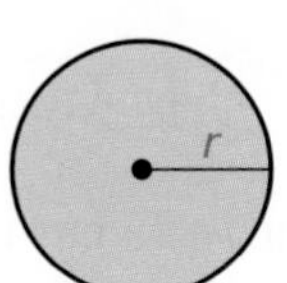

24. $A = 45\pi$ cm^2

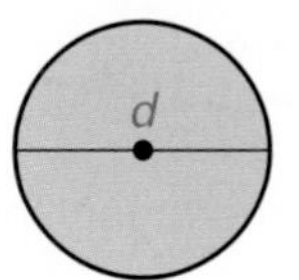

25. **Flower Seed** A manufacturer is making a cylindrical can that will hold and dispense flower seeds through small holes in the top of the can. The manufacturer wants the can to have a volume of 42 cubic inches and be 6 inches tall. What should the diameter of the can be? (*Hint:* Use the formula for volume, $V = \pi r^2 h$, where V is the volume, r is the radius, and h is the height.) Round your answer to the nearest inch.

26. **Stockpile** You can find the diameter D (in feet) of a conical pile of sand, dirt, etc., by using the formula $V = 0.2618hD^2$ where h is the height of the pile (in feet) and V is the volume of the pile (in cubic feet). Find the diameter of each stockpile in the table. Round your answers to the nearest foot.

Stockpile	Height (ft)	Diameter (ft)	Volume (ft^3)
A	10	?	68
B	15	?	230
C	20	?	545

UNIT 2

LESSON 2.13 **Exercise Set B**

MM1A3a Solve quadratic equations in the form $ax^2 + bx + c = 0$, where $a = 1$, by using factorization and finding square roots where applicable.

Solve the equation.

1. $4x^2 - 29 = 7$
2. $2x^2 - 50 = 48$
3. $5x^2 - 120 = -40$
4. $\frac{1}{2}x^2 - 2 = 0$
5. $\frac{1}{3}x^2 - 8 = 4$
6. $0.1x^2 - 6.4 = 0$

Solve the equation. Round the solutions to the nearest hundredth.

7. $4x^2 - 8 = 122$
8. $7x^2 - 43 = 34$
9. $2x^2 + 7 = 1$
10. $3x^2 + 23 = 74$
11. $6x^2 - 27 = 9$
12. $5(x - 8)^2 = 15$
13. $4(x + 9)^2 = 24$
14. $\frac{1}{2}(x - 4)^2 = 7$
15. $\frac{3}{4}(x + 7)^2 = 9$
16. $\frac{2}{5}(x - 4)^2 = 16$
17. $7x^2 - 34 = 2x^2 + 16$
18. $24 = 3(x^2 + 7)$
19. $9x^2 + 3 = 4(3x^2 - 6)$
20. $\left(\frac{x - 4}{5}\right)^2 = 36$
21. $(16x^2 - 8)^2 = 81$

Solve the equation without graphing.

22. $x^2 + 6x + 9 = 16$
23. $x^2 - 4x + 4 = 100$
24. $x^2 - 10x + 25 = 121$
25. $2x^2 - 28x + 98 = 72$
26. $-3x^2 + 6x - 3 = -27$
27. $\frac{1}{2}x^2 + 4x + 8 = 8$

28. **Speed** To estimate the speed s (in feet per second) of a car involved in an accident, investigators use the formula $s = \frac{11}{2}\sqrt{\frac{3}{4}\ell}$ where ℓ represents the length (in feet) of tire skid marks on the pavement. After an accident, an investigator measures skid marks that are 180 feet long. Approximately how fast was the car traveling?

29. **Doyle Log rule** The Doyle log rule is a formula used to estimate the amount of lumber that can be sawn from logs of various sizes. The amount of lumber V (in board feet) is given by $V = \frac{L(D - 4)^2}{16}$ where L is the length (in feet) of a log and D is the small-end diameter (in inches) of the log. Solve the formula for D. Then use the rewritten formula to find the diameters, to the nearest tenth of a foot, of logs that will yield 60 board feet and have the following lengths: 16 feet, 20 feet, 25 feet, and 32 feet.

30. **Multiple Representations** A ride at an amusement park lifts seated riders 240 feet straight above the ground. Then the riders are dropped. They experience free fall until the brakes are activated at 90 feet above the ground.

    a. **Writing an Equation** Use the vertical motion model to write an equation for the height h (in feet) of the riders as a function of the time t (in seconds) into the free fall.

    b. **Making a Table** Make a table that shows the height of the riders after 0, 1, 2, 3, and 4 seconds. Use the table to estimate the amount of time the riders experience free fall.

    c. **Interpreting an Equation** Use the equation to find the amount of time, to the nearest tenth of a second, that the riders experience free fall.

TEST | for Unit 2

Find the sum or difference.

1. $(x^2 + 3x + 4) + (-2x^2 + 10x - 5)$
2. $(4b^3 - 2b) + (b^3 + 6b^2 + 3b - 7)$
3. $(12y^2 - 8y + 4) - (9y^2 + 5y + 1)$
4. $(3a^3 + 10a - 15) - (-a^3 + 2a^2 + 6a - 9)$

Find the product.

5. $(2x - 3)(x + 5)$
6. $(4x + 7)(3x + 7)$
7. $(x - 1)(x^2 - 4x + 6)$
8. $(2z^2 + 3z - 4)(4z + 5)$
9. $(2a + 5)(2a - 5)$
10. $(3m + 4n)^2$

Use the Binomial Theorem and Pascal's triangle to write the binomial expansion.

11. $(y - 3)^3$
12. $(x + 4)^5$
13. $(2a - 1)^4$

Factor the polynomial.

14. $t^2 - 4t - 21$
15. $6x^2 - 5x - 25$
16. $4y^2 - 20yz + 25z^2$
17. $9b^2 - 36$
18. $10m^3 + 2m^2 - 36m$
19. $z^3 + 2z^2 + z + 2$

Solve the equation by factoring.

20. $2x^2 = 32x$
21. $b^2 - 8b + 16 = 0$
22. $2x^2 + 5x = 12$
23. $4y^2 + 15y = 25$
24. $x^3 - 19x^2 + 84x = 0$
25. $v^3 + 4v^2 = 4v + 16$

Graph the function. Label the vertex and axis of symmetry.

26. $y = x^2 - 9$
27. $y = x^2 - 4x + 4$
28. $y = -x^2 + 6x - 5$
29. $y = -4x^2 + 12x - 9$
30. $y = 3x^2 - 6x + 4$
31. $y = \frac{1}{2}x^2 + 2x + 1$

Graph the functions in the same coordinate plane. *Describe* how the graphs are related.

32. $f(x) = x^2 + 4x + 3$; $g(x) = -x^2 - 4x - 3$
33. $f(x) = x^2 - 8x + 12$; $g(x) = -x^2 + 8x - 12$

Solve the equation by graphing.

34. $4x^2 + x + 3 = 0$
35. $x^2 + 2x = -1$
36. $-x^2 + 8 = 7x$

Find the zeros of the function by graphing.

37. $f(x) = -x^2 + 5x + 14$
38. $f(x) = 2x^2 - 17$
39. $f(x) = -3x^2 - 2x + 5$

Solve the equation. Round your solutions to the nearest hundredth, if necessary.

40. $6x^2 - 54 = 0$
41. $3x^2 + 5 = 53$
42. $g^2 + 11 = 24$
43. $7n^2 + 5 = 9$
44. $2(a + 7)^2 = 34$
45. $3(w - 4)^2 = 5$

46. Box Dimensions A cardboard box that is rectangular prism has the dimensions shown.

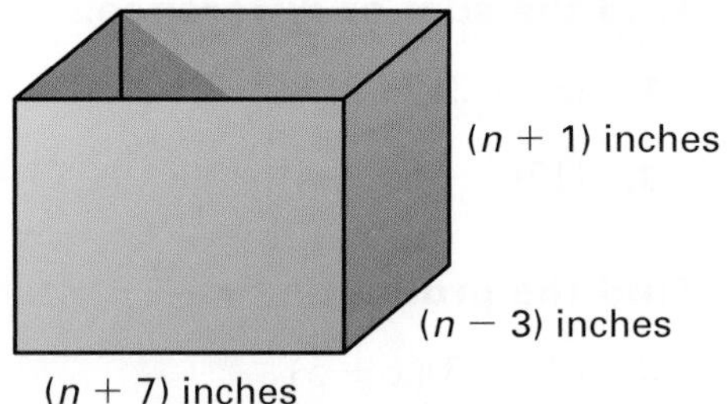

a. Write a polynomial that represents the area of the base of the box.

b. Write a polynomial that represents the volume of the box.

c. Write a polynomial for the area of the base if the length and width increase by 2 inches.

47. Vertical Motion A cat jumps straight up from the ground with an initial vertical velocity of 9 feet per second.

a. Write an equation that models the height h (in feet) of the cat as a function of the time t (in seconds) since it jumps.

b. After how many seconds does the cat land on the ground?

48. Profit A company's yearly profits from 1996 to 2006 can be modeled by the function

$$y = x^2 - 10x + 125$$

where y is the profit (in thousands of dollars) and x is the number of years since 1996.

a. In what year did the company experience its lowest yearly profit?

b. What was the lowest yearly profit?

49. Diving During a cliff diving competition, a diver begins a dive with his center of gravity 70 feet above the water. The initial vertical velocity of his dive is 8 feet per second.

a. Write and graph an equation that models the height h (in feet) of the diver's center of gravity as a function of time t (in seconds).

b. How long after the diver begins his dive does his center of gravity reach the water?

Performance Task

Juggling

A circus performer is juggling clubs while standing on stilts. He releases a club from a point 8 feet above the ground with an initial vertical velocity of 10 feet per second.

a. Write an equation that models the height h (in feet) of the club as a function of the time t (in seconds).

b. Graph the function from part (a). Label the vertex of the graph.

c. How high does the club go? Round your answer to the nearest tenth.

d. How long after the club is released does it reach its maximum height? Round your answer to the nearest tenth.

e. When is the club at a height of 9 feet?

f. After the performer releases the club, how much time does he have to catch the club on its way down when the club reaches a height of 7 feet? Round your answer to the nearest tenth.

g. If the performer does not catch the club, when will it land on the ground? Round your answer to the nearest tenth.

UNIT 3
Algebra: Cubic, Square Root, and Rational Functions

LESSON 3.1

Graph Cubic Functions

Georgia Performance Standards: MM1A1b, MM1A1c, MM1A1d, MM1A1h

Goal Graph and analyze cubic functions.

Vocabulary

A **cubic function** is a nonlinear function that can be written in the standard form $y = ax^3 + bx^2 + cx + d$ where $a \neq 0$.

A function f is an **odd function** if $f(-x) = -f(x)$. The graphs of odd functions are symmetric about the origin.

A function f is an **even function** if $f(-x) = f(x)$. The graphs of even functions are symmetric about the y-axis.

The **end behavior** of a function's graph is the behavior of the graph as x approaches positive infinity $(+\infty)$ or negative infinity $(-\infty)$.

If the degree is odd and the leading coefficient is positive:
$f(x) \to -\infty$ as $x \to -\infty$ and $f(x) \to +\infty$ as $x \to +\infty$.

If the degree is odd and the leading coefficient is negative:
$f(x) \to +\infty$ as $x \to -\infty$ and $f(x) \to -\infty$ as $x \to +\infty$.

UNIT 3

Example 1 Graph $y = x^3 + c$

Graph $y = x^3 + 2$. Compare the graph with the graph of $y = x^3$.

Make a table of values for $y = x^3 + 2$.

x	−2	−1	0	1	2
y	−6	1	2	3	10

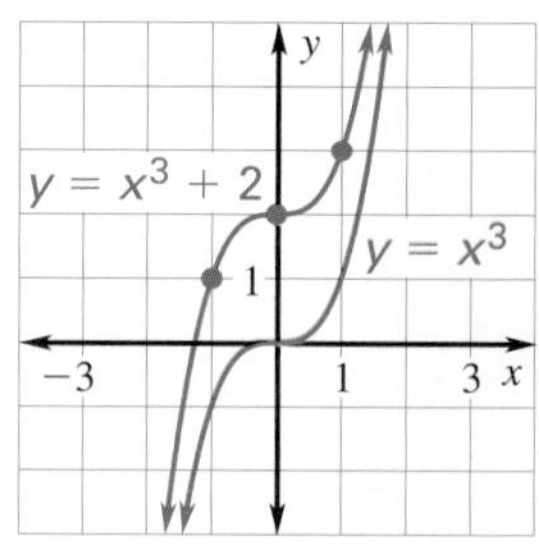

Plot points from the table and connect them with a smooth curve. The degrees of both functions are odd and leading coefficients are positive, so the graphs have the same end behavior. The graph of $y = x^3 + 2$ is a vertical translation (of 2 units up) of the graph of $y = x^3$.

Example 2 Graph $y = ax^3$

Graph $y = -4x^3$. Compare the graph with the graph of $y = x^3$.

Make a table of values for $y = -4x^3$.

x	−2	−1	0	1	2
y	32	4	0	−4	−32

Georgia Performance Standards

MM1A1b Graph the basic functions $f(x) = x^n$, where $n = 1$ to 3, $f(x) = \sqrt{x}$, $f(x) = |x|$, and $f(x) = \frac{1}{x}$.

MM1A1c Graph transformations of basic functions including vertical shifts, stretches, and shrinks, as well as reflections across the x- and y-axes.

MM1A1d Investigate and explain the characteristics of a function: domain, range, zeros, intercepts, intervals of increase and decrease, maximum and minimum values, and end behavior.

MM1A1h Determine graphically and algebraically whether a function has symmetry and whether it is even, odd, or neither.

Example 2 Graph $y = ax^3$ *(continued)*

Plot points from the table and connect them with a smooth curve. The degrees of both functions are odd but the leading coefficients do not have the same sign, so the graphs have different end behavior. The graph of $y = -4x^3$ is narrower than the graph of $y = x^3$. This is because the graph of $y = -4x^3$ is a vertical stretch (by a factor of 4) with a reflection in the x-axis of the graph of $y = x^3$. The graphs could also be viewed as being reflected in the y-axis.

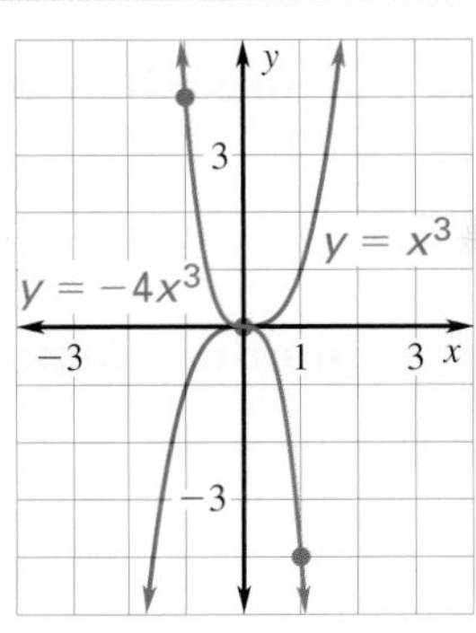

Example 3 Analyze cubic functions

Consider the cubic function $f(x) = \frac{1}{3}x^3 - 3x$.

a. Tell whether the function is *even*, *odd*, or *neither*. Does the graph of the function have symmetry?

b. Identify the intervals of increase and decrease of the graph of the function.

Solution

a. The function is odd because

$f(-x) = \frac{1}{3}(-x)^3 - 3(-x) = -\frac{1}{3}x^3 + 3x = -f(x)$.

Therefore, the graph is symmetric about the origin.

b. You can see from the graph that the function is increasing on the interval $x < -1.73$, decreasing on the interval $-1.73 < x < 1.73$, and increasing on the interval $x > 1.73$. You can use a graphing calculator to verify the turning points.

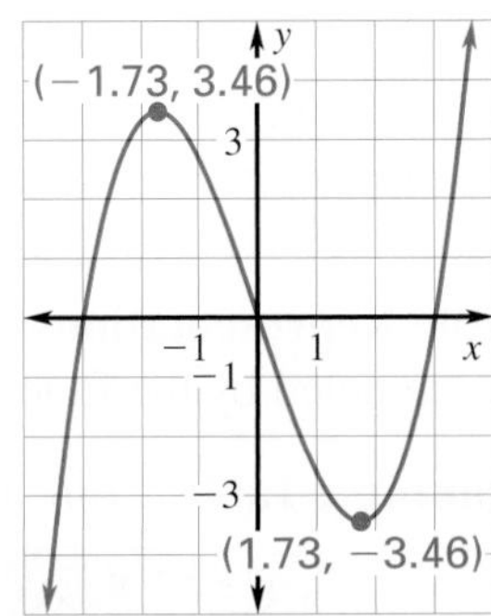

Guided Practice for Example 1, 2, and 3

1. Graph the function $y = 2x^3 + 1$. *Compare* the graph with the graph of $y = x^3$.

2. Is the function $f(x) = x^3 - 3x^2$ *even*, *odd*, or *neither*? Does the graph of the function have symmetry? What are the intervals of increase and decrease?

LESSON 3.1 **Exercise Set A**

MM1A1b Graph the basic functions $f(x) = x^n$, where $n = 1$ to 3, $f(x) = \sqrt{x}$, $f(x) = |x|$, and $f(x) = \frac{1}{x}$.

MM1A1c Graph transformations of basic functions including vertical shifts, stretches, and shrinks, as well as reflections across the x- and y-axes.

MM1A1d Investigate and explain the characteristics of a function: domain, range, zeros, intercepts, intervals of increase and decrease, maximum and minimum values, and end behavior.

MM1A1h Determine graphically and algebraically whether a function has symmetry and whether it is even, odd, or neither.

Describe **the end behavior of the graph of the function.**

1. $f(x) = x^3$

2. $f(x) = -3x^3$

3. $f(x) = \frac{1}{2}x^3 - 2$

Graph the function. *Compare* the graph with the graph of $y = x^3$.

4. $y = x^3 + 1$

5. $y = x^3 - 2$

6. $y = 4x^3$

7. $y = -2x^3$

8. $y = -x^3 - 1$

9. $y = \frac{1}{3}x^3 + 1$

Tell whether the function is *even, odd,* or *neither.*

10. $f(x) = -x^3$

11. $f(x) = 5x^3$

12. $f(x) = x^2 + 4$

13. $f(x) = x^3 - x^2$

14. $f(x) = -x^3 + 2x$

15. $f(x) = x^3 + 4x + 1$

16. Error Analysis *Describe* and correct the student's error in analyzing the function $f(x) = x^3 + x$.

The function is an odd function because

$$f(-x) = (-x)^3 + (-x) = -x^3 - x = -f(x).$$

So the function is symmetric about the y-axis.

17. Multiple Representations The number of fish F in a small pond t years after 2000 can be modeled by the function $F = t^3 - 9t^2 + 18t + 12$.

a. Making a Table Copy and complete the table.

t (years since 2000)	0	1	2	3	4	5	6	7
F (number of fish)	?	?	?	?	?	?	?	?

b. Drawing a Graph Use the table to graph the function.

c. Interpreting a Graph Did the number of fish increase or decrease between 2002 and 2004?

LESSON 3.1

Exercise Set B

MM1A1b Graph the basic functions $f(x) = x^n$, where $n = 1$ to 3, $f(x) = \sqrt{x}$, $f(x) = |x|$, and $f(x) = \frac{1}{x}$.

MM1A1c Graph transformations of basic functions including vertical shifts, stretches, and shrinks, as well as reflections across the x- and y-axes.

MM1A1d Investigate and explain the characteristics of a function: domain, range, zeros, intercepts, intervals of increase and decrease, maximum and minimum values, and end behavior.

MM1A1h Determine graphically and algebraically whether a function has symmetry and whether it is even, odd, or neither.

Describe **the end behavior of the graph of the function.**

1. $f(x) = -x^3 - 2x$

2. $f(x) = -\frac{2}{3}x^3 + 2$

3. $f(x) = 0.4x^3 - 2x^2$

4. **Open-Ended** Give an example of a transformation or a series of transformations that would change the end behavior of a function.

Graph the function. ***Compare*** **the graph with the graph of $y = x^3$.**

5. $y = 3x^3 - 2$

6. $y = -2x^3 + 1$

7. $y = -\frac{3}{4}x^3$

8. **Multiple Choice** The graph of which function is a vertical stretch and a reflection in the x-axis of the graph of $y = x^3$?

A. $y = -5x^3$ **B.** $y = -\frac{3}{4}x^3$ **C.** $y = -x^3 + 4$ **D.** $y = 2x^3$

Tell whether the function is *even, odd,* or *neither*.

9. $f(x) = \frac{1}{2}x^3 + 9x$

10. $f(x) = -5x^2 - 9$

11. $f(x) = x^3 - x + 1$

12. **Reasoning** Can a cubic function be an even function? *Explain* your answer algebraically. Also explain your answer using what you know about the end behavior of cubic functions.

13. **Stock Market** The balance B (in thousands of dollars) in Ed's stock market account between 2000 and 2007 can be modeled by the cubic function graphed at the right, where t is the number of years since 2000.

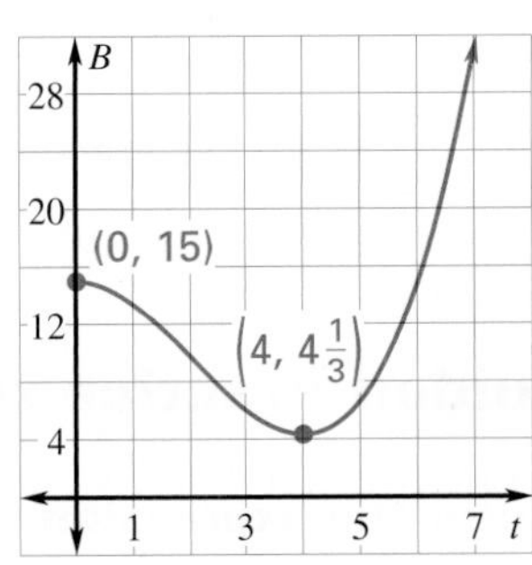

a. How much was in Ed's account in 2000?

b. Between what years did his account value decrease?

c. Between what years did his account value increase?

LESSON 3.2

Use Special Products to Factor Cubics

Georgia Performance Standards: MM1A2f

Goal Factor cubics using special product patterns.

Vocabulary

Special Product Patterns

$(x + y)^3 = x^3 + 3x^2y + 3xy^2 + y^3$

$(x - y)^3 = x^3 - 3x^2y + 3xy^2 - y^3$

Example 1 Use special product patterns

Factor the expression.

a. $x^3 + 6x^2 + 12x + 8$ **b.** $x^3 - 9x^2 + 27x - 27$

Solution

a. $x^3 + 6x^2 + 12x + 8 = x^3 + 3x^2(2) + 3x(2^2) + 2^3$ Rewrite.

$= (x + 2)^3$ Use pattern.

b. $x^3 - 9x^2 + 27x - 27 = x^3 - 3x^2(3) + 3x(3^2) - 3^3$ Rewrite.

$= (x - 3)^3$ Use pattern.

UNIT 3

Guided Practice for Example 1

Factor the expression.

1. $x^3 + 3x^2 + 3x + 1$ **2.** $x^3 - 12x^2 + 48x - 64$

Example 2 Factor out a monomial first

Factor $2x^3 - 6x^2 + 6x - 2$.

Solution

$2x^3 - 6x^2 + 6x - 2 = 2(x^3 - 3x^2 + 3x - 1)$ Factor common monomial.

$= 2[x^3 - 3x^2(1) + 3x(1^2) - 1^3]$ Rewrite.

$= 2(x - 1)^3$ Use pattern.

Guided Practice for Example 2

Factor the expression.

3. $-3x^3 + 18x^2 - 36x + 24$ **4.** $x^4 + 15x^3 + 75x^2 + 125x$

Georgia Performance Standards

MM1A2f Factor expressions by greatest common factor, grouping, trial and error, and special products.

Example 3 Factor cubics with multiple variables

Factor the expression.

a. $a^3b^3 + 12a^2b^2 + 48ab + 64$

$= (ab)^3 + 3(ab)^2(4) + 3(ab)(4^2) + 4^3$ Rewrite.

$= (ab + 4)^3$ Use pattern.

b. $343x^3 - 147x^2y + 21xy^2 - y^3$

$= (7x)^3 - 3(7x)^2(y) + 3(7x)(y^2) - y^3$ Rewrite

$= (7x - y)^3$ Use pattern.

Guided Practice for Example 3

Factor the expression.

5. $8x^3 + 12x^2y + 6xy^2 + y^3$

6. $p^3q^3 - 18p^2q^2 + 108pq - 216$

7. $r^3s^3 + 15r^2s^2 + 75rs + 125$

Example 4 Solve a real-world problem

Interest The amount y (in dollars) that is in Jessica's savings account after t years can be modeled by the equation $y = a(1 + r)^t$ where a is the initial amount and r is the annual interest rate expressed as a decimal. The polynomial $1000 + 3000r + 3000r^2 + 1000r^3$ represents the amount of money in her account after 3 years. What was the initial amount of her investment?

Solution

Factor the polynomial so that it is of the form $a(1 + r)^t$.

$$1000 + 3000r + 3000r^2 + 1000r^3 = 1000(1 + 3r + 3r^2 + r^3)$$

$$= 1000(1 + r)^3$$

The polynomial factors to $1000(1 + r)^3$, so the initial amount of her investment was \$1000.

Guided Practice for Example 4

8. In Example 4, suppose the polynomial given is $500 + 1500r + 1500r^2 + 500r^3$. What was the initial amount of the investment?

LESSON **3.2**

Exercise Set A

MM1A2f Factor expressions by greatest common factor, grouping, trial and error, and special products.

Factor the expression.

1. $x^3 - 6x^2 + 12x - 8$

2. $x^3 + 18x^2 + 108x + 216$

3. $8x^3 - 12x^2 + 6x - 1$

4. $27x^3 + 27x^2 + 9x + 1$

5. $x^3 + 30x^2 + 300x + 1000$

6. $729x^3 - 486x^2 + 108x - 8$

Match the polynomial with the appropriate factorization.

7. $32x^2 - 24x^2 + 6x - \frac{1}{2}$

A. $\frac{1}{2}(x - 4)^3$

8. $\frac{1}{2}x^3 + 6x^2 + 24x + 32$

B. $\frac{1}{2}(4x - 1)^3$

9. $\frac{1}{2}x^3 - 6x^2 + 24x - 32$

C. $\frac{1}{2}(x + 4)^3$

10. **Multiple Choice** Which expression is equivalent to $125x^3 - 225x^2 + 135x - 27$?

A. $(3x - 5)^3$ **B.** $(5x - 3)^3$ **C.** $(3x + 5)^3$ **D.** $(5x + 3)^3$

Factor the expression.

11. $x^3y^3 + 3x^2y^2 + 3xy + 1$

12. $m^3n^3 - 9m^2n^2 + 27mn - 27$

13. $27x^3 - 54x^2y + 36xy^2 - 8y^3$

14. $64x^3 + 240x^2y + 300xy^2 + 125y^3$

15. **Error Analysis** *Describe* and correct the student's error in factoring $a^3b^3 - 3a^2b^2cd + 3abc^2d^2 - c^3d^3$.

$$a^3b^3 - 3a^2b^2cd + 3abc^2d^2 - c^3d^3 = (ab)^3 - 3(ab)^2(cd) + 3(ab)(cd)^2 - (cd)^3$$
$$= (ab + cd)^3$$

X

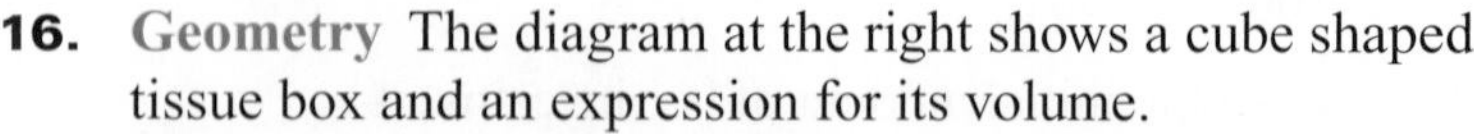

16. **Geometry** The diagram at the right shows a cube shaped tissue box and an expression for its volume.

a. Find a binomial that represents an edge length of the tissue box.

b. Write an expression for the surface area of the tissue box.

c. If x is 4 centimeters, what is the surface area of the tissue box?

Volume:
$27x^3 - 27x^2 + 9x - 1$

UNIT 3

LESSON 3.2 **Exercise Set B**

MM1A2f Factor expressions by greatest common factor, grouping, trial and error, and special products.

Factor the expression.

1. $a^3 + 9a^2 + 27a + 27$
2. $125 - 75y + 15y^2 - y^3$
3. $2 - 12y + 24y^2 - 16y^3$
4. $2x^4 + 30x^3 + 150x^2 + 250x$
5. **Reasoning** Adrianna and Lauren factor the expression $8w^3 - 6w^2 + \frac{3}{2}w - \frac{1}{8}$. Adrianna's answer is $\left(2w - \frac{1}{2}\right)^3$ and Lauren's answer is $\frac{1}{8}(4w - 1)^3$. Who is correct? *Explain.*

Factor the expression.

6. $s^3t^3 + 6s^2t^2 + 12st + 8$
7. $1 - 3gh + 3g^2h^2 - g^3h^3$
8. $x^3 - 9x^2y + 27xy^2 - 27y^3$
9. $512x^3 + 960x^2y + 600xy^2 + 125y^3$

Determine the value of *k* for which the expression can be factored using a special product pattern.

10. $x^3 + 6x^2 + kx + 8$
11. $64z^3 - kz^2 + 108z - 27$
12. $kx^3y^3 - 12x^2y^2z + 6xyz^2 - z^3$
13. $\frac{1}{8}x^3 + 6x^2 + kx + 512$

Complete the statement with +, −, •, or =.

14. $(x - y)^3$ __?__ $(y - x)^3$ __?__ (-1)
15. $(x + y)^3$ __?__ $(x - y)^3$ __?__ $6x^2y$ __?__ $2y^3$
16. **Savings** You have a savings account like the one described in Example 3 on page 131. The polynomial $900 + 2700r + 2700r^2 + 900r^3$ represents the amount of money in the account after 3 years.
    a. What was the initial amount of your investment?
    b. If $r = 0.03$, what is the amount in the savings account after 3 years to the nearest cent?
17. **Packaging** You are shipping a cube-shaped package. The volume of the package can be represented by the polynomial $8x^3 - 12x^2 + 6x - 1$. The area A of one of the faces of a larger cube-shaped package is shown at the right. How much longer is an edge length of the larger package?

$A = 16x^2 - 16x + 4$

UNIT 3

Georgia Performance Standards

MM1A1c Graph transformations of basic functions including vertical shifts, stretches, and shrinks, as well as reflections across the x- and y-axes.

Investigating Math Activity

Graphing Square Root Functions

Use before Lesson 3.3

Materials	**graph paper and pencil**

Question

How does the value of k affect the shape of the graph of the square root function $y = \sqrt{x} + k$?

Explore

Graph $y = \sqrt{x} + k$.

STEP 1 **Complete table**

Copy and complete the table of values for the function $y = \sqrt{x}$. Round to the nearest tenth.

x	0	1	2	3	4	5
y	?	?	?	?	?	?

STEP 2 **Graph $y = \sqrt{x}$**

Plot the points from your table. Graph the function.

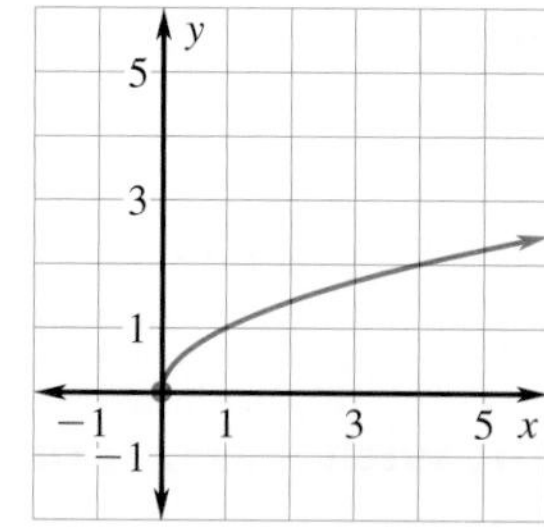

STEP 3 **Repeat Steps 1 and 2**

Graph $y = \sqrt{x} + k$ using -2 and 2 as values of k. Compare each graph to the graph of $y = \sqrt{x}$. Describe how the value of k affects the graph of $y = \sqrt{x}$.

Draw Conclusions

1. **Reasoning** In the Explore, what are the domain and range of the function? Why are negative values of x not included in the domain?

2. Which of the square root functions could be shown by the graph at the right? *Explain* your reasoning.

   A. $y = -3\sqrt{x}$ **B.** $y = \sqrt{x - 3}$

   C. $y = \sqrt{x} - 3$ **D.** $y = \sqrt{x} + 3$

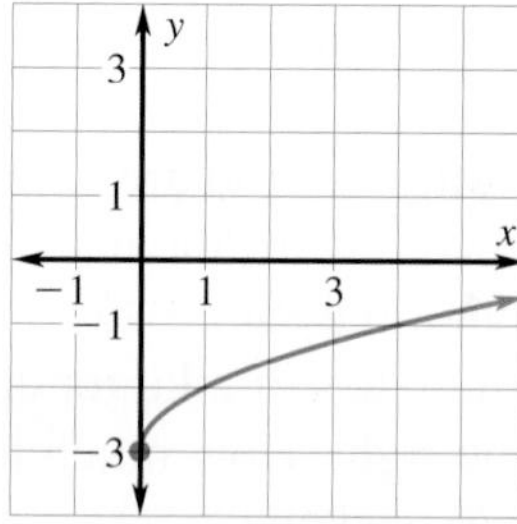

LESSON 3.3

Graph Square Root Functions

Georgia Performance Standards: MM1A1b, MM1A1c, MM1A1d

Goal Graph square root functions.

Vocabulary

A **radical expression** is an expression that contains a radical, such as a square root, cube root, or other root.

A **radical function** contains a radical expression with the independent variable in the radicand.

If the radical is a square root, then the function is called a **square root function**.

The most basic square root function in the family of all square root functions, called the **parent square root function**, is $y = \sqrt{x}$.

Example 1 Graph $y = a\sqrt{x}$ where $|a| > 1$

Graph the function $y = 5\sqrt{x}$ and identify its domain and range. Compare the graph with the graph of $y = \sqrt{x}$.

Solution

STEP 1 **Make** a table. Because the square root of a negative number is undefined, x must be non-negative. So the domain is $x \geq 0$.

x	0	1	2	3
y	0	5	7.1	8.7

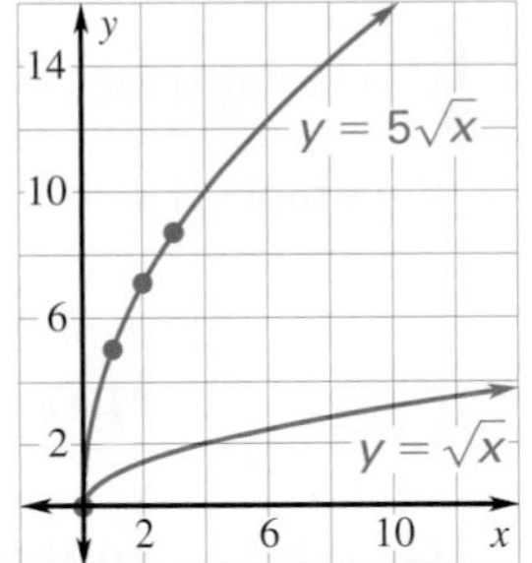

STEP 2 **Plot** the points.

STEP 3 **Draw** a smooth curve through the points. From either the table or the graph, you can see the range of the function is $y \geq 0$.

STEP 4 **Compare** the graph with the graph of $y = \sqrt{x}$. The graph of $y = 5\sqrt{x}$ is a vertical stretch (by a factor of 5) of the graph of $y = \sqrt{x}$.

Guided Practice for Example 1

1. Graph $y = 4\sqrt{x}$ and identify its domain and range. *Compare* the graph with the graph of $y = \sqrt{x}$.

2. Graph $y = 1.5\sqrt{x}$ and identify its domain and range. *Compare* the graph with the graph of $y = \sqrt{x}$.

UNIT 3

Georgia Performance Standards

MM1A1b Graph the basic functions $f(x) = x^n$, where $n = 1$ to 3, $f(x) = \sqrt{x}$, $f(x) = |x|$, and $f(x) = \frac{1}{x}$. ☑

MM1A1c Graph transformations of basic functions including vertical shifts, stretches, and shrinks, as well as reflections across the x- and y-axes. ☑

MM1A1d Investigate and explain the characteristics of a function: domain, range, zeros, intercepts, intervals of increase and decrease, maximum and minimum values, and end behavior. ☑

Example 2 Graph $y = a\sqrt{-x}$

Graph the function $y = \frac{1}{2}\sqrt{-x}$ and identify its domain and range.

Compare the graph with the graph of $y = \sqrt{x}$.

Solution

To graph the function, make a table, plot the points, and draw a smooth curve through the points. The domain is $x \le 0$.

x	−4	−3	−2	−1	0
y	1	0.9	0.7	0.5	0

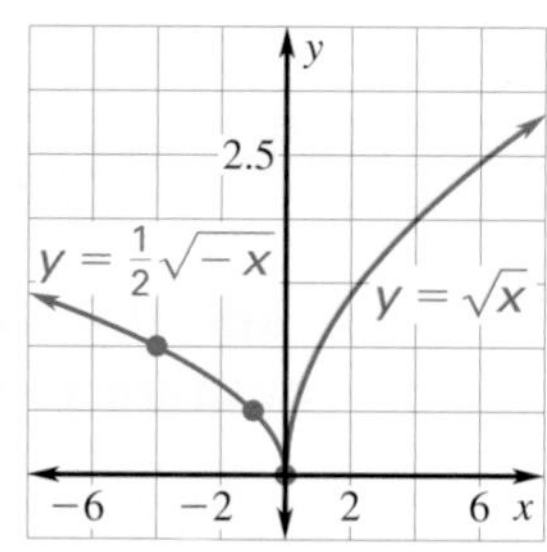

The range is $y \ge 0$. The graph of $y = \frac{1}{2}\sqrt{-x}$ is a vertical shrink $\left(\text{by a factor of } \frac{1}{2}\right)$ with a reflection in the y-axis of the graph of $y = \sqrt{x}$.

Example 3 Graph $y = a\sqrt{x}$ where $|a| < 1$

Graph the function $y = -\frac{1}{2}\sqrt{x}$ and identify its domain and range.

Compare the graph with the graph of $y = \sqrt{x}$.

Solution

To graph the function, make a table, plot the points, and draw a smooth curve through the points. The domain is $x \ge 0$.

x	0	1	2	3	4
y	0	−0.5	−0.7	−0.9	−1

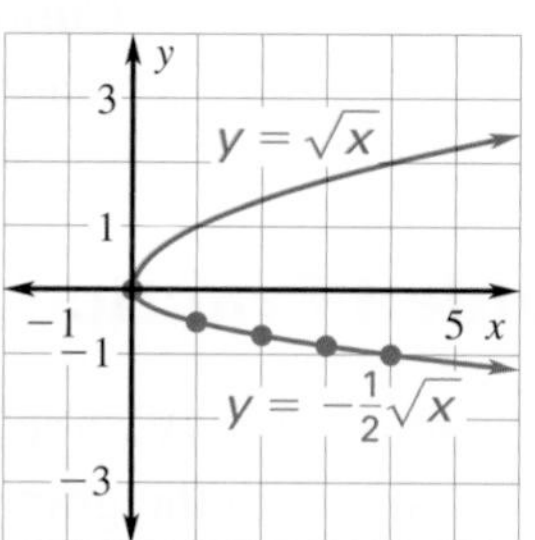

The range is $y \le 0$. The graph of $y = -\frac{1}{2}\sqrt{x}$ is a vertical shrink $\left(\text{by a factor of } \frac{1}{2}\right)$ with a reflection in the x-axis of the graph of $y = \sqrt{x}$.

Guided Practice for Examples 2 and 3

Graph the function and identify its domain and range. *Compare* the graph with the graph of $y = \sqrt{x}$.

3. $y = -6\sqrt{x}$

4. $y = -\frac{3}{4}\sqrt{x}$

Example 4 Graph a function in the form $y = \sqrt{x} + k$

Graph the function $y = \sqrt{x} - 2$ and identify its domain and range. Compare the graph with the graph of $y = \sqrt{x}$.

Solution

To graph the function, make a table, plot the points, and draw a smooth curve through the points. The domain is $x \geq 0$.

x	0	1	2	3	4
y	-2	-1	-0.6	-0.3	0

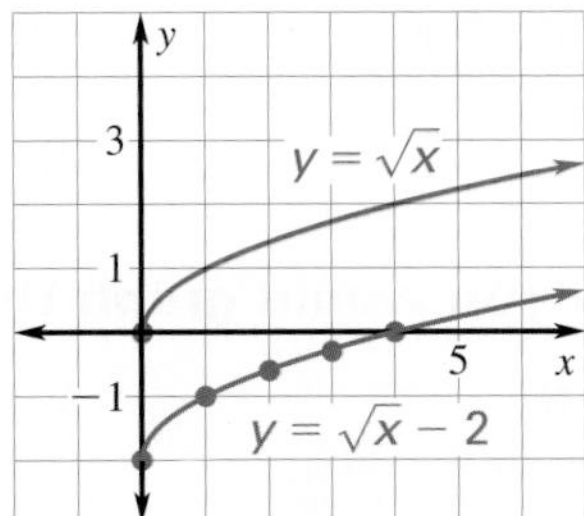

The range is $y \geq -2$. The graph of $y = \sqrt{x} - 2$ is a vertical translation (of 2 units down) of the graph of $y = \sqrt{x}$.

Example 5 Graph a function in the form $y = a\sqrt{x - h} + k$

Graph the function $y = 3\sqrt{x + 2} - 4$.

Solution

STEP 1 **Sketch** the graph of $y = 3\sqrt{x}$.

STEP 2 **Shift** the graph $|h|$ units horizontally and $|k|$ units vertically. Notice that $y = 3\sqrt{x + 2} - 4 = 3\sqrt{x - (-2)} + (-4)$. So, $h = -2$ and $k = -4$. Shift the graph left 2 units and down 4 units.

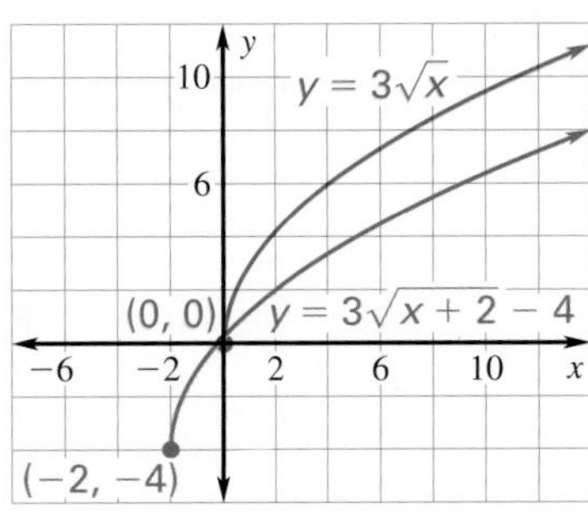

Guided Practice for Examples 4 and 5

Graph the function and identify its domain and range. *Compare* the graph with the graph of $y = \sqrt{x}$.

5. $y = \sqrt{x} + 1$

6. $y = \sqrt{x - 3} + 2$

7. Identify the domain and range of the function in Example 5.

UNIT 3

LESSON 3.3

Exercise Set A

MM1A1b Graph the basic functions $f(x) = x^n$, where $n = 1$ to 3, $f(x) = \sqrt{x}$, $f(x) = |x|$, and $f(x) = \frac{1}{x}$.

MM1A1c Graph transformations of basic functions including vertical shifts, stretches, and shrinks, as well as reflections across the x- and y-axes.

MM1A1d Investigate and explain the characteristics of a function: domain, range, zeros, intercepts, intervals of increase and decrease, maximum and minimum values, and end behavior.

Graph the function and identify its domain and range. *Compare* the graph with the graph of $y = \sqrt{x}$.

1. $y = 7\sqrt{x}$ **2.** $y = \frac{1}{5}\sqrt{x}$ **3.** $y = -4\sqrt{x}$

***Describe* how you would graph the function by using the graph of $y = \sqrt{x}$.**

4. $y = \sqrt{x - 8}$ **5.** $y = \sqrt{x} + 3$ **6.** $y = \sqrt{x + 7}$

7. $y = \sqrt{x} - 5$ **8.** $y = \sqrt{-x} + 3.5$ **9.** $y = \sqrt{x - \frac{1}{2}}$

UNIT 3

Match the function with its graph.

10. $y = \sqrt{x + 4} - 3$ **11.** $y = \sqrt{x - 3} + 4$ **12.** $y = \sqrt{x - 4} + 3$

13. $y = \sqrt{x - 4} - 3$ **14.** $y = \sqrt{x + 3} - 4$ **15.** $y = \sqrt{x + 3} + 3$

A.

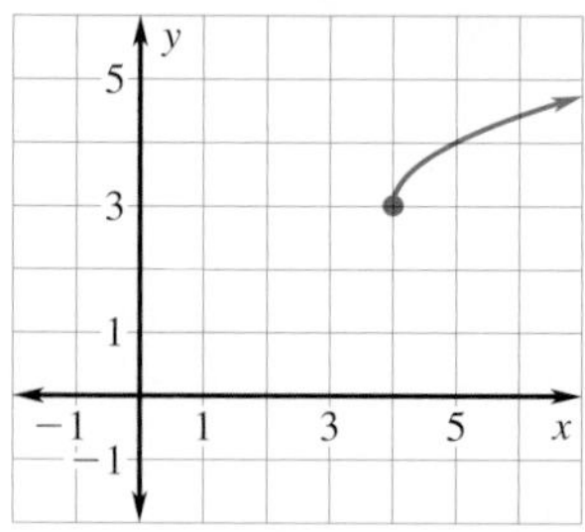

B.

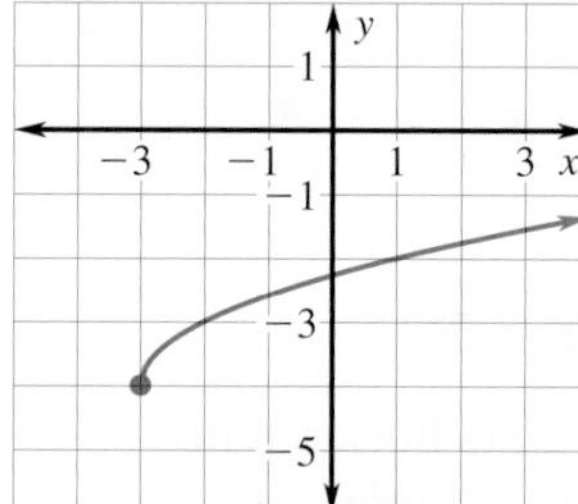

C.

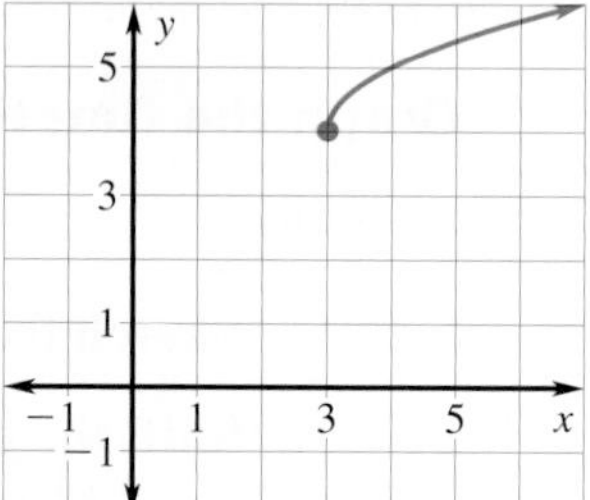

D.

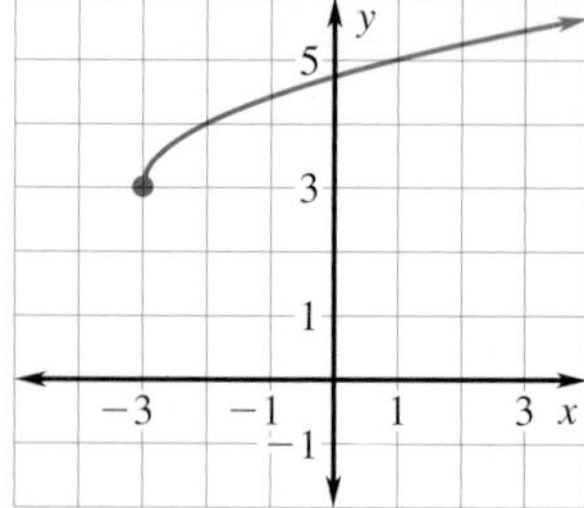

E.

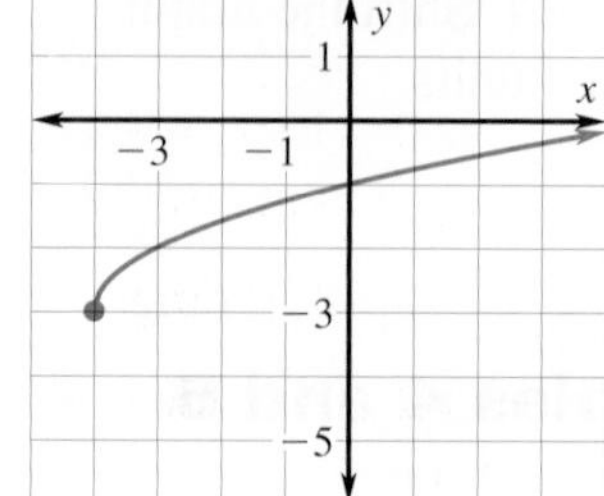

F.

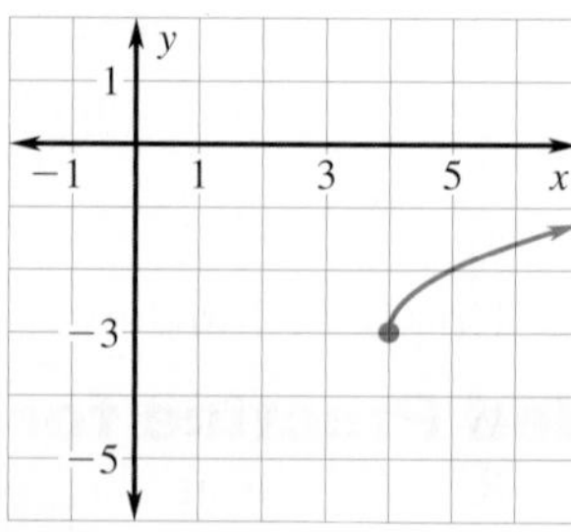

Exercise Set A *(continued)*

16. **Multiple Choice** The graph of which function is a horizontal translation of 3 units to the right of the graph of $y = \sqrt{x}$?

A. $y = \sqrt{x} + 3$ **B.** $y = \sqrt{x} - 3$

C. $y = \sqrt{x + 3}$ **D.** $y = \sqrt{x - 3}$

Graph the function and identify its domain and range. *Compare* the graph with the graph of $y = \sqrt{x}$.

17. $y = \sqrt{x + 4} - 4$ **18.** $y = \sqrt{x + 5} + 1$ **19.** $y = \sqrt{x - 6} + 4$

20. $y = \sqrt{x - 5} - 7$ **21.** $y = \sqrt{x - 1} + 2$ **22.** $y = \sqrt{x + 5} - 4$

23. **Multiple Representations** The time t (in seconds) it takes an object dropped from a height h (in feet) to reach the ground is given by the function $t = \frac{1}{4}\sqrt{h}$.

a. **Making a Table** Make a table that shows the values of t for $h = 0, 25, 100,$ and 225 feet.

b. **Graphing an Equation** Use the table in part (a) to graph the function. Estimate the height of a building if it takes a stone 4 seconds to reach the sidewalk below when dropped from the top of the building.

c. **Checking Reasonableness** Is your solution from part (b) reasonable in this situation? *Explain.*

24. **Box Design** You are designing a box with a square base that will hold popcorn. The box must be 9 inches tall. The side length y (in inches) of the box is given by the function $y = \frac{1}{3}\sqrt{V}$ where V is the volume (in cubic inches) of the box.

a. Graph the function and identify its domain and range.

b. What is the volume of a box with a side length of 5 inches?

c. What is the volume of a box with a side length of 8 inches?

25. **Steel Pipe** The inside diameter d of a steel pipe (in inches) and the weight w of water in the pipe (in pounds) are related by the function $d = 1.71\sqrt{w}$.

a. Graph the function and identify its domain and range.

b. What does the water weigh in a pipe with an inside diameter of 17 inches? Round your answer to the nearest pound.

c. What does the water weigh in a pipe with an inside diameter of 3.5 inches? Round your answer to the nearest pound.

LESSON 3.3

Exercise Set B

MM1A1b Graph the basic functions $f(x) = x^n$, where $n = 1$ to 3, $f(x) = \sqrt{x}$, $f(x) = |x|$, and $f(x) = \frac{1}{x}$.

MM1A1c Graph transformations of basic functions including vertical shifts, stretches, and shrinks, as well as reflections across the x- and y-axes.

MM1A1d Investigate and explain the characteristics of a function: domain, range, zeros, intercepts, intervals of increase and decrease, maximum and minimum values, and end behavior.

Graph the function and identify its domain and range. *Compare* the graph with the graph of $y = \sqrt{x}$.

1. $y = 2.5\sqrt{x}$ **2.** $y = -\frac{3}{5}\sqrt{x}$ **3.** $y = -0.25\sqrt{x}$

***Describe* how you would graph the function by using the graph of $y = \sqrt{x}$.**

4. $y = \sqrt{x + 2.5}$ **5.** $y = \sqrt{x} - \frac{3}{2}$ **6.** $y = \sqrt{-x} + 12$

7. $y = \sqrt{x - \frac{1}{4}}$ **8.** $y = \sqrt{x + 5.5}$ **9.** $y = \sqrt{x} + \frac{3}{4}$

Match the function with its graph.

10. $y = 3\sqrt{x + 2} - 1$ **11.** $y = 2\sqrt{x - 1} + 3$ **12.** $y = 3\sqrt{x - 1} + 2$

13. $y = \sqrt{x - 3} - 2$ **14.** $y = 3\sqrt{x + 1} - 2$ **15.** $y = \sqrt{x + 2} + 3$

A.

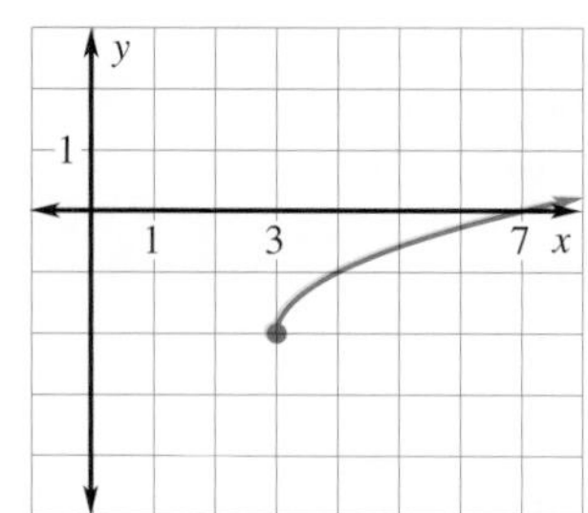

B.

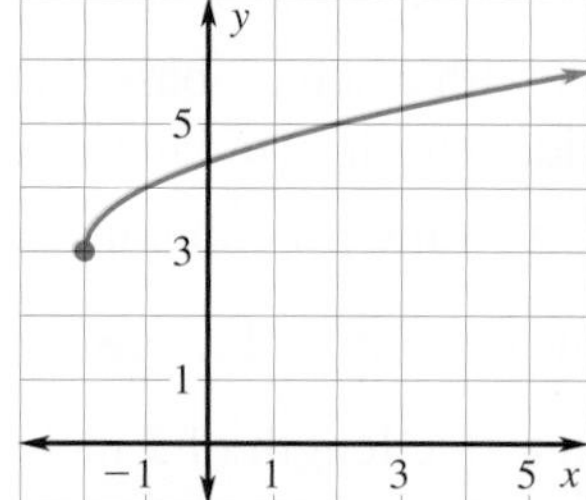

C.

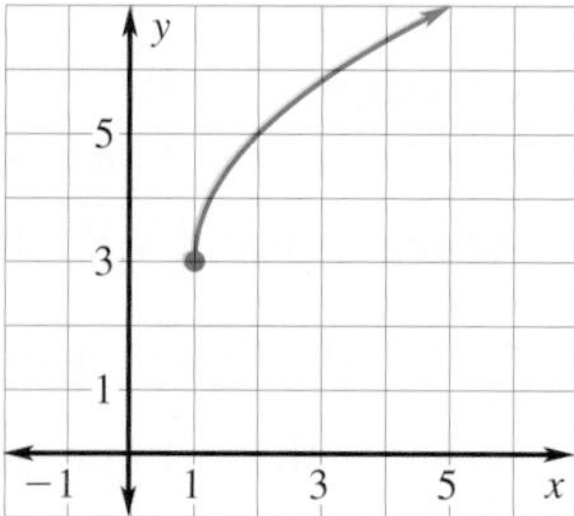

D.

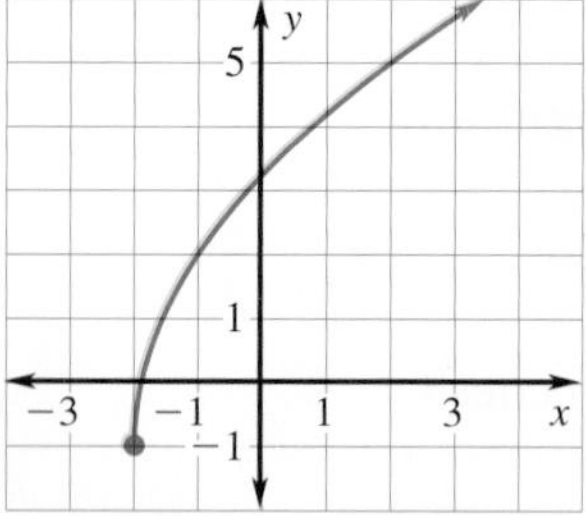

E.

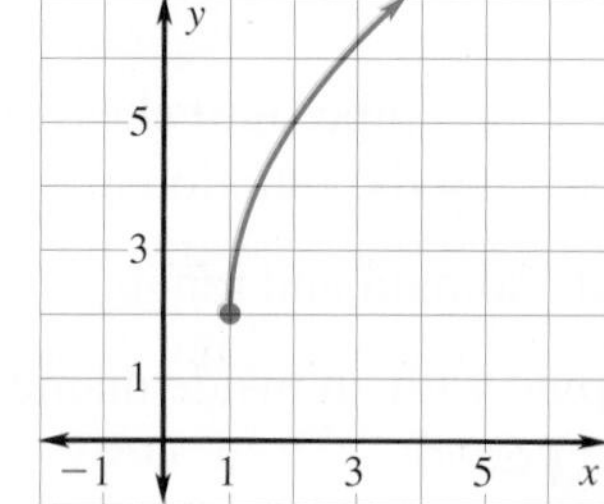

F.

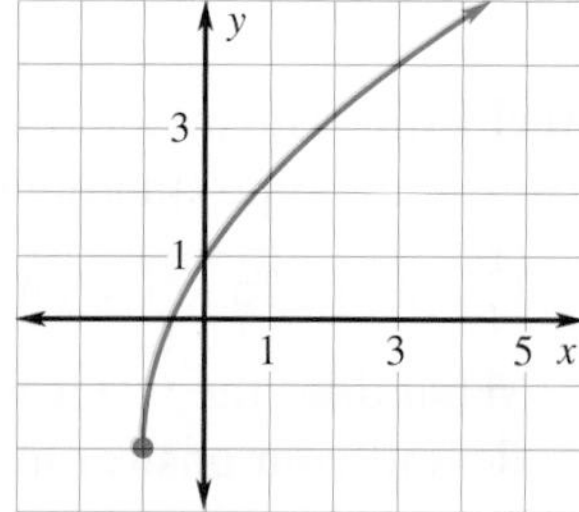

UNIT 3

Exercise Set B *(continued)*

Graph the function and identify its domain and range. *Compare* the graph with the graph of $y = \sqrt{x}$.

16. $y = \sqrt{x + 6} - 4$

17. $y = -\sqrt{x - 1} + 5$

18. $y = \sqrt{x - 3} - 3$

19. $y = -\sqrt{x + 6} + 2$

20. $y = \sqrt{x - 7} + 8$

21. $y = -\sqrt{x - 4.5} + 2.5$

22. **Error Analysis** *Describe* and correct the error in explaining how to graph the function $y = -5\sqrt{x - 8} - 12$.

To graph $y = -5\sqrt{x - 8} - 12$, sketch the graph of $y = -5\sqrt{x}$. Then shift the graph 8 units to the left and 12 units down.

23. **Multiple Choice** How is the graph of $g(x) = 4\sqrt{x} - 2$ related to the graph of $h(x) = 4\sqrt{x} + 2$?

A. It is a vertical stretch by a factor of 2 of the graph of h.

B. It is a vertical translation of 2 units down of the graph of h.

C. It is a vertical translation of 4 units down of the graph of h.

D. It is a horizontal translation of 4 units to the left of the graph of h.

24. **Challenge** Write a rule for a radical function that has a domain of all real numbers greater than or equal to -4 and a range of all real numbers less than or equal to 3.

25. **Bridge** The time t (in seconds) it takes an object dropped from a height h (in meters) to reach the ground is given by the function $t = \frac{\sqrt{10}}{7}\sqrt{h}$.

a. Graph the function and identify its domain and range.

b. You are on a bridge that passes over a river. It takes about 1.5 seconds for a stone dropped from the bridge to reach the river. About how high is the bridge?

26. **Steel Pipe** The radius of gyration of a steel pipe is a number that describes a pipe's resistance to buckling. The greater value of r, the more resistance to buckling. The radius of gyration r (in inches) of a steel pipe is given by the function $r = \frac{1}{4}\sqrt{D^2 + d^2}$ where D is the outside diameter of the pipe (in inches) and d is the inside diameter of the pipe (in inches). One standard outside pipe diameter is 4 inches.

a. Write a function for r and d using $D = 4$.

b. Graph the function and identify its domain and range.

c. If you want a pipe with a 4-inch outside diameter and a radius of gyration of 1.3 inches, what must its inside diameter be? Round your answer to the nearest tenth.

LESSON 3.4

Simplify Radical Expressions

Georgia Performance Standards: MM1A2a, MM1A2b

Goal Simplify radical expressions.

Vocabulary

A radical expression is in **simplest form** if no perfect square factors other than 1 are in the radicand, no fractions are in the radicand, and no radicals appear in the denominator of the fraction.

The process of eliminating a radical from an expression's denominator is called **rationalizing the denominator.**

The binomials $a + \sqrt{b}$ and $a - \sqrt{b}$ are called **radical conjugates.**

In this lesson, whenever a variable appears in the radicand, assume that it has only *nonnegative* values.

The **Product Property of Radicals** states that the square root of a product equals the product of the square roots of the factors. ($\sqrt{ab} = \sqrt{a} \cdot \sqrt{b}$ where $a \geq 0$ and $b \geq 0$)

The **Quotient Property of Radicals** states that the square root of a quotient equals the quotient of the square roots of the numerator and denominator.
$\left(\sqrt{\frac{a}{b}} = \frac{\sqrt{a}}{\sqrt{b}} \text{ where } a \geq 0 \text{ and } b > 0\right)$

UNIT 3

Example 1 Use the product property of radicals

Simplify the expression.

Solution

a. $\sqrt{28} = \sqrt{4 \cdot 7}$
$= \sqrt{4} \cdot \sqrt{7}$
$= 2\sqrt{7}$

b. $\sqrt{50y^3} = \sqrt{25 \cdot 2 \cdot y^2 \cdot y}$
$= \sqrt{25} \cdot \sqrt{2} \cdot \sqrt{y^2} \cdot \sqrt{y}$
$= 5y\sqrt{2y}$

Example 2 Multiply radicals

Simplify the expression.

Solution

a. $\sqrt{2} \cdot \sqrt{18} = \sqrt{2 \cdot 18}$
$= \sqrt{36}$
$= 6$

b. $5\sqrt{2xy} \cdot \sqrt{32y} = 5\sqrt{2xy \cdot 32y}$
$= 5\sqrt{64xy^2}$
$= 5\sqrt{64} \cdot \sqrt{x} \cdot \sqrt{y^2}$
$= 40y\sqrt{x}$

Georgia Performance Standards

MM1A2a Simplify algebraic and numeric expressions involving square root. 

MM1A2b Perform operations with square roots. ☑

Example 3 Use the quotient property of radicals

a. $\sqrt{\frac{17}{25}} = \frac{\sqrt{17}}{\sqrt{25}}$

$= \frac{\sqrt{17}}{5}$

b. $\sqrt{\frac{4}{49y^2}} = \frac{\sqrt{4}}{\sqrt{49y^2}}$

$= \frac{2}{7y}$

Guided Practice for Examples 1, 2, and 3

Simplify the expression.

1. $\sqrt{72}$ **2.** $\sqrt{3x^2}$ **3.** $\sqrt{45y^5}$ **4.** $3\sqrt{12x^2}$

5. $\sqrt{5} \cdot \sqrt{10}$ **6.** $\sqrt{3x} \cdot \sqrt{15xy}$ **7.** $\sqrt{\frac{5}{81}}$ **8.** $\sqrt{\frac{2x^2}{9y^2}}$

Example 4 Rationalize the denominator

a. $\frac{3}{\sqrt{6x}} = \frac{3}{\sqrt{6x}} \cdot \frac{\sqrt{6x}}{\sqrt{6x}}$

$= \frac{3\sqrt{6x}}{\sqrt{36x^2}}$

$= \frac{3\sqrt{6x}}{6|x|} = \frac{\sqrt{6x}}{2|x|}$

b. $\frac{1}{3 + \sqrt{2}} = \frac{1}{3 + \sqrt{2}} \cdot \frac{3 - \sqrt{2}}{3 - \sqrt{2}}$

$= \frac{3 - \sqrt{2}}{9 - 3\sqrt{2} + 3\sqrt{2} - 2}$

$= \frac{3 - \sqrt{2}}{7}$

Example 5 Add and subtract radicals

a. $3\sqrt{3} + 6\sqrt{27} = 3\sqrt{3} + 6\sqrt{9 \cdot 3}$ Factor using perfect square factor.

$= 3\sqrt{3} + 6 \cdot \sqrt{9} \cdot \sqrt{3}$ Product property of radicals

$= 3\sqrt{3} + 18\sqrt{3} = 21\sqrt{3}$ Simplify.

b. $11\sqrt{5} - 2\sqrt{20} = 11\sqrt{5} - 2\sqrt{4 \cdot 5}$ Factor using perfect square factor.

$= 11\sqrt{5} - 2 \cdot \sqrt{4} \cdot \sqrt{5}$ Product property of radicals

$= 11\sqrt{5} - 4\sqrt{5} = 7\sqrt{5}$ Simplify.

Guided Practice for Examples 4 and 5

Simplify the expression.

9. $\frac{3}{\sqrt{2x}}$ **10.** $6\sqrt{7} + 8\sqrt{10} - 3\sqrt{7}$ **11.** $3\sqrt{5} + 2\sqrt{500}$

UNIT 3

LESSON 3.4 **Exercise Set A**

MM1A2a Simplify algebraic and numeric expressions involving square root.

MM1A2b Perform operations with square roots.

Simplify the expression.

1. $\sqrt{200}$
2. $\sqrt{45}$
3. $\sqrt{112}$
4. $\sqrt{400d}$
5. $\sqrt{9y^2}$
6. $\sqrt{25n^3}$
7. $\sqrt{3} \cdot \sqrt{21}$
8. $\sqrt{20} \cdot \sqrt{15}$
9. $\sqrt{10x} \cdot \sqrt{2x}$
10. $\sqrt{\frac{16}{81}}$
11. $\sqrt{\frac{5}{49}}$
12. $\sqrt{\frac{x^2}{144}}$

Simplify the expression by rationalizing the denominator.

13. $\frac{4}{\sqrt{5}}$
14. $\frac{2}{\sqrt{p}}$
15. $\frac{9}{\sqrt{2x}}$
16. $\frac{1}{5 + \sqrt{3}}$
17. $\frac{6}{4 + \sqrt{5}}$
18. $\frac{9}{7 - \sqrt{2}}$

Simplify the expression.

19. $10\sqrt{7} + 3\sqrt{7}$
20. $4\sqrt{5} - 7\sqrt{5}$
21. $\sqrt{7}(4 - \sqrt{7})$
22. $\sqrt{5}(8\sqrt{10} + 1)$
23. $(2\sqrt{3} + 5)^2$
24. $(6 + \sqrt{3})(6 - \sqrt{3})$

25. **Water Flow** You can measure the speed of water by using an L-shaped tube. The speed V of the water (in miles per hour) is given by the function $V = \sqrt{\frac{5}{2}h}$ where h is the height of the column of water above the surface (in inches).

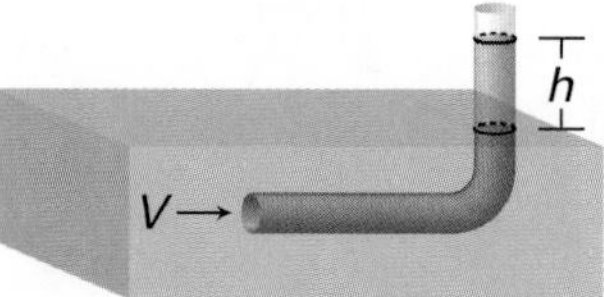

   a. If you use the tube in a river and find that h is 6 inches, what is the speed of the water? Round your answer to the nearest hundredth.
   b. If you use the tube in a river and find that h is 8.5 inches, what is the speed of the water? Round your answer to the nearest hundredth.

26. **Walking Speed** The maximum walking speed S (in feet per second) of an animal is given by the function $S = \sqrt{gL}$ where g is 32 feet per second squared and L is the length of the animal's leg (in feet).
   a. How fast can an animal whose legs are 9 inches long walk? Round your answer to the nearest hundredth.
   b. How fast can an animal whose legs are 3 feet long walk? Round your answer to the nearest hundredth.

LESSON 3.4 **Exercise Set B**

MM1A2a Simplify algebraic and numeric expressions involving square root.

MM1A2b Perform operations with square roots.

Simplify the expression.

1. $\sqrt{45s^3}$
2. $\sqrt{196r^4}$
3. $\sqrt{450c^5}$
4. $\sqrt{124m^4n^{10}}$
5. $11\sqrt{x^7y^8}$
6. $\sqrt{a^3b} \cdot \sqrt{ab}$
7. $\sqrt{27xy} \cdot \sqrt{5y^3}$
8. $\sqrt{\frac{121}{16m^2}}$
9. $\sqrt{\frac{5d^2}{125}}$

Simplify the expression by rationalizing the denominator.

10. $\sqrt{\frac{5}{8}}$
11. $\sqrt{\frac{7m^5}{11}}$
12. $\sqrt{\frac{125}{4x^3}}$
13. $\frac{2}{5 - \sqrt{3}}$
14. $\frac{1}{\sqrt{7} + 1}$
15. $\frac{\sqrt{5}}{6 + \sqrt{5}}$

Simplify the expression.

16. $\sqrt{15} + 5\sqrt{3} - 2\sqrt{27}$
17. $\sqrt{7}(3 - 2\sqrt{7})$
18. $\sqrt{2}(3\sqrt{14} - \sqrt{7})$
19. $(3\sqrt{12} + 5)^2$
20. $(8\sqrt{3} + \sqrt{2})(1 - \sqrt{3})$
21. $\sqrt{\frac{250m^3}{2n}}$
22. $\frac{5}{\sqrt{7}} + \frac{2}{\sqrt{14}}$
23. $\frac{4\sqrt{10}}{\sqrt{30}} - \frac{2}{\sqrt{3}}$
24. $\frac{4}{\sqrt{x}} + \frac{5}{2\sqrt{x}}$

25. **Electricity** Current, power, and resistance are related by the formula $I = \sqrt{\frac{P}{R}}$ where I is the current (in amps), P is the power (in watts), and R is the resistance (in ohms).
    - **a.** A light bulb with a 283-ohm resistor is using 0.42 amp of current. What is the wattage of the light bulb? Round your answer to the nearest whole watt.
    - **b.** A light bulb with a 145-ohm resistor is using 0.83 amp of current. What is the wattage of the light bulb? Round your answer to the nearest whole watt.

26. **Medicine** A doctor may need to know a person's body surface area to prescribe the correct amount of medicine. A person's body surface area A (in square meters) is given by the function $A = \sqrt{\frac{hw}{3131}}$ where h is the height (in inches) and w is the weight (in pounds).
    - **a.** Find the body surface area of a person who is 5 feet 5 inches tall and weighs 110 pounds. Round your answer to the nearest tenth of a meter.
    - **b.** Find the body surface area of a person who is 5 feet 10 inches tall and weighs 150 pounds. Round your answer to the nearest tenth of a meter.

LESSON 3.5

Solve Radical Equations

Georgia Performance Standards: MM1A3b

Goal Solve radical equations.

Vocabulary

An equation that contains a radical expression with a variable in the radicand is a **radical equation.**

Squaring both sides of the equation $a = b$ can result in a solution of $a^2 = b^2$ that is *not* a solution of the original equation. Such a solution is called an **extraneous solution.**

Example 1 Solve a radical equation

Solve $\sqrt{x} + \frac{1}{2} = \frac{3}{4}$.

Solution

$\sqrt{x} + \frac{1}{2} = \frac{3}{4}$ Write original equation.

$\sqrt{x} = \frac{1}{4}$ Subtract $\frac{1}{2}$ from each side.

$(\sqrt{x})^2 = \left(\frac{1}{4}\right)^2$ Square each side.

$x = \frac{1}{16}$ Simplify.

The solution is $\frac{1}{16}$.

CHECK Check your solution by substituting it in the original equation.

$\sqrt{x} + \frac{1}{2} = \frac{3}{4}$ Write original equation.

$\sqrt{\frac{1}{16}} + \frac{1}{2} \stackrel{?}{=} \frac{3}{4}$ Substitute $\frac{1}{16}$ for x.

$\frac{1}{4} + \frac{1}{2} \stackrel{?}{=} \frac{3}{4}$ Simplify.

$\frac{3}{4} = \frac{3}{4}$ ✓ Solution checks.

Guided Practice for Example 1

Solve the equation.

1. $\sqrt{x} - 7 = 10$

2. $5\sqrt{x} - 15 = 0$

UNIT 3

Georgia Performance Standards

MM1A3b Solve equations involving radicals such as $\sqrt{x} + b = c$, using algebraic techniques.

Example 2 Solve an equation with an extraneous solution

Solve $x = \sqrt{20 - x}$.

Solution

$x = \sqrt{20 - x}$	Write original equation.
$x^2 = (\sqrt{20 - x})^2$	Square each side.
$x^2 = 20 - x$	Simplify.
$x^2 + x - 20 = 0$	Write in standard form.
$(x - 4)(x + 5) = 0$	Factor.
$x - 4 = 0$ or $x + 5 = 0$	Zero-product property
$x = 4$ or $x = -5$	Solve for x.

CHECK Check 4 and -5 in the original equation.

If $x = 4$: $4 \stackrel{?}{=} \sqrt{20 - 4}$ **If $x = -5$:** $-5 \stackrel{?}{=} \sqrt{20 - (-5)}$

$4 = 4$ ✓ $-5 = 5$ ✗

Because -5 does not check in the original equation, it is an extraneous solution. The only solution of the equation is 4.

Example 3 Solve an equation with radicals on both sides

Solve $\sqrt{x + 3} = \sqrt{3x - 5}$.

Solution

$\sqrt{x + 3} = \sqrt{3x - 5}$	Write original equation.
$(\sqrt{x + 3})^2 = (\sqrt{3x - 5})^2$	Square each side.
$x + 3 = 3x - 5$	Simplify.
$3 = 2x - 5$	Subtract x from each side.
$8 = 2x$	Add 5 to each side.
$4 = x$	Divide each side by 2.

The solution is 4. Check the solution.

Guided Practice for Examples 2 and 3

Solve the equation.

3. $x = \sqrt{x + 42}$

4. $\sqrt{x + 2} = \sqrt{4x - 7}$

5. $\sqrt{5x - 12} - \sqrt{2x + 9} = 0$

UNIT 3

LESSON 3.5

Exercise Set A

MM1A3b Solve equations involving radicals such as $\sqrt{x} + b = c$, using algebraic techniques.

Tell whether the given value is a solution of the equation.

1. $4\sqrt{2x - 3} = 12; 2$
2. $2\sqrt{9x - 1} = 20; 7$
3. $\sqrt{4x + 8} = \sqrt{6 + 2x}; -1$
4. $\sqrt{7x - 2} = \sqrt{8 - 3x}; -1$
5. $x = \sqrt{4x - 3}; 3$
6. $\sqrt{4x - 3} = x - 2; 7$

Describe **the steps you would use to solve the equation. Do not solve the equation.**

7. $\sqrt{7x + 3} - 5 = 2$
8. $6\sqrt{4 - x} - 3 = 1$
9. $\sqrt{12x - 7} = \sqrt{9x + 3}$
10. $10\sqrt{6 - x} = 2\sqrt{x + 4}$
11. $\sqrt{5x - 3} - \sqrt{10 - 4x} = 0$
12. $\sqrt{9x + 1} - 2 = x$

Solve the equation. Check for extraneous solutions.

13. $8\sqrt{x} - 32 = 0$
14. $\sqrt{x} - 4 = 16$
15. $\sqrt{x + 3} + 8 = 15$
16. $\sqrt{x - 6} - 2 = 4$
17. $\sqrt{x} + 5 = 14$
18. $\sqrt{8 - 3x} + 5 = 6$
19. $\sqrt{5x + 4} - 12 = -6$
20. $3\sqrt{x + 5} - 3 = 6$
21. $4\sqrt{2x + 1} - 7 = 1$
22. $\sqrt{x} = \sqrt{5x - 1}$
23. $\sqrt{7x - 6} = \sqrt{x}$
24. $\sqrt{6x - 8} = \sqrt{4x - 10}$
25. $\sqrt{7x - 5} = \sqrt{3x + 19}$
26. $\sqrt{x - 15} - \sqrt{x - 7} = 0$
27. $\sqrt{10x - 3} - \sqrt{8x - 11} = 0$
28. $\sqrt{5x - 6} = x$
29. $x = \sqrt{2x + 24}$
30. $\sqrt{2x - 15} = x$

31. **Market Research** A marketing department determines that the price of a magazine subscription and the demand to subscribe are related by the function $P = 40 - \sqrt{0.0004x + 1}$ where P is the price per subscription and x is the number of subscriptions sold.
    a. If the subscription price is set at \$25, how many subscriptions would be sold? Round your answer to the nearest whole subscription.
    b. If the subscription price is set at \$30, how many more subscriptions are sold in part (a) than when the price is \$30? Round your answer to the nearest whole subscription.

32. **Awning** The area A of a portion of a circle bounded by two radii r and angle t of a sector of a circle are related by the function

$$r = \sqrt{\frac{2A}{t}}.$$

The length of a side (radius) of the top view of the awning shown at the right is 6 feet and the angle that is formed by the awning is $\frac{5\pi}{3}$. Find the area of the awning. Round your answer to the nearest hundredth.

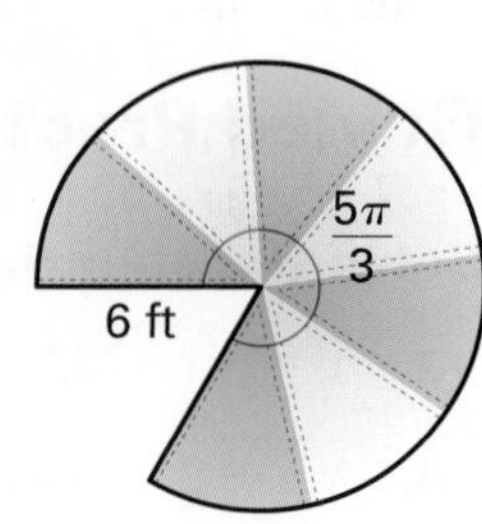

UNIT 3

LESSON 3.5

Exercise Set B

MM1A3b Solve equations involving radicals such as $\sqrt{x} + b = c$, using algebraic techniques.

Describe **how you would solve the equation. Do not solve the equation.**

1. $1 + \sqrt{x + 6} = 13$

2. $15 - \sqrt{2x + 2} = 13$

3. $4 - 2\sqrt{1 - 4x} = -6$

4. $6\sqrt{5x + 3} - 5 = 2$

5. $\sqrt{10 - 6x} = \sqrt{\frac{3}{2}x - 1}$

6. $\sqrt{3 - 2x} - \sqrt{2 + 4x} = 0$

7. $6\sqrt{5 - 2x} = 3\sqrt{5x - 2}$

8. $x + 1 = \sqrt{3 - 2x}$

9. $x + \sqrt{1 - 3x} = -5$

Solve the equation. Check for extraneous solutions.

10. $\sqrt{x} + 4 = 9$

11. $7\sqrt{3x - 4} + 7 = 35$

12. $14 - 5\sqrt{8 - 3x} = 19$

13. $\sqrt{x} - 8 = 4$

14. $10 + 4\sqrt{3 - 2x} = 14$

15. $2\sqrt{5 - 2x} - 13 = -17$

16. $\sqrt{4x - 3} - \sqrt{6x - 11} = 0$

17. $\sqrt{\frac{1}{4}x - 5} - \sqrt{x - 9} = 0$

18. $\sqrt{8 - 6x} = 3x$

19. $2x = \sqrt{11x + 3}$

20. $\sqrt{3x + 6} = x - 4$

21. $x + 3 = \sqrt{2x + 21}$

22. $\sqrt{x} + 3 = \sqrt{x + 12}$

23. $4 - \sqrt{x - 3} = \sqrt{x + 5}$

24. $\sqrt{4x + 3} + \sqrt{4x} = 3$

25. Write a radical equation that has 3 and 4 as solutions.

26. **Writing** A student solves the equation $\sqrt{x + 6} = x$ and finds that $x = 3$ or $x = -2$. Without checking by substituting into the equation, which is the extraneous solution, 3 or -2? How do you know?

27. **Speed of Sound** The speed of sound near Earth's surface depends on the temperature. The speed v (in meters per second) is given by the function $v = 20\sqrt{t + 273}$ where t is the temperature (in degrees Celsius).

a. A friend is throwing a tennis ball against a wall 200 meters from you. You hear the sound of the ball hitting the wall 0.6 second after seeing the ball hit the wall. What is the temperature? Round your answer to the nearest tenth.

b. The temperature $-273°C$ is called absolute zero. What is the speed of sound at this temperature?

28. **Pendulum** The period T (in seconds) of a pendulum is the time it takes for the pendulum to swing back and forth. The period is related to the length L (in inches) of the pendulum by the model $T = 2\pi\sqrt{\frac{L}{384}}$.

a. Find the length of a pendulum with a period of 2 seconds. Round your answer to the nearest tenth.

b. What is the length of a pendulum whose period is double the period of the pendulum in part (a)? Round your answer to the nearest tenth.

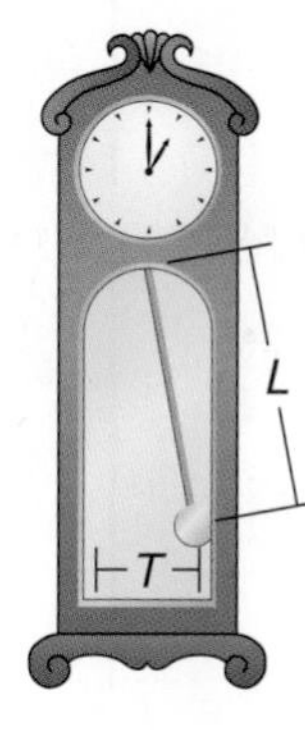

UNIT 3

LESSON 3.6

Graph Rational Functions

Georgia Performance Standards: MM1A1b, MM1A1c, MM1A1d

Goal Graph rational functions.

Vocabulary

A **rational function** has a rule given by a fraction whose numerator and denominator are polynomials and whose denominator is not 0.

An **asymptote** is a line that a graph approaches more and more closely.

Example 1 Compare graphs of $y = \frac{a}{x}$ where $a > 0$ with graph of $y = \frac{1}{x}$

a. The graph of $y = \frac{3}{x}$ is a vertical stretch of the graph of $y = \frac{1}{x}$.

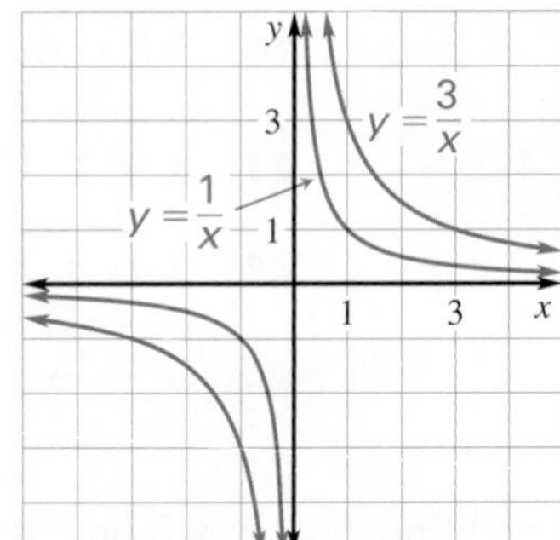

b. The graph of $y = \frac{1}{3x}$ is a vertical shrink of the graph of $y = \frac{1}{x}$.

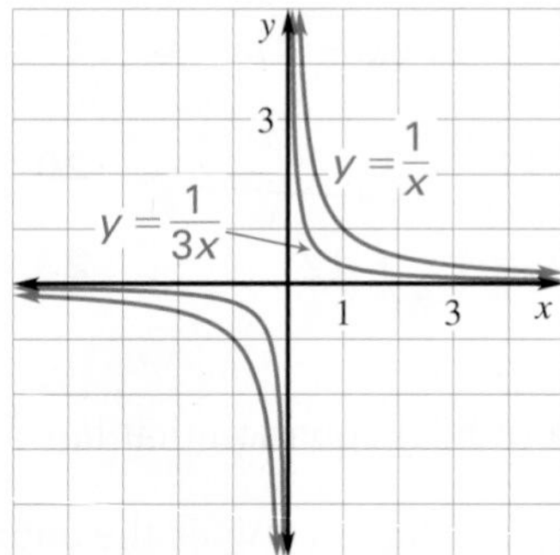

Example 2 Compare graphs of $y = \frac{a}{x}$ where $a < 0$ with graph of $y = \frac{1}{x}$

a. The graph of $y = \frac{-2}{x}$ is a vertical stretch with a reflection in the x-axis of the graph of $y = \frac{1}{x}$.

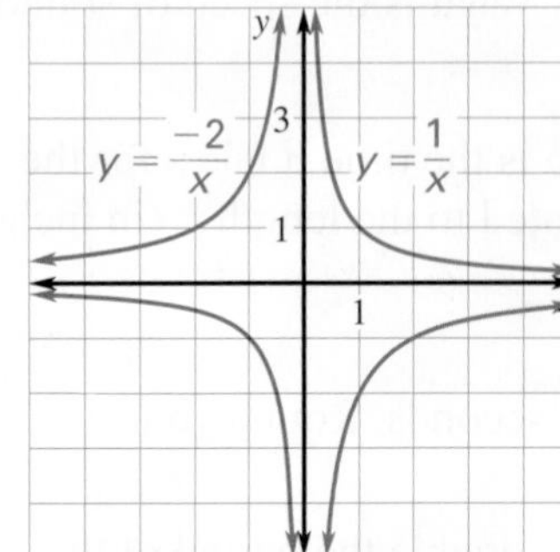

b. The graph of $y = \frac{1}{-2x}$ is a vertical shrink with a reflection in the x-axis of the graph of $y = \frac{1}{x}$.

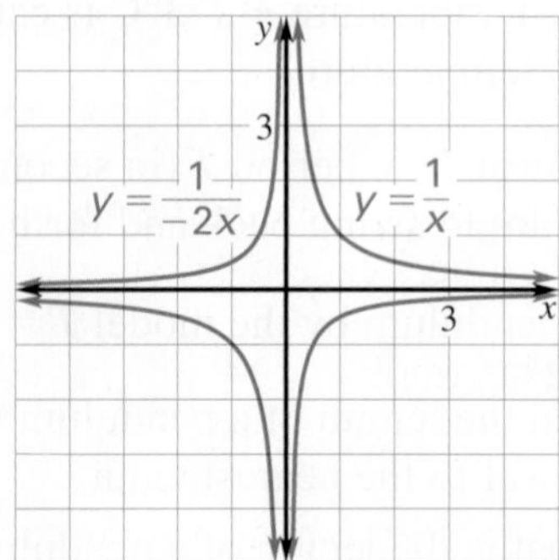

Note that in both parts of Example 2, the graphs could also be viewed as being reflected in the y-axis.

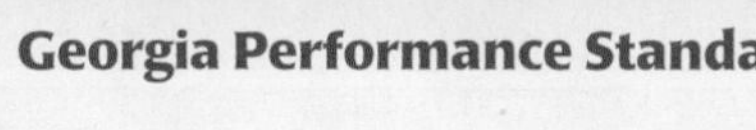

Georgia Performance Standards

MM1A1b Graph the basic functions $f(x) = x^n$, where $n = 1$ to 3, $f(x) = \sqrt{x}$, $f(x) = |x|$, and $f(x) = \frac{1}{x}$.

MM1A1c Graph transformations of basic functions including vertical shifts, stretches, and shrinks, as well as reflections across the x- and y-axes.

MM1A1d Investigate and explain the characteristics of a function: domain, range, zeros, intercepts, intervals of increase and decrease, maximum and minimum values, and end behavior.

Example 3 Graph $y = \frac{1}{x} + k$

Graph $y = \frac{1}{x} - 2$ and identify its domain and range. Compare the graph with the graph of $y = \frac{1}{x}$.

Graph the function using a table of values.

The domain is all real numbers except 0. The range is all real numbers except −2.

The graph of $y = \frac{1}{x} - 2$ is a vertical translation (of 2 units down) of the graph of $y = \frac{1}{x}$.

x	y
−2	−2.5
−1	−3
−0.5	−4
0	undefined
0.5	0
1	−1
2	−1.5

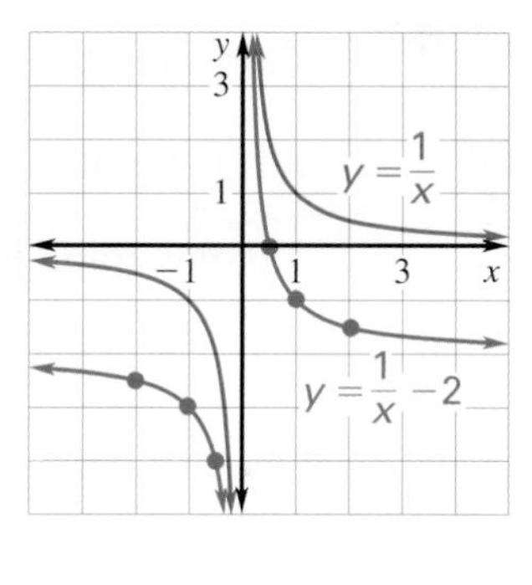

Example 4 Graph $y = \frac{1}{x - h}$

Graph $y = \frac{1}{x - 4}$ and identify its domain and range. Compare the graph with the graph of $y = \frac{1}{x}$.

Graph the function using a table of values.

The domain is all real numbers except 4. The range is all real numbers except 0.

The graph of $y = \frac{1}{x - 4}$ is a horizontal translation (of 4 units to the right) of the graph of $y = \frac{1}{x}$.

x	y
2	−0.5
3	−1
3.5	−2
4	undefined
4.5	2
5	1
6	0.5

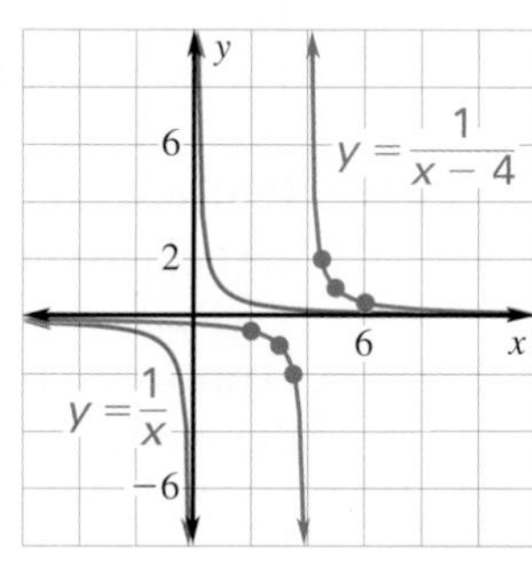

UNIT 3

Guided Practice for Examples 1, 2, 3, and 4

Graph the function and identify its domain and range. *Compare* the graph with the graph of $y = \frac{1}{x}$.

1. $y = \frac{8}{x}$

2. $y = \frac{1}{-3x}$

3. $y = \frac{1}{x} + 5$

4. $y = \frac{1}{x + 10}$

Graph of $y = \frac{a}{x - h} + k$

The graph of $y = \frac{a}{x - h} + k$ has the following characteristics:

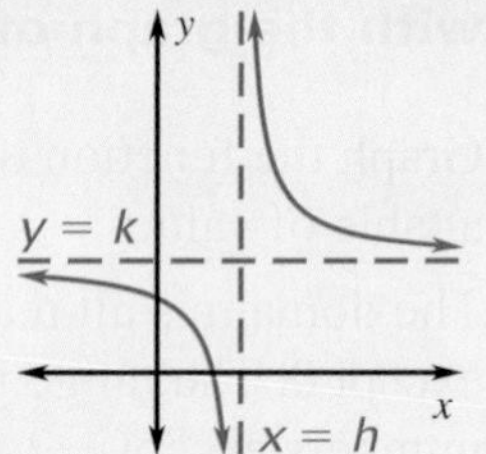

- If $|a| > 1$, the graph is a vertical stretch of the graph of $y = \frac{1}{x}$. If $0 < |a| < 1$, the graph is a vertical shrink of the graph of $y = \frac{1}{x}$. If $a < 0$, the graph is a reflection in the x-axis of the graph of $y = \frac{1}{x}$.
- The horizontal asymptote is $y = k$. The vertical asymptote is $x = h$.

The domain of the function is all real numbers except $x = h$. The range is all real numbers except $y = k$.

Example 5 Graph $y = \frac{a}{x - h} + k$

Graph $y = \frac{5}{x + 3} - 2$.

Solution

STEP 1 **Identify** the asymptotes of the graph. The vertical asymptote is $x = -3$. The horizontal asymptote is $y = -2$.

STEP 2 **Plot** several points on each side of the vertical asymptote.

STEP 3 **Graph** two branches that pass through the plotted points and approach the asymptotes.

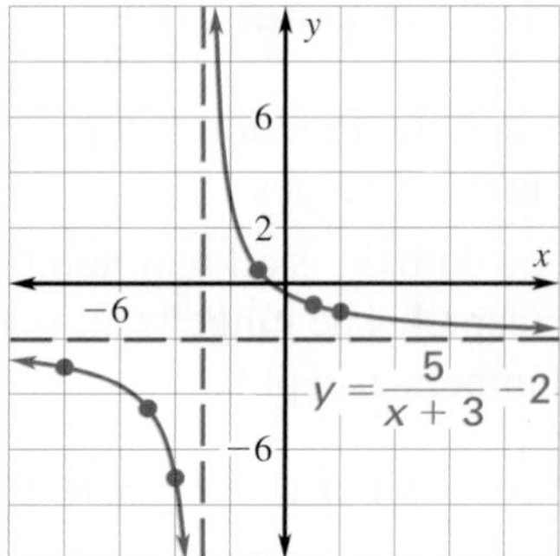

Guided Practice for Example 5

5. Graph $y = \frac{2}{x - 2} + 1$.

LESSON 3.6

Exercise Set A

MM1A1b Graph the basic functions $f(x) = x^n$, where $n = 1$ to 3, $f(x) = \sqrt{x}$, $f(x) = |x|$, and $f(x) = \frac{1}{x}$.

MM1A1c Graph transformations of basic functions including vertical shifts, stretches, and shrinks, as well as reflections across the *x*- and *y*-axes.

MM1A1d Investigate and explain the characteristics of a function: domain, range, zeros, intercepts, intervals of increase and decrease, maximum and minimum values, and end behavior.

Identify the domain and range of the function from its graph.

1.

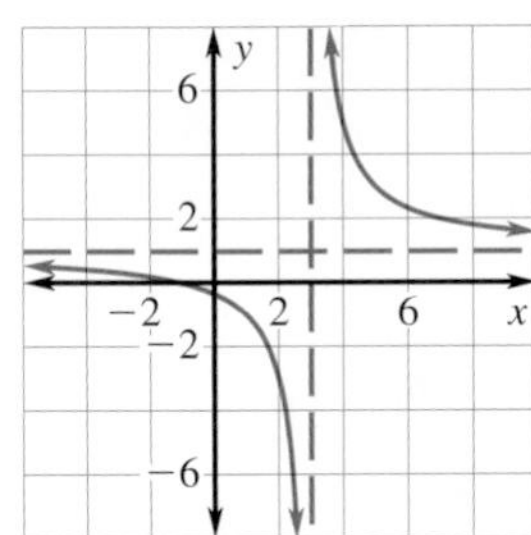

2.

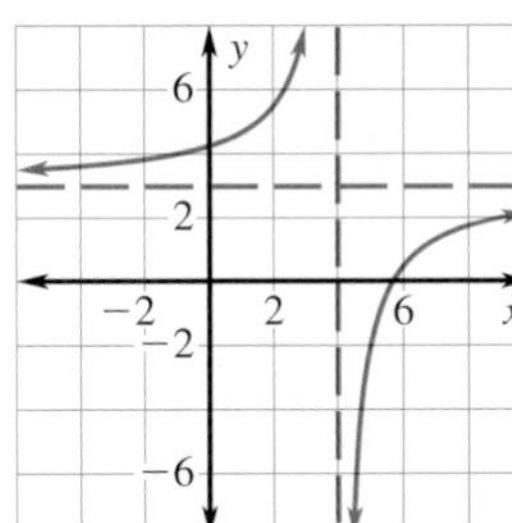

3.

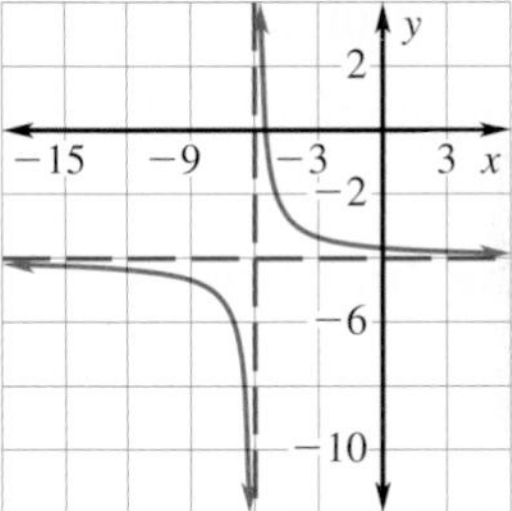

4.

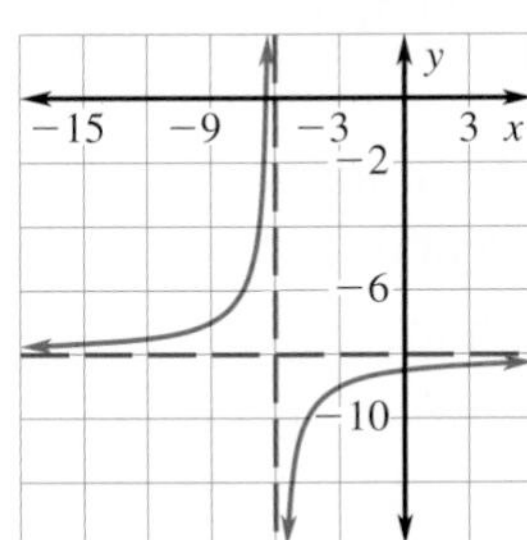

5.

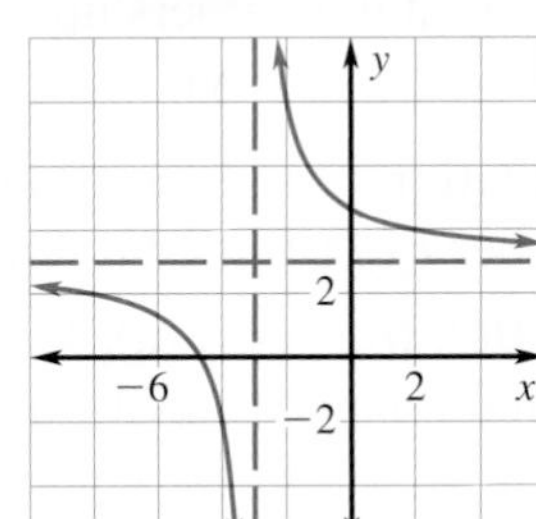

6.

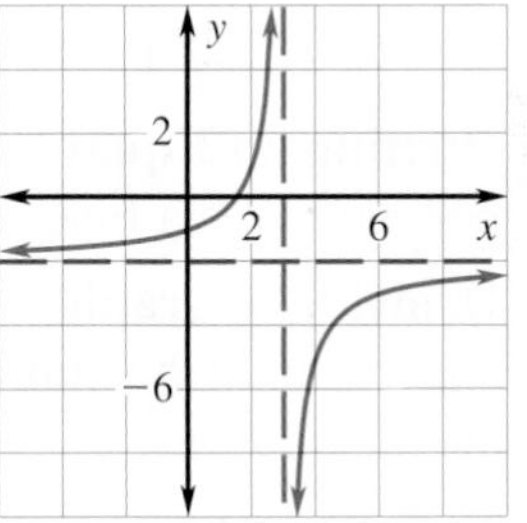

7. **Multiple Choice** For which function is the domain all real numbers except -6 and the range all real numbers except 0?

A. $y = \frac{6}{x}$ **B.** $y = \frac{6}{x - 6}$ **C.** $y = \frac{6}{x + 6}$ **D.** $y = \frac{-6}{x - 6}$

8. Graph $y = \frac{1}{x}$. Identify the domain and range of the function.

Graph the function and identify its domain and range. Then compare the graph with the graph of $y = \frac{1}{x}$.

9. $y = \frac{5}{x}$

10. $y = \frac{1}{6x}$

11. $y = \frac{-3}{2x}$

12. $y = \frac{1}{x} - 7$

13. $y = \frac{1}{x} + 10$

14. $y = \frac{1}{x - 4}$

15. **Open-Ended** Give an example of a rational function whose graph has the same horizontal asymptote as the graph of $y = \frac{1}{x}$.

UNIT 3

Exercise Set A *(continued)*

Determine the asymptotes of the graph of the function.

16. $y = \frac{10}{x - 6} + 4$

17. $y = \frac{-8}{x + 5} - 6$

18. $y = \frac{14}{x - 3} - 8$

19. $y = \frac{12}{x + 7} + 7$

20. $y = \frac{-4}{x - 8} + 12$

21. $y = \frac{9}{x + 5} + 10$

22. $y = \frac{14}{x - 14} + 1$

23. $y = \frac{-12}{x + 12} - 3$

24. $y = \frac{7}{x - 5} - 14$

25. **Error Analysis** *Describe* and correct the error in identifying the asymptotes of the graph of $y = \frac{3}{x + 1} - 5$.

Vertical asymptote: $x = 1$
Horizontal asymptote: $y = -5$
X

Graph the function.

26. $y = \frac{2}{x} + 5$

27. $y = \frac{1}{x - 4} + 2$

28. $y = \frac{-3}{x + 6} - 1$

29. **Multiple Representations** Your movie rental membership lets you rent any number of movies for \$28 per month. You rent at least 2 movies per month.

a. **Writing an Equation** Write an equation that gives the average cost C (in dollars per rental) as a function of the number r of additional rentals beyond 2 rentals.

b. **Drawing a Graph** Graph the equation from part (a). Then use the graph to approximate the number of additional rentals needed per month so that the average cost is \$2 per rental.

30. **Baseball Hall of Fame** Your baseball team is planning a bus trip to the National Baseball Hall of Fame. The cost for renting a bus is \$515, and the cost will be divided equally among the people who are going on the trip. One admission costs \$14.50.

a. Write an equation that gives the cost C (in dollars per person) of the trip as a function of the number p of people going on the trip.

b. Graph the equation.

c. What would the cost per person be if 20 people go on the trip?

31. **Fundraiser** A pizza shop makes pizzas that organizations sell for fundraisers. One organization has placed an order for 450 pizzas. Currently, 4 people are scheduled to put together the pizzas. The owner of the shop hopes to call in some extra workers to complete all of the pizzas.

a. Write an equation that gives the average number n of pizzas made per person as a function of the number p of extra workers that can come in and help complete the work.

b. Graph the equation.

c. If 2 people come in to help out, what is the average number of pizzas made per person?

LESSON 3.6 **Exercise Set B**

MM1A1b Graph the basic functions $f(x) = x^n$, where $n = 1$ to 3, $f(x) = \sqrt{x}$, $f(x) = |x|$, and $f(x) = \frac{1}{x}$.

MM1A1c Graph transformations of basic functions including vertical shifts, stretches, and shrinks, as well as reflections across the x- and y-axes.

MM1A1d Investigate and explain the characteristics of a function: domain, range, zeros, intercepts, intervals of increase and decrease, maximum and minimum values, and end behavior.

Graph the function and identify its domain and range. Then compare the graph with the graph of $y = \frac{1}{x}$.

1. $y = \frac{-1}{8x}$

2. $y = \frac{4}{5x}$

3. $y = \frac{-5}{3x}$

4. $y = \frac{-2}{3x}$

5. $y = \frac{7}{2x}$

6. $y = \frac{1}{x} - 9$

7. $y = \frac{1}{x} + 5$

8. $y = \frac{1}{x - 6}$

9. $y = \frac{1}{x + 8}$

10. **Multiple Choice** For graph of which function has the same vertical asymptote as the graph of $y = \frac{3}{x + 2}$?

A. $y = \frac{1}{x} - 2$ **B.** $y = \frac{1}{x} + 2$ **C.** $y = \frac{1}{x - 2}$ **D.** $y = \frac{1}{x + 2}$

Determine the asymptotes of the graph of the function.

11. $y = \frac{22}{x + 13} - 10$

12. $y = \frac{4}{4x - 8} + 2$

13. $y = \frac{-10}{5x + 5} - 3$

Graph the function.

14. $y = \frac{4}{x - 3} + 5$

15. $y = \frac{-2}{x + 2} - 1$

16. $y = \frac{5}{x + 4} + 2$

17. $y = \frac{-2}{x - 4} - 4$

18. $y = \frac{3}{x + 6} - 2$

19. $y = \frac{-4}{x + 2} - 4$

Write an equation whose graph has the given asymptotes and passes through the given point.

20. $x = 7, y = 8; (2, 0)$

21. $x = -2, y = 5; (0, -2)$

22. $x = 3, y = -2; (6, -1)$

23. $x = -4, y = -4; (-5, 3)$

Exercise Set B *(continued)*

24. **Writing** Let f be a function of the form $f(x) = \frac{a}{x - h} + k$. Can you graph f if you know only two points on the graph? *Explain.*

25. **Geometry** The height h of a trapezoid is given by the formula $h = \frac{2A}{b_1 + b_2}$ where A is the area and b_1 and b_2 are the bases.

    a. Let $A = 40$ and $b_1 = 5$. Write h as a function of b_2. Then graph the function and identify its domain and range.

    b. Use the graph to approximate the value of b_2 when $h = 6$.

26. **Challenge** *Describe* how to find the asymptotes of the graph of $g(x) = \frac{3}{2x - 4} + 7$. Then graph the function.

27. **Zoo Trip** A grade school is taking a trip to the zoo. A parent group of 6 people is responsible for putting together 225 box lunches for the trip. The group hopes to recruit extra people for the task. Write an equation that gives the average number n of box lunches made per person as a function of the number p of parents that can come in and help complete the task. Then graph the equation. How many people need to come in so that the average number of box lunches made per person is 15 box lunches?

28. **Multiple Representations** You rent video games from a web site for $17.25 per month. You can rent any number of games per month, but you usually rent at least 4 games per month.

    a. **Writing an Equation** Write an equation that gives the average cost C per rental as a function of the number r of additional rentals beyond 4 rentals.

    b. **Drawing a Graph** Graph the equation from part (a). Then use the graph to approximate the number of additional rentals needed per month so that the average cost is $2.25.

29. **Challenge** To decide whether a person qualifies for a loan to buy a house, a lender uses the ratio r of the person's expected monthly housing expenses to monthly income. Suppose the person has a monthly income of $4200 and expects to pay $1200 per month in housing expenses. The person also expects to receive a raise of x dollars this month.

    a. Write and graph an equation that gives r as a function of x.

    b. The person will qualify for a loan if the ratio is 0.28. What must the amount of the raise be in order for the person to qualify for a loan?

LESSON 3.7

Divide Polynomials

Georgia Performance Standards: MM1A2c

Goal Divide polynomials.

Example 1 Divide a polynomial by a monomial

Divide $15x^3 - 10x^2 - 20x$ by $-5x$.

Solution

METHOD 1 Write the division as a fraction.

$$(15x^3 - 10x^2 - 20x) \div (-5x) = \frac{15x^3 - 10x^2 - 20x}{-5x}$$ Write as fraction.

$$= \frac{15x^3}{-5x} + \frac{-10x^2}{-5x} + \frac{-20x}{-5x}$$ Divide each term by $-5x$.

$$= -3x^2 + 2x + 4$$ Simplify.

METHOD 2 Use long division.

Think: $15x^3 \div -5x = ?$	Think: $-10x^2 \div -5x = ?$	Think: $-20x \div -5x = ?$

$$\begin{array}{r} -3x^2 + 2x + 4 \\ -5x \overline{)\,15x^3 - 10x^2 - 20x} \end{array}$$

$$(15x^3 - 10x^2 - 20x) \div (-5x) = -3x^2 + 2x + 4$$

CHECK $$-5x(-3x^2 + 2x + 4) \stackrel{?}{=} 15x^3 - 10x^2 - 20x$$

$$-5x(-3x^2) + (-5x)(2x) + (-5x)(4) \stackrel{?}{=} 15x^3 - 10x^2 - 20x$$

$$15x^3 - 10x^2 - 20x = 15x^3 - 10x^2 - 20x \checkmark$$

Guided Practice for Example 1

Divide.

1. $(14p^3 - 35p^2 + 42p) \div 7p$
2. $(12r^3 + 8r^2 - 22r) \div 2r$
3. $(15t^3 + 6t^2 - 18t) \div (-3t)$
4. $(-42w^3 - 30w^2 + 36w) \div (-6w)$

Georgia Performance Standards

MM1A2c Add, subtract, multiply, and divide polynomials.

Example 2 Divide a polynomial by a binomial

Divide $6x^2 - 13x + 2$ by $2x - 5$.

Solution

First divide the first term of $6x^2 - 13x + 2$ by the first term of $2x - 5$.

$$\begin{array}{r} 3x + 1 \\ 2x - 5 \overline{)6x^2 - 13x + 2} \\ \underline{6x^2 - 15x} \\ 2x + 2 \\ \underline{2x - 5} \\ 7 \end{array}$$

Multiply $3x$ and $2x - 5$.

Subtract $6x^2 - 15x$. Bring down 2. Divide the first term of $2x + 2$ by the first term of $2x - 5$.

Multiply 1 and $2x - 5$.

Subtract $2x - 5$.

$(6x^2 - 13x + 2) \div (2x - 5) = 3x + 1 + \frac{7}{2x - 5}$

Example 3 Insert missing terms

Divide $16y^2 - 7$ by $3 + 4y$.

Solution

$$\begin{array}{r} 4y - 3 \\ 4y + 3 \overline{)16y^2 + 0y - 7} \\ \underline{16y^2 + 12y} \\ -12y - 7 \\ \underline{-12y - 9} \\ 2 \end{array}$$

Rewrite polynomials. Insert missing term.

Multiply $4y$ and $4y + 3$.

Subtract $16y^2 + 12y$. Bring down -7.

Multiply -3 and $4y + 3$.

Subtract $-12y - 9$.

$(16y^2 - 7) \div (3 + 4y) = 4y - 3 + \frac{2}{4y + 3}$

Guided Practice for Examples 2 and 3

Divide.

5. $(8x^2 - 22x - 21) \div (2x - 7)$

6. $(24x^2 - 19x + 6) \div (8x - 1)$

7. $(4x^2 - 25) \div (-5 + 2x)$

8. $(16x^2 - 46) \div (4x + 7)$

UNIT 3

LESSON 3.7 **Exercise Set A**

MM1A2c Add, subtract, multiply, and divide polynomials.

Divide.

1. $(18x^3 - 24x^2 + 12x) \div 6x$
2. $(-5x^3 + 15x^2 - 30x) \div (-5x)$
3. $(22x^4 - 18x^2 + 6x) \div (-2x)$
4. $(x^2 + 6x + 5) \div (x + 5)$
5. $(5x^2 + 7x - 6) \div (x + 2)$
6. $(4x^2 + x - 5) \div (x - 1)$
7. $(6x^2 + 22x - 8) \div (x + 4)$
8. $(4x^2 + x - 8) \div (x - 2)$
9. $(9x^2 + 5x - 6) \div (x + 1)$
10. $(3x^2 - 7x + 14) \div (3x + 2)$

11. **Error Analysis** *Describe* and correct the error in dividing $(5x + 4)$ by $(x + 2)$.

$$\begin{array}{r} 5 \\ x + 2\overline{)5x + 4} \\ \underline{5x + 10} \\ -6 \end{array}$$

$$(5x + 4) \div (x + 2) = 5 + \frac{-6}{5x + 4} \quad \times$$

Match the function with its graph.

12. $y = \dfrac{x + 8}{x}$

13. $y = \dfrac{3x - 5}{x}$

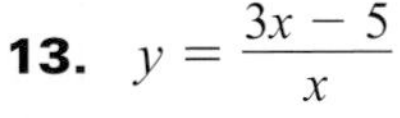

14. $y = \dfrac{x + 5}{x - 2}$

A.

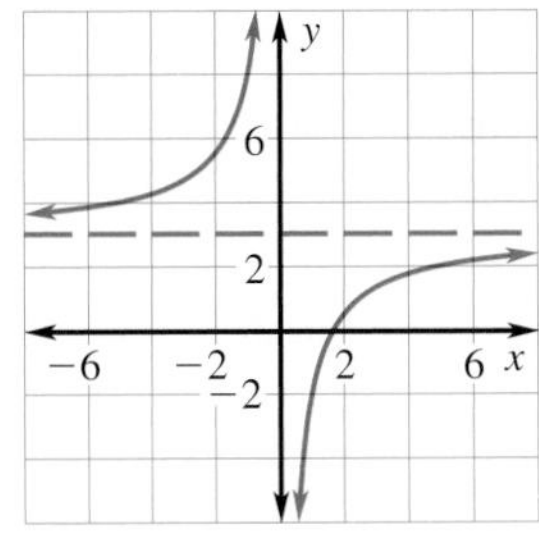

B.

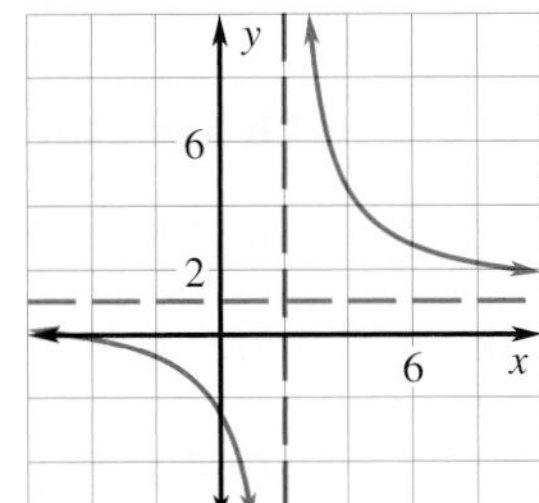

C.

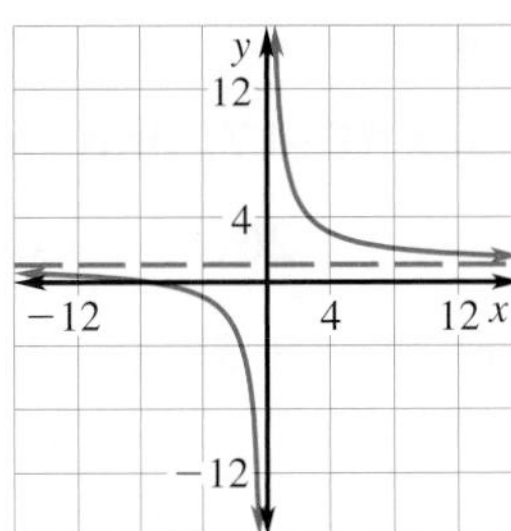

15. **Scootcar Rental** A resort area offers rentals of scootcars (a cross between a scooter and a small car) for \$40 per hour plus a \$4.50 gasoline fill-up fee.
   a. Write an equation that gives the average cost C per hour as a function of the number t of hours the scootcar is rented.
   b. Rewrite the equation in the form $y = \dfrac{a}{x - h} + k$. Then graph the equation.

16. **Juice Bar** Between 1995 and 2004, the number V of vegetable drinks (in thousands) sold at a juice bar can be modeled by $V = 4t + 18$ where t is the number of years since 1995. The number F of drinks (in thousands) made from fruit juice can be modeled by $F = 2t + 32$.
   a. Use long division to find a model for the ratio R of the number of fruit drinks sold to the number of vegetable drinks sold.
   b. Graph the model.

UNIT 3

LESSON 3.7 **Exercise Set B**

MM1A2c Add, subtract, multiply, and divide polynomials.

Divide.

1. $(45x^4 - 60x^2 + 30x) \div 15x$
2. $(96x^3 - 64x^2 - 24x) \div (-8x)$
3. $(7x^2 + 2x - 5) \div (x - 2)$
4. $(9 - 3x - x^2) \div (1 - x)$
5. $(22 - 4x + 3x^2) \div (x - 4)$
6. $(6x + x^2 + 5) \div (3 + x)$
7. $(8x + x^2 - 3) \div (2 - x)$
8. $(9x^2 - 4) \div (3x + 1)$
9. $(7 - x^2) \div (x + 4)$
10. $(18x - 8x^2) \div (5 - 4x)$

Rewrite the function in the form $y = \frac{a}{x - h} + k$. Then graph the function.

11. $y = \frac{5 - x}{x + 7}$
12. $y = \frac{3 + 6x}{x - 2}$
13. $y = \frac{8 - 5x}{x + 4}$

14. **Multiple Choice** The graph of which function is shown?

 A. $y = \frac{x + 5}{x - 3}$ B. $y = \frac{x + 5}{x + 3}$

 C. $y = \frac{x - 5}{x - 3}$ D. $y = \frac{x - 5}{x + 3}$

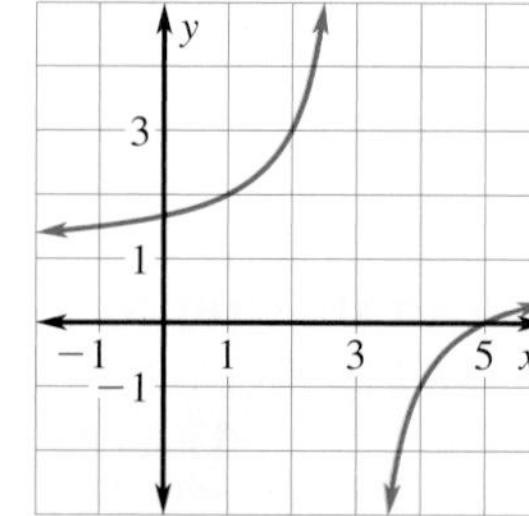

In Exercises 15–17, find the value of k using the given information.

15. When $8x^2 + 26x + k$ is divided by $x + 2$, the remainder is -10.
16. When $100x^2 + k$ is divided by $5x + 1$, the remainder is 0.
17. The graph of $y = \frac{kx + 4}{x - 6}$ has $y = -7$ as its horizontal asymptote.
18. **Car Rental** A local car rental company offers an economy car rental for \$72 per day plus \$.06 per mile. You want to rent the car for three days.
    a. Write an equation that gives the average cost C per mile as a function of the number m of miles you drive the rental.
    b. Rewrite the equation in the form $y = \frac{a}{x - h} + k$. Then graph the equation.
19. **Athletic Shoes** Between 1999 and 2002, the sales S of athletic and sport footwear (in millions of dollars) can be modeled by $S = 546t + 12{,}552$ where t is the number of years since 1999. The sales W of walking shoes (in millions of dollars) can be modeled by $W = 91t + 3141$.
    a. Use long division to find a model for the ratio R of walking shoe sales to all athletic shoe sales.
    b. Graph the model.

UNIT 3

LESSON 3.8

Simplify Rational Expressions

Georgia Performance Standards: MM1A2c

Goal Simplify rational expressions.

Vocabulary

A **rational expression** is an expression that can be written as a ratio of two polynomials.

A rational expression is undefined when the denominator is 0. A number that makes a rational expression undefined is called an **excluded value.**

A rational expression is in **simplest form** if the numerator and denominator have no factors in common other than 1.

Example 1 Find excluded values

Find the excluded values, if any, of the expression.

a. $\frac{8}{-2x}$ **b.** $\frac{x}{3x - 9}$ **c.** $\frac{x + 2}{x^2 + 2x - 15}$ **d.** $\frac{12}{5x^2 + 2x + 7}$

Solution

a. The expression $\frac{8}{-2x}$ is undefined when $-2x = 0$, or $x = 0$. The excluded value is 0.

b. The expression $\frac{x}{3x - 9}$ is undefined when $3x - 9 = 0$, or $x = 3$. The excluded value is 3.

c. The expression $\frac{x + 2}{x^2 + 2x - 15}$ is undefined when $x^2 + 2x - 15 = 0$, or $(x - 3)(x + 5) = 0$.
The solutions of the equation are 3 and -5. The excluded values are 3 and -5.

d. The expression $\frac{12}{5x^2 + 2x + 7}$ is undefined when $5x^2 + 2x + 7 = 0$.

The graph of $y = 5x^2 + 2x + 7$ does not cross the x-axis. So, the quadratic equation has no real roots. There are no excluded values.

Guided Practice for Example 1

Find the excluded values, if any, of the expression.

1. $\frac{9x}{5x - 15}$

2. $\frac{x - 1}{x^2 - 16}$

3. $\frac{7}{2x^2 - 5x + 6}$

4. $\frac{x + 6}{x^2 + 4x - 12}$

UNIT 3

Georgia Performance Standards

MM1A2c Add, subtract, multiply, and divide polynomials.

Example 2 Simplify expressions by dividing out monomials

Simplify the rational expression, if possible. State the excluded values.

a. $\frac{2m}{8m(m-1)}$ **b.** $\frac{11}{y+6}$ **c.** $\frac{7q^2-14q}{14q^3}$

Solution

a. $\frac{2m}{8m(m-1)} = \frac{\cancel{2} \cdot \cancel{m}}{\cancel{2} \cdot 4 \cdot \cancel{m} \cdot (m-1)}$ Divide out common factors.

$= \frac{1}{4(m-1)}$ Simplify.

The excluded values are 0 and 1.

b. The expression $\frac{11}{y+6}$ is already in simplest form. The excluded value is -6.

c. $\frac{7q^2-14q}{14q^3} = \frac{\cancel{7} \cdot \cancel{q} \cdot (q-2)}{\cancel{7} \cdot 2 \cdot \cancel{q} \cdot q^2}$ Divide out common factors.

$= \frac{q-2}{2q^2}$ Simplify.

The excluded value is 0.

Example 3 Simplify an expression by dividing out binomials

Simplify $\frac{x^2+4x-21}{x^2-5x+6}$. State the excluded values.

Solution

$\frac{x^2+4x-21}{x^2-5x+6} = \frac{(x+7)(x-3)}{(x-2)(x-3)}$ Factor numerator and denominator.

$= \frac{(x+7)\cancel{(x-3)}}{(x-2)\cancel{(x-3)}}$ Divide out common factors.

$= \frac{x+7}{x-2}$ Simplify.

The excluded values are 2 and 3.

Guided Practice for Examples 2 and 3

Simplify the expression. State the excluded value(s).

5. $\frac{3x^3}{15x^5}$

6. $\frac{28x}{7x-21}$

7. $\frac{3x^2}{2x+6}$

8. $\frac{5x+10}{3x^2+6x}$

9. $\frac{x^2+13x+42}{x^2-2x-63}$

10. $\frac{4x^2+20x+25}{4x^2-25}$

UNIT 3

LESSON 3.8

Exercise Set A

MM1A2c Add, subtract, multiply, and divide polynomials.

Find the excluded values, if any, of the expression.

1. $\frac{14}{3x}$

2. $\frac{-8}{x-5}$

3. $\frac{5x}{x+10}$

4. $\frac{-x}{4x-8}$

5. $\frac{3x}{7x+21}$

6. $\frac{x+1}{3x+7}$

7. $\frac{x+6}{x^2-2x+1}$

8. $\frac{8}{x^2+4x-12}$

9. $\frac{7x}{x^2-25}$

Simplify the rational expression, if possible. Find the excluded values.

10. $\frac{-36x^2}{18x}$

11. $\frac{6x-24}{x-4}$

12. $\frac{4x-12}{3-x}$

13. $\frac{x+11}{x^2-121}$

14. $\frac{x+3}{x^2+10x+21}$

15. $\frac{x-4}{x^2+11x+24}$

Write and simplify a rational expression for the ratio of the perimeter to the area of the given figure.

16. Square

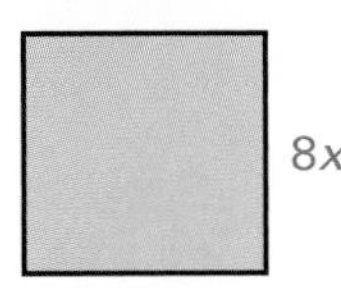

17. Rectangle

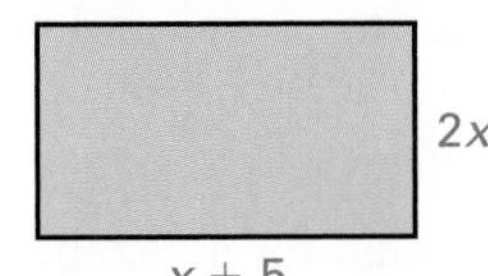

18. Triangle

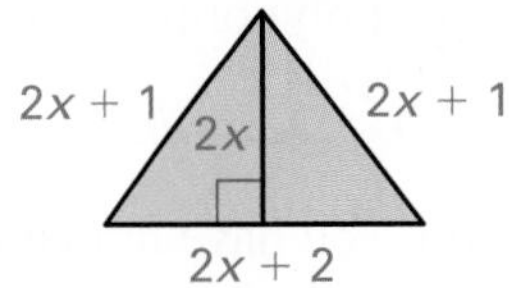

19. Zoo Exhibit The directors of a zoo have drawn up preliminary plans for a rectangular exhibit. They have decided on dimensions that are related as shown.

a. Write a rational expression for the ratio of the perimeter to the area of the exhibit.

b. Simplify your expression from part (a).

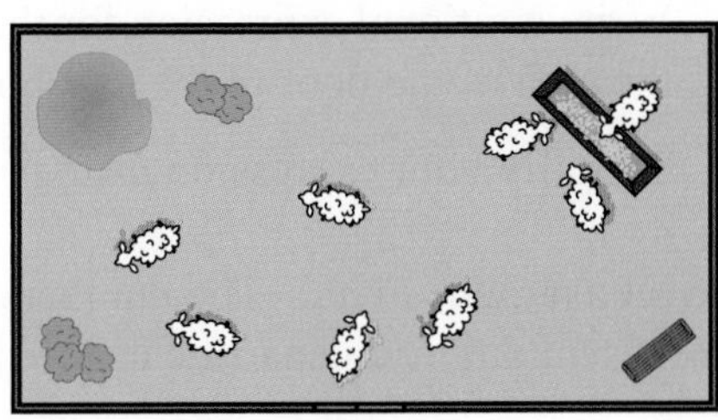

20. Materials Used The material consumed M (in thousands of pounds) by a plastic injection molding machine per year between 1995 and 2004 can be modeled by

$$M = \frac{8t^2 + 66t + 70}{(3 - 0.2t + 0.1t^2)(t + 7)}$$

where t is the number of years since 1995. Simplify the model and approximate the number of pounds consumed in 2000.

UNIT 3

LESSON 3.8 **Exercise Set B**

MM1A2c Add, subtract, multiply, and divide polynomials.

Find the excluded values, if any, of the expression.

1. $\frac{-x}{3x^2 + 11x - 4}$

2. $\frac{12}{8x^2 - 3x - 5}$

3. $\frac{5x^2}{x^2 - 14x + 49}$

Simplify the rational expression, if possible. Find the excluded values.

4. $\frac{x - 7}{x^2 - 6x - 7}$

5. $\frac{-8x^3}{12x^2 - 20x}$

6. $\frac{9x^2 - 36x}{12x - 24x^2}$

7. $\frac{15x^4}{15x^2 + 20x}$

8. $\frac{2x - 4}{x^2 + 8x - 20}$

9. $\frac{4x^2 - 12x}{2x^2 - 5x - 3}$

10. $\frac{x^2 + 4x - 60}{2x^2 + 23x + 30}$

11. $\frac{x - 4}{x^3 - 8x^2 + 16x}$

12. $\frac{x^2 + 7x + 10}{2x^3 - 8x}$

13. Are the rational expressions $\frac{x^2 + 2x}{x^2 - 4}$ and $\frac{x^2}{x^2 - 2x}$ equivalent? *Explain* how you know. What are the excluded values, if any, of the rational expressions.

14. The expression $\frac{a}{15x^2 + 13x + 2}$ simplifies to $\frac{5x + 1}{3x + 2}$. What is the value of a? *Explain* how you got your answer.

15. Find two polynomials whose ratio simplifies to $\frac{3x - 1}{5x + 1}$ and whose sum is $8x^2 + 24x$. *Describe* your steps.

16. **Gazebo** You have drawn up a preliminary plan for a gazebo that you want to build in your backyard. Your plan for the base is to use two identical trapezoids as shown at the right.

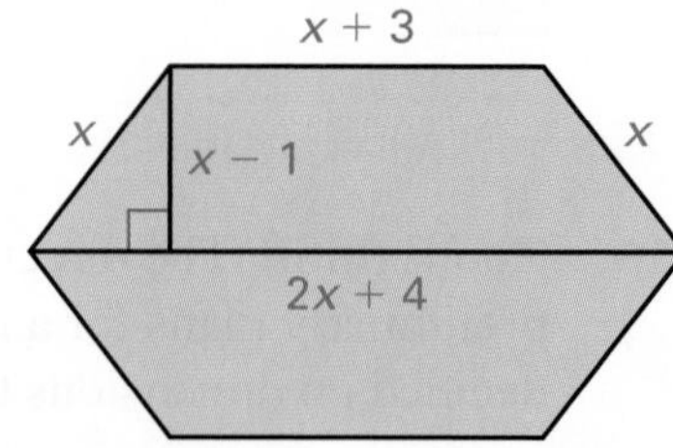

a. Write a rational expression for the ratio of the perimeter to the area of the floor of the gazebo.

b. Simplify your expression from part (a).

17. **Advertisement Flyers** The number A (in hundreds of thousands) of advertising flyers sent out by a department store between 1995 and 2004 can be modeled by

$$A = \frac{6t^2 + 102t + 312}{(18 - 0.5t + 0.01t^2)(t + 13)}$$

where t is the number of years since 1995.

a. Simplify the model.

b. Use the model to approximate how many flyers were sent out in 2001.

c. Graph the model. *Describe* how the number of flyers sent out changed over time.

UNIT 3

LESSON 3.9

Multiply and Divide Rational Expressions

Georgia Performance Standards: MM1A2e

Goal Multiply and divide rational expressions.

Example 1 Multiply rational expressions involving polynomials

Find the product $\frac{x^2 + x - 6}{10x^2 - 20x} \cdot \frac{5x^2 + 15x}{x^2 - 2x - 15}$.

$$\frac{x^2 + x - 6}{10x^2 - 20x} \cdot \frac{5x^2 + 15x}{x^2 - 2x - 15}$$

$$= \frac{(x^2 + x - 6)(5x^2 + 15x)}{(10x^2 - 20x)(x^2 - 2x - 15)}$$ Multiply numerators and denominators.

$$= \frac{\cancel{(x - 2)}(x + 3)\cancel{5x}\cancel{(x + 3)}}{2 \cdot \cancel{5x}\cancel{(x - 2)}(x - 5)\cancel{(x + 3)}}$$ Factor and divide out common factors.

$$= \frac{x + 3}{2(x - 5)}$$ Simplify.

Example 2 Multiply a rational expression by a polynomial

Find the product $\frac{4x^2}{2x^3 + 10x^2 - 48x} \cdot (x + 8)$.

$$\frac{4x^2}{2x^3 + 10x^2 - 48x} \cdot (x + 8)$$

$$= \frac{4x^2}{2x^3 + 10x^2 - 48x} \cdot \frac{x + 8}{1}$$ Rewrite polynomial as a fraction.

$$= \frac{4x^2(x + 8)}{2x^3 + 10x^2 - 48x}$$ Multiply numerators and denominators.

$$= \frac{\cancel{2x}(2x)\cancel{(x + 8)}}{\cancel{2x}\cancel{(x + 8)}(x - 3)}$$ Factor and divide out common factors.

$$= \frac{2x}{x - 3}$$ Simplify.

Guided Practice for Examples 1 and 2

Find the product.

1. $\frac{x^2 - 1}{2x^2 - 3x + 1} \cdot \frac{4x - 2}{3x + 18}$

2. $\frac{9x}{3x^2 + 9x - 30} \cdot (x + 5)$

UNIT 3

Georgia Performance Standards

MM1A2e Add, subtract, multiply, and divide rational expressions.

Example 3 Divide rational expressions involving polynomials

Find the quotient $\frac{8x^2 + 24x}{x^2 - 5x} \div \frac{x^2 + 7x + 12}{x^2 - 7x + 10}$.

$$\frac{8x^2 + 24x}{x^2 - 5x} \div \frac{x^2 + 7x + 12}{x^2 - 7x + 10}$$

$$= \frac{8x^2 + 24x}{x^2 - 5x} \cdot \frac{x^2 - 7x + 10}{x^2 + 7x + 12}$$ Multiply by multiplicative inverse.

$$= \frac{(8x^2 + 24x)(x^2 - 7x + 10)}{(x^2 - 5x)(x^2 + 7x + 12)}$$ Multiply numerators and denominators.

$$= \frac{8\cancel{x}\cancel{(x + 3)}(x - 2)\cancel{(x - 5)}}{\cancel{x}\cancel{(x - 5)}(x + 4)\cancel{(x + 3)}}$$ Factor and divide out common factors.

$$= \frac{8(x - 2)}{x + 4}$$ Simplify.

Example 4 Divide a rational expression by a polynomial

Find the quotient $\frac{5x^2 - 10x}{4x^2 + 12} \div (x - 2)$.

$$\frac{5x^2 - 10x}{4x^2 + 12} \div (x - 2)$$

$$= \frac{5x^2 - 10x}{4x^2 + 12} \div \frac{x - 2}{1}$$ Rewrite polynomial as a fraction.

$$= \frac{5x^2 - 10x}{4x^2 + 12} \cdot \frac{1}{x - 2}$$ Multiply by multiplicative inverse.

$$= \frac{5x^2 - 10x}{(4x^2 + 12)(x - 2)}$$ Multiply numerators and denominators.

$$= \frac{5x\cancel{(x - 2)}}{4(x^2 + 3)\cancel{(x - 2)}}$$ Factor and divide out common factor.

$$= \frac{5x}{4(x^2 + 3)}$$ Simplify.

Guided Practice for Examples 3 and 4

Find the quotient.

3. $\frac{x^2 + 3x - 10}{3x^2 - 3x} \div \frac{x^2 - 8x + 12}{x - 1}$

4. $\frac{2x^4 - 6x^3 - 56x^2}{x^3 - 5x^2} \div (x - 7)$

LESSON 3.9

Exercise Set A

MM1A2e Add, subtract, multiply, and divide rational expressions.

Find the product.

1. $\dfrac{4x^2}{15} \cdot \dfrac{5}{8x^5}$

2. $\dfrac{24}{7x^2} \cdot \dfrac{14x^6}{40}$

3. $\dfrac{21}{2x + 12} \cdot \dfrac{4x + 24}{15}$

4. $\dfrac{5x + 10}{2x - 6} \cdot \dfrac{x - 3}{10x + 20}$

5. $\dfrac{x - 3}{2x + 8} \cdot \dfrac{x + 4}{x^2 + 2x - 15}$

6. $\dfrac{x^2 + 4x - 12}{x^2 + 7x + 10} \cdot \dfrac{x + 5}{2x - 4}$

7. $\dfrac{6x}{4x^2 - 1} \cdot \dfrac{2x^2 + 7x + 3}{18}$

8. $\dfrac{x^4}{x^4 + 5x^3} \cdot (x + 5)$

9. $\dfrac{3x - 6}{x^2 - x - 2} \cdot (x^2 + 6x + 5)$

Find the quotient.

10. $\dfrac{24}{5x^3} \div \dfrac{6}{25x^2}$

11. $\dfrac{11x^4}{18} \div \dfrac{22}{9x^2}$

12. $\dfrac{7x + 21}{30} \div \dfrac{21x + 63}{20}$

13. $\dfrac{4x - 24}{3x + 15} \div \dfrac{12x - 72}{x + 5}$

14. $\dfrac{x + 2}{3x - 3} \div \dfrac{x^2 + 11x + 18}{x - 1}$

15. $\dfrac{x^2 + 4x}{4x} \div \dfrac{x^2 + x - 12}{x - 3}$

16. $\dfrac{2x + 10}{x^2 - 25} \div \dfrac{4x^2}{2x^2 - 10x}$

17. $\dfrac{2x - 14}{x^2 - 4x - 21} \div (x + 3)$

18. **Wall Art** You want to create a rectangular picture from 2-inch by 3-inch tiles. You want the picture's dimensions to be related as shown.

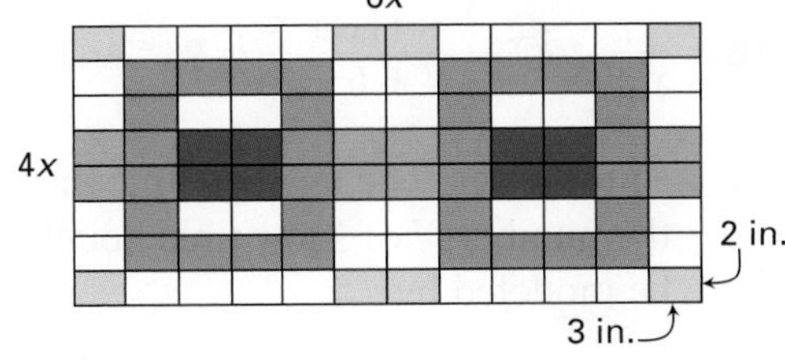

   a. Write and simplify an expression that you can use to determine the number of 2-inch by 3-inch tiles that will be needed for the picture.

   b. If $x = 5$, how many tiles will you need?

19. **Profit** The total profit P (in millions of dollars) earned by a company from 1995 to 2004 can be modeled by

$$P = \frac{3500 + 500t}{98 - t}$$

where t is the number of years since 1995. The number N (in hundreds of thousands) of units sold can be modeled by

$$N = \frac{(t + 7)(3000 - 20t)}{490 - 5t}$$

where t is the number of years since 1995. Write a model that gives the profit earned per unit per year. Then approximate the profit per unit in 2002.

UNIT 3

LESSON 3.9 **Exercise Set B**

MM1A2e Add, subtract, multiply, and divide rational expressions.

Find the product.

1. $\dfrac{8x}{2x^2 + x - 3} \cdot \dfrac{4x^2 + 2x - 6}{16}$

2. $\dfrac{x^2 - x - 2}{18x^3} \cdot \dfrac{14x^2}{x^2 + x - 6}$

3. $\dfrac{-x - 3}{5x^2 + 10x} \cdot \dfrac{10x^2 + 20x}{4x + 12}$

4. $\dfrac{x^2 + 8x + 15}{x^2 + 7x + 10} \cdot \dfrac{x^2 - 2x - 8}{3x^2 + 9x}$

5. $\dfrac{x^6}{9x^3 + 63x} \cdot (x^2 + 7)$

6. $\dfrac{4x - 12}{x^2 + 5x - 24} \cdot (2x^2 + 11x - 40)$

Find the quotient.

7. $\dfrac{x^2 - 2x - 48}{4x^2 + 24} \div \dfrac{x - 8}{8x + 24}$

8. $\dfrac{x^2 - 5x - 36}{5x^2 + 16x} \div \dfrac{x^2 - 8x - 9}{x + 1}$

9. $\dfrac{2x^2 - 9x - 5}{5 - x} \div \dfrac{2x^2 + 7x + 3}{x + 3}$

10. $\dfrac{x^2 + 4x}{5x^3 + 20x^2} \div \dfrac{x^2 - 16}{10x - 40}$

11. $\dfrac{4x^4 - 20x^2}{x + 7} \div \dfrac{16x^2 - 112}{x^2 - 49}$

12. $\dfrac{3x^2 - 10x - 8}{5x^2 - 20x} \div \dfrac{6x^2 + x - 2}{30x^2 - 120x}$

13. $\dfrac{x^2 + 2x - 35}{x^2 - 3x - 10} \div \dfrac{3x^2 + 21x}{9x + 18}$

14. $\dfrac{x^3 - x^2 + 4x - 4}{10x^3} \div \dfrac{x^2 + 7x - 8}{5x^2 + 40x}$

Let *a* be a polynomial in the given equation. Find *a*.

15. $\dfrac{a}{x + 5} \cdot \dfrac{2x^2 + 11x + 5}{x + 6} = 2x^2 - 11x - 6$

16. $\dfrac{4x^2 + 7x - 15}{2x + 1} \div \dfrac{x + 3}{a} = 4x^2 - 33x + 35$

17. **Snow Tires** The average amount C (in dollars) of money spent per snow tire and the number N of snow tires bought by an auto body shop from 2000 to 2004, can be modeled by

$$C = \frac{t + 80}{1 - 0.05t} \quad \text{and} \quad N = \frac{500(t + 20)}{t + 80}$$

where t is the number of years since 2000. Write a model that gives the total amount A spent by the shop each year on snow tires. Then approximate the amount spent in 2003.

18. **Drive-in Movies** The average monthly revenue R (in dollars) from admissions at a drive-in theater and the average price p (in dollars) per car from 1988 to 2000 can be modeled by

$$R = \frac{13{,}124 + 3122t}{26 - t} \quad \text{and} \quad p = \frac{294 + 7t}{130 - 5t}$$

where t is the number of years since 1988.

a. Write a model that gives the average number x of cars admitted per month to the theater.

b. Graph the model on a graphing calculator and describe how the number of cars admitted changed over time.

UNIT 3

Georgia Performance Standards

MM1A2e Add, subtract, multiply, and divide rational expressions.

Technology Activity

Checking the Product or Quotient

Use after Lesson 3.9

Question

How can you use a graphing calculator to check the product (or quotient) of two rational expressions?

Example

Use a graphing calculator to check the product or quotient.

Use a graphing calculator to check the product:

$$\frac{2x^2 + 2x}{3x^2 - 15x + 12} \cdot \frac{5x^2 - 5x}{x^2 + x} = \frac{10x}{3(x - 4)}.$$

STEP 1 **Press** Y= .

Enter $y_1 = \frac{2x^2 + 2x}{3x^2 - 15x + 12} \cdot \frac{5x^2 - 5x}{x^2 + x}$

and $y_2 = \frac{10x}{3(x - 4)}$.

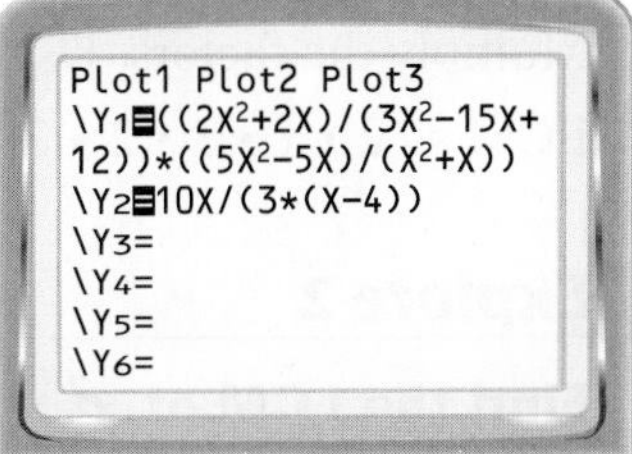

STEP 2 **Graph** y_1 and y_2 using a friendly viewing window. The graphs coincide. So, the expressions are equivalent for all values of x other than the excluded values (-1, 0, 1, and 4).

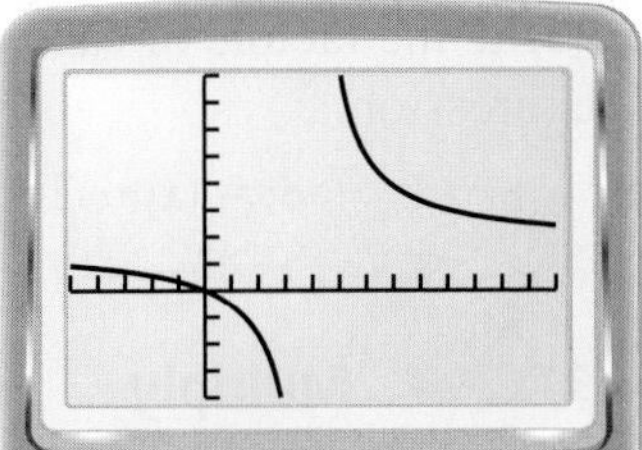

Practice

Use a graphing calculator to check the product or quotient.

1. $\frac{3x^2}{4x} \cdot \frac{8x}{16x^3} = \frac{3}{8x}$

2. $\frac{x}{x + 4} \div \frac{x + 3}{x + 4} = \frac{x}{x + 3}$

3. $\frac{4x}{x^2 - 9} \cdot \frac{x - 3}{8x^2 + 12x} = \frac{1}{(x + 3)(2x + 3)}$

4. $\frac{x^2 - 2x}{x^2 - 6x + 8} \div \frac{2x}{3x - 12} = \frac{3}{2}$

Georgia Performance Standards

MM1A2f Factor expressions by greatest common factor, grouping, trial and error, and special products.

Investigating Math Activity

Least Common Multiple

Use before Lesson 3.10

Question

How can you find the least common multiple of polynomials?

Explore 1

Find the LCM of $6x$ and $8x^2$.

STEP 1 **Factor**
Write the factors of each expression.

$6x = 2 \cdot 3 \cdot x$

$8x^2 = 2 \cdot 2 \cdot 2 \cdot x \cdot x$

STEP 2 **Find common factors**
Circle the factors that both expressions have in common.

$6x = (2) \cdot 3 \cdot (x)$

$8x^2 = (2) \cdot 2 \cdot 2 \cdot (x) \cdot x$

STEP 3 **Multiply**
Multiply the factors. Use the common factors only once.

$\text{LCM} = 2 \cdot x \cdot 3 \cdot 2 \cdot 2 \cdot x = 24x^2$

Explore 2

Find the LCM of $x^2 + 2x - 8$ and $x^2 + 7x + 12$.

STEP 1 **Factor**
Write the factors of each expression.

$x^2 + 2x - 8 = (x - 2)(x + 4)$

$x^2 + 7x + 12 = (x + 3)(x + 4)$

STEP 2 **Find common factors**
Circle the factors that both expressions have in common.

$x^2 + 2x - 8 = (x - 2)(x + 4)$

$x^2 + 7x + 12 = (x + 3)(x + 4)$

STEP 3 **Multiply**
Multiply the factors. Use the common factors only once.

$\text{LCM} = (x + 4)(x - 2)(x + 3)$

Draw Conclusions

1. Find the LCM of $9x$ and $4x^3$.

2. Find the LCM of $x^2 - x - 2$ and $x^2 + 3x - 10$.

3. **Reasoning** When adding or subtracting rational expressions, when would finding the LCM of polynomials be necessary?

LESSON 3.10

Add and Subtract Rational Expressions

Georgia Performance Standards: MM1A2e

Goal Add and subtract rational expressions.

Vocabulary

The **least common denominator (LCD)** of two or more rational expressions is the product of the factors of the rational expressions with each common factor used only once.

Example 1 Add and subtract with the same denominator

Find the sum or difference.

a. $\frac{2}{5x} + \frac{8}{5x} = \frac{10}{5x}$ Add numerators.

$= \frac{\cancel{5} \cdot 2}{\cancel{5} \cdot x}$ Factor and divide out common factors.

$= \frac{2}{x}$ Simplify.

b. $\frac{11r}{r-7} - \frac{3r-5}{r-7} = \frac{11r - (3r-5)}{r-7}$ Subtract numerators.

$= \frac{8r+5}{r-7}$ Simplify.

Guided Practice for Example 1

Find the sum or difference.

1. $\frac{x+3}{7x} + \frac{x-2}{7x}$

2. $\frac{5x+7}{3x-4} - \frac{2x-9}{3x-4}$

Example 2 Find the LCD of rational expressions

Find the LCD of the rational expressions.

a. $\frac{3x}{x^2 - 5x + 6}, \frac{x+2}{x^2 - 7x + 10}$

b. $\frac{1}{2x-1}, \frac{7}{4x-5}$

Solution

a. Find the least common multiple of $x^2 - 5x + 6$ and $x^2 - 7x + 10$.

$x^2 - 5x + 6 = \boxed{(x-2)} \cdot (x-3)$
$x^2 - 7x + 10 = \boxed{(x-2)} \cdot (x-5)$

The LCD of $x^2 - 5x + 6$ and $x^2 - 7x + 10$ is $(x-2)(x-3)(x-5)$.

b. Find the least common multiple of $2x - 1$ and $4x - 5$. Because $2x - 1$ and $4x - 5$ cannot be factored, they don't have any factors in common. The LCD is their product, $(2x-1)(4x-5)$.

Georgia Performance Standards

MM1A2e Add, subtract, multiply, and divide rational expressions.

Guided Practice for Example 2

Find the LCD of the rational expressions.

3. $\frac{3}{10x^2}, \frac{x+7}{15x^5}$

4. $\frac{9}{3x-1}, \frac{2x}{x+6}$

5. $\frac{8x}{(x+5)^2}, \frac{4x+1}{x^2+8x+15}$

Example 3 Add expressions with different denominators

Find the sum $\frac{11}{12x^2} + \frac{15}{16x^5}$.

$$\frac{11}{12x^2} + \frac{15}{16x^5} = \frac{11 \cdot 4x^3}{12x^2 \cdot 4x^3} + \frac{15 \cdot 3}{16x^5 \cdot 3}$$ Rewrite fraction using LCD, $48x^5$.

$$= \frac{44x^3}{48x^5} + \frac{45}{48x^5}$$ Simplify numerators and denominators.

$$= \frac{44x^3 + 45}{48x^5}$$ Add fractions.

Example 4 Subtract expressions with different denominators

Find the difference $\frac{12}{x+2} - \frac{4x}{x-3}$.

$$\frac{12}{x+2} - \frac{4x}{x-3} = \frac{12(x-3)}{(x+2)(x-3)} - \frac{4x(x+2)}{(x-3)(x+2)}$$ Rewrite fraction using LCD, $(x+2)(x-3)$.

$$= \frac{12(x-3) - 4x(x+2)}{(x+2)(x-3)}$$ Subtract fractions.

$$= \frac{-4x^2 + 4x - 36}{(x+2)(x-3)}$$ Simplify numerator.

$$= -\frac{4(x^2 - x + 9)}{(x+2)(x-3)}$$ Factor numerator to check for common factors in numerator and denominator.

Guided Practice for Examples 3 and 4

Find the sum or difference.

6. $\frac{7}{18r^2} + \frac{12}{9r^3}$

7. $\frac{x}{x^2 - 2x - 15} + \frac{3}{x^2 - 9}$

8. $\frac{t+1}{t-7} - \frac{t-2}{t+3}$

UNIT 3

LESSON 3.10 **Exercise Set A**

MM1A2e Add, subtract, multiply, and divide rational expressions.

Find the sum or difference.

1. $\frac{8}{x+5} + \frac{x}{x+5}$

2. $\frac{10x}{x-4} - \frac{6x}{x-4}$

3. $\frac{x+3}{x-9} + \frac{5x}{x-9}$

4. $\frac{x-5}{x+2} - \frac{x+6}{x+2}$

5. $\frac{3x-4}{x^2-9} + \frac{7x-3}{x^2-9}$

6. $\frac{2x+4}{3x^2} - \frac{x-1}{3x^2}$

Find the LCD of the rational expressions.

7. $\frac{6}{5x^3}, \frac{7}{15x}$

8. $\frac{10}{x}, \frac{9x}{x+7}$

9. $\frac{3x+1}{x-4}, \frac{x-4}{x+6}$

10. $\frac{x+5}{2x-4}, \frac{4x}{x-2}$

11. $\frac{1}{x^2-5x}, \frac{8}{x^2-3x-10}$

12. $\frac{3}{x^2+5x+4}, \frac{4x}{x^2+2x+1}$

Find the sum or difference.

13. $\frac{11}{2x} + \frac{4}{7x}$

14. $\frac{8}{3x^3} - \frac{5}{12x}$

15. $\frac{8x}{x-5} - \frac{3x}{x+2}$

16. $\frac{x}{6x-5} + \frac{1}{5x-3}$

17. $\frac{4}{x^2-7x} - \frac{3}{x}$

18. $\frac{5}{x^2} + \frac{x+3}{x-1}$

19. $\frac{x+3}{x-1} + \frac{x+2}{x+1}$

20. $\frac{2x}{x^2-3x} + \frac{x+4}{x-3}$

21. $\frac{1}{x^2+5x+4} - \frac{1}{x^2-16}$

22. **Paddle Boat** You paddle a boat 8 miles upstream (against the current) and 8 miles downstream (with the current). The speed of the current is 1 mile per hour.

a. Write an equation that gives the total travel time t (in hours) as a function of your average speed r (in miles per hour) in still water.

b. Find your total travel time if your average speed in still water is 3 miles per hour.

c. How much faster is your total travel time if you increased your average speed in still water to 3.5 miles per hour? Round your answer to the nearest tenth.

23. **Bike Ride** You bike 50 miles from home. On your way back home, your average speed increases by 3 miles per hour.

a. Write an equation that gives the total biking time t (in hours) as a function of your average speed r (in miles per hour) when you are biking away from home.

b. Find the total biking time if you bike away from your home at an average speed of 15 miles per hour. Round your answer to the nearest tenth.

c. How much longer is your total biking time if you bike away from your home at an average speed of 12 miles per hour?

LESSON 3.10 **Exercise Set B**

MM1A2e Add, subtract, multiply, and divide rational expressions.

Find the sum or difference.

1. $\frac{x - 9}{x + 3} + \frac{2x + 3}{x + 3}$

2. $\frac{2x - 4}{x - 5} - \frac{x + 4}{x - 5}$

3. $\frac{3x}{2x - 5} - \frac{6x - 2}{2x - 5}$

4. $\frac{10x}{x - 5} + \frac{x + 4}{x + 2}$

5. $\frac{x + 9}{x + 10} - \frac{3x}{x - 1}$

6. $\frac{6x - 5}{2x - 3} - \frac{4x + 3}{x + 5}$

7. $\frac{3x - 5}{x - 2} - \frac{x - 1}{3x^2}$

8. $\frac{x + 6}{5x^2} + \frac{x - 4}{x + 2}$

9. $\frac{x - 5}{8x} - \frac{2x}{x + 6}$

10. $\frac{4x}{x^2 - 1} - \frac{x + 1}{x^2 + 8x + 7}$

11. $\frac{x - 2}{x^2 - 6x + 9} - \frac{x + 1}{x^2 + 2x - 15}$

12. $\frac{x + 6}{x^2 - 4x - 12} + \frac{x - 1}{x^2 + 3x + 2}$

Use the order of operations to write the expression as a single rational expression.

13. $4\left(\frac{x}{x + 2}\right) - 5\left(\frac{x - 5}{x + 1}\right)$

14. $6\left(\frac{4x}{x - 3} + \frac{7}{x^2 + 5x - 24}\right)$

15. $\frac{x - 2}{x^2 + 10x + 24} + \frac{4x}{x + 1} \cdot \frac{5}{x + 6}$

16. $\frac{x + 3}{x - 7} - \frac{2x^2 + 3x + 1}{x - 3} \div \frac{x^2 + 3x + 2}{x^2 - 9}$

17. Suppose that $a = 4b - b^2$ and $b = \frac{c - 5}{3c + 4}$. Write a in terms of c.

18. **In-line Skating** You in-line skate 10 miles from the beginning of a trail. On your way back, your average speed decreases by 2.75 miles per hour.

a. Write an equation that gives the total skating time t (in hours) as a function of your average speed r (in miles per hour) when you are skating away from the beginning of the trail.

b. Find the total skating time if you skate away from the beginning of the trail at an average speed of 10 miles per hour. Round your answer to the nearest tenth.

c. How much faster is your total skating time if you skate away from the beginning of the trail at an average speed of 10.75 miles per hour?

19. **Advertisement Delivery** You and your friend plan to spend 45 minutes delivering pizza shop advertisements to houses in the shop's delivery area. You can deliver all of the advertisements on your own in two and a half hours.

a. Write an equation that gives the fraction y of advertisements that your friend can deliver alone as a function of the time t (in minutes).

b. Suppose that your friend can deliver the advertisements alone in two hours and fifteen minutes. Can you deliver all of the advertisements if you and your friend work together for 45 minutes? *Explain.*

Georgia Performance Standards

MM1A2e Add, subtract, multiply, and divide rational expressions.

LESSON 3.10

Problem Solving Workshop

Problem Beth drives 135 miles to another city. On the drive back home, her average speed decreases by 9 miles per hour. Write an equation that gives the total driving time t (in hours) as a function of her average speed r (in miles per hour) when driving to the city. Then find the total driving time if she drives to the city at an average speed of 45 miles per hour.

STEP 1 **Read and Understand**

What do you know? The distance that Beth drives and the decrease of her average speed on the way back.

What do you want to find out? The total driving time.

STEP 2 **Make a Plan** Use what you know to write and solve an equation.

STEP 3 **Solve the Problem** An equation to represent the situation is

$t = \frac{135}{r} + \frac{135}{r - 9}$ where $\frac{135}{r}$ is the time to drive to the other city and $\frac{135}{r - 9}$ is the time to drive back home. Find the sum of the expressions.

$$t = \frac{135(r - 9)}{r(r - 9)} + \frac{135r}{r(r - 9)}$$ Rewrite fractions using the LCD, $r(r - 9)$.

$$= \frac{270r - 1215}{r(r - 9)}$$ Add fractions and simplify.

Calculate the value of t when $r = 45$.

$$t = \frac{270(45) - 1215}{45(45 - 9)} = \frac{10,935}{1620} = 6.75 \text{ hours}$$

The total travel time is 6.75 hours.

STEP 4 **Look Back** The time of the trip to the city is $\frac{135}{45} = 3$ hours and the time of the trip back home is $\frac{135}{45 - 9} = 3.75$ hours. The total time of the trip is 6.75 hours.

Practice

1. **What If?** Suppose in the example that on the drive back home, Beth's average speed decreases by 15 miles per hour because of construction. Write an equation that gives the total driving time t (in hours) as a function of her average speed r (in miles per hour) when driving to the city. Find the total travel time.

2. **Boat Travel** A boat travels 25 kilometers against the current and 25 kilometers with the current. The speed of the current is 5 kilometers per hour. Write an equation that gives the total travel time t (in hours) as a function of the boat's average speed r (in kilometers per hour) in still water. The boat's speed in still water is 15 kilometers per hour. Find the total travel time.

UNIT 3

LESSON 3.11

Solve Rational Equations

Georgia Performance Standards: MM1A3d

Goal Solve rational equations.

Vocabulary

A **rational equation** is an equation that contains rational expressions.

Example 1 Use the cross products property

Solve $\frac{6}{x+5} = \frac{x}{6}$. Check your solution.

Solution

$\frac{6}{x+5} = \frac{x}{6}$	Write original equation.
$36 = x^2 + 5x$	Cross products property
$0 = x^2 + 5x - 36$	Subtract 36 from each side.
$0 = (x + 9)(x - 4)$	Factor polynomial.
$x + 9 = 0$ *or* $x - 4 = 0$	Zero-product property
$x = -9$ *or* $x = 4$	Solve for x.

The solutions are -9 and 4.

CHECK **If $x = -9$:** $\frac{6}{-9+5} \stackrel{?}{=} \frac{-9}{6}$ → $-1.5 = -1.5$ ✓

If $x = 4$: $\frac{6}{4+5} \stackrel{?}{=} \frac{4}{6}$ → $\frac{2}{3} = \frac{2}{3}$ ✓

Example 2 Multiply by the LCD

Solve $\frac{3x}{x+5} - \frac{5}{2} = \frac{5}{x+5}$.

$\frac{3x}{x+5} - \frac{5}{2} = \frac{5}{x+5}$	Write original equation.
$\frac{3x}{x+5} \cdot 2(x+5) - \frac{5}{2} \cdot 2(x+5) = \frac{5}{x+5} \cdot 2(x+5)$	Multiply by LCD.
$\frac{3x \cdot 2\cancel{(x+5)}}{\cancel{x+5}} - \frac{5 \cdot \cancel{2}(x+5)}{\cancel{2}} = \frac{5 \cdot 2\cancel{(x+5)}}{\cancel{x+5}}$	Multiply. Divide out common factors.
$6x - 5x - 25 = 10$	Simplify.
$x - 25 = 10$	Combine like terms.
$x = 35$	Add 25 to each side.

The solution is 35.

Georgia Performance Standards

MM1A3d Solve simple rational equations that result in linear equations or quadratic equations with leading coefficient of 1.

Example 3 Factor to find the LCD

Solve $\frac{4}{x-4} + 1 = \frac{14}{x^2 + x - 20}$. Check your solution.

Solution

Write each denominator in factored form. The LCD is $(x - 4)(x + 5)$.

$$\frac{4}{x-4} + 1 = \frac{14}{x^2 + x - 20}$$

$$\frac{4}{x-4} \cdot (x-4)(x+5) + 1 \cdot (x-4)(x+5) = \frac{14}{(x-4)(x+5)} \cdot (x-4)(x+5)$$

$$\frac{4\cancel{(x-4)}(x+5)}{\cancel{x-4}} + (x-4)(x+5) = \frac{14\cancel{(x-4)}\cancel{(x+5)}}{\cancel{(x-4)}\cancel{(x+5)}}$$

$$4(x+5) + (x^2 + x - 20) = 14$$

$$x^2 + 5x = 14$$

$$x^2 + 5x - 14 = 0$$

$$(x+7)(x-2) = 0$$

$$x + 7 = 0 \text{ or } x - 2 = 0$$

$$x = -7 \text{ or } \quad x = 2$$

The solutions are -7 and 2.

CHECK **If $x = 2$:**

$$\frac{4}{2-4} + 1 \stackrel{?}{=} \frac{14}{2^2 + 2 - 20}$$

$$-1 = -1 \checkmark$$

If $x = -7$:

$$\frac{4}{-7-4} + 1 \stackrel{?}{=} \frac{14}{(-7)^2 - 7 - 20}$$

$$\frac{7}{11} = \frac{7}{11} \checkmark$$

Guided Practice for Examples 1, 2, and 3

Solve the equation. Check your solution.

1. $\frac{-12}{x} = \frac{x - 14}{4}$

2. $\frac{6}{x-3} = \frac{x}{18}$

3. $\frac{x}{x+10} + \frac{1}{5} = \frac{-7}{x+10}$

4. $\frac{x}{x+4} - \frac{4}{x-2} = \frac{11}{x^2 + 2x - 8}$

UNIT 3

LESSON 3.11 **Exercise Set A**

MM1A3d Solve simple rational equations that result in linear equations or quadratic equations with leading coefficient of 1.

Solve the equation. Check your solution.

1. $\frac{x}{27} = \frac{3}{x}$

2. $\frac{3}{x} = \frac{2}{x + 4}$

3. $\frac{4}{x - 7} = \frac{2}{x}$

4. $\frac{10}{x + 2} = \frac{7}{x - 4}$

5. $\frac{-5}{x + 4} = \frac{x}{x + 4}$

6. $\frac{8}{x + 8} = \frac{x}{x + 2}$

7. $\frac{-1}{x + 2} = \frac{x}{x + 2}$

8. $\frac{2}{x} = \frac{x + 1}{2x + 5}$

9. $\frac{x - 3}{x + 2} = \frac{-2}{x + 2}$

Find the LCD of the rational expressions in the equation.

10. $\frac{7x}{x - 3} + 4 = \frac{x + 1}{x - 3}$

11. $\frac{3}{2x - 2} + 4 = \frac{7x}{x - 1}$

12. $\frac{7}{x - 2} + 1 = \frac{4}{x - 3}$

Solve the equation. Check your solution.

13. $\frac{2x}{x + 4} - 3 = \frac{-12}{x + 4}$

14. $\frac{3}{x + 2} + 5 = \frac{4}{x + 2}$

15. $\frac{2x}{x - 1} - 2 = \frac{10}{x + 2}$

16. Stain Mixing You are staining a coffee table you just made. After testing some sample pieces of wood, you decide that you want a mix of a yellow stain and a red stain. You estimate that you want a mix that contains 75% of the yellow stain. You only have 1 pint that is made up of equal parts of the two stains. How many pints of the yellow stain do you have to add to the current mixture?

17. Wallpaper Working together, an expert wallpaper hanger and an assistant can hang the wallpaper in a room in 3 hours. The assistant can hang the wallpaper in one and one-half times the time it takes the expert wallpaper hanger to hang the wallpaper alone. Let x represent the time (in hours) that the assistant can hang the wallpaper alone.

a. Copy and complete the table.

Person	Fraction of room papered each hour	Time (hours)	Fraction of room papered
Assistant	$\frac{1}{x}$	3	?
Expert	?	3	?

b. *Explain* why the sum of the expressions in the last column must be 1.

c. Write a rational equation that you can use to find the amount of time it takes the assistant to wallpaper the room alone. Then solve the equation.

LESSON 3.11 **Exercise Set B**

MM1A3d Solve simple rational equations that result in linear equations or quadratic equations with leading coefficient of 1.

Solve the equation. Check your solution.

1. $\frac{14}{2-x} = \frac{2}{x}$

2. $\frac{x+2}{x+1} - x = \frac{-6}{x+1}$

3. $\frac{2}{x-4} + 2 = \frac{6}{x-4}$

4. $\frac{10}{x+2} = \frac{4}{x-1}$

5. $\frac{3x+2}{3x-5} = \frac{x}{x-1}$

6. $\frac{8}{x-4} = \frac{2}{x-2}$

7. $\frac{1}{3x} + \frac{1}{x+4} = \frac{1}{3}$

8. $\frac{x}{x-5} + 3 = \frac{4x-3}{x-4}$

9. $\frac{7}{x-2} - \frac{4}{x+2} = \frac{3}{x^2-4}$

10. $\frac{2x+3}{x+2} + 3x = \frac{-2}{x+2}$

11. $\frac{2}{x+3} - \frac{6}{2x+6} = \frac{x}{2}$

12. $\frac{5}{2x-2} = \frac{3}{x-1} + \frac{x+3}{8}$

13. $1 - \frac{x-1}{(x+1)^2} = \frac{1}{x+1}$

14. $2x + \frac{3x-4}{x-2} = \frac{2}{x-2}$

15. $\frac{x+2}{x-4} - \frac{2x}{x-1} = \frac{18}{x^2-5x+4}$

16. Let a and b be real numbers. The solutions of the equation $ax + b = \frac{24}{x+3} - 1$ are -9 and 9. What are the values of a and b?

17. Paint Mixing You have a 6-pint mixture of paint that is made up of equal amounts of red paint and yellow paint. To create a certain shade of orange, you need a paint mixture that is 30% red. How many pints of yellow paint do you need to add to the mixture?

18. Roofing Working together, an expert roofer and an assistant can complete the roof on a certain building in 24 hours. The expert roofer can roof the building alone in about three fifths of the time it takes the assistant to roof the building alone. Let x represent the time (in hours) that the expert can roof the building alone.

a. Copy and complete the table.

Person	Fraction of roof completed each hour	Time (hours)	Fraction of roof completed
Expert	$\frac{1}{x}$	24	?
Assistant	?	24	?

b. *Explain* why the sum of the expressions in the last column must be 1.

c. Write a rational equation that you can use to find the time that the expert can roof the building alone. Then solve the equation.

d. How long does it take the assistant to roof the building alone?

UNIT 3

LESSON 3.12

Use Graphs of Functions

Georgia Performance Standards: MM1A1g, MM1A1i

Goal Find average rates of change and use graphs to solve equations.

Vocabulary

For a function f, the **average rate of change** between any two points $(x_1, f(x_1))$ and $(x_2, f(x_2))$ is the slope of the line through the two points.

Average rate of change of f from x_1 to $x_2 = \dfrac{f(x_2) - f(x_1)}{x_2 - x_1}$.

Example 1 Find an average rate of change

Find the average rate of change of $f(x) = x^3 - 3x$ from x_1 to x_2.

a. $x_1 = -2, x_2 = 0$

b. $x_1 = 0, x_2 = 1$

Solution

a. Average rate of change of f from $x_1 = -2$ to $x_2 = 0$:

$$\frac{f(x_2) - f(x_1)}{x_2 - x_1} = \frac{f(0) - f(-2)}{0 - (-2)}$$

$$= \frac{0 - (-2)}{2}$$

$$= 1$$

b. Average rate of change of f from $x_1 = 0$ to $x_2 = 1$:

$$\frac{f(x_2) - f(x_1)}{x_2 - x_1} = \frac{f(1) - f(0)}{1 - 0}$$

$$= \frac{-2 - 0}{1}$$

$$= -2$$

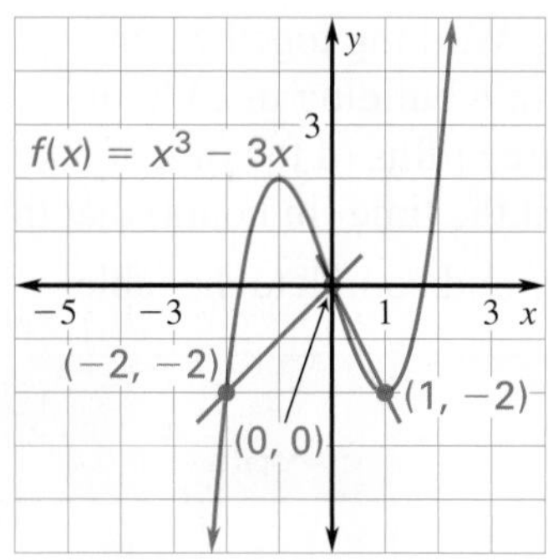

Guided Practice for Example 1

Find the average rate of change of the function from x_1 to x_2.

1. $f(x) = x^3 - 1; x_1 = -2, x_2 = 0$

2. $f(x) = \frac{1}{2}x^2; x_1 = 0, x_2 = 2$

UNIT 3

Georgia Performance Standards

MM1A1g Explore rates of change, comparing constant rates of change (i.e., slope) versus variable rates of change. Compare rates of change of linear, quadratic, square root, and other function families. 

MM1A1i Understand that any equation in x can be interpreted as the equation $f(x) = g(x)$, and interpret the solutions of the equation as the x-value(s) of the intersection point(s) of the graphs of $y = f(x)$ and $y = g(x)$. 

Example 2 Compare average rates of change

Compare the average rates of change of the functions from $x_1 = 0$ to $x_2 = 4$.

a. $f(x) = 2x$ **b.** $g(x) = \sqrt{x}$ **c.** $h(x) = -\frac{1}{8}x^2 + 2$

Solution

a. The function is linear, so the rate of change, 2, is constant. The average rate of change from $x_1 = 0$ to $x_2 = 4$ is 2.

b. Average rate of change of g from $x_1 = 0$ to $x_2 = 4$:

$$\frac{g(x_2) - g(x_1)}{x_2 - x_1} = \frac{g(4) - g(0)}{4 - 0} = \frac{2 - 0}{4} = \frac{1}{2}$$

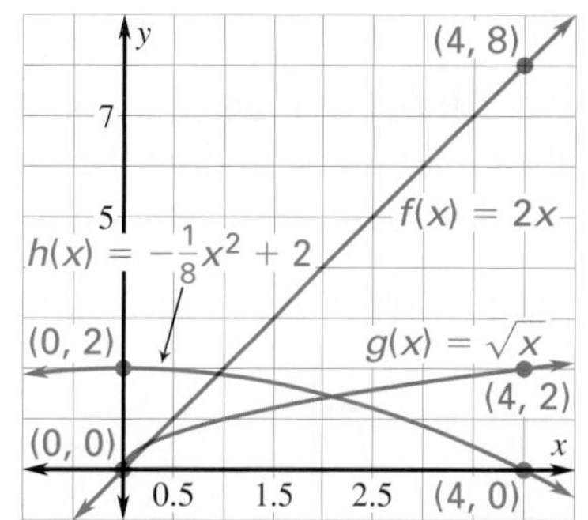

c. Average rate of change of h from $x_1 = 0$ to $x_2 = 4$:

$$\frac{h(x_2) - h(x_1)}{x_2 - x_1} = \frac{h(4) - h(0)}{4 - 0} = \frac{0 - 2}{4} = -\frac{1}{2}$$

The average rate of change of h is negative because the function is decreasing on the interval. The average rates of change of f and g are positive because the functions are increasing on the intervals. The graph of $f(x) = 2x$ is steeper, so its average rate of change is greater.

Guided Practice for Example 2

In Exercises 3 and 4, find the average rate of change of the function from $x_1 = -1$ to $x_2 = 2$.

3. $f(x) = -2\sqrt{x + 2}$

4. $g(x) = \frac{1}{4}(x - 2)^3$

5. *Compare* the average rates of change from Exercises 3 and 4.

UNIT 1

Example 3 Solve an equation using a graph

Solve $\frac{1}{2}x^3 = \frac{1}{2}x$.

Solution

METHOD 1 Solve the equation by factoring.

$\frac{1}{2}x^3 = \frac{1}{2}x$	Write original equation.
$\frac{1}{2}x^3 - \frac{1}{2}x = 0$	Subtract $\frac{1}{2}x$ from each side.
$\frac{1}{2}x(x^2 - 1) = 0$	Factor out $\frac{1}{2}x$.
$\frac{1}{2}x(x + 1)(x - 1) = 0$	Difference of two squares pattern
$\frac{1}{2}x = 0$ *or* $x + 1 = 0$ *or* $x - 1 = 0$	Zero-product property
$x = 0$ *or* $x = -1$ *or* $x = 1$	Solve equations.

The solutions are 0, −1, and 1.

METHOD 2 If an equation cannot be easily solved algebraically, you can solve the equation by finding the intersection of two graphs. The solution will be the x-values of the intersection points.

Graph both sides of the equation and find the points of intersection.

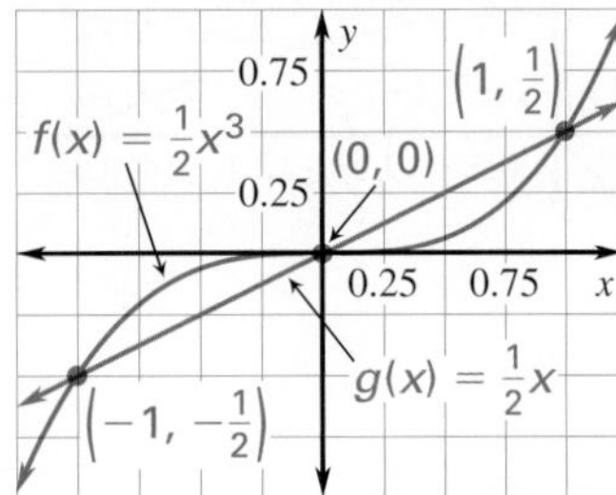

The solutions are 0, −1, and 1.

Guided Practice for Example 3

Solve the equation by graphing. If necessary, use a graphing calculator and round your answer to the nearest hundredth.

6. $\sqrt{x - 1} = x - 3$

7. $\frac{1}{2}x^3 + x^2 = -x$

8. $\frac{1}{3}x^3 = -\frac{1}{2}x + 2$

9. $\sqrt{x + 5} = x^2 - 3$

LESSON 3.12

Exercise Set A

MM1A1g Explore rates of change, comparing constant rates of change (i.e., slope) versus variable rates of change. Compare rates of change of linear, quadratic, square root, and other function families.

MM1A1i Understand that any equation in x can be interpreted as the equation $f(x) = g(x)$, and interpret the solutions of the equation as the x-value(s) of the intersection point(s) of the graphs of $y = f(x)$ and $y = g(x)$.

Find the average rate of change of the function from x_1 to x_2.

1. $f(x) = -3x + 15; x_1 = 0, x_2 = 2$
2. $f(x) = 2x + 8; x_1 = -1, x_2 = 4$
3. $f(x) = -\sqrt{x - 2} + 4; x_1 = 2, x_2 = 11$
4. $f(x) = -\sqrt{x + 1} + 2; x_1 = 0, x_2 = 8$

Compare **the average rates of change of the functions from x_1 to x_2.**

5. $f(x) = x^2 + 12x - 3, g(x) = 7\sqrt{16x}; x_1 = 0, x_2 = 4$
6. $f(x) = x^3 - 2x^2 - x, g(x) = 12x + 5; x_1 = -1, x_2 = 5$
7. **Error Analysis** *Describe* and correct the student's error in finding the average rate of change of $f(x) = x^3 + 2x^2$ from $x_1 = -1$ to $x_2 = 0$.

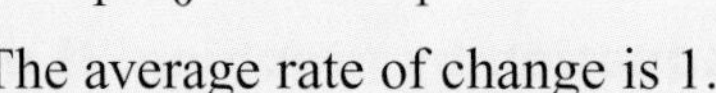

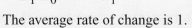

$$\frac{f(0) - f(-1)}{-1 - 0} = \frac{0 - 1}{-1} = 1$$

The average rate of change is 1.

Solve the equation by graphing. If necessary, use a graphing calculator and round your answer to the nearest hundredth.

8. $x^2 + 1 = -x + 3$
9. $\frac{1}{3}x^3 + x = -\frac{1}{8}x^2$
10. $\sqrt{x - 1} = x^3 - 7$
11. $2\sqrt{x} + 1 = \frac{1}{4}(x^2 + x)$
12. $x^3 - \sqrt{2} = 2x$
13. $-\sqrt{x + 10} = x^2 - 7$
14. **Multiple Choice** The graphs of $f(x)$ and $g(x)$ intersect at the points $(-1, 3)$ and $(4, -2)$. What are the solutions of the equation $f(x) = g(x)$?

A. -2 and -1 **B.** -2 and 3 **C.** -1 and 4 **D.** -1 and 3

15. **Multiple Representations** Two objects are thrown upward at the same time. One is thrown from a height of 6 feet with an initial vertical velocity of 64 feet per second. The other is thrown from a height of 20 feet with an initial vertical velocity of 48 feet per second.

    a. Writing Functions Write functions $f(t)$ and $g(t)$ for the height (in feet) t seconds after each was thrown.

    b. Drawing a Graph Graph the functions on the same graph.

    c. Interpreting a Solution Solve $f(t) = g(t)$. Interpret the solution in the context of the problem.

UNIT 3

LESSON 3.12

Exercise Set B

MM1A1g Explore rates of change, comparing constant rates of change (i.e., slope) versus variable rates of change. Compare rates of change of linear, quadratic, square root, and other function families.

MM1A1i Understand that any equation in *x* can be interpreted as the equation $f(x) = g(x)$, and interpret the solutions of the equation as the *x*-value(s) of the intersection point(s) of the graphs of $y = f(x)$ and $y = g(x)$.

Find the average rate of change of the function from x_1 to x_2.

1. $f(x) = -\frac{2}{3}x + 5;\ x_1 = -5, x_2 = 3$

2. $f(x) = -x^2 + 8x - 4;\ x_1 = 0, x_2 = 4$

3. $f(x) = 1 - \sqrt{x + 3};\ x_1 = 1, x_2 = 6$

4. $f(x) = 2 - \sqrt{x + 1};\ x_1 = 3, x_2 = 7$

***Compare* the average rates of change of the functions from x_1 to x_2.**

5. $f(x) = 5x + 3,\ g(x) = 6\sqrt{9x + 9};\ x_1 = 0, x_2 = 3$

6. $f(x) = x^2 + 8x,\ g(x) = x^3 - x^2 + 4;\ x_1 = -1, x_2 = 4$

7. **Open-Ended** For the function $f(x) = -x^3 + 5x^2$, state values of x_1 and x_2 so that the average rate of change from x_1 to x_2 is (a) positive and (b) negative.

Solve the equation by graphing. If necessary, use a graphing calculator and round your answer to the nearest hundredth.

8. $14 - x^2 = -\sqrt{x}$

9. $-x^3 + x = \frac{3}{2}x^2$

10. $-\sqrt{x + 4} - 2 = x^3$

11. $\sqrt{x - 2} = x^2 + 2$

In Exercises 12–14, complete the statement.

12. The equation $f(x) = g(x)$ has __?__ solution(s) when the graphs of $f(x)$ and $g(x)$ do not intersect.

13. If a cubic equation has a maximum in the second quadrant and a minimum in the fourth quadrant, then the sign of the average rate of change from the maximum to the minimum is __?__.

14. If the graphs of two equations intersect at (a, b) and (c, d), then the average rates of change for both equations are the same from $x_1 =$ __?__ to $x_2 =$ __?__.

15. **Profit** The profit P (in thousands of dollars) of a company from 1997 to 2007 can be approximated by $P = 0.4t^3 - 4t^2 + 55.6$ where t represents the year, with $t = 0$ corresponding to 1997.

a. Use a graphing calculator to graph the function.

b. Find the average rate of change of the function from 2004 to 2007. Interpret your answer in the context of the problem.

c. Find the three-year time periods when the average rate of change was the most positive and the most negative.

LESSON 3.13

Use Sequences

Georgia Performance Standards: MM1A1f

Goal Write terms of sequences and use terms to write rules.

Vocabulary

A **sequence** is a function whose domain is a set of consecutive whole numbers. If a domain is not specified, it is understood that the domain starts with 1.

The values in the range are called the **terms** of the sequence.

Domain:	1	2	3	4 . . . n	relative position of each term
	↓	↓	↓	↓ ↓	
Range:	a_1	a_2	a_3	$a_4 \ldots a_n$	terms of the sequence

A sequence can be specified by an equation, or a *rule*.

Example 1 Write terms of a sequence

Write the first six terms of the sequence. Identify the domain and range.

a. $a_n = 2n - 3$

b. $a_n = (-2)^{n+1}$

Solution

a.
$a_1 = 2(1) - 3 = -1$ 1st term
$a_2 = 2(2) - 3 = 1$ 2nd term
$a_3 = 2(3) - 3 = 3$ 3rd term
$a_4 = 2(4) - 3 = 5$ 4th term
$a_5 = 2(5) - 3 = 7$ 5th term
$a_6 = 2(6) - 3 = 9$ 6th term

Domain: 1, 2, 3, 4, 5, 6

Range: −1, 1, 3, 5, 7, 9

b.
$a_1 = (-2)^{1+1} = 4$ 1st term
$a_2 = (-2)^{2+1} = -8$ 2nd term
$a_3 = (-2)^{3+1} = 16$ 3rd term
$a_4 = (-2)^{4+1} = -32$ 4th term
$a_5 = (-2)^{5+1} = 64$ 5th term
$a_6 = (-2)^{6+1} = -128$ 6th term

Domain: 1, 2, 3, 4, 5, 6

Range: 4, −8, 16, −32, 64, −128

Guided Practice for Example 1

Write the first six terms of the sequence. Identify the domain and range.

1. $a_n = n - 3$

2. $a_n = (-3)^{n-1}$

3. $a_n = \frac{n}{n+2}$

UNIT 3

Georgia Performance Standards

MM1A1f Recognize sequences as functions with domains that are whole numbers.

Example 2 Write rules for sequences

Describe the pattern, write the next term, and write a rule for the nth term of the sequence (a) −1, −4, −9, −16, . . . and (b) 2, 6, 12, 20, ...

Solution

a. You can write the terms as $-1^2, -2^2, -3^2, -4^2, \ldots$. The next term is $a_5 = -5^2 = -25$. A rule for the nth term is $a_n = -n^2$.

b. You can write the terms as 1(2), 2(3), 3(4), 4(5), ... The next term is 5(6) = 30. A rule for the nth term is $a_n = n(n + 1)$.

Example 3 Solve a multi-step problem

Stacking Wood You stack logs 6 rows tall. The top three rows are shown. Write a rule for the number of logs in each row. Then graph the sequence.

Solution

STEP 1 **Make** a table showing the number of logs in the first three rows. Let a_n represent the number of logs in row n.

Row, *n*	1	2	3
Number of logs, a_n	$2 = 1^2 + 1$	$5 = 2^2 + 1$	$10 = 3^2 + 1$

STEP 2 **Write** a rule for the number of logs in each row. From the table, you can see that $a_n = n^2 + 1$.

STEP 3 **Plot** the points (1, 2), (2, 5), (3, 10), (4, 17), (5, 26), and (6, 37). The graph is shown at the right. Notice that the graph is a function.

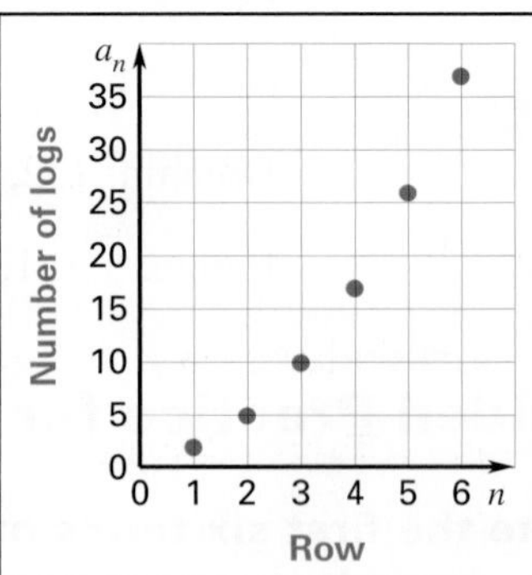

Guided Practice for Examples 2 and 3

4. For the sequence −1, −8, −27, −64, . . ., describe the pattern, write the next term, and write a rule for the nth term.

5. In Example 3, suppose there are 8 rows of logs. How many logs are in the 8th row?

LESSON 3.13

Exercise Set A

MM1A1f Recognize sequences as functions with domains that are whole numbers.

Write the first six terms of the sequence.

1. $a_n = 2n$

2. $a_n = n + 4$

3. $a_n = 3 - n$

4. $a_n = n^2 - 2$

5. $a_n = (n + 1)^2$

6. $a_n = (-1)^n$

7. $a_n = (-2)^n$

8. $a_n = \frac{2}{n}$

9. $a_n = \frac{n}{3n + 1}$

For the sequence, describe the pattern, write the next term, and write a rule for the *n*th term.

10. 4, 6, 8, 10, . . .

11. 3, 1, −1, −3, . . .

12. −3, −24, −81, −192, . . .

13. 1, 7, 17, 31, . . .

14. $\frac{1}{2}, \frac{1}{4}, \frac{1}{6}, \frac{1}{8}, \ldots$

15. $-\frac{1}{2}, -\frac{4}{2}, -\frac{9}{2}, -\frac{16}{2}, \ldots$

16. Multiple Choice Which rule gives the total number of circles in the *n*th figure of the pattern shown?

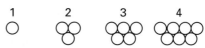

1 2  3 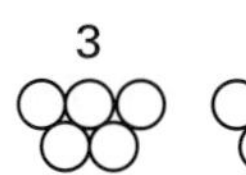 4

A. $a_n = 3n$ **B.** $a_n = n + 1$ **C.** $a_n = 2n - 1$ **D.** $a_n = \frac{n(n + 1)}{2}$

Match the sequence with the graph of its first 6 terms.

17. $a_n = n^2 + 3$

18. $a_n = 2(n + 1)$

19. $a_n = 4n$

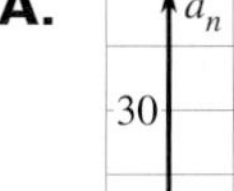

A.

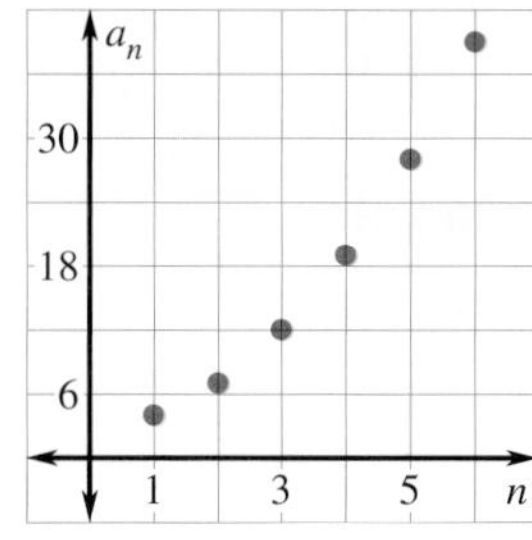

B.

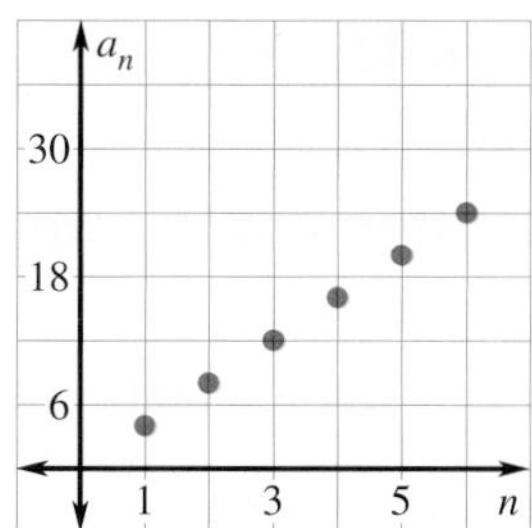

C.

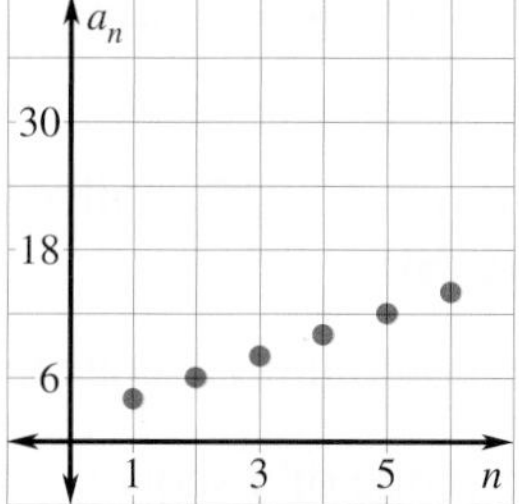

20. Multiple Representations A grocery store employee stacks tissue boxes six layers tall. The top four layers are shown.

a. Making a Table Copy and complete the table.

Layer, n	1	2	3	4
Number of boxes, a_n	?	?	?	?

b. Writing a Rule Write a rule for the number of tissue boxes in each layer.

c. Drawing a Graph Graph the function from part (b) using the domain 1, 2, 3, 4, 5, 6.

LESSON 3.13

Exercise Set B

MM1A1f Recognize sequences as functions with domains that are whole numbers.

Write the first six terms of the sequence.

1. $a_n = -5n$

2. $a_n = 2n^2 + 3$

3. $a_n = 8 - n^2$

4. $a_n = \frac{3 - 2n}{n}$

5. $a_n = n^2(n - 1)$

6. $a_n = (-1)^n(n + 1)$

Find the indicated term of the sequence.

7. $a_n = n(n^2 + 1); a_{10}$

8. $a_n = (-1)^n(3n - 5); a_{25}$

9. $a_n = \frac{-(n + 1)}{n^3 + 1}; a_{12}$

For the sequence, describe the pattern, write the next term, and write a rule for the *n*th term.

10. 7, 19, 31, 43, . . .

11. $-2, 4, -6, 8, \ldots$

12. $-\frac{3}{2}, -\frac{9}{3}, -\frac{27}{4}, -\frac{81}{5}, \ldots$

13. **Error Analysis** *Describe* and correct the student's error in writing a rule for the *n*th term of the sequence $1, -4, 9, -16, \ldots$.

> You can write the terms as $(-1)^{1+1}(1^2), (-1)^{2+1}(2^2), (-1)^{3+1}(3^2), (-1)^{4+1}(4^2)$.
> So, $a_n = (-1)^n(n^2)$. ✗

Graph the sequence.

14. $-1, -3, -5, -7, -9, \ldots$

15. 0, 3, 8, 15, 24, . . .

16. $\frac{2}{1}, \frac{3}{3}, \frac{4}{5}, \frac{5}{7}, \frac{6}{9}, \ldots$

In Exercises 17–19, tell whether the statement is *true* or *false*. If it is false, explain why.

17. The domain of a sequence consists only of whole numbers.

18. The range of a sequence consists only of whole numbers.

19. An input of a sequence may be paired with more than one output.

20. **Building Blocks** A child stacks building blocks as shown at the right.

a. Write the number of blocks in each layer that are visible from the front view of the solid. Repeat for the side view and top view.

b. Write a rule for the number of building blocks a_n visible in each layer n from each view in part (a).

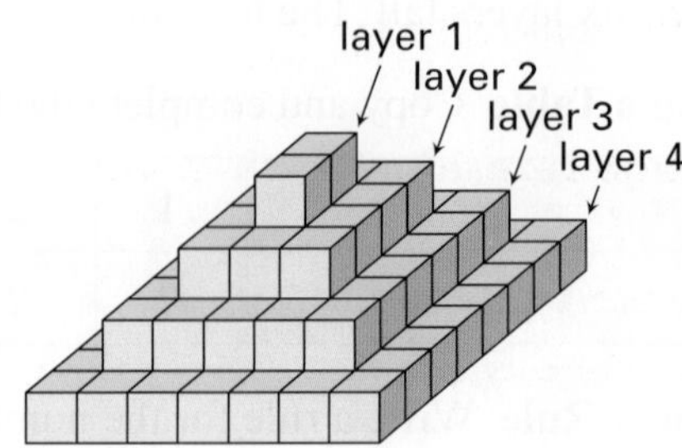

TEST | for Unit 3

1. Graph the function $y = x^3 + 3$ and identify its domain and range. *Compare* the graph with the graph of $y = x^3$.

Factor the expression.

2. $3x^3 - 27x^2 + 81x - 81$

3. $p^3 + 6p^2q + 12pq^2 + 8q^3$

4. Graph the function $y = \sqrt{x + 2}$ and identify its domain and range. *Compare* the graph with the graph of $y = \sqrt{x}$.

Simplify the expression.

5. $\sqrt{12x^5} \cdot \sqrt{6x}$

6. $\sqrt{\frac{15}{2y^2}}$

7. $(6 + \sqrt{6})(6 - 2\sqrt{6})$

Solve the equation. Check for extraneous solutions.

8. $\sqrt{20 - x} = x$

9. $\sqrt{2x - 14} = \sqrt{x + 17}$

10. $3\sqrt{x - 6} + 8 = 32$

11. What are the asymptotes of the graph of $y = \frac{2}{x + 1} - 3$?

Divide.

12. $(2r^2 + 19r + 29) \div (r + 8)$

13. $(6t^2 - 19t + 13) \div (2t - 5)$

Simplify the rational expression. Find the excluded values.

14. $\frac{x - 5}{x^2 + 2x - 35}$

15. $\frac{x^2 - 16}{x^2(x + 4)}$

Find the product or quotient.

16. $\frac{5y}{2y^2 - y - 1} \cdot \frac{2y^2 + 2y - 4}{10y + 20}$

17. $\frac{x^2 + 25}{x + 3} \div \frac{x^2 + 25}{x^2 - 9}$

Find the sum or difference.

18. $\frac{9}{z + 2} + \frac{z}{z + 2}$

19. $\frac{3x + 1}{4x} - \frac{x - 2}{4x}$

20. $\frac{1}{w^2 + 2w - 3} - \frac{1}{w + 3}$

21. What are the solutions of $\frac{x}{x - 5} - 2 = \frac{9}{x - 1}$?

Find the average rate of change of the function from x_1 to x_2.

22. $f(x) = x^3 - 5x^2; x_1 = 0, x_2 = 2$

23. $f(x) = \sqrt{x - 2} + 1; x_1 = 2, x_2 = 6$

Write the first six terms of the sequence.

24. $a_n = 8n - 10$

25. $a_n = n(-1)^n$

UNIT 3

26. Vertical Motion The time t (in seconds) it takes an object dropped from a height h (in feet) to reach the ground is given by the function $t = \frac{1}{4}\sqrt{h}$.

A rock is dropped from a bridge 225 feet above the water. How long does it take the rock to reach the water?

27. Population The resident population P (in thousands) of Georgia from 2001 through 2005 can be modeled by $P = 7854 + 533\sqrt{x}$ where x is the number of years since 2000. When was the resident population in Georgia about 8,920,000 people?

28. Baseball You order baseball tickets from an online vendor for $46 each. The total cost of your order includes a $5 processing fee.

a. Write an equation that gives the average cost C (in dollars per ticket) as a function of the number t of tickets ordered.

b. Rewrite the equation in the form $y = \frac{a}{x - h} + k$.

29. Flying An airplane flies 480 miles against the wind to another city and then returns with the wind. The speed of the wind is a constant 15 miles per hour.

a. Write an equation that gives the total flying time t (in hours) as a function of the airplane's average speed r (in miles per hour) in still air.

b. Find the total flying time if the airplane's average speed in still air is 300 miles per hour.

Performance Task

Payroll

The payroll (in millions of dollars) of a software company from 1990 through 2007 can be modeled by $P(x) = 5\sqrt{x} + 1$ where x is the number of years since 1990.

a. Write a radical expression for the payroll in 2002. Simplify the expression.

b. In what year was the payroll about 21 million dollars?

c. Suppose that a hardware company's payroll from 1990 to 2007 can be modeled by $Q(x) = -\frac{1}{100}x^2 + 16.81$ where x is the number of years since 1990. Graph both payroll functions on the same graph. Find the solution of $P(x) = Q(x)$ and interpret its meaning in the context of the problem.

d. In which three-year time period was the average rate of change the greatest for the software company? In which three-year time period was the average rate of change the most negative for the hardware company?

UNIT 4
Geometry: Reasoning and Proof, Lines, and Congruent Triangles

4.1 Apply the Distance and Midpoint Formulas (MM1G1a, MM1G1c)

4.2 Use Inductive Reasoning (MM1G2a)

4.3 Analyze Conditional Statements (MM1G2b)

4.4 Apply Deductive Reasoning (MM1G2a)

4.5 Prove Statements About Segments and Angles (MM1G2a)

4.6 Prove Angle Pair Relationships (MM1G2a)

4.7 Prove Theorems About Perpendicular Lines (MM1G1b)

4.8 Prove Triangles Congruent by SSS (MM1G1e, MM1G3c)

4.9 Prove Triangles Congruent by SAS and HL (MM1G3c)

4.10 Prove Triangles Congruent by ASA and AAS (MM1G3c)

Georgia Performance Standards

MM1G1d Understand the distance formula as an application of the Pythagorean theorem.

Investigating Math Activity

The Pythagorean Theorem and the Distance Formula

Use before Lesson 4.1

Materials graph paper

Question

How can you use the Pythagorean Theorem to find the distance between two points in a coordinate plane?

Recall that the Pythagorean Theorem states that in a right triangle, the square of the length of the hypotenuse is equal to the sum of the squares of the lengths of the legs.

Explore

Find the distance between *A*(−2, −1) and *B*(3, 2) in a coordinate plane.

STEP 1 Draw a right triangle

To find the distance between points A and B, draw a right triangle as shown. Label point $C(3, -1)$.

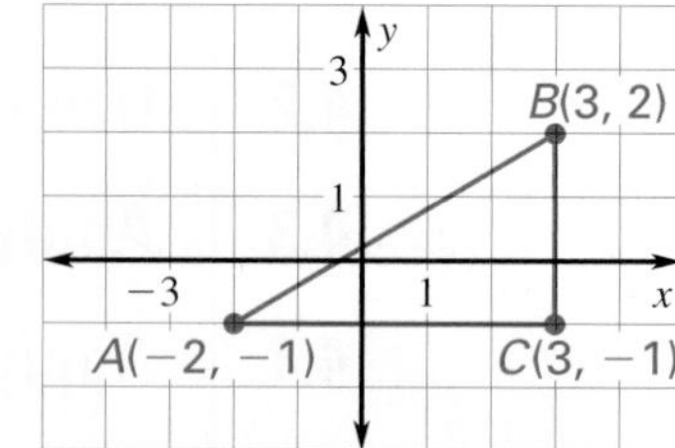

STEP 2 Find the lengths of the legs

Points A and C lie on a horizontal line. The distance between points A and C is the absolute value of the difference of their x-coordinates. Points B and C lie on a vertical line. The distance between points B and C is the absolute value of the difference of their y-coordinates. The lengths of the legs of $\triangle ABC$ are:

$AC = |3 - (-2)| = 5$ $\qquad$ $BC = |2 - (-1)| = 3$

STEP 3 Find *AB*

Because AB is the length of the hypotenuse of the triangle, use the Pythagorean Theorem to find AB.

$(AB)^2 = (AC)^2 + (BC)^2$ Pythagorean Theorem

$AB = \sqrt{(AC)^2 + (BC)^2}$ Take positive square root of each side.

$AB = \sqrt{5^2 + 3^2} = \sqrt{34}$ Substitute 5 for AC and 3 for BC and simplify.

Draw Conclusions

Use the Pythagorean Theorem to find the distance between the points.

1. $A(-3, 2), B(4, 6)$ **2.** $A(6, 3), B(5, 7)$ **3.** $A(-2, 1), B(2, 5)$

4. **Reasoning** Use your observations to write a formula that can be used to find the distance between any two points (x_1, y_1) and (x_2, y_2) in a coordinate plane.

UNIT 4

LESSON 4.1

Apply the Distance and Midpoint Formulas

Georgia Performance Standards: MM1G1a, MM1G1c

Goal Use the distance and midpoint formulas.

Vocabulary

The Distance Formula

The distance d between any two points (x_1, y_1) and (x_2, y_2) is
$d = \sqrt{(x_2 - x_1)^2 + (y_2 - y_1)^2}$.

The **midpoint** of a line segment is the point on the segment that is equidistant from the endpoints. The midpoint of a segment divides the segment into two congruent segments.

The Midpoint Formula

The midpoint M of the line segment with endpoints $A(x_1, y_1)$ and
$B(x_2, y_2)$ is $\left(\frac{x_1 + x_2}{2}, \frac{y_1 + y_2}{2}\right)$.

Example 1 Find the distance between two points

Find the distance between (3, −2) and (−2, 4).

Solution

Let $(x_1, y_1) = (3, -2)$ and $(x_2, y_2) = (-2, 4)$.

$d = \sqrt{(x_2 - x_1)^2 + (y_2 - y_1)^2}$	Distance formula
$= \sqrt{(-2 - 3)^2 + [4 - (-2)]^2}$	Substitute.
$= \sqrt{(-5)^2 + (6)^2}$	Simplify.
$= \sqrt{61}$	Simplify.

The distance between the points is $\sqrt{61}$ units.

Guided Practice for Example 1

Find the distance between the two points.

1. (5, 2), (3, 8)
2. (−2, 0), (−4, 5)
3. (7, −1), (−5, 3)
4. (4, −1), (−1, 6)

UNIT 4

Georgia Performance Standards

MM1G1a Determine the distance between two points. ☑

MM1G1c Determine the midpoint of a segment. ☑

Example 2 Find a missing coordinate

The distance between (4, 1) and (*a*, −3) is $\sqrt{52}$ units. Find the possible values of *a*.

Solution

Use the distance formula with $d = \sqrt{52}$. Let $(x_1, y_1) = (4, 1)$ and $(x_2, y_2) = (a, -3)$. Then solve for a.

$d = \sqrt{(x_2 - x_1)^2 + (y_2 - y_1)^2}$	Distance formula
$\sqrt{52} = \sqrt{(a - 4)^2 + (-3 - 1)^2}$	Substitute.
$\sqrt{52} = \sqrt{a^2 - 8a + 16 + 16}$	Multiply.
$\sqrt{52} = \sqrt{a^2 - 8a + 32}$	Simplify.
$52 = a^2 - 8a + 32$	Square each side.
$0 = a^2 - 8a - 20$	Write in standard form.
$0 = (a - 10)(a + 2)$	Factor.
$a - 10 = 0$ *or* $a + 2 = 0$	Zero-product property
$a = 10$ *or* $a = -2$	Solve for a.

The value of a is 10 or −2.

Guided Practice for Example 2

5. The distance between (5, 7) and (−3, b) is 17 units. Find the possible values of b.

Example 3 Find a midpoint of a line segment

Find the midpoint of the line segment with endpoints (7, −1) and (5, 7).

Solution

Let $(x_1, y_1) = (7, -1)$ and $(x_2, y_2) = (5, 7)$.

$\left(\frac{x_1 + x_2}{2}, \frac{y_1 + y_2}{2}\right) = \left(\frac{7 + 5}{2}, \frac{-1 + 7}{2}\right)$	Substitute.
$= (6, 3)$	Simplify.

The midpoint of the line segment is (6, 3).

Guided Practice for Example 3

Find the midpoint of the line segment with the given endpoints.

6. (14, 3), (6, 9)

7. (−11, −3), (2, −5)

UNIT 4

LESSON 4.1

Exercise Set A

MM1G1a Determine the distance between two points.

MM1G1c Determine the midpoint of a segment.

Find the distance between the two points.

1. (8, 3), (10, 4) **2.** (2, 7), (5, 6) **3.** (9, 6), (4, 1)

4. (0, 4), (8, −2) **5.** (−5, 3), (1, 2) **6.** (1, −6), (−2, 4)

7. (8, −7), (4, −3) **8.** (−10, −2), (6, 5) **9.** (−1, −8), (−5, −2)

The distance *d* between two points is given. Find the possible values of *b*.

10. $(b, 4), (2, -1); d = 5$ **11.** $(-3, 2), (7, b); d = 10$ **12.** $(3, 2), (b, -9); d = 11$

13. $(4, 1), (5, b); d = \sqrt{17}$ **14.** $(b, 2), (3, -1); d = \sqrt{58}$ **15.** $(-4, b), (5, -2); d = \sqrt{106}$

Find the midpoint of the line segment with the given endpoints.

16. (2, 5), (4, 12) **17.** (−7, 2), (−10, 14) **18.** (−9, −5), (7, −14)

19. (8, −8), (3, 5) **20.** (20, 5), (30, −5) **21.** (−11, 7), (8, −3)

22. Error Analysis *Describe* and correct the error in finding the midpoint of the line segment with endpoints (−15, −4) and (3, 6).

$$\left(\frac{3-(-15)}{2}, \frac{6-(-4)}{2}\right) = (9, 5)$$

23. **Walking Trail** A walking trail follows the path shown on the map. The distance between consecutive grid lines is 1 mile. Find the total distance of the trail from start to finish. Round your answer to the nearest mile.

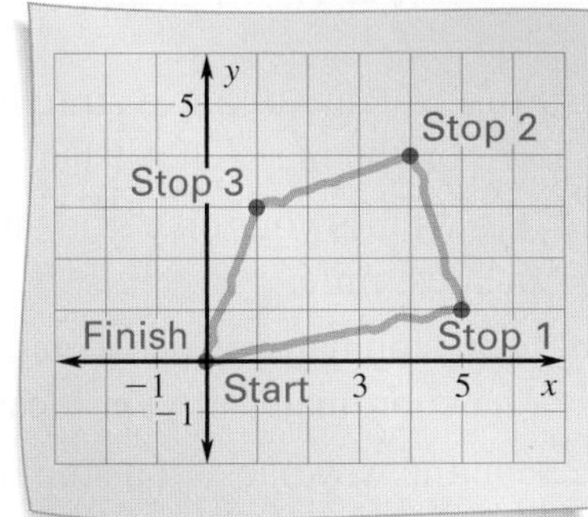

24. **Amusement Park** An amusement park designer wants to place a Ferris wheel midway between the two largest coasters. The distance between consecutive grid lines is 500 feet.

a. Determine the coordinates of where the Ferris wheel should be.

b. How far will the Ferris wheel be from each of the coasters? Round your answer to the nearest foot.

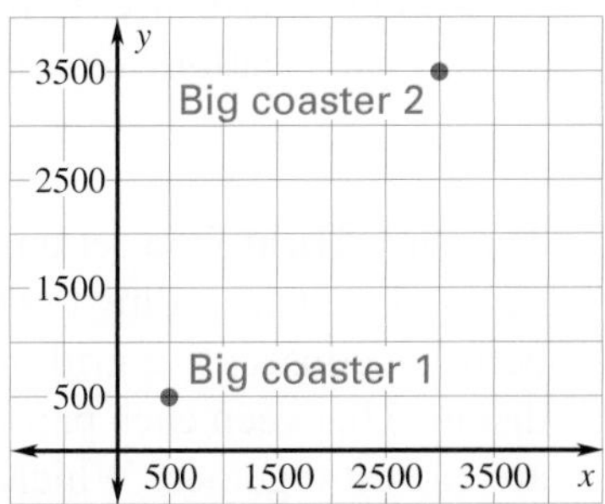

25. **Reading** You have 30 days left to read the books on your summer reading list. As of today, you have read 5 books. By the end of the 30 days, you have to have read 12 books. Assume that the books are all approximately the same length and you read at a relatively constant pace. After 15 days, how many books should you have read?

UNIT 4

LESSON 4.1 **Exercise Set B**

MM1G1a Determine the distance between two points.

MM1G1c Determine the midpoint of a segment.

Find the distance between the two points.

1. $(1, -5), (6, 7)$ **2.** $(-3, -3), (8, -2)$ **3.** $(14, -5), (-3, 8)$

4. $(-11, -4), (9, -2)$ **5.** $(4, -15), (-2, 10)$ **6.** $(1.5, 6), (1.5, -2)$

7. $(4.1, 6), (5.1, 17)$ **8.** $\left(\frac{1}{2}, 8\right), \left(\frac{3}{2}, 5\right)$ **9.** $\left(-\frac{1}{3}, \frac{2}{3}\right), \left(\frac{5}{3}, \frac{1}{3}\right)$

The distance *d* between two points is given. Find the possible values of *b*.

10. $(7, b), (-1, 3); d = 2\sqrt{17}$ **11.** $(4, -2), (b, 9); d = 5\sqrt{5}$ **12.** $(b, 1), (-2, 8); d = 5\sqrt{2}$

13. $(9, -5), (b, 6); d = \sqrt{290}$ **14.** $(-8, b), (1, -3); d = 3\sqrt{10}$ **15.** $(10, -10), (b, -2); d = 2\sqrt{65}$

Find the midpoint of the line segment with the given endpoints.

16. $(-14, 3), (10, -4)$ **17.** $(-11, -6), (16, 22)$ **18.** $(105, -214), (97, 45)$

19. $(3.5, 8), (4, 10.5)$ **20.** $(7.25, -1.5), (2.25, -2)$ **21.** $(-8.4, 3.5), (-2.6, 4.5)$

The midpoint and an endpoint of a line segment are given. Find the other endpoint.

22. Midpoint: $(-4, 6)$
Endpoint: $(2, 1)$

23. Midpoint: $(-3, 3)$
Endpoint: $(-4, -2)$

24. Midpoint: $\left(\frac{3}{2}, 1\right)$
Endpoint: $(5, -7)$

25. Biking You are biking a straight-line distance between the two towns shown on the map. The distance between consecutive grid lines is 1 mile.

a. How far is your bike ride one way? Round your answer to the nearest mile.

b. You stop halfway between the two towns to eat a snack. What are the coordinates of your location?

c. On the way back, you stop one-quarter of the way from your destination to visit a friend. How far are you from your destination? Round your answer to the nearest mile. What are the coordinates of your location? *Explain* how you got your answers.

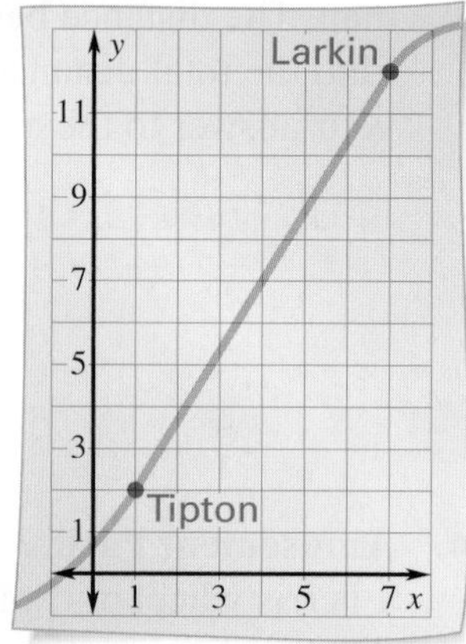

26. Treasure Hunt You set up a treasure hunt with the items placed according to the map shown. The distance between consecutive grid lines is 200 feet. What is the distance between each pair of objects? Which two objects are closest together? Which two objects are farthest apart? Round your answers to the nearest foot.

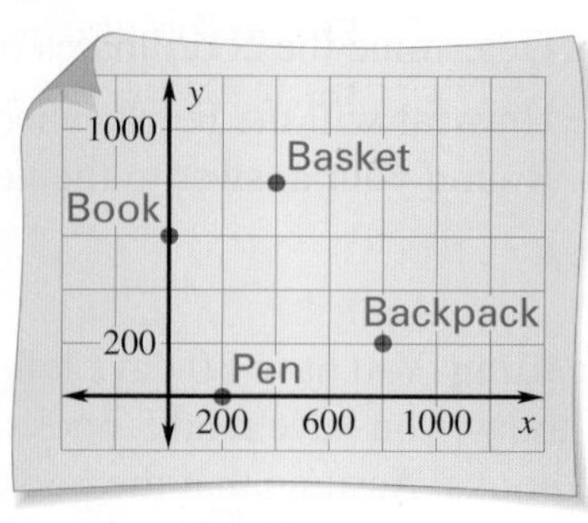

UNIT 4

LESSON 4.2

Use Inductive Reasoning

Georgia Performance Standards: MM1G2a

Goal Describe patterns and use inductive reasoning.

Vocabulary

A **conjecture** is an unproven statement that is based on observations.

You use **inductive reasoning** when you find a pattern in specific cases and then write a conjecture for the general case.

A **counterexample** is a specific case for which a conjecture is false.

Example 1 Describe a visual pattern

Describe how to sketch the next figure in the pattern. Then sketch the next figure.

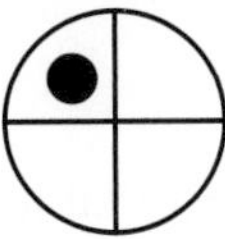 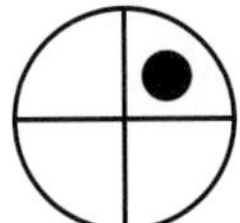 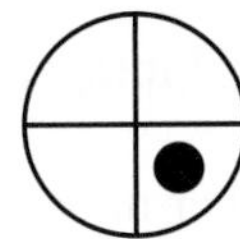

Solution

Each figure looks like the one before it except that it has been rotated 90° clockwise. Sketch the next figure by rotating the last figure 90° clockwise.

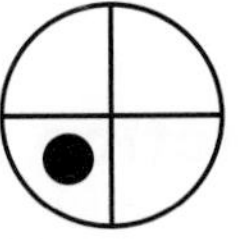

Guided Practice for Example 1

1. Sketch the next figure in the pattern.

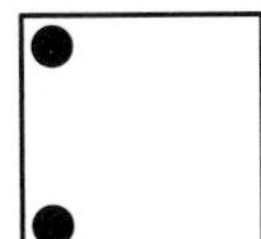  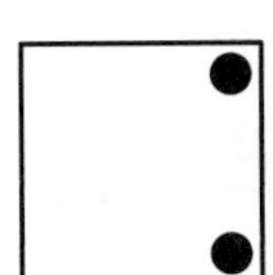

Example 2 Describe a number pattern

Describe the pattern in the numbers 2, 8, 32, 128, . . . and write the next three numbers in the pattern.

Solution

Notice that each number in the pattern is four times the previous number.

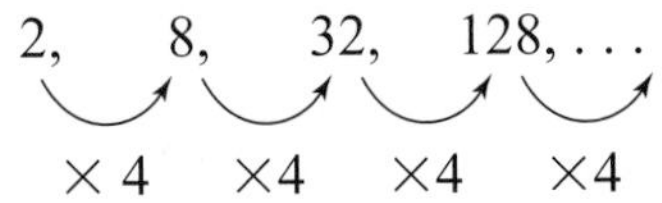

Continue the pattern. The next three numbers are 512, 2048, and 8192.

UNIT 4

Georgia Performance Standards

MM1G2a Use conjecture, inductive reasoning, deductive reasoning, counterexamples, and indirect proof as appropriate.

Guided Practice for Example 2

Describe the pattern in the numbers. Then give the next number in the pattern.

2. 1, 5, 9, 13, . . .

3. 1, 3, 9, 27, 81, . . .

Example 3 Make and test a conjecture

Make and test a conjecture about the product of any two odd integers.

Solution

STEP 1 **Find** a pattern using a few groups of small numbers.

$3 \times 13 = 39$ $\quad$ $5 \times 9 = 45$

$7 \times 21 = 147$ $\quad$ $11 \times 15 = 165$

Conjecture The product of any two odd integers is odd.

STEP 2 **Test** your conjecture using other numbers. For example, test that it works with the pairs 17, 19 and 23, 31.

$17 \times 19 = 323$ ✓ $\quad$ $23 \times 31 = 713$ ✓

Guided Practice for Example 3

4. Make and test a conjecture about the product of any two even integers.

5. Make and test a conjecture about the sum of an even integer and an odd integer.

Example 4 Find a counterexample

Find a counterexample to show that the conjecture is false.

Conjecture All odd numbers are prime.

Solution

To find a counterexample, you need to find an odd number that is a composite number.

The number 9 is odd but is a composite number, not a prime number.

Because a counterexample exists, the conjecture is false.

Guided Practice for Example 4

6. Find a counterexample to show that the conjecture is false.

Conjecture The difference of two positive numbers is always positive.

LESSON 4.2 **Exercise Set A**

MM1G2a Use conjecture, inductive reasoning, deductive reasoning, counterexamples, and indirect proof as appropriate.

Sketch the next figure in the pattern.

1.

2. 

3. 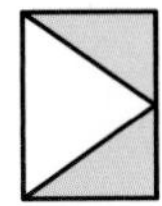 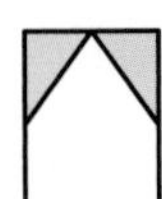 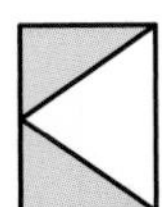

4.  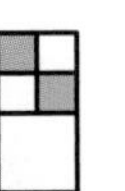 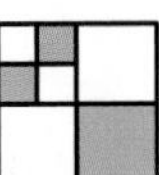 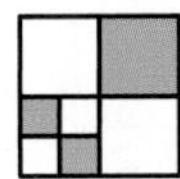

5. 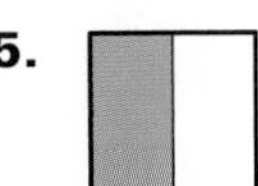 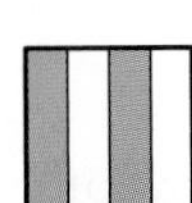 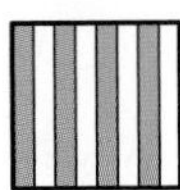

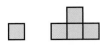

6.  

Describe a pattern in the numbers. Write the next number in the pattern.

7. 113, 224, 335, 446, . . .

8. 4, 6, 9, 13, 18, . . .

9. $\frac{1}{3}, \frac{3}{4}, \frac{5}{5}, \frac{7}{6}, \ldots$

10. $\frac{7}{8}, \frac{6}{7}, \frac{5}{6}, \frac{4}{5}, \ldots$

11. $3, 0, -3, -6, \ldots$

12. 1, 4, 9, 16, . . .

13. 2, 5, 11, 23, . . .

14. 2, 3, 5, 7, 11, . . .

15. **Patterns** Describe a pattern in the numbers. Write the first three numbers in the pattern.

$$\underline{\ ?\ }, \underline{\ ?\ }, \underline{\ ?\ }, \frac{1}{3}, \frac{2}{3}, 1$$

The first three objects in a pattern are shown. How many squares are in the next object?

16. 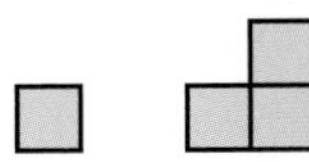 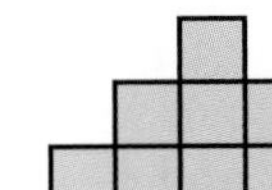

17. 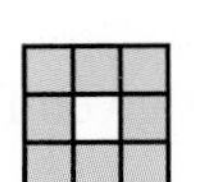 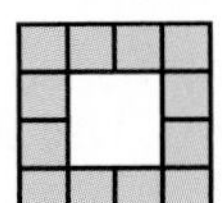 

Show the conjecture is false by finding a counterexample.

18. The quotient of two whole numbers is a whole number.

19. The difference of the absolute value of two numbers is positive, meaning $|a| - |b| > 0$.

20. If $m \neq -1$, then $\frac{m}{m+1} < 1$.

21. The square root of a number x is always less than x.

Exercise Set A *(continued)*

Write a function rule relating x and y.

22.

x	1	2	3
y	1	8	27

23.

x	1	2	3
y	−5	−3	−1

24.

x	1	2	3
y	4	3	2

25.

x	1	2	4
y	1	0.5	0.25

26. **Flowers** Your neighbor is planting yellow Y and pink P carnations in one row of her garden. You notice that the order of the color of the carnations is

Y, P, Y, Y, P, P, Y, Y, Y.

Assuming this pattern continues, predict the color of the next five carnations.

27. **Bacteria Growth** Suppose you are studying bacteria in biology class. The table shows the number of bacteria after n doubling periods. Your teacher asks you to predict the number of bacteria after 7 doubling periods. What would your prediction be?

***n* (periods)**	0	1	2	3	4	5
Billions of bacteria	4	8	16	32	64	128

28. **Chemistry** The half-life of an isotope is the amount of time it takes for half of the isotope to decay. Suppose you begin with 25 grams of Platinum-191, which has a half-life of 3 days. How many days will it take before there is less than 1 gram of the isotope?

29. **Multiple Representations** Use the given function table relating x and y.

x	−2	?	5	?	12	18
y	−5	1	16	25	37	55

a. **Making a Table** Copy and complete the table.

b. **Drawing a Graph** Graph the table of values.

c. **Writing an Equation** *Describe* the pattern in words and then write an equation relating x and y.

UNIT 4

LESSON 4.2

Exercise Set B

MM1G2a Use conjecture, inductive reasoning, deductive reasoning, counterexamples, and indirect proof as appropriate.

Sketch the next figure in the pattern.

1.

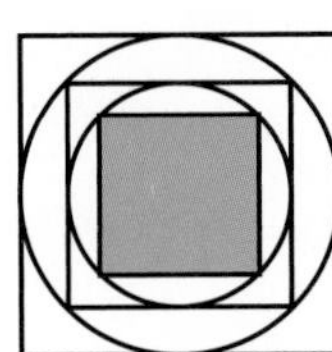 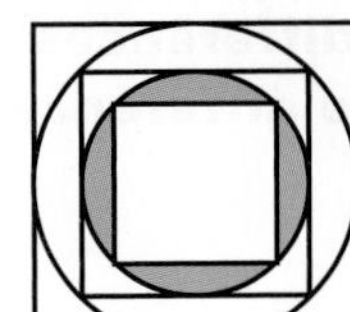 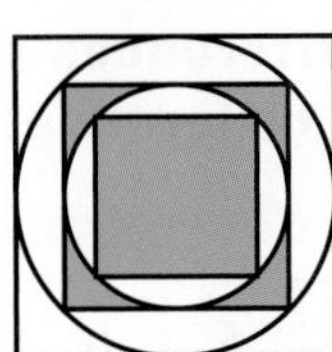 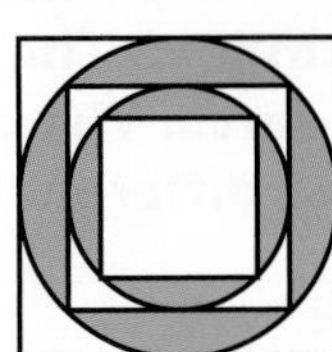

2.

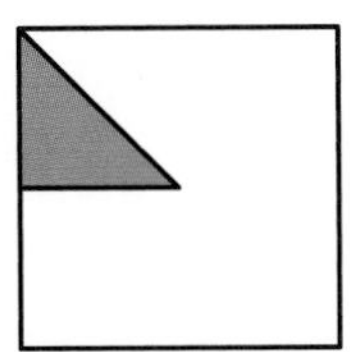 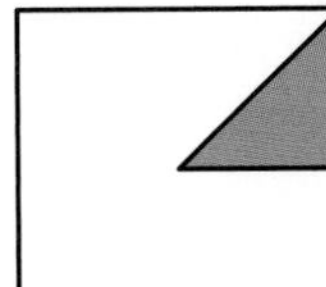 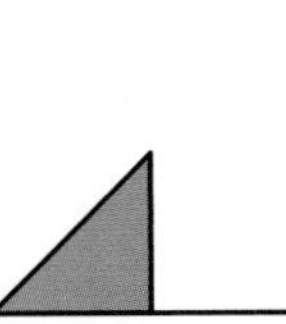 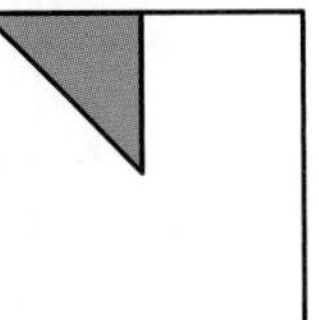 

3.

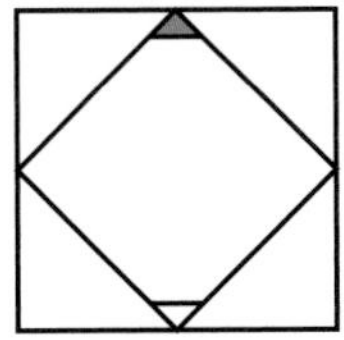 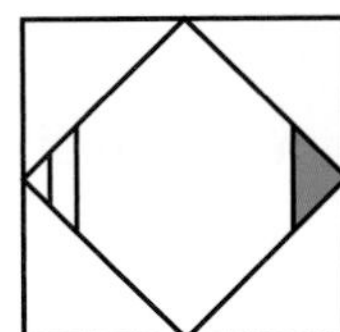 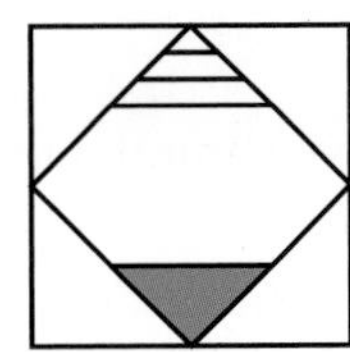 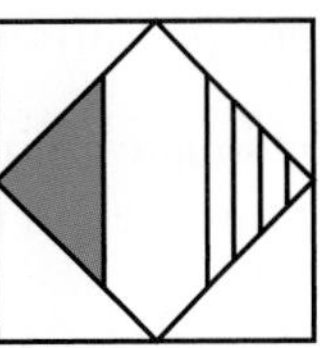

4.

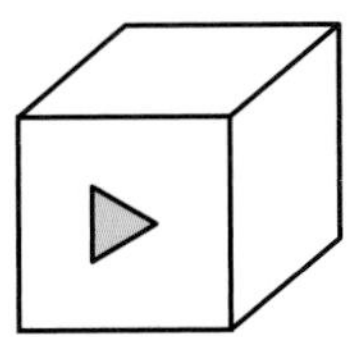 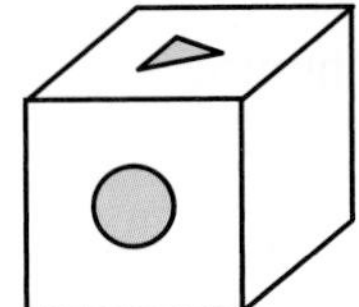  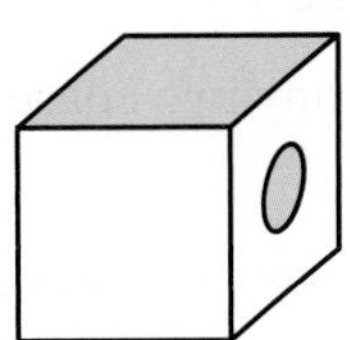

Describe **a pattern in the numbers. Write the next number in the pattern.**

5. $-5, 7, -9, 11, -13, \dots$

6. $22, 21, 19, 16, 12, \dots$

7. $5.1, -6.2, 7.3, -8.4, \dots$

8. $100, 101, 98, 103, 96, 105, \dots$

9. $\frac{10}{11}, \frac{9}{10}, \frac{8}{9}, \frac{7}{8}, \dots$

10. $-\frac{1}{2}, \frac{3}{3}, -\frac{5}{4}, \frac{7}{5}, \dots$

11. $-1, 1, 5, 13, 29, \dots$

12. $1.1, 3.3, 13.2, 66, 396, \dots$

13. $40, 35, 25, 10, \dots$

14. $1, 2, 6, 15, \dots$

15. $3, 30, 15, 150, \dots$

16. $3, \frac{3}{2}, \frac{3}{8}, \frac{3}{48}, \dots$

Describe **a pattern in the numbers and write the next three numbers in the pattern. Then describe a different pattern in the numbers and write the next three numbers in the pattern.**

17. $1, 2, 4, \dots$

18. $3, 6, 12, \dots$

19. $1, 4, 8, \dots$

UNIT 4

Exercise Set B *(continued)*

In Exercises 20 and 21, complete the conjecture based on the pattern you observe in the table. The table shows the squares of several natural numbers. The first differences are the differences of consecutive squares. The second differences are the differences of consecutive first differences.

Whole Numbers	1	2	3	4	5	6	7	8
Squares	1	4	9	16	25	36	49	64
First Differences	3	5	7	9	11	13	15	
Second Differences	2	2	2	2	2	2		

20. **Conjecture** For squares of consecutive natural numbers, each first difference is _?_ the previous first difference.

21. **Conjecture** For squares of consecutive natural numbers, each second difference is _?_ the previous second difference.

Show the conjecture is false by finding a counterexample.

22. The sum of the squares of any two consecutive squared natural numbers is an even number.

23. The sum of the squares of any two squared natural numbers is an odd number.

For the given ordered pairs, write a function rule relating *x* and *y*.

24. $(1, -3), (2, -4), (3, -5), (4, -6)$

25. $(1, 4), (2, 9), (3, 16), (4, 25)$

26. **Circumference** A circular pond has a circumference of 280 feet. You are going to install a fence around the pond, 7 feet from the water's edge. You need to know how much fencing to buy.

a. First, explore a pattern of the relationship between a circle's radius and its circumference by using the circumference formula to complete the following table.

Radius	1	2	3	4	5
Circumference	2π	4π	?	?	?
First Differences	2π	?	?	?	

b. Based on the table, make a conjecture about how the circumference of a circle changes with each 1 unit increase in its radius.

c. Use your conjecture to determine the length of fencing you need to the nearest foot.

UNIT 4

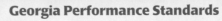

Georgia Performance Standards

MM1G2a Use conjecture, inductive reasoning, deductive reasoning, counterexamples, and indirect proof as appropriate.

Technology Activity

Statistics for Inductive Reasoning

Use after Lesson 4.2

Question

How can you use technology and inductive reasoning to predict sales based on money spent on advertising?

Example

The table shows the annual sales (in thousands of dollars) and the amount (in thousands of dollars) a company spent on advertising for several years. Use a graphing calculator and inductive reasoning to predict the annual sales if the company spends $3700 next year on advertising.

Advertising	2.4	3.5	2.8	3.0	4.0	3.2
Sales	46	59	51	55	65	58

STEP 1 **Create a scatter plot of the data.**
Use a graphing calculator to create a scatter plot of the data, with an appropriate viewing window. Use the money spent on advertising for the x-values and the annual sales for the y-values.

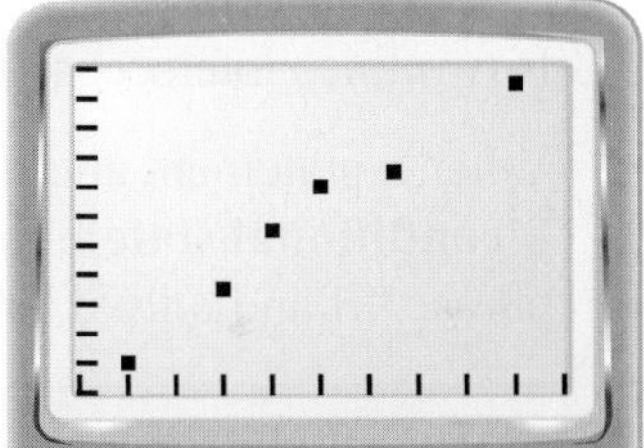

STEP 2 **Find a pattern in the data.**
The data show a linear increase in the annual sales as the amount spent on advertising increases from $2400 to $6500. Use the graphing calculator to graph a model for the data.

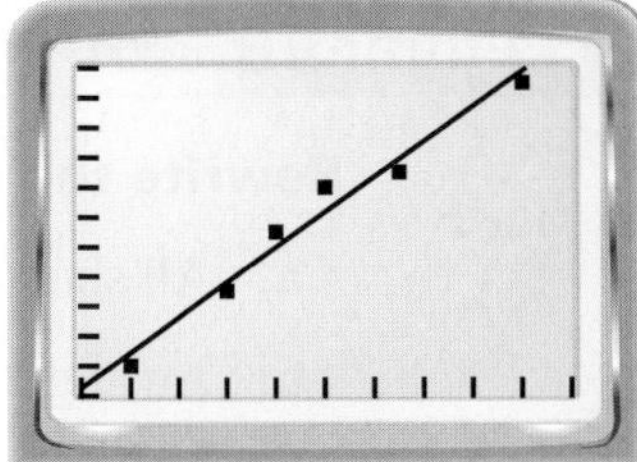

STEP 3 **Make a prediction.**
Using the model, the annual sales will be about $62,100 if the company spends $3700 in advertising.

Practice

1. The table shows the temperature for various elevations based on a temperature of 59°F at sea level. Use a graphing calculator and inductive reasoning to predict the temperature at an elevation of 18,000 feet.

Elevation (ft)	1000	5000	10,000	15,000	20,000	30,000
Temperature (°F)	56	41	23	5	−15	−47

2. **Writing** A linear model for predicting a company's profits is based on data for 3 years. *Describe* the potential accuracy or inaccuracy of such a model.

UNIT 4

LESSON 4.3

Analyze Conditional Statements

Georgia Performance Standards: MM1G2b

Goal Write definitions as conditional statements.

Vocabulary

A **conditional statement** is a logical statement that has two parts, a hypothesis and a conclusion.

When a conditional statement is written in **if-then form,** the "if" part contains the **hypothesis** and the "then" part contains the **conclusion.**

The **negation** of a statement is the opposite of the original statement.

To write the **converse** of a conditional statement, switch the hypothesis and conclusion.

To write the **inverse** of a conditional statement, negate both the hypothesis and conclusion.

To write the **contrapositive** of a conditional statement, first write the converse and then negate both the hypothesis and the conclusion.

When two statements are both true or both false, they are called **equivalent statements.**

If two lines intersect to form a right angle, then they are **perpendicular lines.**

When a statement and its converse are both true, you can write them as a single **biconditional statement**. A biconditional statement is a statement that contains the phrase "if and only if." Any valid definition can be written as a biconditional statement.

UNIT 4

Example 1 Rewrite a statement in if-then form

Rewrite the conditional statement in if-then form.

a. All sharks have a boneless skeleton.

b. An angle is an acute angle if its measure is less than 90°.

c. When $n = 6, n^2 = 36$.

Solution

First identify the **hypothesis** and the **conclusion.** When you rewrite the statement in if-then form, you may need to reword the hypothesis or conclusion.

a. **All sharks** have **a boneless skeleton.**

If **a fish is a shark,** then **it has a boneless skeleton.**

b. **An angle is an acute angle** if **its measure is less than 90°.**

If **the measure of an angle is less than 90°**, then **it is an acute angle.**

c. When $n = 6, n^2 = 36$.

If $n = 6$, then $n^2 = 36$.

Georgia Performance Standards

MM1G2b Understand and use the relationships among a statement and its converse, inverse, and contrapositive.

Guided Practice for Example 1

Rewrite the conditional statement in if-then form.

1. On Saturday, Mary has a soccer game.
2. $4x - 8 = -28$, because $x = -5$.
3. An object weighs one ton if it weighs 2000 pounds.
4. When $n = 121$, $\sqrt{n} = 11$.
5. The measure of a right angle is 90°.

Example 2 Write four related conditional statements

Write the if-then form, the converse, the inverse, and the contrapositive of the statement "Basketball players are athletes." Decide whether each statement is *true* or *false*.

Solution

If-then form If you are a basketball player, then you are an athlete.
True, basketball players are athletes.

Converse If you are an athlete, then you are a basketball player.
False, not all athletes play basketball.

Inverse If you are not a basketball player, then you are not an athlete.
False, even if you don't play basketball, you can still be an athlete.

Contrapositive If you are not an athlete, then you are not a basketball player.
True, a person who is not an athlete cannot be a basketball player.

Guided Practice for Example 2

Write the if-then form, the converse, the inverse, and the contrapositive of the statement. Decide whether each statement is *true* or *false*.

6. All 180° angles are straight angles.
7. All cats are mammals.
8. An even number greater than two is not prime.
9. A midpoint bisects a segment.
10. A hexagon is a polygon.

UNIT 4

Example 3 Use definitions

Decide whether each statement about the diagram is true. *Explain* your answer using the definitions you have learned.

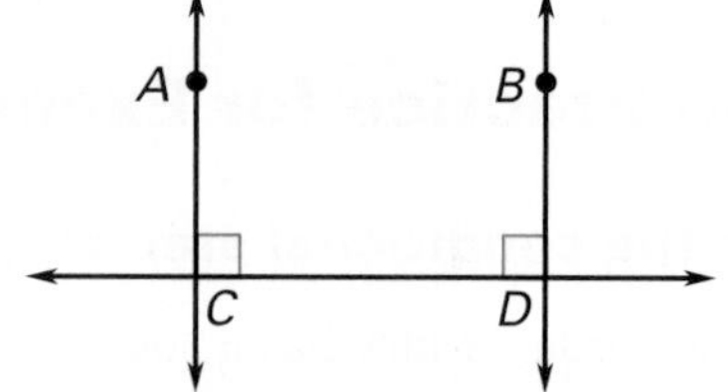

a. $\overleftrightarrow{AC} \perp \overleftrightarrow{CD}$

b. $\angle ACD$ and $\angle BDC$ are complementary.

Solution

a. This statement is true. The right angle symbol in the diagram indicates that the lines intersect to form a right angle. So the lines are perpendicular.

b. This statement is false. Both angles are right angles, so the sum of their measures is not 90°.

Guided Practice for Example 3

Use the diagram in Example 3. Decide whether each statement about the diagram is true. *Explain* your answer using the definitions you have learned.

11. $\overleftrightarrow{BD} \perp \overleftrightarrow{CD}$

12. $\angle ACD$ and $\angle BDC$ are supplementary.

13. $\overleftrightarrow{AC} \perp \overleftrightarrow{BD}$

UNIT 4

Example 4 Write a biconditional

Write the definition of supplementary angles as a biconditional.

Solution

Definition If two angles are supplementary angles, then the sum of their measures is 180°.

Converse If the sum of the measures of two angles is 180°, then they are supplementary angles.

Biconditional Two angles are supplementary angles if and only if the sum of their measures is 180°.

Guided Practice for Example 4

Rewrite the definition or statement as a biconditional.

14. If two angles are complementary angles, then the sum of their measures is 90°.

15. If a polygon is equilateral, then all of its sides are congruent.

16. If Mary is in theater class, she will be in the fall play. If Mary is in the fall play, she must be taking theater class.

LESSON 4.3 **Exercise Set A**

MM1G2b Understand and use the relationships among a statement and its converse, inverse, and contrapositive.

Rewrite the conditional statement in if-then form.

1. It is time for dinner if it is 6 P.M.
2. There are 12 eggs if the carton is full.
3. An obtuse angle is an angle that measures more than 90° and less than 180°.
4. The car runs when there is gas in the tank.

Write the converse, inverse, and contrapositive of each statement.

5. If you like hockey, then you go to the hockey game.
6. If x is odd, then $3x$ is odd.

Decide whether the statement is *true* or *false*. If false, provide a counterexample.

7. The equation $4x - 3 = 12 + 2x$ has exactly one solution.
8. If $x^2 = 36$, then x must equal 18 or -18.
9. If $m\angle A = 122°$, then the measure of the supplement of $\angle A$ is 58°.
10. Two lines intersect in at most one point.

Write the converse of each true statement. If the converse is also true, combine the statements to write a true biconditional statement.

11. If an angle measures 30°, then it is acute.
12. If two angles are supplementary, then their sum is 180°.
13. If two circles have the same diameter, then they have the same circumference.
14. If an animal is a panther, then it lives in the forest.

Rewrite the biconditional statement as a conditional statement and its converse.

15. Two lines are perpendicular if and only if they intersect to form right angles.
16. A point is a midpoint of a segment if and only if it divides the segment into two congruent segments.

Decide whether the statement is a valid definition.

17. If a number is divisible by 2 and 3, then it is divisible by 6.
18. If two angles have the same measure, then they are congruent.
19. If an angle is a right angle, then its measure is greater than that of an acute angle.

Exercise Set A *(continued)*

20. Error Analysis *Describe* and correct the error made in writing the if-then statement.

Given statement: All high school students take four Mathematics courses.

If-then statement: If a high school student takes four courses, then all four are Mathematics courses. X

In Exercises 21–23, use the information in the table to write a definition for each type of saxophone.

Instrument	Frequency (cycles per second)	
	Lower limit (Hz)	Upper limit (Hz)
E-flat baritone saxophone	69	415
B-flat tenor saxophone	103	622
E-flat alto saxophone	138	830

21. E-flat baritone saxophone

22. B-flat tenor saxophone

23. E-flat alto saxophone

In Exercises 24 and 25, use the information in the table above and the answers to Exercises 21–23.

24. If the frequency of a saxophone was 95 Hz, what could you conclude?

25. If the frequency of a saxophone was 210 Hz, what could you conclude?

26. **Profits** The statements below were made during an executive meeting at a department store. Use these statements in parts (a)–(c).

The department store's profits will decrease if wages are increased.

Offering more sales will increase the department store's profits.

Profits will increase when inventory is increased.

a. Write each statement in if-then form.

b. Write the converse of each of the statements in part (a). Is the converse of each statement true? *Explain* your reasoning.

c. Write a true if-then statement about the department store's profit. Is the converse of your statement *true* or *false*? *Explain*.

LESSON 4.3

Exercise Set B

MM1G2b Understand and use the relationships among a statement and its converse, inverse, and contrapositive.

Rewrite the conditional statement in if-then form.

1. A car with leaking antifreeze has a problem.
2. Don't say anything at all when you don't have something nice to say.
3. You can't teach an old dog new tricks.
4. A vein is a blood vessel that carries blood toward the heart.

The statement is either the converse, the inverse, or the contrapositive of the *meaning* of a well-known saying. What is the saying?

5. If you learn things, then use them to make mistakes.
6. If it isn't lost easily, then it isn't gained easily.
7. If dogs are not lying down, then don't let them sleep.
8. If you don't see something, then you won't get it.

For the given statement, write the if-then form, the converse, the inverse, and the contrapositive and indicate whether each statement is *true* or *false*.

9. A circle with a radius of r has a circumference of $2\pi r$.
10. A regular pentagon has five sides.

In a plane, point F lies between points C and D and $\overleftrightarrow{EF}$ intersects $\overleftrightarrow{CD}$ so that $\angle CFE \cong \angle DFE$. Decide whether the given statement is true. *Explain* your answer using definitions and properties that you have learned.

11. $\overrightarrow{FC}$ and $\overrightarrow{FE}$ are opposite rays.
12. $\angle CFE$ and $\angle DFE$ are supplementary angles.
13. $m\angle CFD = 180°$
14. Points C, F, and E are collinear points.
15. $\angle CFE$ is an obtuse angle.
16. $\overleftrightarrow{CD} \perp \overleftrightarrow{EF}$

Rewrite the definition as a biconditional statement.

17. A conditional statement is a logical statement that has two parts, a hypothesis and a conclusion.
18. A conjecture is an unproven statement that is based on observations.
19. A counterexample is a specific case for which a given conjecture is false.

UNIT 4

Exercise Set B *(continued)*

20. Rewrite the following definition as a biconditional statement: A polygon is a closed plane figure that is formed by three or more sides, with each side intersecting exactly two other sides, one at each endpoint, so that no two sides with a common endpoint are collinear.

Decide whether the statement is a valid definition.

21. If a triangle has one right angle, then it is a right triangle.

22. If a solid is a cylinder, then it has two circular bases.

23. If a number is divisible by 9, then it is divisible by 3.

Write the converse of each true statement. Tell whether the converse is true. If false, explain why.

24. If $x > 5$, then $x > 0$.

25. If $x < 8$, then $-x > -8$.

26. If $-x \geq x$, then $x \leq 0$.

27. Can the statement, "If $x^2 - 14 = x + 6$, then $x = 5$," be combined with its converse to form a true biconditional statement?

UNIT 4

In Exercises 28–32, use the following information.

Cyclones Cyclones are areas of rotating air that can be associated with many types of severe weather. Tornadoes are sometimes considered to be cyclones that occur over land. Tropical cyclones are cyclones that form over tropical ocean waters. A weak tropical cyclone with winds of less than 38 miles per hour is called a tropical depression. A tropical depression turns into a tropical storm if its winds increase to 39 miles per hour or faster. The most severe type of tropical cyclone occurs if the wind speeds increase to greater than 74 miles per hour. This type of storm has many different names, depending on where it forms. Some of the names used in different locations are: *typhoon* over much of the Pacific Ocean, *willy-nilly* near Australia, and *hurricane* over the Atlantic Ocean.

Tell whether the statement is a valid definition of a hurricane. If not, explain why.

28. If a tropical cyclone develops in the Atlantic Ocean, then the storm is a called a hurricane.

29. If a tropical cyclone has winds in excess of 74 miles per hour, then the storm is called a hurricane.

30. If a storm occurs in the tropics over the Atlantic Ocean and the storm has winds of over 74 miles per hour, then the storm is a hurricane.

31. If a cyclone with winds of over 74 miles per hour forms in the Atlantic Ocean, then the storm is a hurricane.

32. If a tropical cyclone is formed over the Atlantic Ocean and develops wind speeds of over 74 miles per hour, then the storm is classified as a hurricane.

LESSON 4.4

Apply Deductive Reasoning

Georgia Performance Standards: MM1G2a

Goal Use deductive reasoning to form a logical argument.

Vocabulary

Deductive reasoning uses facts, definitions, accepted properties, and the laws of logic to form a logical argument.

Law of Detachment If the hypothesis of a true conditional statement is true, then the conclusion is also true.

Law of Syllogism

If **hypothesis** p, then **conclusion** q. ←
If **hypothesis** q, then **conclusion** r. ← If these statements are true,

If **hypothesis** p, then **conclusion** r. ← then the following statement is true.

Example 1 Use the Law of Detachment

Use the Law of Detachment to make a valid conclusion in the true situation.

If two angles have the same measure, then they are congruent. You know that $m\angle A = m\angle B$.

Solution

First, identify the hypothesis and the conclusion of the first statement. The hypothesis is "If two angles have the same measure." The conclusion is "then they are congruent."

Because $m\angle A = m\angle B$ satisfies the hypothesis of a true conditional statement, the conclusion is also true. So, $\angle A \cong \angle B$.

Example 2 Use the Law of Syllogism

If possible, use the Law of Syllogism to write the conditional statement that follows from the pair of true statements.

a. If the electric power is off, then the refrigerator does not run.
If the refrigerator does not run, then the food will spoil.

b. If $2x > 10$, then $2x > 7$.
If $x > 5$, then $2x > 10$.

Solution

a. The conclusion of the first statement is the hypothesis of the second statement, so you can write the following statement.

If the electric power is off, then the food will spoil.

b. Notice that the conclusion of the second statement is the hypothesis of the first statement, so you can write the following statement.

If $x > 5$, then $2x > 7$.

UNIT 4

Georgia Performance Standards

MM1G2a Use conjecture, inductive reasoning, deductive reasoning, counterexamples, and indirect proof as appropriate.

Guided Practice for Examples 1 and 2

1. If $\angle A$ is acute, then $0° < m\angle A < 90°$. Angle B is an acute angle. Using the Law of Detachment, what conclusion can you make?
2. If B is between A and C, then $AB + BC = AC$. E is between D and F. Using the Law of Detachment, what conclusion can you make?
3. If you study hard, you will pass all of your classes. If you pass all of your classes, you will graduate. Using the Law of Syllogism, what statement can you make?
4. If $x^2 > 9$, then $x^2 > 8$. If $x > 4$, then $x^2 > 9$. Using the Law of Syllogism, what statement can you make?

Example 3 Use inductive and deductive reasoning

What conclusion can you make about the sum of two even integers?

Solution

STEP 1 **Look** for a pattern in several examples. Use inductive reasoning to make a conjecture.

$-2 + 4 = 2, -4 + 10 = 6, 6 + 8 = 14, 12 + 6 = 18,$

$-20 + 14 = -6, -12 + 2 = -10, -6 + 2 = -4, -2 + (-6) = -8$

Conjecture: Even integer + Even integer = Even integer

STEP 2 **Let** n and m be any integer. Use deductive reasoning to show the conjecture is true.

$2n$ and $2m$ are even integers because any integer multiplied by 2 is even.

$2n + 2m$ represents the sum of two even integers.

$2n + 2m$ can be written as $2(n + m)$.

$2(n + m)$ is the product of 2 and an integer $(n + m)$. So, $2(n + m)$ is an even integer.

The sum of two even integers is an even integer.

Guided Practice for Example 3

5. What conclusion can you make about the sum of two odd integers? (*Hint:* An odd integer can be written as $2n + 1$, where n is any integer.)
6. What conclusion can you make about the product of an even integer and an odd integer?

UNIT 4

LESSON 4.4

Exercise Set A

MM1G2a Use conjecture, inductive reasoning, deductive reasoning, counterexamples, and indirect proof as appropriate.

Determine if statement (3) follows from statements (1) and (2) by either the Law of Detachment or the Law of Syllogism. If it does, state which law was used. If it does not, write invalid.

1. (1) If an angle measures more than 90°, then it is not acute.

(2) $m\angle ABC = 120°$

(3) $\angle ABC$ is not acute.

2. (1) All 45° angles are congruent.

(2) $\angle A \cong \angle B$

(3) $\angle A$ and $\angle B$ are 45° angles.

3. (1) If you order the apple pie, then it will be served with ice cream.

(2) Matthew ordered the apple pie.

(3) Matthew was served ice cream.

4. (1) If you wear the school colors, then you have school spirit.

(2) If you have school spirit, then the team feels great.

(3) If you wear the school colors, then the team will feel great.

5. (1) If you eat too much turkey, then you will get sick.

(2) Kinsley got sick.

(3) Kinsley ate too much turkey.

6. (1) If $\angle 2$ is acute, then $\angle 3$ is obtuse.

(2) If $\angle 3$ is obtuse, then $\angle 4$ is acute.

(3) If $\angle 2$ is acute, then $\angle 4$ is acute.

In Exercises 7–9, decide whether *inductive* or *deductive* reasoning is used to reach the conclusion. *Explain* your reasoning.

7. Angela knows that Walt is taller than Peter. She also knows that Peter is taller than Natalie. Angela reasons that Walt is taller than Natalie.

8. Josh knows that Brand X computers cost less than Brand Y computers. All other brands that Josh knows of cost less than Brand X. Josh reasons that Brand Y costs more than all other brands.

9. For the past three Wednesdays, the cafeteria has served macaroni and cheese for lunch. Dana concludes that the cafeteria will serve macaroni and cheese for lunch this Wednesday.

Exercise Set A *(continued)*

10. If you live in Nevada and are between the ages of 16 and 18, then you must take driver's education to get your license. Anthony lives in Nevada, is 16 years old, and has his driver's license. Therefore, Anthony took driver's education. Decide whether *inductive* or *deductive* reasoning is used to reach the conclusion. *Explain* your reasoning.

In Exercises 11–14, state whether the argument is valid. *Explain* your reasoning.

11. Jeff knows that if he does not do his chores in the morning, he will not be allowed to play video games later the same day. Jeff does not play video games on Saturday afternoon. So, Jeff did not do his chores on Saturday morning.

12. Katie knows that all sophomores take driver education in her school. Brandon takes driver education. So, Brandon is a sophomore.

13. If Casey is elected, the income tax will be increased. The income tax was increased. So, Casey was elected.

14. If you study every day, then you will receive good grades. If you receive good grades, then you will get a good job. So, if you study every day, then you will get a good job.

In Exercises 15–18, use the true statements below to determine whether you know the conclusion is *true* or *false*. *Explain* your reasoning.

If Dan goes shopping, then he will buy a pretzel.

If the mall is open, then Jodi and Dan will go shopping.

If Jodi goes shopping, then she will buy a pizza.

The mall is open.

15. Dan bought a pizza.

16. Jodi and Dan went shopping.

17. Jodi bought a pizza.

18. Jodi had some of Dan's pretzel.

19. **Robotics** Because robots can withstand higher temperatures than humans, a fire-fighting robot is under development. Write the following statements about the robot in order. Then use the Law of Syllogism to complete the statement, "If there is a fire, then __?__."

A. If the robot sets off the fire alarm, then it concludes there is a fire.

B. If the robot senses high levels of smoke and heat, then it sets off a fire alarm.

C. If the robot locates the fire, then the robot extinguishes the fire.

D. If there is a fire, then the robot senses high levels of smoke and heat.

E. If the robot concludes there is a fire, then it locates the fire.

LESSON 4.4 **Exercise Set B**

MM1G2a Use conjecture, inductive reasoning, deductive reasoning, counterexamples, and indirect proof as appropriate.

Write the statement that follows from the given statements. Indicate whether the *Law of Detachment* or the *Law of Syllogism* is used.

1. If Dr. Klein is well-rested for a surgical procedure, then she operates with precision. Dr. Klein got plenty of sleep to prepare for today's operation.
2. If we don't make any stops, then we'll make it to the stadium by 12:30 P.M. If we make it to the stadium by that time, then we should be in time to see the kickoff.
3. In a recreational basketball league, if a player receives two technical fouls in one game, then the player is ejected from the game. If a player is ejected from a game, then the player has to sit out the following game.
4. If the accused suspect has a valid alibi, then the police will not hold him. The crime occurred at 9:32 A.M. The suspect's place of business confirms that he was working with 22 other people from 7:00 A.M. to 4:00 P.M. on the same day.
5. Even when firefighters follow all relevant safety procedures, if they enter a burning building, then there is significant danger involved. A group of firefighters enters a burning warehouse to look for people.
6. The store manager knows that if tomorrow's sale is not advertised in the newspaper, then the store will lose money. If the newspaper does not receive the order for the advertisement soon enough, then they will not be able to put it in tomorrow's newspaper.

Use deductive reasoning along with one of the laws of logic to write the statement that follows from the given statements. Indicate whether the *Law of Detachment* or the *Law of Syllogism* is used.

7. If a company's taxable income is reduced by $10,000, then it will go into a lower tax bracket. If the company contributes money to a certain charity, then it will reduce its taxable income by 50% of the amount contributed.
8. If you park a car on a hill, then you should set the parking brake. You park the car facing down a steep grade on a busy street.
9. If you take the absolute value of a positive number, then the value of the result is the number. You take the absolute value of a perfect square.
10. If the ice on a lake becomes brittle, it may not be safe to walk on the ice for up to 24 hours. If there is a large, rapid decrease in air temperature, then the lake ice becomes brittle.
11. If an object has a greater volume than an equivalent mass of water, then the object will float in water. A ball has three times the volume of an equivalent mass of water.
12. If a car is moving at a speed of 50 miles per hour, then it takes 175 feet to stop the car on average. The car is traveling at 50 miles per hour when another vehicle pulls directly into its path.

UNIT 4

Exercise Set B *(continued)*

Decide whether *inductive* or *deductive* reasoning is used to reach the conclusion. *Explain* your reasoning.

13. You diet for 3 weeks and lose 3 pounds. You conclude that you can lose 20 more pounds in the next 20 weeks.

14. You use the rise of 8.1 and the run of 2.7 between two points on a line in the coordinate plane to conclude that the slope of the line is 3.

15. It is the last day of the month and you want to buy a new jacket. Because you always run out of money by the end of the month, you conclude that there is not enough money in your checking account for the jacket.

16. Multiple Representations The points $(-2, -1)$, $(-1, 1)$, and $(0, 3)$ lie on a line.

a. Making a Table Copy and complete the table below to find two additional points that lie on the line. Does this method use inductive or deductive reasoning?

x-coordinate	-2	-1	0	1	2
y-coordinate	-1	1	3	?	?

b. Writing an Equation Use the given points to write an equation for the line. Then use the equation to find two additonal points that lie on the line. Does this method use inductive or deductive reasoning?

UNIT 4

In Exercises 17 and 18, use the figure at the right.

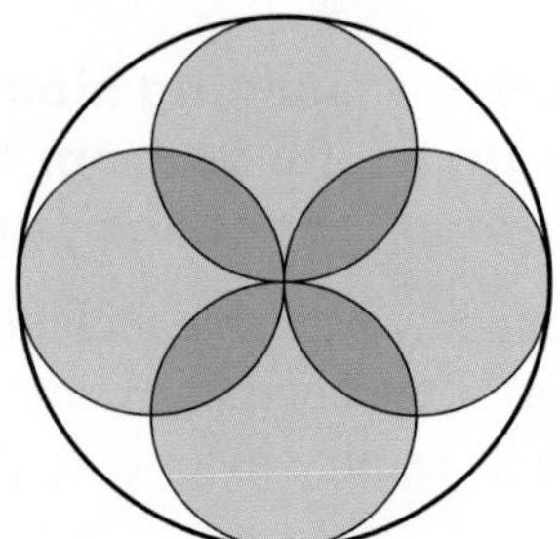

17. Based on the appearance of the circles in the figure, use inductive reasoning to make a conjecture about how the area of one circle compares to the area of another circle with a radius that is twice as long.

18. Use deductive reasoning and the formula for the area of a circle to determine whether your conjecture in Exercise 17 is correct.

In Exercises 19 and 20, use the following information.

A roofing crew is replacing the roof on the house shown in the diagram. Safety guidelines call for a catch platform to be installed below the working area of a roof if it is more than 20 feet from the ground to the eave, or if it is more than 16 feet from the ground to the eave and the pitch rises more than 4 inches for each run of 12 inches. In either case, a catch platform is *not* required if each worker wears a safety belt attached to an approved lifeline.

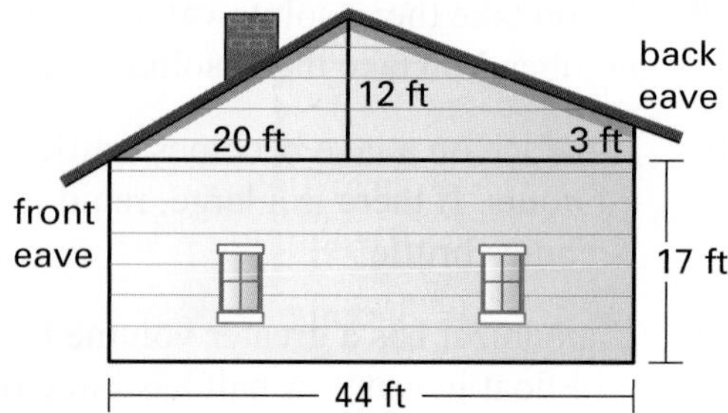

19. What safety precautions are required on the front roof? *Explain* your reasoning.

20. What safety precautions are required on the back roof? *Explain* your reasoning.

LESSON 4.5

Prove Statements about Segments and Angles

Georgia Performance Standards: MM1G2a

Goal Write proofs using geometric theorems.

Vocabulary

A **proof** is a logical argument that shows a statement is true.

A two-column proof has numbered statements and corresponding reasons that show an argument in a logical order.

A **postulate** is a rule that is accepted without proof.

Segment Addition Postulate: If B is between A and C, then $AB + BC = AC$. If $AB + BC = AC$, then B is between A and C.

Angle Addition Postulate: If P is in the interior of $\angle RST$, then the measure of $\angle RST$ is equal to the sum of the measures of $\angle RSP$ and $\angle PST$.

A **theorem** is a statement that can be proven.

Example 1 Write a two-column proof

Write a two-column proof.

GIVEN: $m\angle 1 = m\angle 4$, $m\angle EHF = 90°$
$m\angle GHF = 90°$

PROVE: $m\angle 2 = m\angle 3$

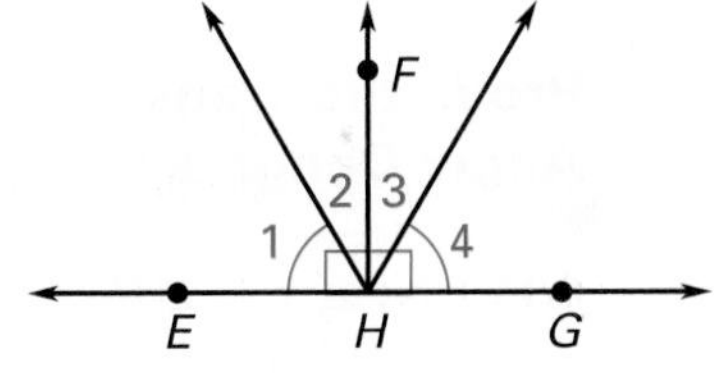

Statements	Reasons
1. $m\angle 1 = m\angle 4$, $m\angle EHF = 90°$ $m\angle GHF = 90°$	**1.** Given
2. $m\angle EHF = m\angle GHF$	**2.** Substitution Property of Equality
3. $m\angle EHF = m\angle 1 + m\angle 2$ $m\angle GHF = m\angle 3 + m\angle 4$	**3.** Angle Addition Postulate
4. $m\angle 1 + m\angle 2 = m\angle 3 + m\angle 4$	**4.** Substitution Property of Equality
5. $m\angle 1 + m\angle 2 = m\angle 3 + m\angle 1$	**5.** Substitution Property of Equality
6. $m\angle 2 = m\angle 3$	**6.** Subtraction Property of Equality

Guided Practice for Example 1

1. Write a two-column proof.

GIVEN: $MP = MN + MN$

PROVE: $MN = NP$

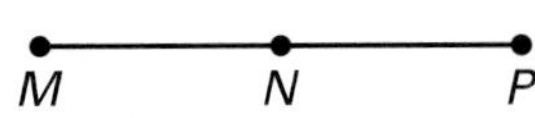

Georgia Performance Standards

MM1G2a Use conjecture, inductive reasoning, deductive reasoning, counterexamples, and indirect proof as appropriate. 

Theorems

Theorem 4.1 Congruence of Segments

Segment congruence is reflexive, symmetric, and transitive.

Reflexive For any segment AB, $\overline{AB} \cong \overline{AB}$.

Symmetric If $\overline{AB} \cong \overline{CD}$ then $\overline{CD} \cong \overline{AB}$.

Transitive If $\overline{AB} \cong \overline{CD}$ and $\overline{CD} \cong \overline{EF}$, then $\overline{AB} \cong \overline{EF}$.

Theorem 4.2 Congruence of Angles

Angle congruence is reflexive, symmetric, and transitive.

Reflexive For any angle A, $\angle A \cong \angle A$.

Symmetric If $\angle A \cong \angle B$, then $\angle B \cong \angle A$.

Transitive If $\angle A \cong \angle B$ and $\angle B \cong \angle C$, then $\angle A \cong \angle C$.

Example 2 Transitive Property of Congruence

Prove the Transitive Property of Angle Congruence.

GIVEN: $\angle A \cong \angle B$, $\angle B \cong \angle C$
PROVE: $\angle A \cong \angle C$

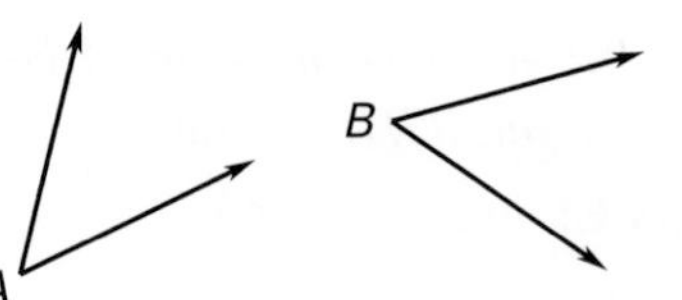

Statements	Reasons
1. $\angle A \cong \angle B$, $\angle B \cong \angle C$	**1.** Given
2. $m\angle A = m\angle B$	**2.** Definition of congruent angles
3. $m\angle B = m\angle C$	**3.** Definition of congruent angles
4. $m\angle A = m\angle C$	**4.** Transitive Property of Equality
5. $m\angle A \cong m\angle C$	**5.** Definition of congruent angles

Guided Practice for Example 2

2. Prove the Transitive Property of Segment Congruence.

GIVEN: $\overline{AB} \cong \overline{BC}$, $\overline{BC} \cong \overline{CD}$
PROVE: $\overline{AB} \cong \overline{CD}$

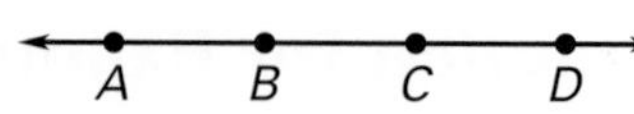

3. Prove the Symmetric Property of Angle Congruence.

GIVEN: $\angle 1 \cong \angle 2$
PROVE: $\angle 2 \cong \angle 1$

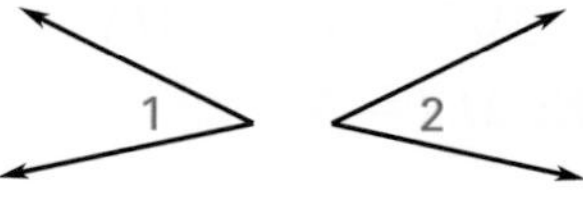

LESSON 4.5 **Exercise Set A**

MM1G2a Use conjecture, inductive reasoning, deductive reasoning, counterexamples, and indirect proof as appropriate.

In Exercises 1–4, copy and complete the proof.

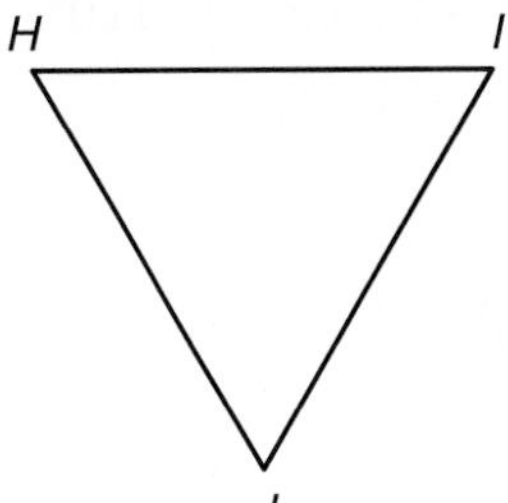

1. GIVEN: $HI = 9, IJ = 9, \overline{IJ} \cong \overline{JH}$

PROVE: $\overline{HI} \cong \overline{JH}$

Statements	Reasons
1. $HI = 9, IJ = 9$	**1.** ?
2. $HI = IJ$	**2.** ?
3. ?	**3.** Definition of congruent segments
4. $\overline{IJ} \cong \overline{JH}$	**4.** ?
5. $\overline{HI} \cong \overline{JH}$	**5.** ?

2. GIVEN: $\angle 3$ and $\angle 2$ are complementary.
$m\angle 1 + m\angle 2 = 90°$

PROVE: $\angle 1 \cong \angle 3$

Statements	Reasons
1. $\angle 3$ and $\angle 2$ are complementary, and $m\angle 1 + m\angle 2 = 90°$	**1.** ?
2. $m\angle 3 + m\angle 2 = 90°$	**2.** ?
3. $m\angle 1 + m\angle 2 = m\angle 3 + m\angle 2$	**3.** ?
4. $m\angle 1 = m\angle 3$	**4.** ?
5. $\angle 1 \cong \angle 3$	**5.** ?

3. GIVEN: $AL = SK$

PROVE: $AS = LK$

Statements	Reasons
1. $AL = SK$	**1.** ?
2. $LS = LS$	**2.** ?
3. $AL + LS = SK + LS$	**3.** ?
4. $AL + LS = AS$	**4.** ?
5. $SK + LS = LK$	**5.** ?
6. $AS = LK$	**6.** ?

Exercise Set A *(continued)*

4. **GIVEN:** $m\angle 4 = 120°$, $\angle 2 \cong \angle 5$, $\angle 5 \cong \angle 4$

PROVE: $m\angle 2 = 120°$

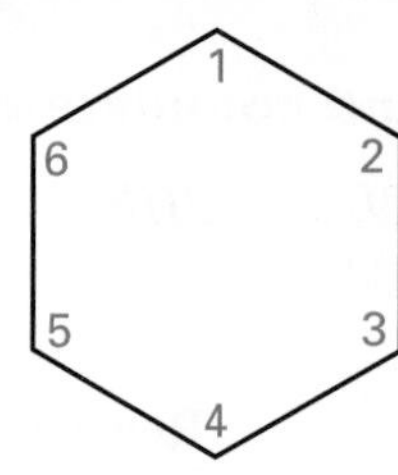

Statements	Reasons
1. $m\angle 4 = 120°$, $\angle 2 \cong \angle 5$, $\angle 5 \cong \angle 4$	1. ?
2. $\angle 2 \cong \angle 4$	2. ?
3. ?	3. Definition of congruent angles
4. $m\angle 2 = 120°$	4. ?

Solve for *x* using the given information. *Explain* your steps.

5. $\angle W \cong \angle Z$

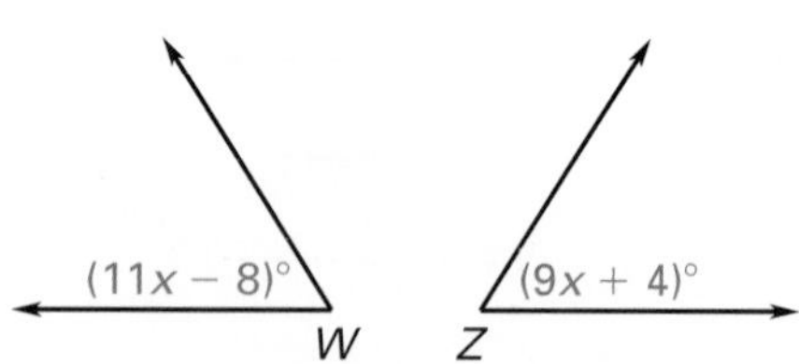

6. $\overline{FG} \cong \overline{FJ}$, $\overline{FJ} \cong \overline{JH}$

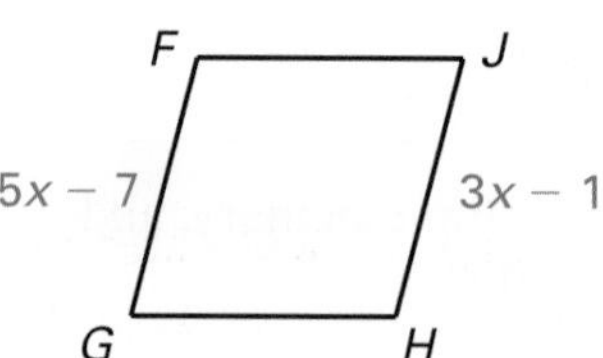

7. $\angle ABD \cong \angle DBE$, $\angle DBE \cong \angle EBC$

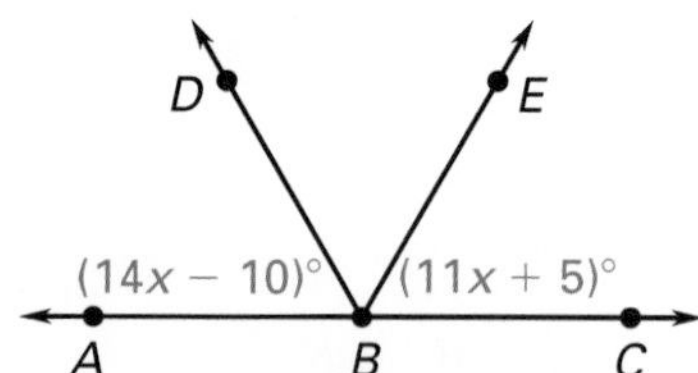

8. $\overline{KP} \cong \overline{PN}$, $KP = 18$

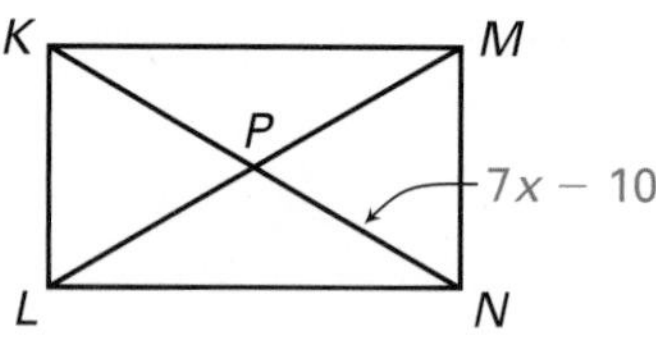

9. **Optical Illusion** To create the illusion at the right, a special grid was used. In the grid, corresponding row heights are the same measure. For instance, $\overline{UV}$ and $\overline{ZY}$ are congruent. You decide to make this design yourself. You draw the grid, but you need to make sure that the row heights are the same. You measure $\overline{UV}$, $\overline{UW}$, $\overline{ZY}$, and $\overline{ZX}$. You find that $\overline{UV} \cong \overline{ZY}$ and $\overline{UW} \cong \overline{ZX}$. Write an argument that allows you to conclude that $\overline{VW} \cong \overline{YX}$.

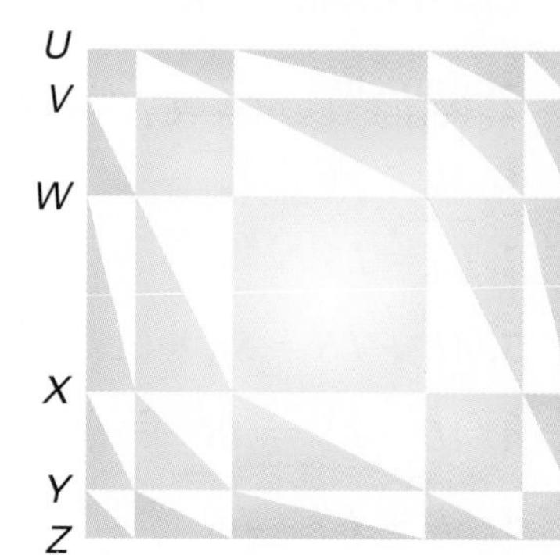

UNIT 4

LESSON 4.5

Exercise Set B

MM1G2a Use conjecture, inductive reasoning, deductive reasoning, counterexamples, and indirect proof as appropriate.

In Exercises 1 and 2, copy and complete the proof.

1. **GIVEN:** $\angle ABC \cong \angle CBD$, $m\angle CBD = 50°$, $m\angle CBE = 100°$

PROVE: $\angle ABC \cong \angle DBE$

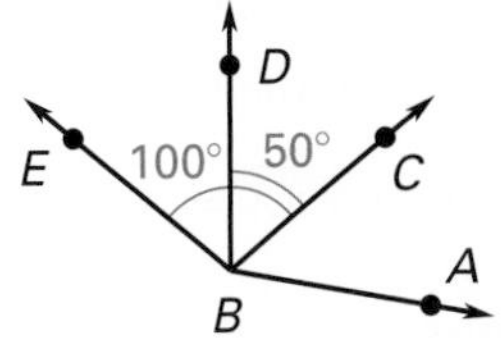

Statements	Reasons
1. $\angle ABC \cong \angle CBD$, $m\angle CBD = 50°$, $m\angle CBE = 100°$	1. ___?___
2. ___?___ $= m\angle CBE$	2. Angle Addition Postulate
3. $50° + m\angle DBE = 100°$	3. ___?___
4. $m\angle DBE = 50°$	4. ___?___
5. $m\angle CBD =$ ___?___	5. Substitution Property of Equality
6. ___?___	6. Definition of congruent angles
7. $\angle ABC \cong \angle DBE$	7. ___?___

2. The lengths of the sides of quadrilateral $ABCD$ are congruent. Prove that the perimeter of $ABCD$ is equal to $4AB$.

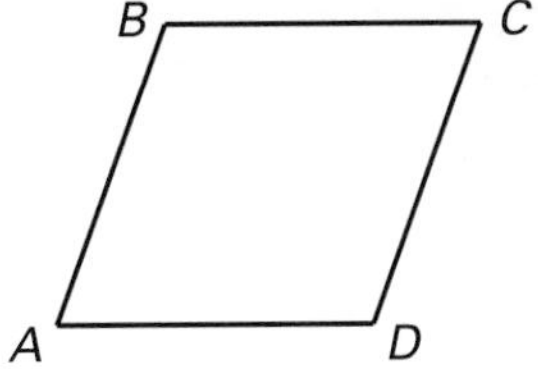

GIVEN: $\overline{AB} \cong \overline{BC}$, $\overline{BC} \cong \overline{CD}$, $\overline{CD} \cong \overline{AD}$

PROVE: Perimeter of $ABCD = 4AB$

Statements	Reasons
1. $\overline{AB} \cong \overline{BC}$, $\overline{BC} \cong \overline{CD}$, $\overline{CD} \cong \overline{AD}$	1. ___?___
2. $AB = BC$, $BC = CD$, $CD = AD$	2. ___?___
3. $AB = CD$, $AB = AD$	3. ___?___
4. Perimeter of $ABCD = AB + BC + CD + AD$	4. ___?___
5. ___?___	5. Substitution Property of Equality
6. ___?___	6. Simplify.

Use the property to complete the statement.

3. Transitive Property of Congruence: If $\angle 1 \cong \angle 5$ and ___?___ , then $\angle 1 \cong \angle 7$.

4. Symmetric Property of Congruence: If $\angle 1 \cong \angle 2$ and $\angle 3 \cong \angle 4$, then ___?___.

UNIT 4

Exercise Set B (continued)

Name the property illustrated by the statement.

5. $\angle ABC \cong \angle CBA$

6. If $\angle RST \cong \angle 5$, then $\angle 5 \cong \angle RST$.

7. If $\overline{QS} \cong \overline{XR}$ and $\overline{RX} \cong \overline{SX}$, then $\overline{QS} \cong \overline{SX}$.

8. **Error Analysis** In the diagram below, $\overline{BC} \cong \overline{AE}$ and $\overline{AE} \cong \overline{DC}$. *Describe* and correct the error in the reasoning.

Because $\overline{BC} \cong \overline{AE}$ and $\overline{AE} \cong \overline{DC}$, then $\overline{BC} \cong \overline{DC}$ by the Reflexive Property of Segment Congruence.

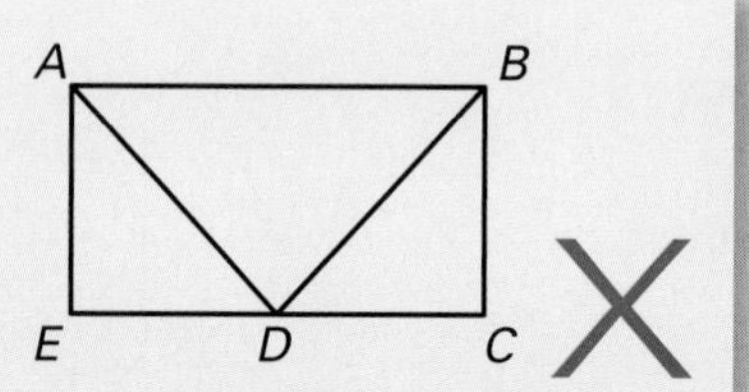

Solve for *x* using the given information. *Explain* your steps.

9. **GIVEN:** S is the midpoint of $\overline{RT}$.
T is the midpoint of $\overline{SU}$.

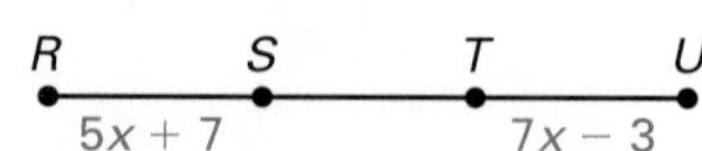

10. **GIVEN:** $\angle D \cong \angle DEG$,
$\overline{EG}$ bisects $\angle DEF$.

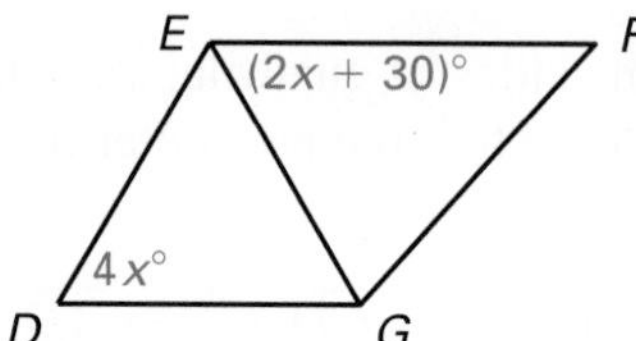

11. **Proof** Write a two-column proof.

GIVEN: $\overline{AE} \cong \overline{CE}$
$\overline{AB}$ and $\overline{CD}$ bisect each other.

PROVE: $\overline{EB} \cong \overline{ED}$

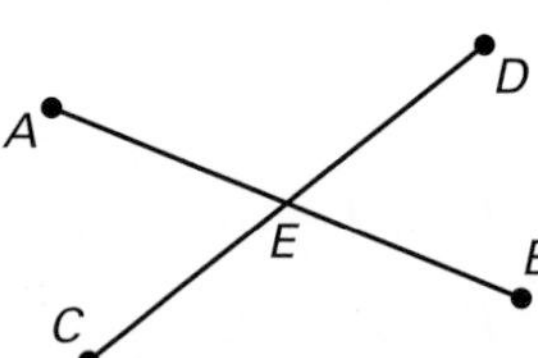

12. **Marching Band** A marching band forms a *company front,* with all of the musicians in a straight line facing the audience. In this formation, Leon is halfway between Marge and Clay, Jade is halfway between Marge and Leon, and Ariel is halfway between Leon and Clay. Use the following steps to prove that the distance between Marge and Jade is the same as the distance between Ariel and Clay.

a. Draw a diagram that represents the five musicians mentioned.

b. Draw separate diagrams to show mathematical relationships.

c. State what is given and what is to be proved.

d. Write a two-column proof.

LESSON 4.6

Prove Angle Pair Relationships

Georgia Performance Standards: MM1G2a

Goal Use properties of special pairs of angles.

Vocabulary

Two angles that share a common vertex and side, but have no common interior points are **adjacent angles.**

Two adjacent angles are a **linear pair** if their noncommon sides are opposite rays.

Theorem 4.3 Right Angles Congruence Theorem: All right angles are congruent.

Theorem 4.4 Congruent Supplements Theorem: If two angles are supplementary to the same angle (or to congruent angles), then they are congruent.

Theorem 4.5 Congruent Complements Theorem: If two angles are complementary to the same angle (or to congruent angles), then they are congruent.

Linear Pair Postulate: If two angles form a linear pair, then they are supplementary.

Theorem 4.6 Vertical Angles Congruence Theorem: Vertical angles are congruent.

Example 1 Find angle measures

Complete the statement given that $m\angle AGF = 90°$.

a. $m\angle CGD = \underline{\ ?\ }$

b. If $m\angle BGF = 113°$, then $m\angle DGE = \underline{\ ?\ }$.

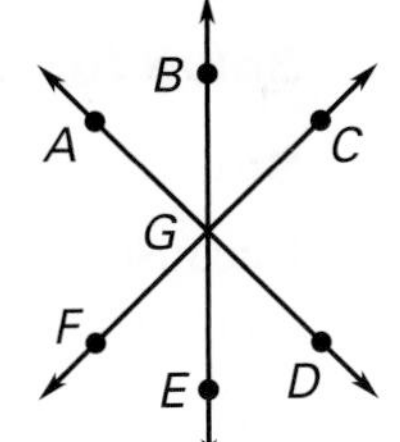

Solution

a. Because $\angle CGD$ and $\angle AGF$ are vertical angles, $\angle CGD \cong \angle AGF$. By the definition of congruent angles, $m\angle CGD = m\angle AGF$. So, $m\angle CGD = 90°$.

b. By the Angle Addition Postulate, $m\angle BGF = m\angle AGF + m\angle AGB$. Substitute to get $113° = 90° + m\angle AGB$. By the Subtraction Property of Equality, $m\angle AGB = 23°$. Because $\angle DGE$ and $\angle AGB$ are vertical angles, $\angle DGE \cong \angle AGB$. By the definition of congruent angles, $m\angle DGE = m\angle AGB$. So, $m\angle DGE = 23°$.

Guided Practice for Example 1

Copy and complete the statement given that $m\angle BHD = m\angle CHE = 90°$.

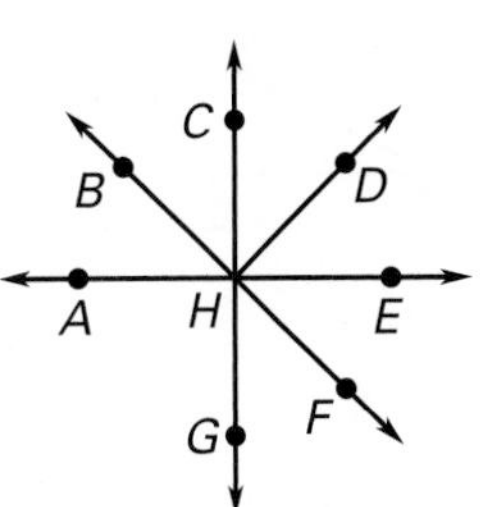

1. $m\angle AHG = \underline{\ ?\ }$

2. $m\angle CHA = \underline{\ ?\ }$

3. If $m\angle CHD = 31°$, then $m\angle EHF = \underline{\ ?\ }$.

4. If $m\angle BHG = 125°$, then $m\angle CHF = \underline{\ ?\ }$.

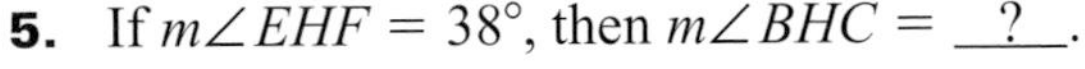

5. If $m\angle EHF = 38°$, then $m\angle BHC = \underline{\ ?\ }$.

UNIT 4

Georgia Performance Standards

MM1G2a Use conjecture, inductive reasoning, deductive reasoning, counterexamples, and indirect proof as appropriate. 

Example 2 Find angle measures

If $m\angle BGD = 90°$ and $m\angle CGD = 26°$, find $m\angle 1$, $m\angle 2$, and $m\angle 3$.

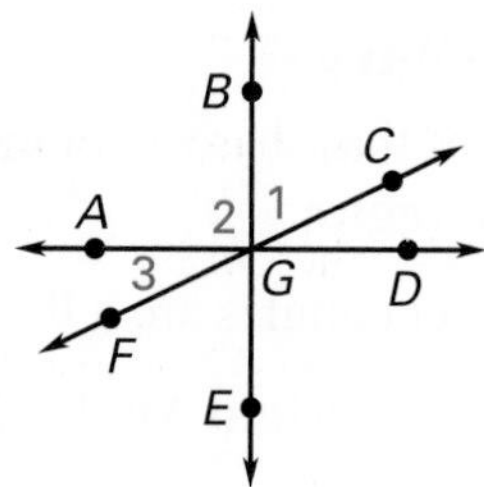

Solution

$\angle BGC$ and $\angle CGD$ are complementary.
So, $m\angle 1 = 90° - 26° = 64°$.

$\angle AGB$ and $\angle BGD$ are supplementary.
So, $m\angle 2 = 180° - 90° = 90°$.

$\angle AGF$ and $\angle CGD$ are vertical angles.
So, $m\angle 3 = 26°$.

Guided Practice for Example 2

In Exercises 6 and 7, refer to Example 2.

6. Find $m\angle FGE$.

7. Find $m\angle DGE$.

Example 3 Use algebra

Solve for *x* in the diagram.

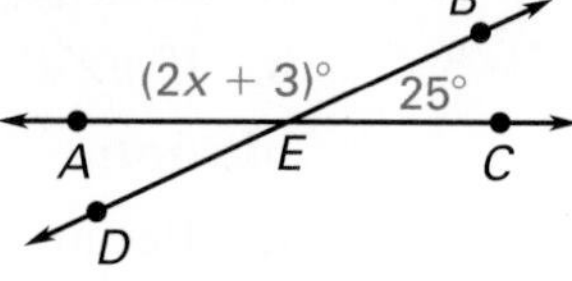

Solution

Because $\angle AEB$ and $\angle BEC$ form a linear pair, the sum of their measures is 180°. So, you can solve for x as follows:

$(2x + 3) + 25 = 180$	Definition of supplementary angles
$2x + 28 = 180$	Combine like terms.
$2x = 152$	Subtract 28 from both sides.
$x = 76$	Divide each side by 2.

Guided Practice for Example 3

Solve for *x* in the diagram.

8.

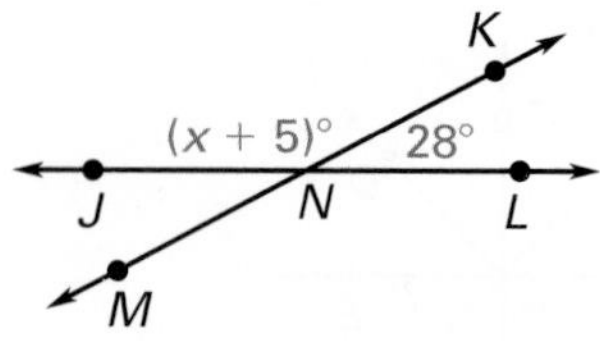

9.

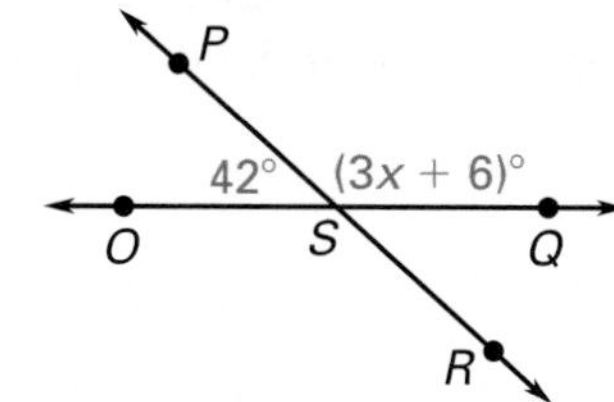

LESSON 4.6

Exercise Set A

MM1G2a Use conjecture, inductive reasoning, deductive reasoning, counterexamples, and indirect proof as appropriate.

Use the diagram to decide whether the statement is *true* or *false*.

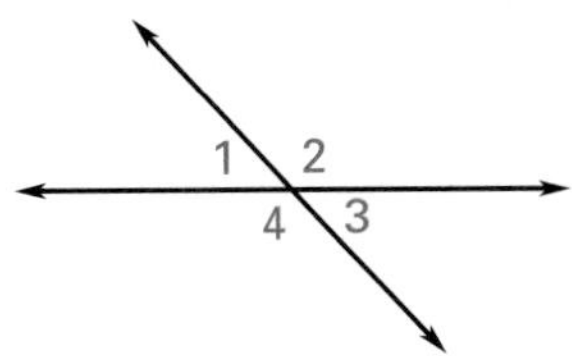

1. If $m\angle 1 = 47°$, then $m\angle 2 = 43°$.
2. If $m\angle 1 = 47°$, then $m\angle 3 = 47°$.
3. $m\angle 1 + m\angle 3 = m\angle 2 + m\angle 4$.
4. $m\angle 1 + m\angle 4 = m\angle 2 + m\angle 3$.

Make a sketch of the given information. Label all angles which can be determined.

5. Adjacent complementary angles where one angle measures 42°
6. Nonadjacent supplementary angles where one angle measures 42°
7. Congruent linear pairs
8. Vertical angles which measure 42°
9. $\angle ABC$ and $\angle CBD$ are adjacent complementary angles. $\angle CBD$ and $\angle DBF$ are adjacent complementary angles.
10. $\angle 1$ and $\angle 2$ are complementary. $\angle 3$ and $\angle 4$ are complementary. $\angle 1$ and $\angle 3$ are vertical angles.

Find the value of the variables and the measure of each angle in the diagram.

11.

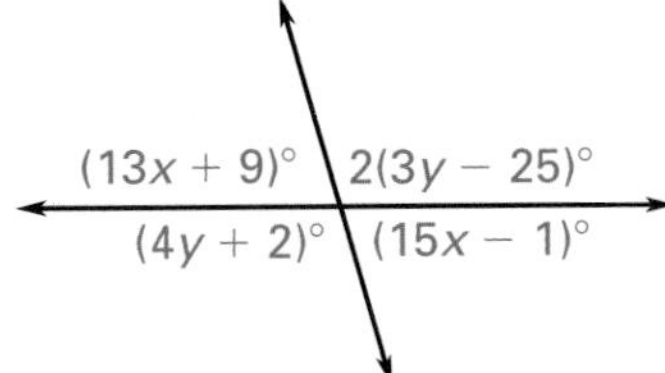

12.

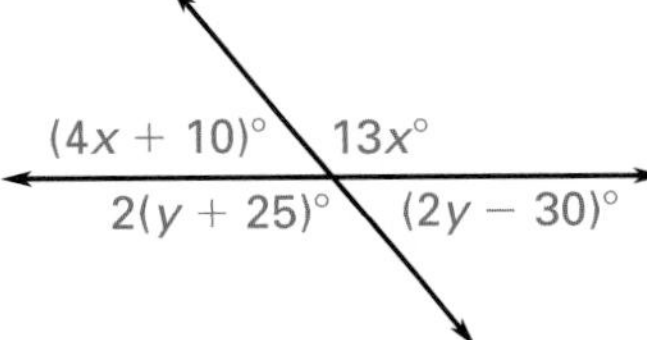

13.

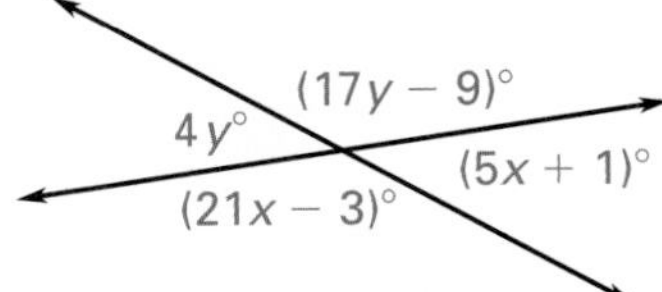

14.

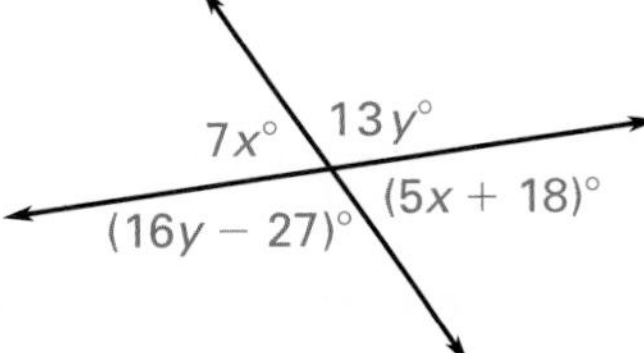

15. **Error Analysis** *Describe* the error in making the statements about the diagram.

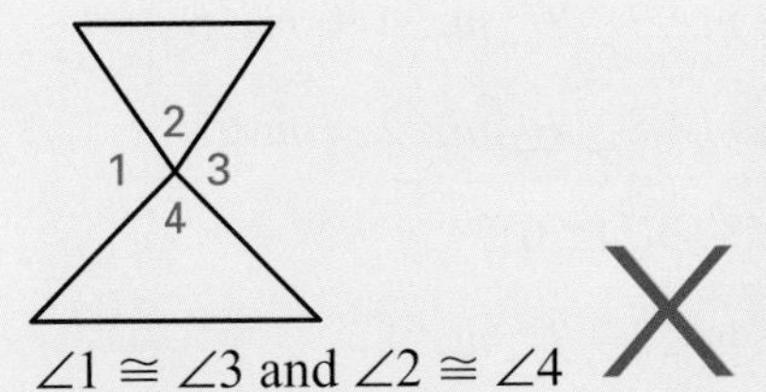

UNIT 4

Exercise Set A *(continued)*

In Exercises 16 and 17, copy and complete the proof.

16. GIVEN: $\angle 2 \cong \angle 3$

PROVE: $\angle 1 \cong \angle 4$

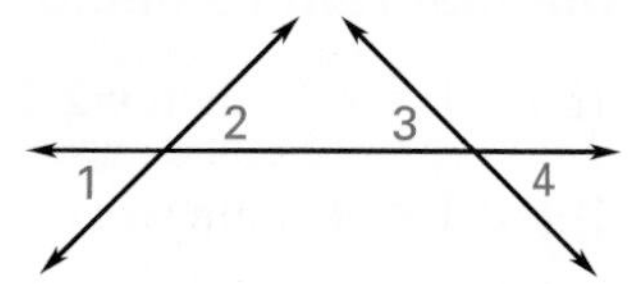

Statements	Reasons
1. $\angle 2 \cong \angle 3$	1. ?
2. $\angle 3 \cong \angle 4$	2. ?
3. $\angle 2 \cong \angle 4$	3. ?
4. $\angle 1 \cong \angle 2$	4. ?
5. $\angle 1 \cong \angle 4$	5. ?

17. GIVEN: $\angle 1$ and $\angle 2$ are complementary.
$\angle 1 \cong \angle 3$, $\angle 2 \cong \angle 4$

PROVE: $\angle 3$ and $\angle 4$ are complementary.

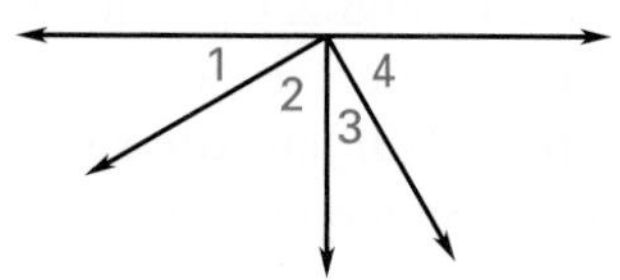

Statements	Reasons
1. $\angle 1$ and $\angle 2$ are complementary.	1. ?
2. $m\angle 1 + m\angle 2 = 90°$	2. ?
3. $\angle 1 \cong \angle 3$, $\angle 2 \cong \angle 4$	3. ?
4. $m\angle 1 = m\angle 3$, $m\angle 2 = m\angle 4$	4. ?
5. $m\angle 3 + m\angle 2 = 90°$	5. ?
6. $m\angle 3 + m\angle 4 = 90°$	6. ?
7. $\angle 3$ and $\angle 4$ are complementary.	7. ?

In the diagram, $\angle 1$ is a right angle and $m\angle 6 = 36°$. Copy and complete the statement with <, >, or =.

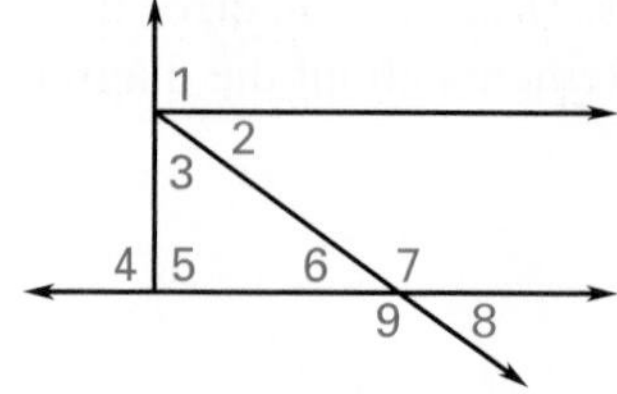

18. $m\angle 6 + m\angle 7$ ___?___ $m\angle 4 + m\angle 5$

19. $m\angle 6 + m\angle 8$ ___?___ $m\angle 2 + m\angle 3$

20. $m\angle 9$ ___?___ $3(m\angle 6)$

21. $m\angle 2 + m\angle 3$ ___?___ $m\angle 1$

LESSON 4.6 **Exercise Set B**

MM1G2a Use conjecture, inductive reasoning, deductive reasoning, counterexamples, and indirect proof as appropriate.

Identify the pair(s) of congruent angles in the figure. *Explain* how you know they are congruent.

1. $\angle 1$ and $\angle 2$ are complementary.
$\angle 2$ and $\angle 3$ are complementary.
$\angle 1$ and $\angle 4$ are complementary.

2. $\angle 1$ and $\angle 7$ are supplementary.
$\angle 8$ and $\angle 1$ are supplementary.
$\angle 5$ and $\angle 1$ are supplementary.

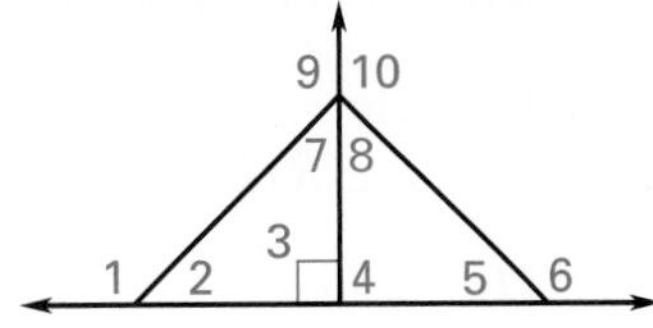

Use the diagram at the right.

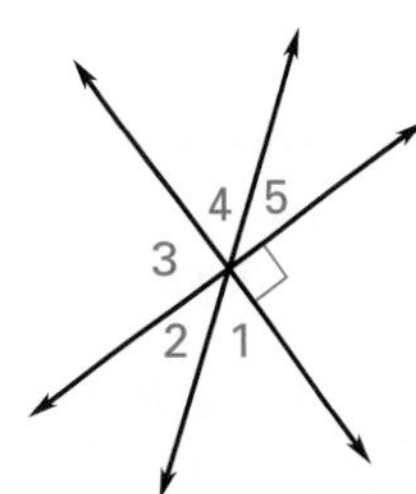

3. If $m\angle 1 = 53°$, find $m\angle 2$, $m\angle 3$, $m\angle 4$, and $m\angle 5$.

4. If $m\angle 2 = 34°$, find $m\angle 1$, $m\angle 3$, $m\angle 4$, and $m\angle 5$.

5. If $m\angle 5 = 39°$, find $m\angle 1$, $m\angle 2$, $m\angle 3$, and $m\angle 4$.

6. If $m\angle 4 + m\angle 3 = 144°$, find $m\angle 1$, $m\angle 2$, and $m\angle 5$.

Find the values of the variables.

7.

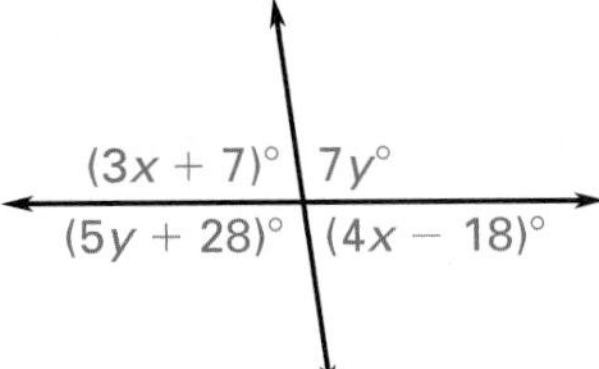

8.

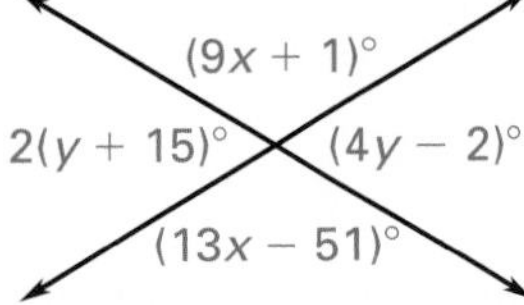

9.

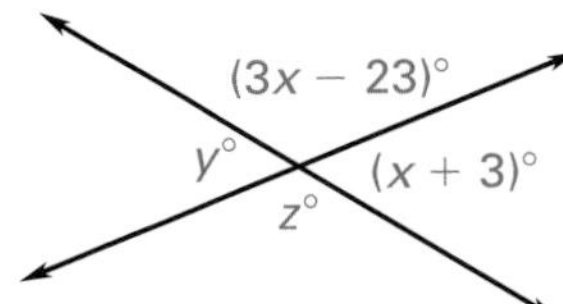

10.

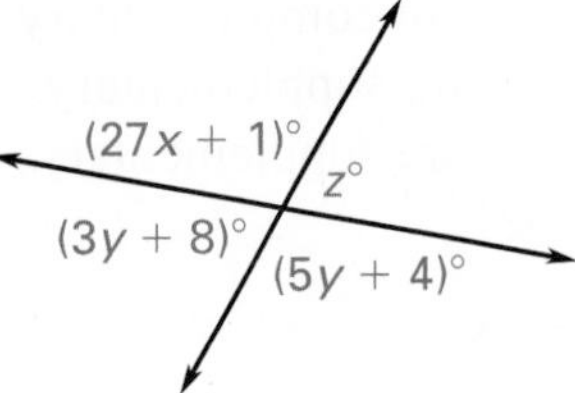

In the diagram, $\overline{AE} \perp \overline{CG}$, $m\angle ASD = 118°$ and $m\angle HSB = 96°$. Find the indicated angle measure.

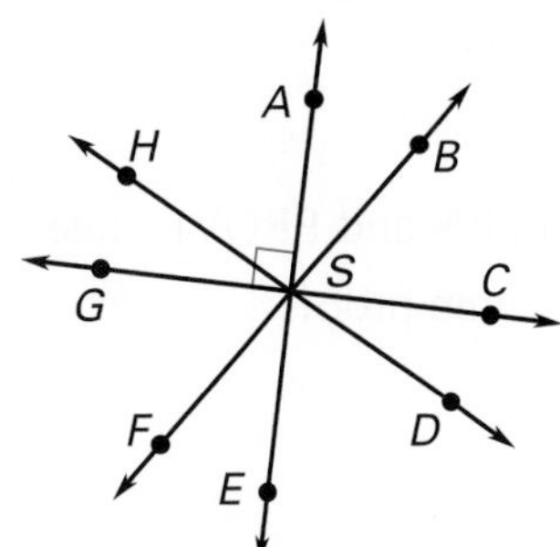

11. Find $m\angle HSE$.

12. Find $m\angle FSD$.

13. Find $m\angle BSD$.

14. Find $m\angle DSE$.

15. Find $m\angle CSD$.

16. Find $m\angle GSF$.

Exercise Set B *(continued)*

Two nonperpendicular lines $\overleftrightarrow{TG}$ and $\overleftrightarrow{SF}$ intersect at *B* so that *B* is between *T* and *G*, and *B* is also between *S* and *F*. Tell whether the statement is true.

17. $\angle TBF \cong \angle SBG$

18. $\angle TBF \cong \angle TBS$

19. $m\angle TBS + m\angle GBF = 180°$

20. $\angle GBF \cong \angle TBG$

21. $\angle TBG \cong \angle SBF$

22. $m\angle TBF + m\angle TBS = 180°$

23. Use the given information and the diagram to complete the proof.

GIVEN: $\angle S$ is a right angle.
$m\angle RTS = 40°$, $m\angle RTU = 50°$

PROVE: $\angle S \cong \angle STU$

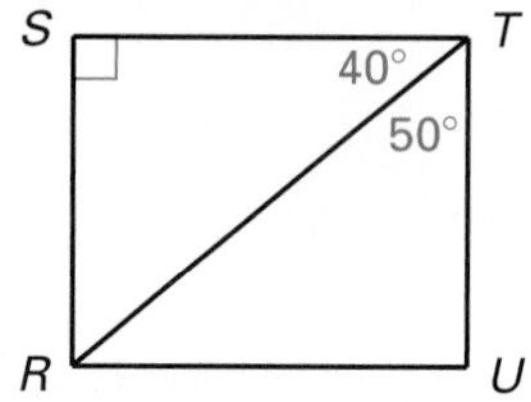

Statements	Reasons
1. $\angle S$ is a right angle. $m\angle RTS = 40°$, $m\angle RTU = 50°$	1. ?
2. ? $= m\angle RTS + m\angle RTU$	2. ?
3. $m\angle STU =$?	3. Substitution Property of Equality
4. $m\angle STU =$?	4. Simplify.
5. $\angle STU$ is a right angle.	5. ?
6. ?	6. Right Angles Congruence Theorem

24. Picture Frame You are making the picture frame shown.

GIVEN: $\angle 1$ and $\angle 4$ are complementary.
$\angle 4$ and $\angle 5$ are complementary.
$\angle 1$ and $\angle 2$ are supplementary.
$\angle 5$ and $\angle 6$ are supplementary.
$m\angle 1 = 52°$

PROVE: $m\angle 6 = 128°$

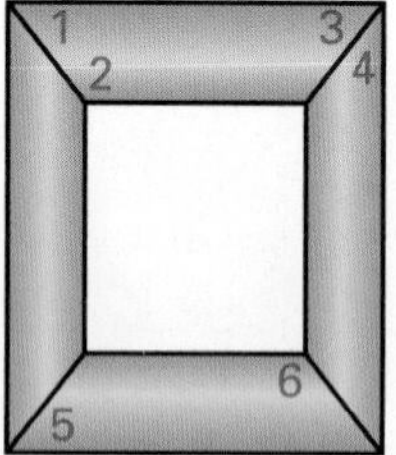

25. $\angle ABC$ is bisected by $\overrightarrow{BD}$, and $\overrightarrow{BD}$ and $\overrightarrow{BE}$ are opposite rays. You want to show that $\angle ABE \cong \angle CBE$.

a. Draw a diagram.

b. Identify the GIVEN and PROVE statements for the situation.

c. Write a two-column proof.

UNIT 4

LESSON 4.7

Prove Theorems About Perpendicular Lines

Georgia Performance Standards: MM1G1b

Goal Find the distance between a point and a line.

Vocabulary

The **distance from a point to a line** is the length of the perpendicular segment from the point to the line.

A **transversal** is a line that intersects two or more coplanar lines at different points.

Theorem 4.7: If two lines intersect to form a linear pair of congruent angles, then the lines are perpendicular.

Theorem 4.8: If two lines are perpendicular, then they intersect to form four right angles.

Theorem 4.9: If two sides of two adjacent acute angles are perpendicular, then the angles are complementary.

Theorem 4.10 Perpendicular Transversal Theorem: If a transversal is perpendicular to one of two parallel lines, then it is perpendicular to the other.

Theorem 4.11 Lines Perpendicular to a Transversal Theorem: In a plane, if two lines are perpendicular to the same line, then they are parallel to each other.

UNIT 4

Example 1 Application of the theorems

Find the value of *x*.

a.

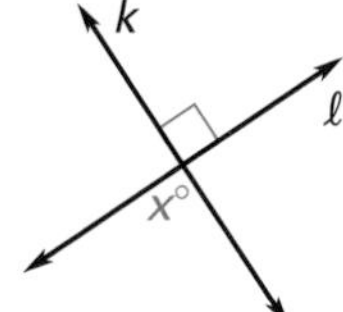

b.

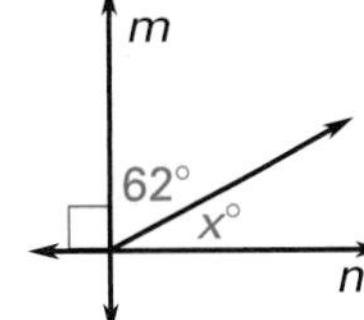

Solution

a. Because k and ℓ are perpendicular, all four angles formed are right angles by Theorem 4.8. By definition of a right angle, $x = 90$.

b. Because m and n are perpendicular, all four angles formed are right angles by Theorem 4.8. By Theorem 4.9, the 62° angle and the $x°$ angle are complementary. Thus $x + 62 = 90$, so $x = 28$.

Guided Practice for Example 1

Find the value of *x*.

1.

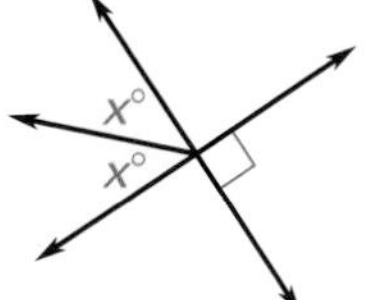

2.

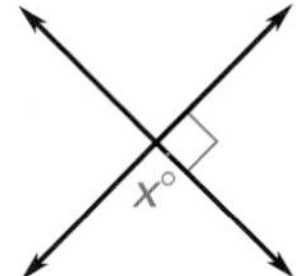

3.

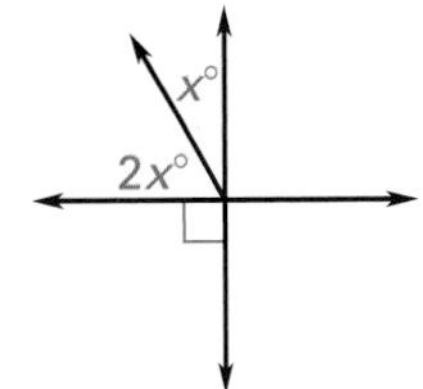

Georgia Performance Standards

MM1G1b Determine the distance between a point and a line.

Example 2 Find the distance between a point and a line

What is the distance from point *A* to line *b*?

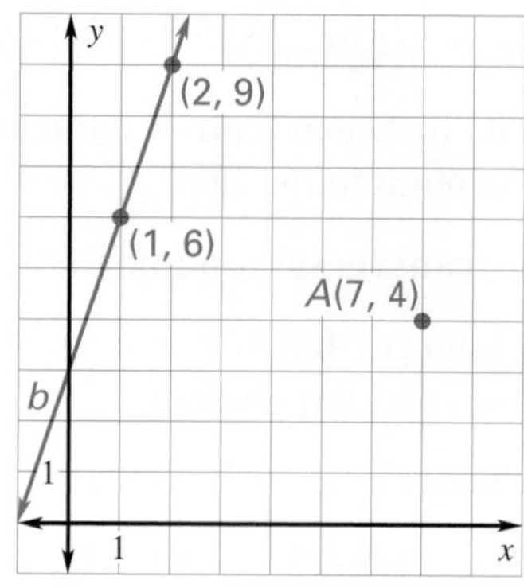

Solution

You need to find the slope of line b. Using the points (1, 6) and (2, 9), the slope of line b is

$$m = \frac{9 - 6}{2 - 1} = 3.$$

The distance from point A to line b is the length of the perpendicular segment from point A to line b. The slope of a perpendicular segment from point A to line b is the negative reciprocal of 3, or $-\frac{1}{3}$. The segment from (1, 6) to (7, 4) has a slope of $-\frac{1}{3}$. So, the segment is perpendicular to line b.

Find the distance between (1, 6) and (7, 4).

$$d = \sqrt{(1 - 7)^2 + (6 - 4)^2} \approx 6.3$$

The distance from point A to line b is about 6.3 units.

Guided Practice for Example 2

Use the graph at the right.

4. What is the distance from point H to line j?

5. What is the distance from line j to line k?

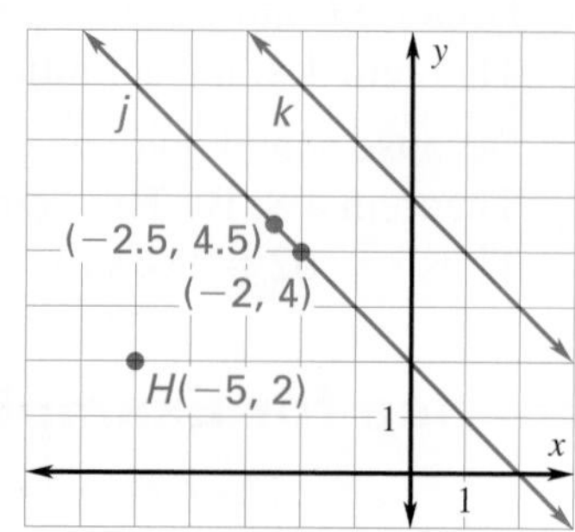

6. Graph the line $y = x + 2$. Which point on the line is the shortest distance from the point (2, 0)? What is the distance? Round your answer to the nearest tenth.

LESSON 4.7

Exercise Set A

MM1G1b Determine the distance between a point and a line.

What can you conclude from the given information? State the reason for your conclusion.

1. $\angle 1 \cong \angle 2$

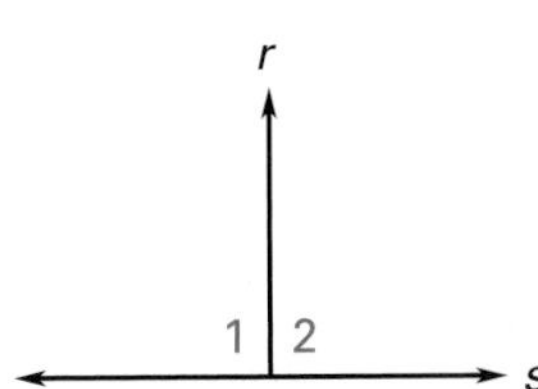

2. $n \perp m$

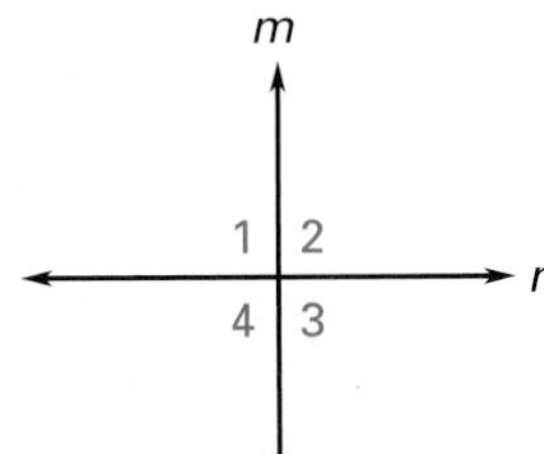

3. $\overrightarrow{BA} \perp \overrightarrow{BC}$

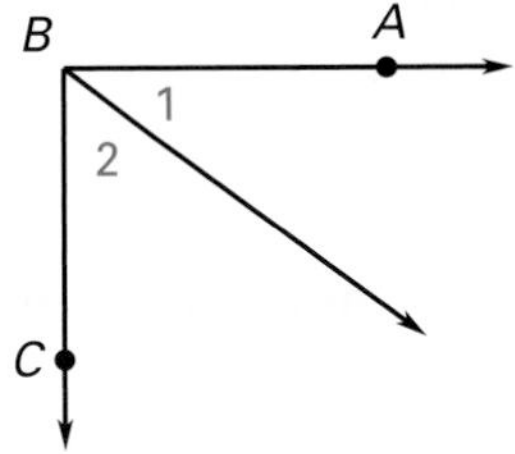

Find the value of *x*.

4.

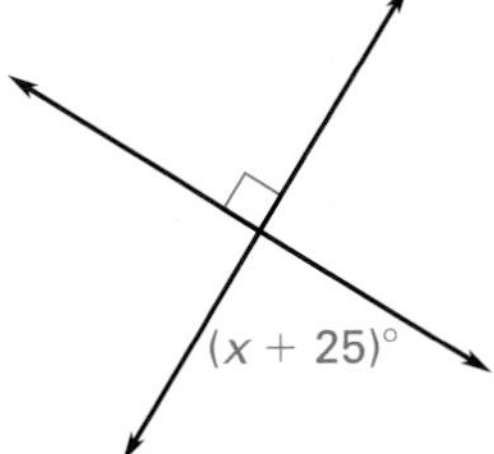

5.

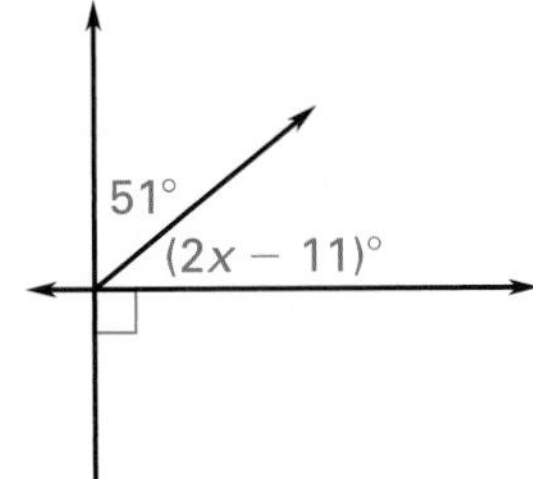

6.

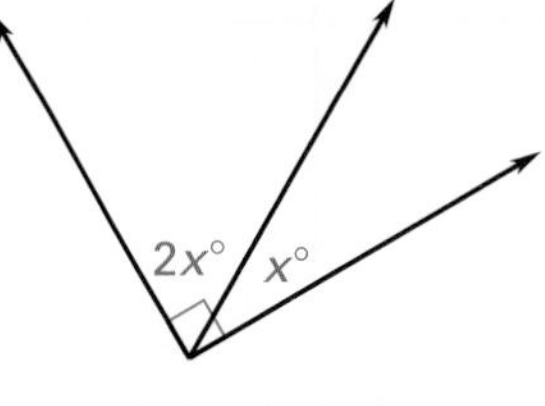

7.

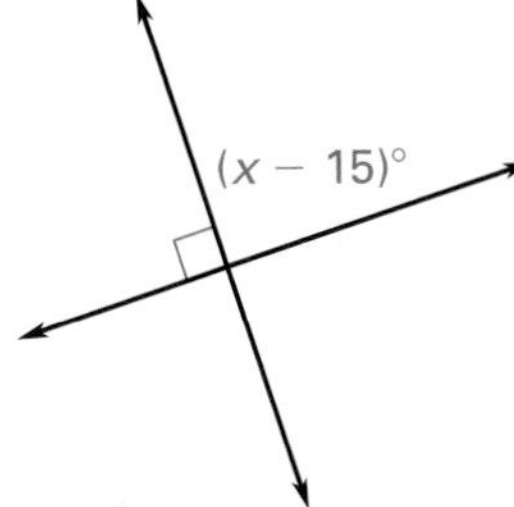

8.

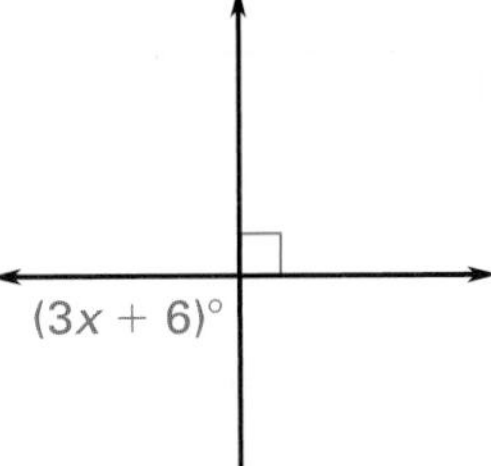

9.

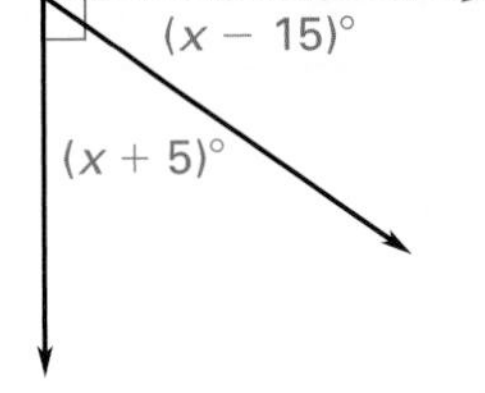

Find the measure of the indicated angle.

10. $\angle 1$

11. $\angle 2$

12. $\angle 3$

13. $\angle 4$

14. $\angle 5$

15. $\angle 6$

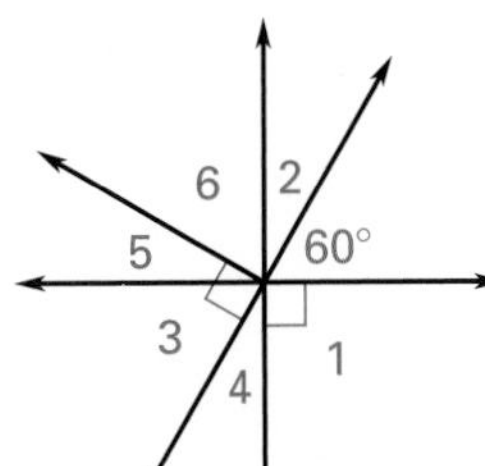

UNIT 4

Exercise Set A *(continued)*

In Exercises 16–18, use the diagram.

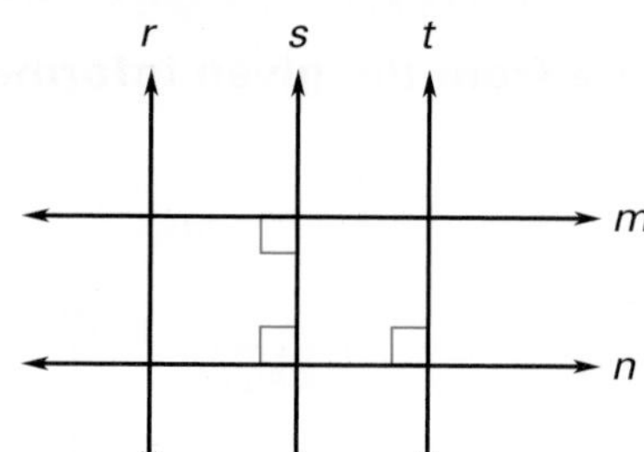

16. Is $r \parallel s$?

17. Is $m \parallel n$?

18. Is $s \parallel t$?

Find the distance from point *A* to line *c*. Round your answer to the nearest tenth.

19.

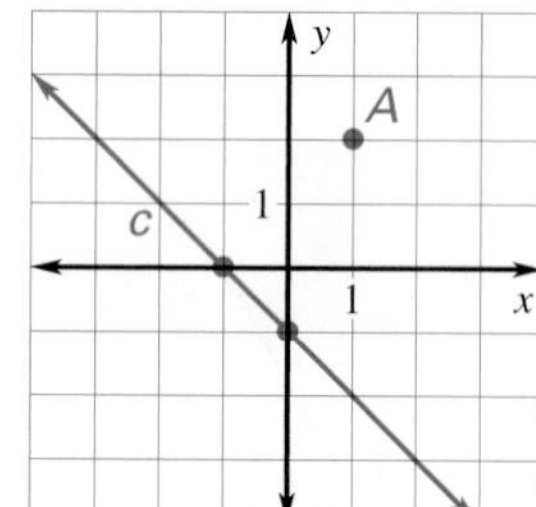

20.

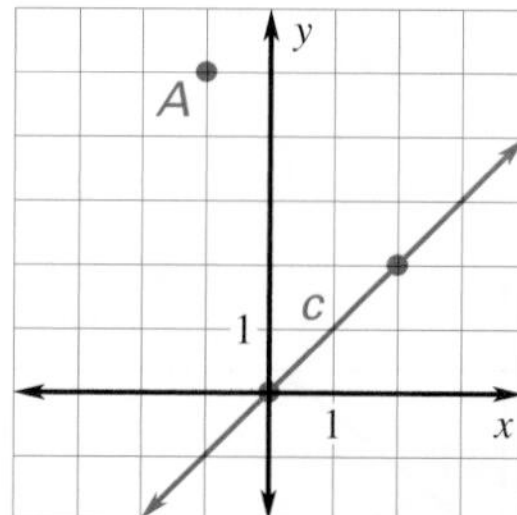

21.

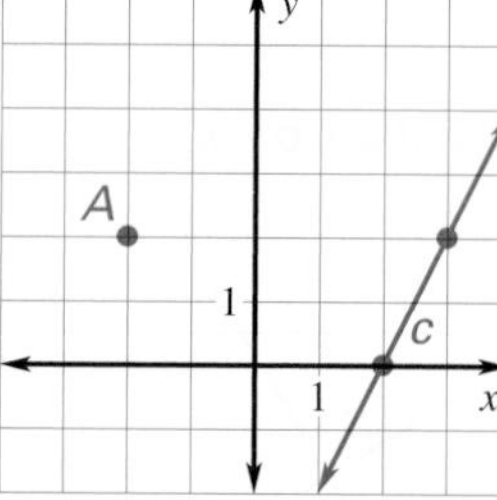

22.

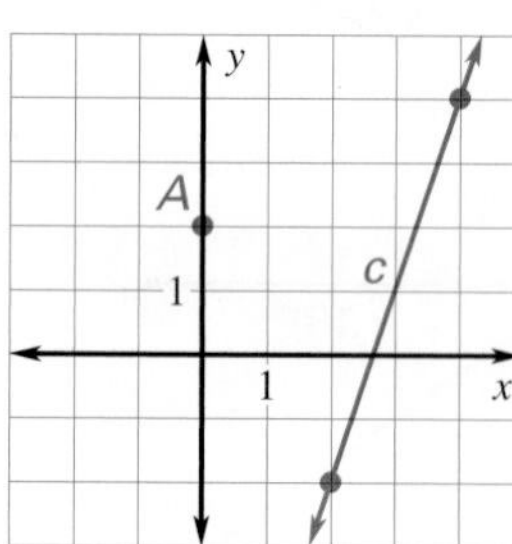

23.

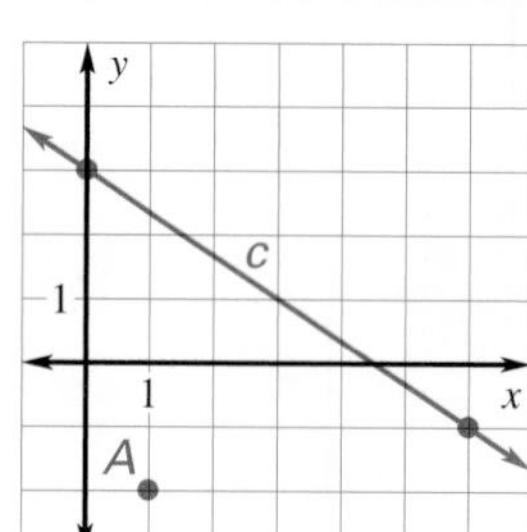

24.

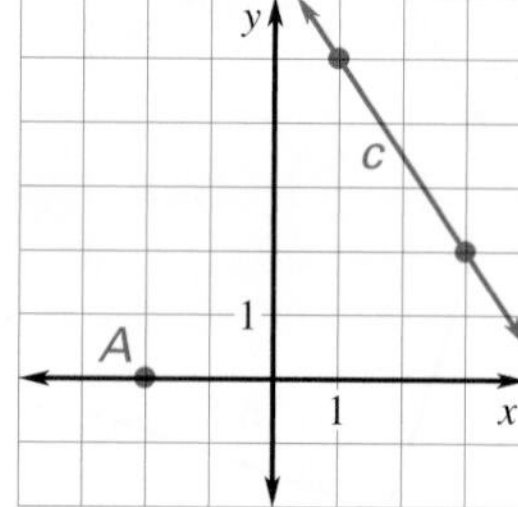

25. Maps A map of a neighborhood is drawn on a graph where units are measured in feet.

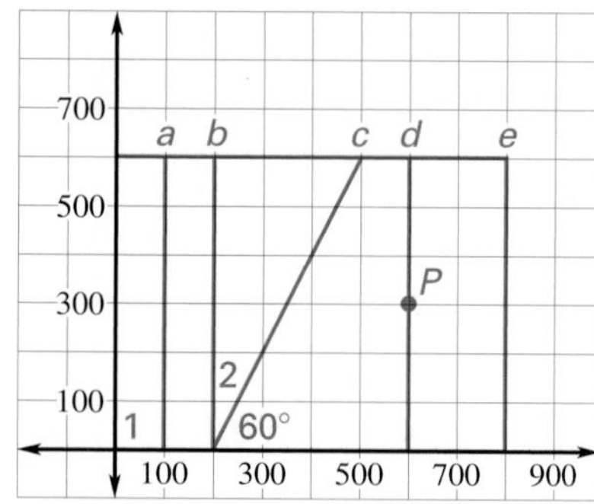

a. Find $m\angle 1$.

b. Find $m\angle 2$.

c. Find the distance from point P to street a.

d. Find the distance from point P to street c. Round your answer to the nearest foot.

LESSON 4.7 **Exercise Set B**

MM1G1b Determine the distance between a point and a line.

Find $m\angle 1$.

1.

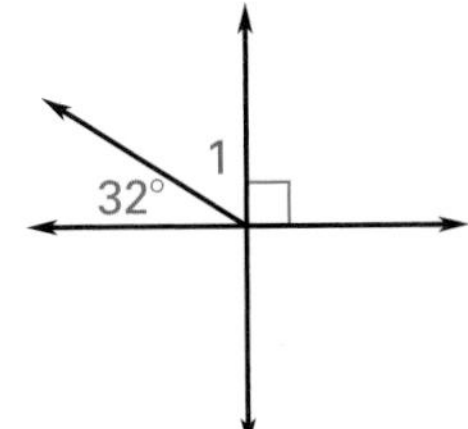

2.

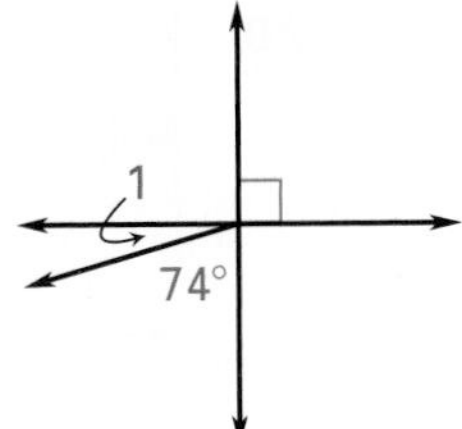

3.

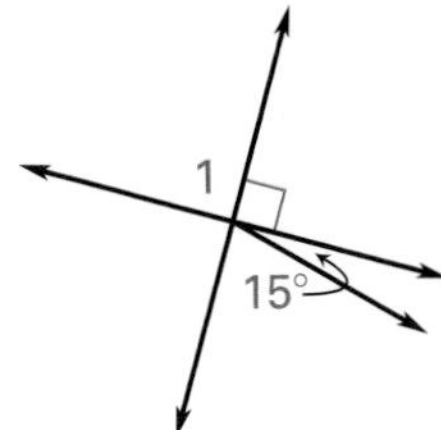

Find the measure of the indicated angle.

4. $\angle 1$

5. $\angle 2$

6. $\angle 3$

7. $\angle 4$

8. $\angle 5$

9. $\angle 6$

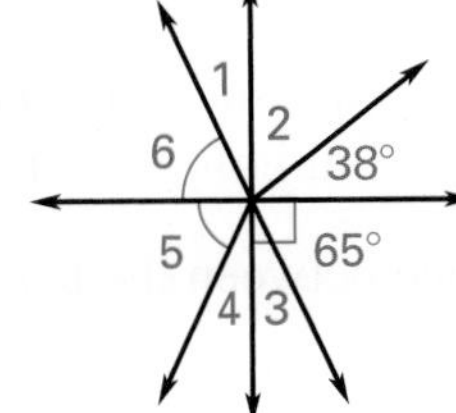

In Exercises 10–12, use the diagram.

10. Is $r \parallel s$?

11. Is $m \parallel n$?

12. Is $r \parallel t$?

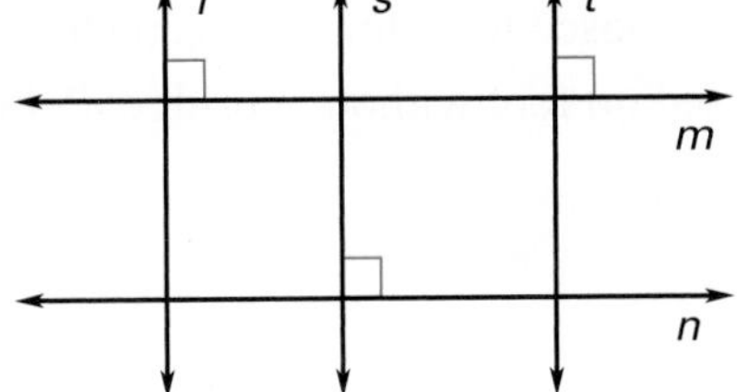

In the diagram, $\overleftrightarrow{RS} \perp \overleftrightarrow{ST}$. Find the value of *x*.

13.

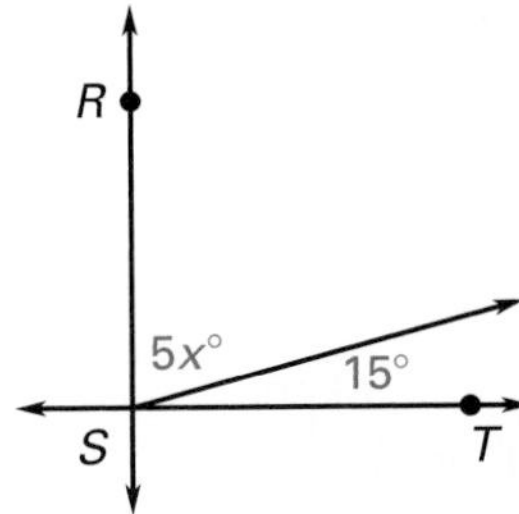

14.

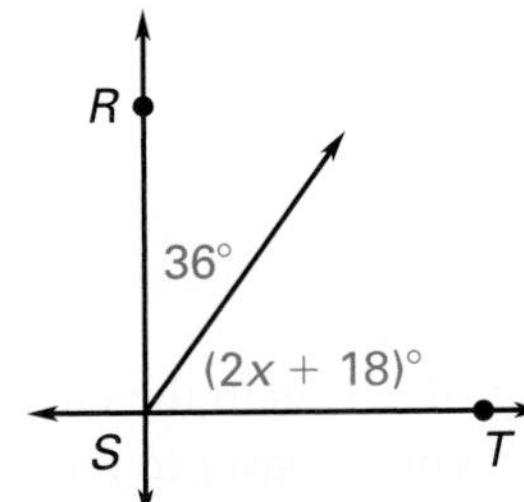

15.

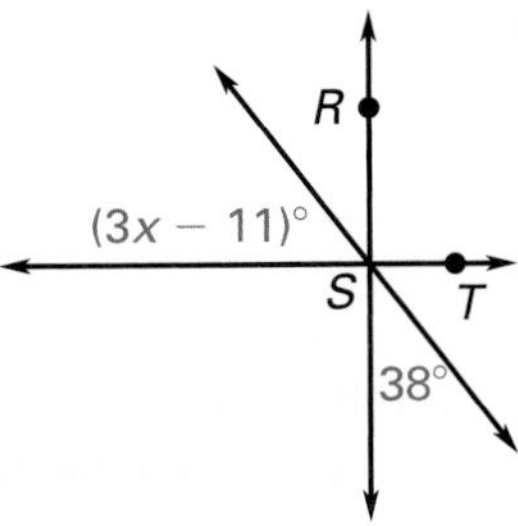

16.

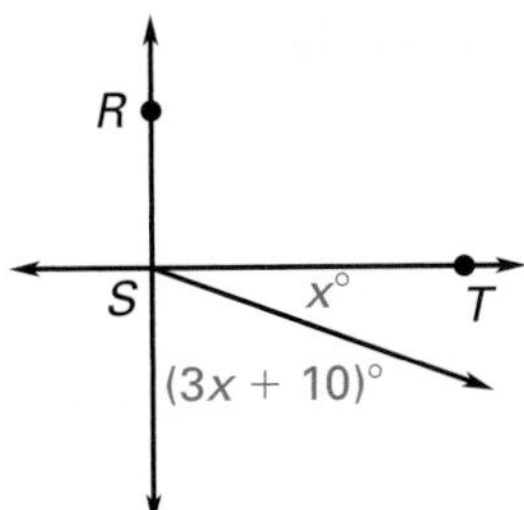

17.

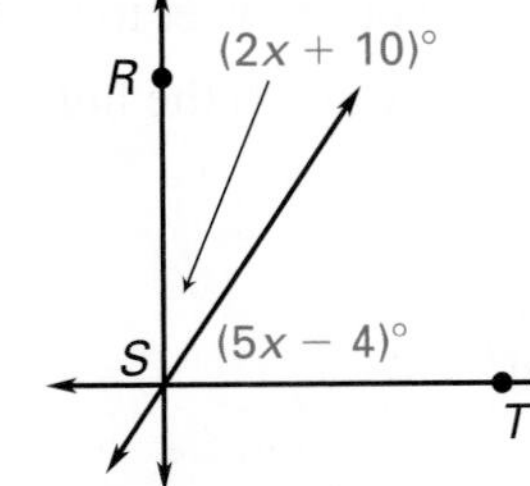

18.

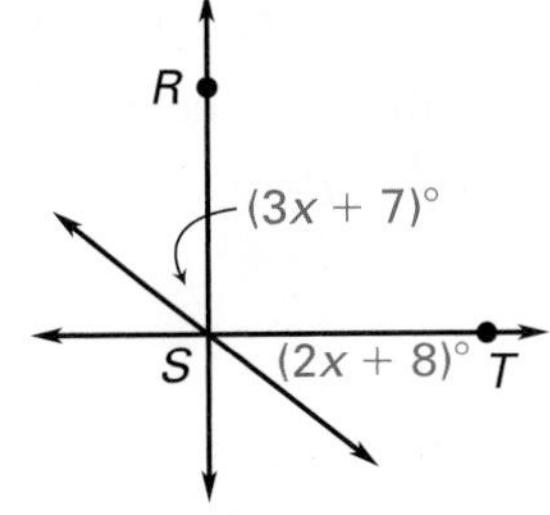

Exercise Set B *(continued)*

Find the distance between the two parallel lines. Round to the nearest tenth, if necessary.

19.

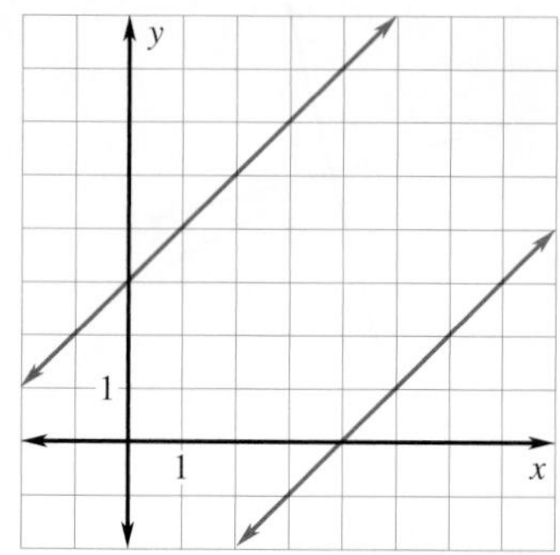

20.

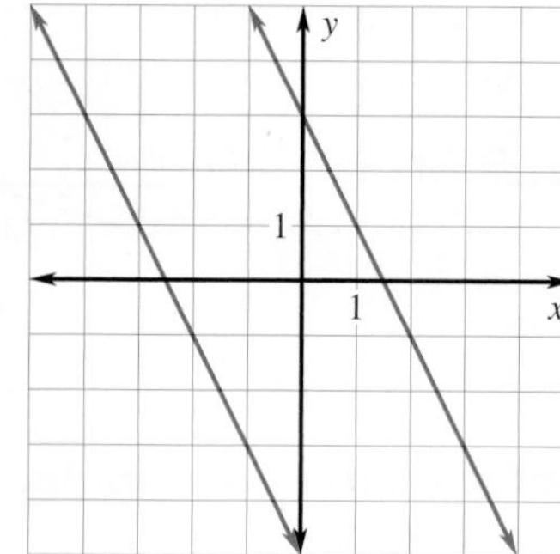

21. Finding Coordinates Find the value of k such that the line containing point $(2, k)$ is perpendicular to the line $y = 2x - 3$ at point $(4, 5)$.

22. Finding Distances Find the distance between the parallel lines with the equations $y = \frac{2}{7}x + 4$ and $y = \frac{2}{7}x - 2$.

23. **Maps** A partial map of a wooded hiking area is drawn on a graph where units are measured in miles. Line HY represents the main highway through the area and line WT represents the hiking trail that hikers are supposed to follow between check points. Line RV represents a river that cannot be crossed on foot without a bridge. Point L represents a lost group of hikers.

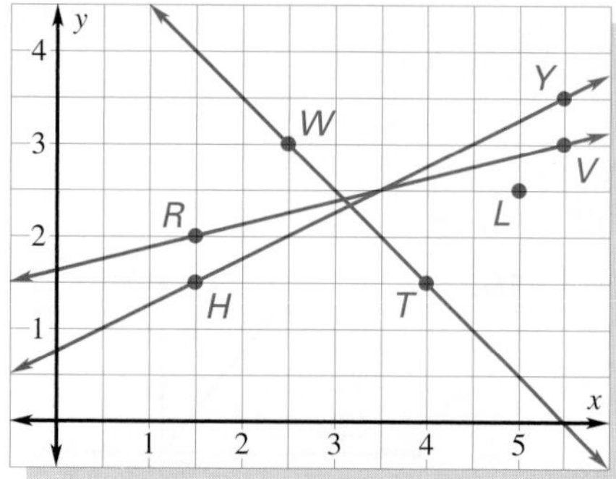

a. Find the distance from the lost group of hikers to the closest point where the hikers are able to reach the highway. Round your answer to the nearest tenth of a mile.

b. Find the distance from the lost group of hikers to the closest point where the hikers are able to reach the hiking trail. Round your answer to the nearest tenth of a mile.

c. Would it be shorter for the lost hikers to walk to the highway or to the hiking trail? *Explain.*

UNIT 4

LESSON 4.7

Problem Solving Workshop

Problem You are measuring the distance between two parallel pieces of lattice work on a fence. The diagram shows the lattice work, with coordinates in inches. What is the approximate distance?

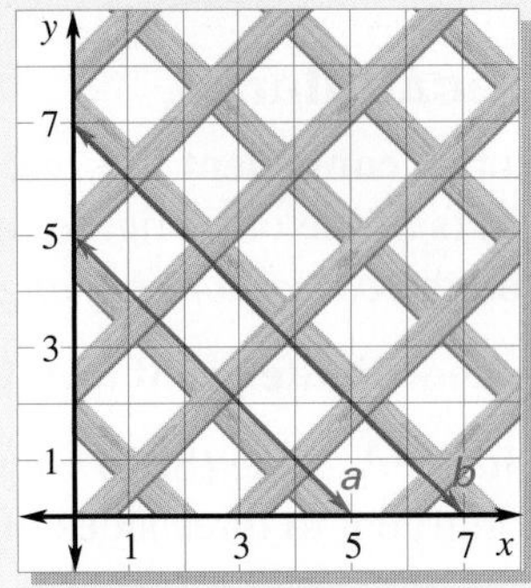

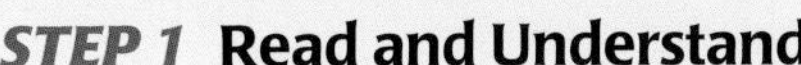

STEP 1 **Read and Understand**

What do you know? You know how to find the slope of each piece of lattice work.

What do you want to find out? You need to find the distance between two parallel pieces of lattice work.

STEP 2 **Make a Plan** Use what you know to find the length of the perpendicular segment from one piece of lattice work to the other.

STEP 3 **Solve the Problem** Use the points (5, 0) and (0, 5) to find the slope of line *a*.

$$m = \frac{5 - 0}{0 - 5} = -1 \qquad \text{Slope of line } a.$$

The slope of a segment perpendicular to line *a* is the negative reciprocal of -1, or 1. A segment from line *a* to line *b* with endpoints (0, 5) and (1, 6) has a slope of 1. So, the segment is perpendicular to line *a*. The distance between (0, 5) and (1, 6) is

$$d = \sqrt{(1 - 0)^2 + (6 - 5)^2} \approx 1.4 \text{ inches.}$$

The distance between two pieces of lattice work is about 1.4 inches.

STEP 4 **Look Back** By looking at the graph, you can estimate that the perpendicular distance between each parallel piece of lattice work is greater than 1 inch, but less than 2 inches. So, the answer seems reasonable.

Practice

1. **Maps** What is the distance between you and Fifth Avenue? (Units are measured in meters.)

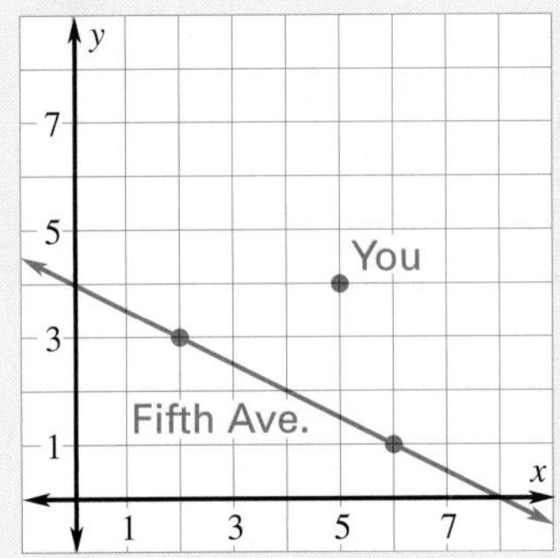

2. **Maps** Maple Lane and Lilac Street are parallel. What is the distance between the two streets? (Units are measured in miles.)

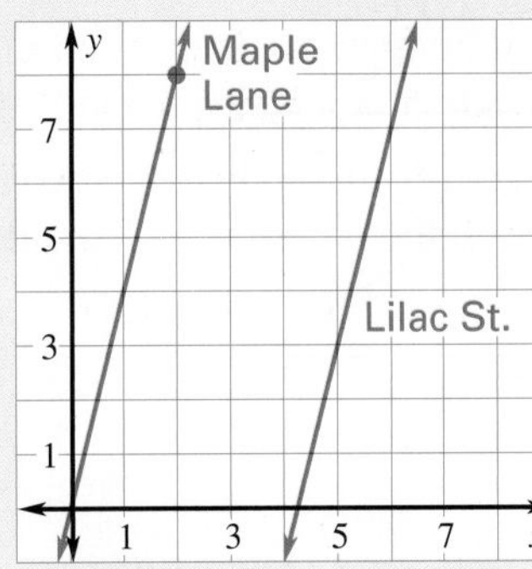

LESSON 4.8

Prove Triangles Congruent by SSS

Georgia Performance Standards: MM1G1e, MM1G3c

Goal Use side lengths to prove triangles are congruent.

Vocabulary

In two **congruent figures,** all the parts of one figure are congruent to the **corresponding parts** of the other figure. In congruent polygons, this means that the *corresponding sides* and the *corresponding angles* are congruent.

A **coordinate proof** involves placing geometric figures in a coordinate plane.

Side-Side-Side (SSS) Congruence Postulate: If three sides of one triangle are congruent to three sides of a second triangle, then the two triangles are congruent.

Example 1 Use the SSS Congruence Postulate

Show that $\triangle JKL \cong \triangle MLN$.

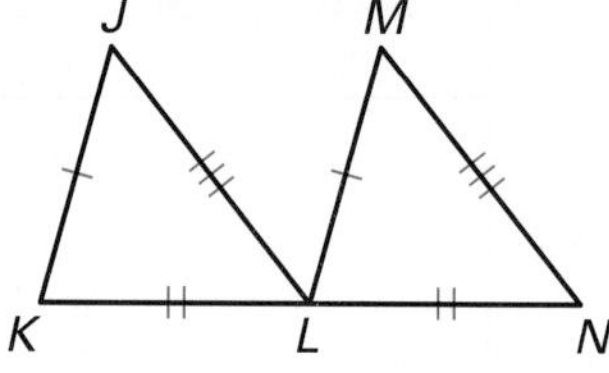

Solution

It is given that $\overline{JK} \cong \overline{ML}$, $\overline{KL} \cong \overline{LN}$, and $\overline{JL} \cong \overline{MN}$.

So, by the SSS Congruence Postulate, $\triangle JKL \cong \triangle MLN$.

Guided Practice for Example 1

Decide whether the congruence statement is true. *Explain* your reasoning.

1. $\triangle ABD \cong \triangle CDB$

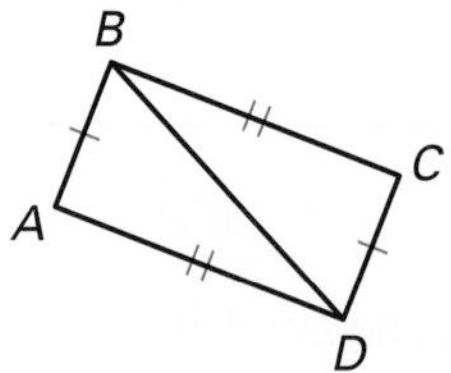

2. $\triangle XWY \cong \triangle WZY$

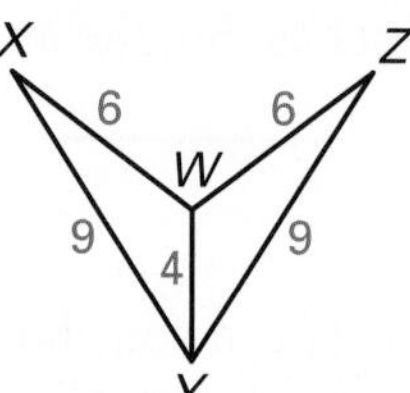

3. $\triangle RST \cong \triangle VUT$

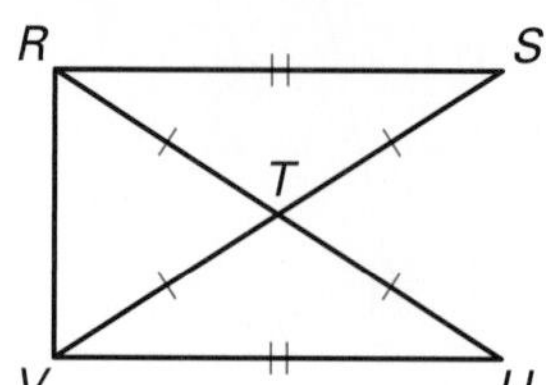

4. $\triangle FGH \cong \triangle JHG$

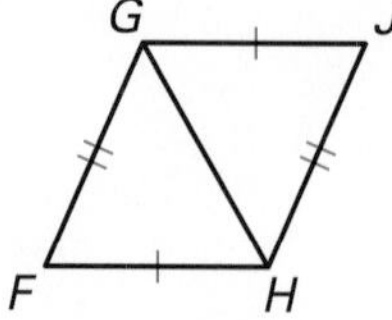

UNIT 4

Georgia Performance Standards

MM1G1e Use the coordinate plane to investigate properties of and verify conjectures related to triangles and quadrilaterals.

MM1G3c Understand and use congruence postulates and theorems for triangles (SSS, SAS, ASA, AAS, HL).

Example 2 Congruent triangles in a coordinate plane

Use the SSS Congruence Postulate to show that $\triangle ABC \cong \triangle CDE$.

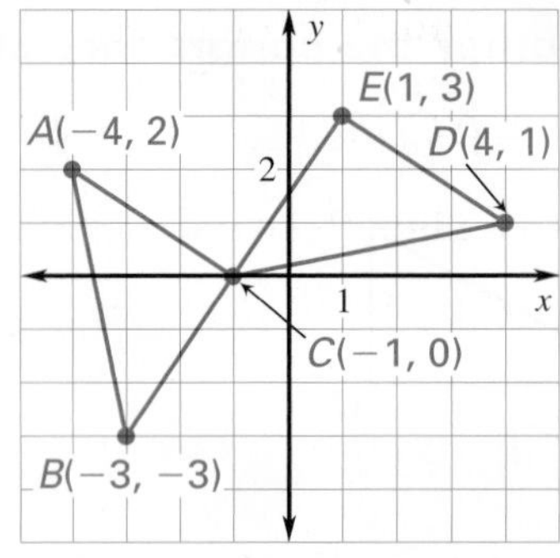

Solution

Use the Distance Formula to show that corresponding sides are the same length.

$$AB = \sqrt{(-3 - (-4))^2 + (-3 - 2)^2} = \sqrt{1^2 + (-5)^2} = \sqrt{26}$$

$$CD = \sqrt{(4 - (-1))^2 + (1 - 0)^2} = \sqrt{5^2 + 1^2} = \sqrt{26}$$

So, $AB = CD$, and hence $\overline{AB} \cong \overline{CD}$.

$$BC = \sqrt{(-1 - (-3))^2 + (0 - (-3))^2} = \sqrt{2^2 + 3^2} = \sqrt{13}$$

$$DE = \sqrt{(1 - 4)^2 + (3 - 1)^2} = \sqrt{(-3)^2 + 2^2} = \sqrt{13}$$

So, $BC = DE$, and hence $\overline{BC} \cong \overline{DE}$.

$$CA = \sqrt{(-4 - (-1))^2 + (2 - 0)^2} = \sqrt{(-3)^2 + 2^2} = \sqrt{13}$$

$$EC = \sqrt{(-1 - 1)^2 + (0 - 3)^2} = \sqrt{(-2)^2 + (-3)^2} = \sqrt{13}$$

So, $CA = EC$, and hence $\overline{CA} \cong \overline{EC}$.

So, by the SSS Congruence Postulate, you know that $\triangle ABC \cong \triangle CDE$.

Guided Practice for Example 2

5. Show that $\triangle ABC \cong \triangle DEF$.

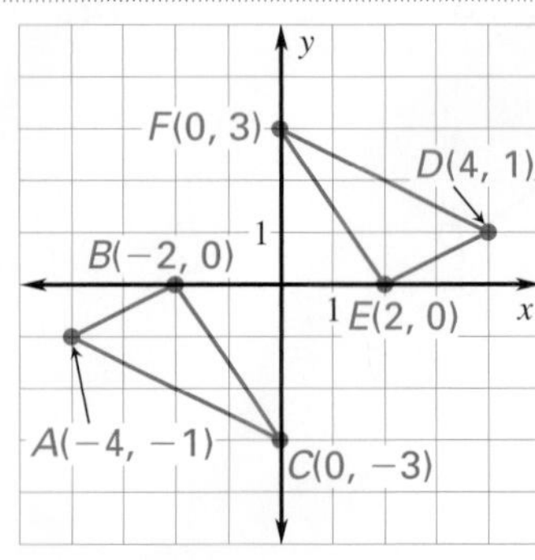

UNIT 4

LESSON 4.8 **Exercise Set A**

MM1G1e Use the coordinate plane to investigate properties of and verify conjectures related to triangles and quadrilaterals.

MM1G3c Understand and use congruence postulates and theorems for triangles (SSS, SAS, ASA, AAS, HL).

Decide whether the congruence statement is true. *Explain* your reasoning.

1. $\triangle ABD \cong \triangle CDB$

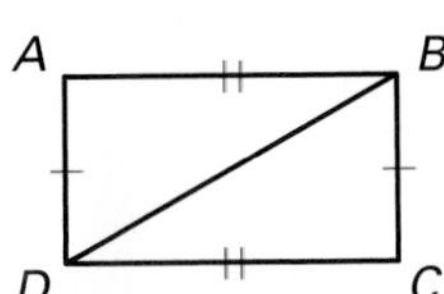

2. $\triangle RST \cong \triangle RQT$

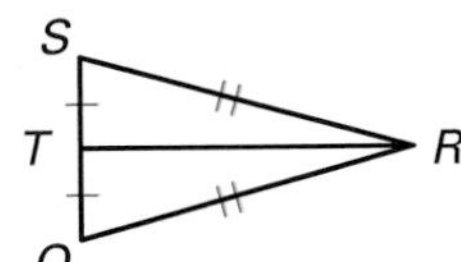

3. $\triangle ABC \cong \triangle DEF$

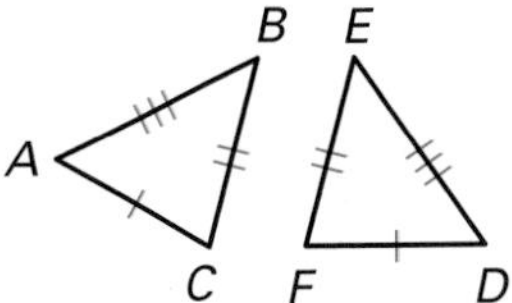

Use the given coordinates to determine if $\triangle ABC \cong \triangle DEF$.

4. $A(1, 2), B(4, -3), C(2, 5), D(4, 7), E(7, 2), F(5, 10)$

5. $A(1, 1), B(4, 0), C(7, 5), D(4, -5), E(6, -6), F(9, -1)$

6. $A(2, -2), B(5, 1), C(4, 8), D(7, 5), E(10, 8), F(9, 13)$

7. $A(-3, 0), B(6, 2), C(-1, 9), D(4, -10), E(13, -8), F(6, -1)$

8. $A(0, 0), B(6, 5), C(9, 0), D(0, -1), E(6, -6), F(9, -1)$

9. $A(-5, 7), B(-5, 2), C(0, 2), D(0, 6), E(0, 1), F(4, 1)$

Use the SSS Congruence Postulate to decide whether the figure is stable. *Explain* your reasoning.

10.

11.

12.

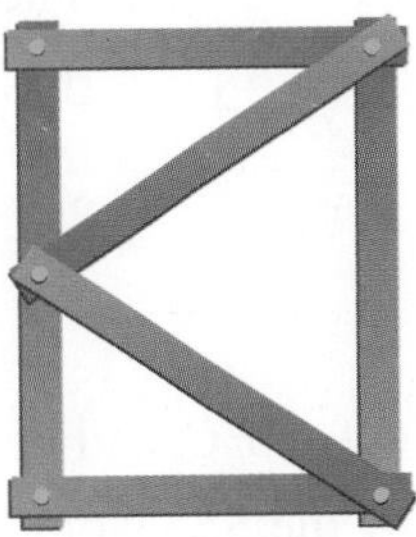

Determine whether $\triangle ABC \cong \triangle DEF$. *Explain* your reasoning.

13.

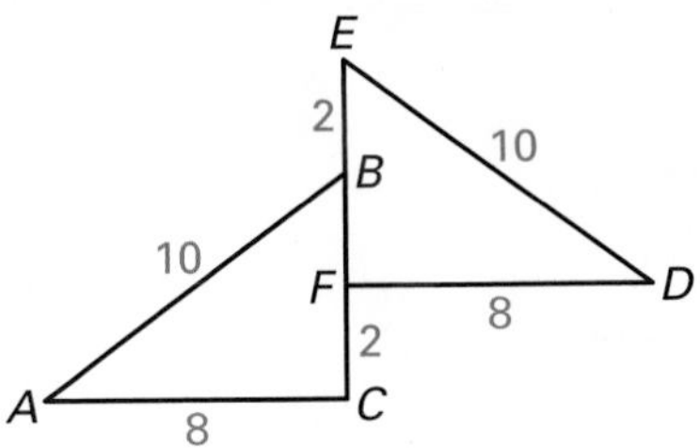

14.

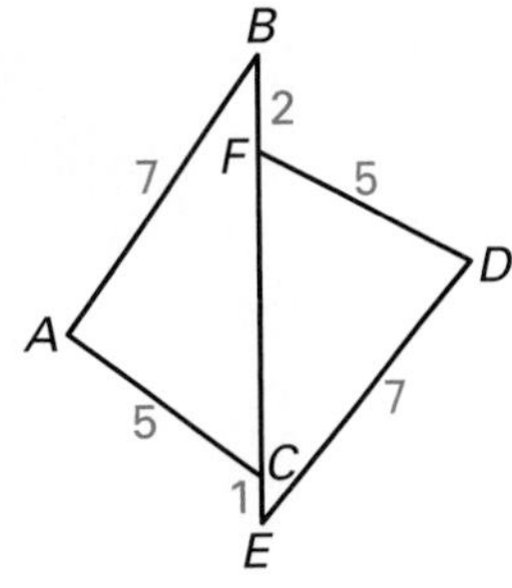

Exercise Set A *(continued)*

15. **Proof** Copy and complete the proof.

GIVEN: $\overline{AB} \cong \overline{CD}$, $\overline{BC} \cong \overline{AD}$

PROVE: $\triangle ABC \cong \triangle CDA$

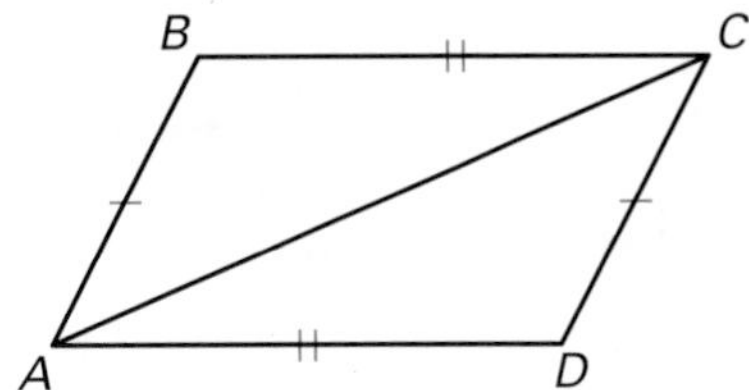

Statements	Reasons
1. $\overline{AB} \cong \overline{CD}$	1. ?
2. $\overline{BC} \cong \overline{AD}$	2. ?
3. $\overline{AC} \cong \overline{AC}$	3. ?
4. $\triangle ABC \cong \triangle CDA$	4. ?

16. **Proof** Copy and complete the proof.

GIVEN: $\overline{AB} \cong \overline{CB}$, D is the midpoint of $\overline{AC}$.

PROVE: $\triangle ABD \cong \triangle CBD$

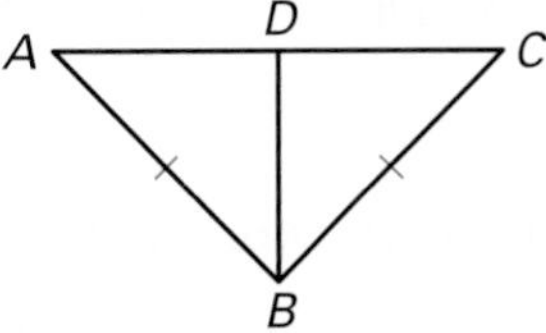

Statements	Reasons
1. $\overline{AB} \cong \overline{CB}$	1. ?
2. D is the midpoint of $\overline{AC}$.	2. ?
3. $\overline{AD} \cong \overline{CD}$	3. ?
4. $\overline{BD} \cong \overline{BD}$	4. ?
5. $\triangle ABD \cong \triangle CBD$	5. ?

17. **Picture Frame** The backs of two different picture frames are shown below. Use the SSS Congruence Postulate to decide which picture frame is stable. *Explain* your reasoning.

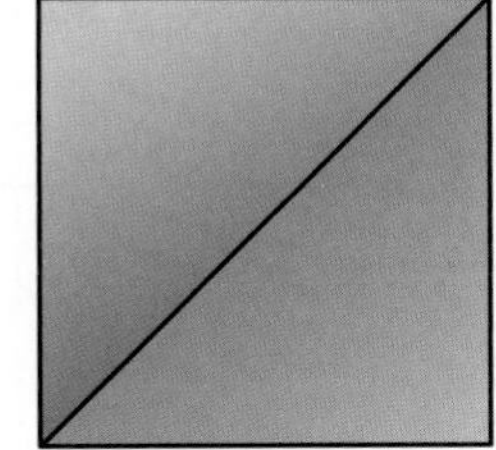

UNIT 4

LESSON 4.8 **Exercise Set B**

MM1G1e Use the coordinate plane to investigate properties of and verify conjectures related to triangles and quadrilaterals.

MM1G3c Understand and use congruence postulates and theorems for triangles (SSS, SAS, ASA, AAS, HL).

Decide whether the congruence statement is true. *Explain* your reasoning.

1. $\triangle ABC \cong \triangle FED$

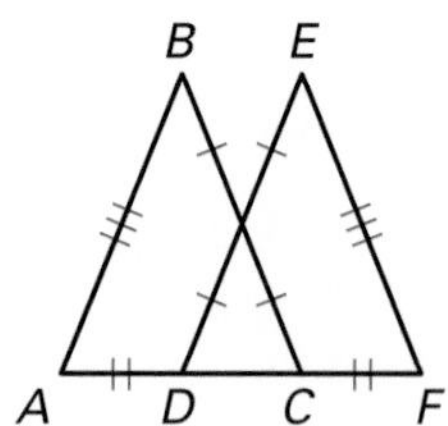

2. $\triangle LMN \cong \triangle UVW$

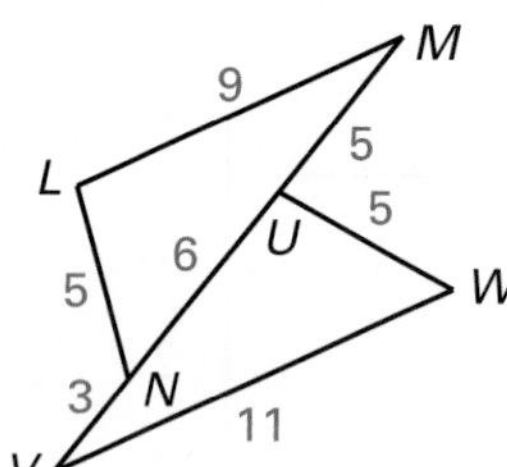

3. $\triangle PQR \cong \triangle RTS$

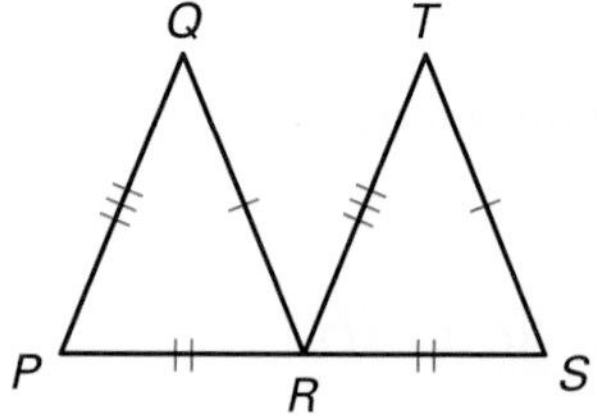

Use the given coordinates to determine if $\triangle ABC \cong \triangle DEF$.

4. $A(1, 3), B(4, 1), C(5, 3), D(3, -3), E(6, -5), F(7, -3)$

5. $A(1, -1), B(-2, 2), C(-3, -4), D(3, 2), E(6, -1), F(7, 5)$

6. $A(-3, 2), B(6, 1), C(-3, 4), D(6, 5), E(-2, 4), F(-1, -7)$

7. $A(1, 1), B(-4, 2), C(-2, -4), D(4, -2), E(9, -3), F(8, 3)$

Use the SSS Congruence Postulate to decide whether the figure is stable. *Explain* your reasoning.

8.

9.

10. **Error Analysis** *Describe* and correct the error in writing a congruence statement for the triangles in the coordinate plane.

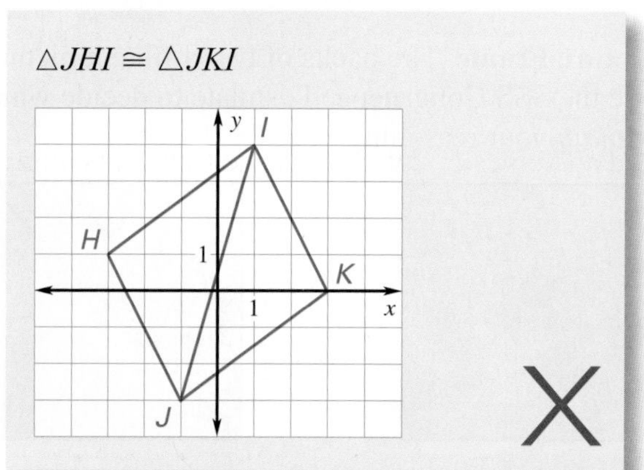

UNIT 4

Exercise Set B *(continued)*

11. **Proof** Copy and complete the proof.

GIVEN: $\overline{HI} \cong \overline{JK}$,
$\overline{IJ} \cong \overline{KH}$

PROVE: $\triangle HIJ \cong \triangle JKH$

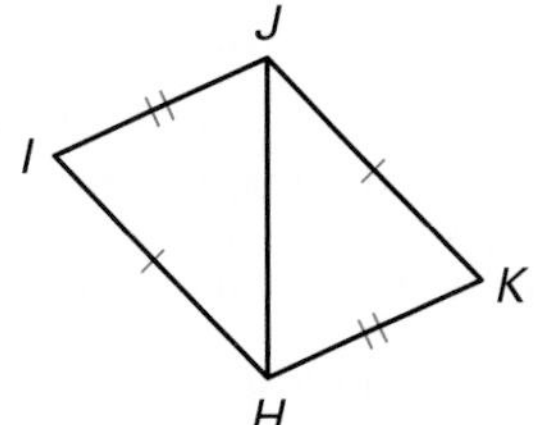

Statements	Reasons
1. ?	1. Given
2. ?	2. Given
3. ?	3. Reflexive Property of Congruence
4. ?	4. SSS Congruence Postulate

12. **Proof** Copy and complete the proof.

GIVEN: $\overline{WX} \cong \overline{YX}$,
Z is the midpoint of $\overline{WY}$.

PROVE: $\triangle WXZ \cong \triangle YXZ$

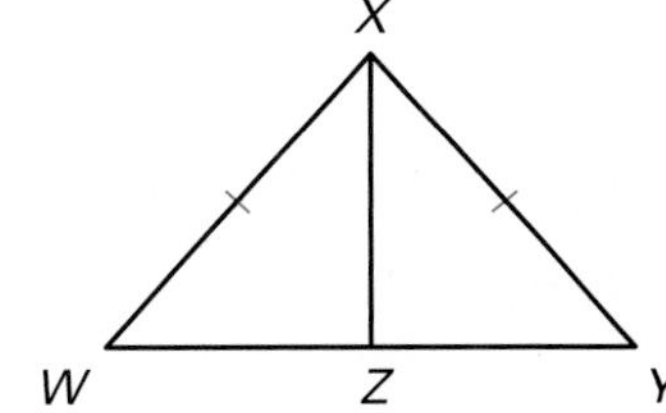

Statements	Reasons
1. ?	1. Given
2. ?	2. Given
3. ?	3. Definition of Midpoint
4. ?	4. Reflexive Property of Congruence
5. ?	5. SSS Congruence Postulate

13. Find all values of x that make the triangles congruent. *Explain.*

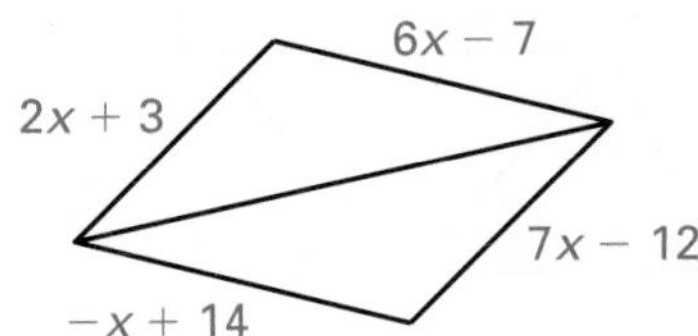

UNIT 4

LESSON 4.9

Prove Triangles Congruent by SAS and HL

Georgia Performance Standards: MM1G3c

Goal Use sides and angles to prove congruence.

Vocabulary

In a right triangle, the sides adjacent to the right angle are called the **legs.**

The side opposite the right angle is called the **hypotenuse** of the right triangle.

Side-Angle-Side (SAS) Congruence Postulate: If two sides and the included angle of one triangle are congruent to two sides and the included angle of a second triangle, then the two triangles are congruent.

Theorem 4.12 Hypotenuse-Leg Congruence Theorem: If the hypotenuse and a leg of a right triangle are congruent to the hypotenuse and a leg of a second right triangle, then the two triangles are congruent.

Example 1 Use the SAS Congruence Postulate

Show that $\triangle ABC \cong \triangle DEF$.

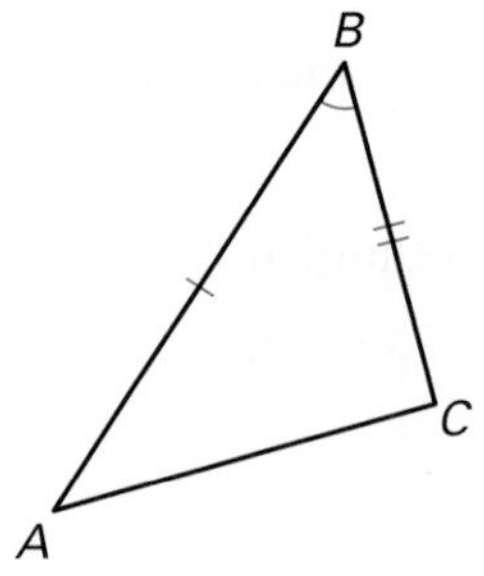

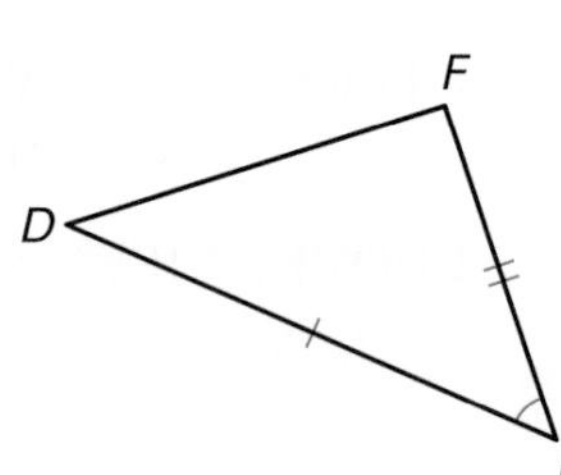

Solution

It is given that $\overline{AB} \cong \overline{DE}$, $\overline{BC} \cong \overline{EF}$, and $\angle B \cong \angle E$.

So, by the SAS Congruence Postulate, $\triangle ABC \cong \triangle DEF$.

Guided Practice for Example 1

Decide whether enough information is given to prove that the triangles are congruent using the SAS Congruence Postulate.

1. $\triangle PQT$, $\triangle RQS$

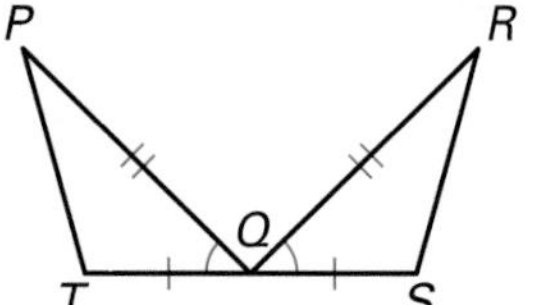

2. $\triangle NKJ$, $\triangle LKM$

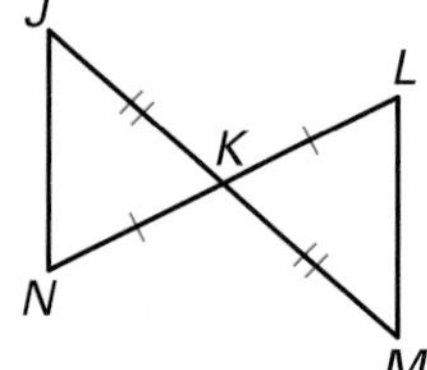

3. $\triangle WXY$, $\triangle ZXY$

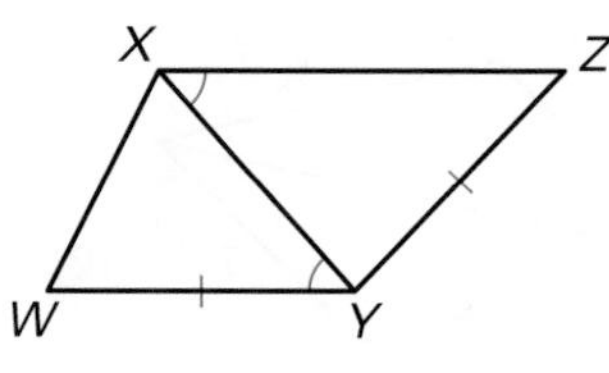

UNIT 4

Georgia Performance Standards

MM1G3c Understand and use congruence postulates and theorems for triangles (SSS, SAS, ASA, AAS, HL).

Example 2 Use the Hypotenuse-Leg Congruence Theorem

Write a proof.

GIVEN: $\overline{AB} \cong \overline{DC}$, $\overline{BA} \perp \overline{AC}$, $\overline{CD} \perp \overline{DB}$

PROVE: $\triangle ABC \cong \triangle DCB$

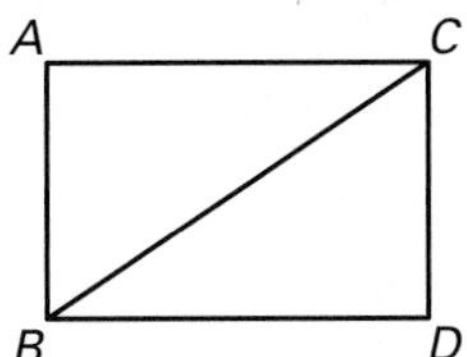

Solution

Redraw the triangles so they are side by side with the corresponding parts in the same position. Mark the given information in the diagram.

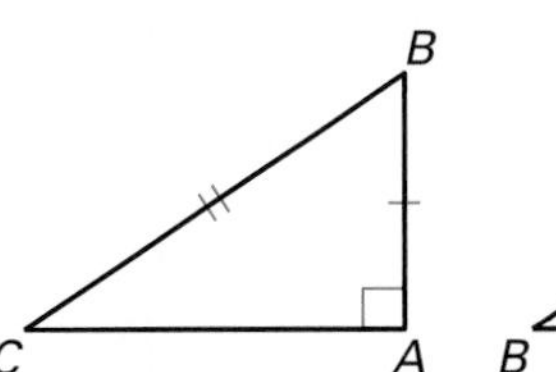

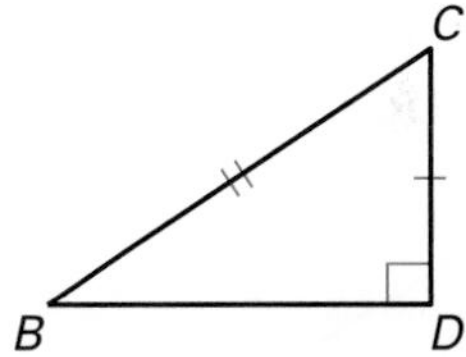

Statements	Reasons
1. $\overline{BA} \perp \overline{AC}$, $\overline{CD} \perp \overline{DB}$	**1.** Given
2. $\angle A$ and $\angle D$ are right angles.	**2.** Definition of $\perp$ lines
3. $\triangle ABC$ and $\triangle DCB$ are right triangles.	**3.** Definition of a right triangle
4. $\overline{CB} \cong \overline{BC}$	**4.** Reflexive Property of Congruence
5. $\overline{AB} \cong \overline{DC}$	**5.** Given
6. $\triangle ABC \cong \triangle DCB$	**6.** HL Congruence Theorem

Guided Practice for Example 2

Write a proof.

4. **GIVEN:** $\overline{AB} \cong \overline{DB}$, $\overline{BC} \perp \overline{AD}$

PROVE: $\triangle ABC \cong \triangle DBC$

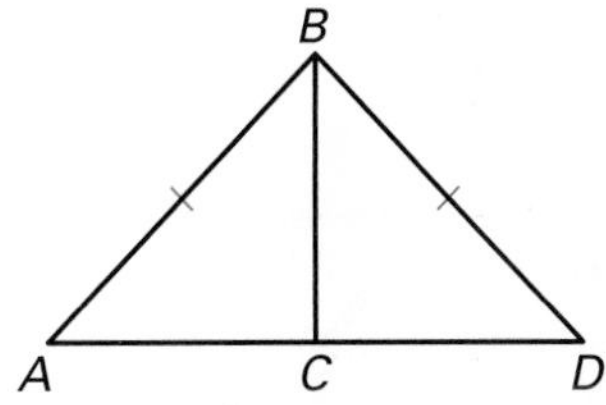

5. **GIVEN:** $m\angle JKL = m\angle MLK = 90°$

$\overline{JL} \cong \overline{MK}$

PROVE: $\triangle JKL \cong \triangle MLK$

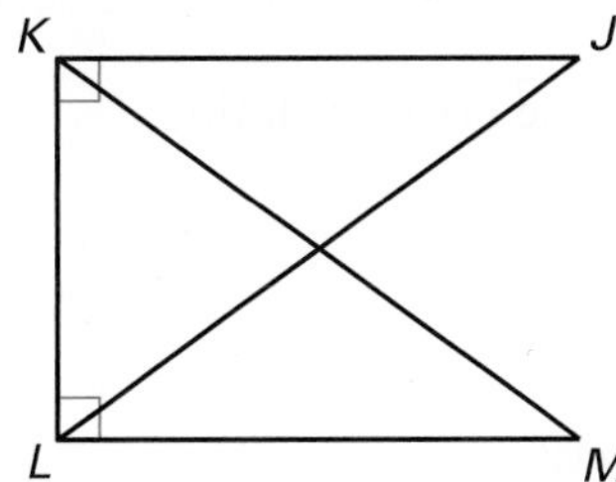

UNIT 4

LESSON 4.9 **Exercise Set A**

MM1G3c Understand and use congruence postulates and theorems for triangles (SSS, SAS, ASA, AAS, HL).

Use the diagram to name the included angle between the given pair of sides.

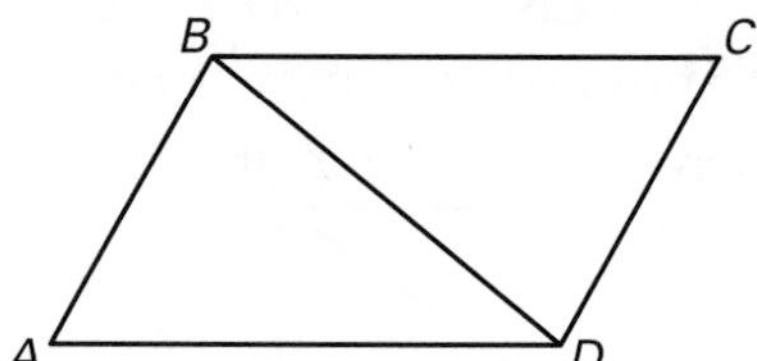

1. $\overline{AB}$ and $\overline{BC}$
2. $\overline{BC}$ and $\overline{CD}$
3. $\overline{AB}$ and $\overline{BD}$
4. $\overline{BD}$ and $\overline{DA}$
5. $\overline{DA}$ and $\overline{AB}$
6. $\overline{CD}$ and $\overline{DB}$

Decide whether enough information is given to prove that the triangles are congruent using the SAS Congruence Postulate.

7. $\triangle MAE, \triangle TAE$

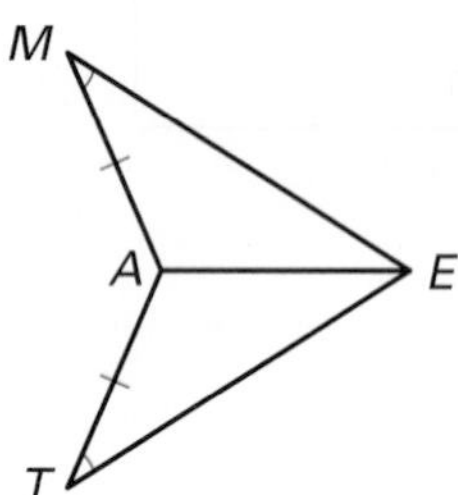

8. $\triangle DKA, \triangle TKS$

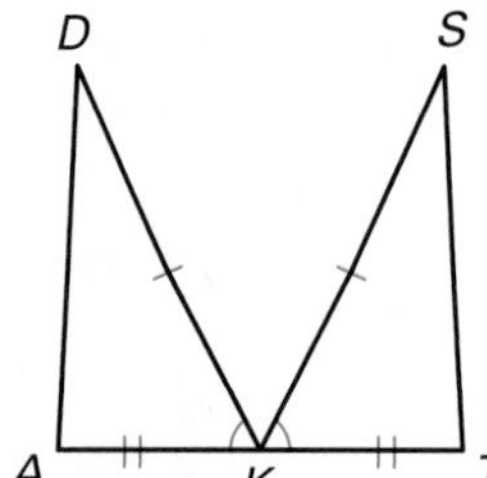

9. $\triangle JRM, \triangle JTM$

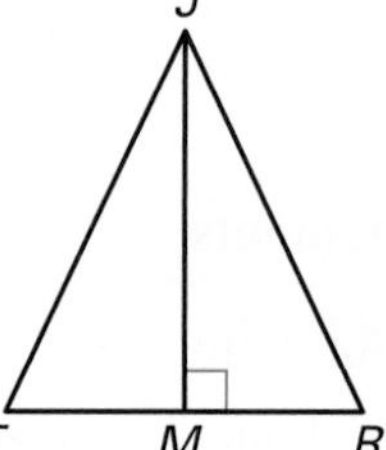

Decide whether enough information is given to prove that the triangles are congruent. If there is enough information, state the congruence postulate or theorem you would use.

10. $\triangle ABC, \triangle DEF$

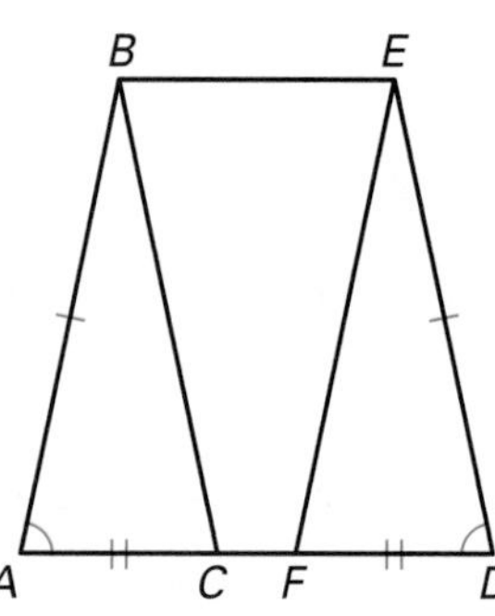

11. $\triangle MNO, \triangle RON$

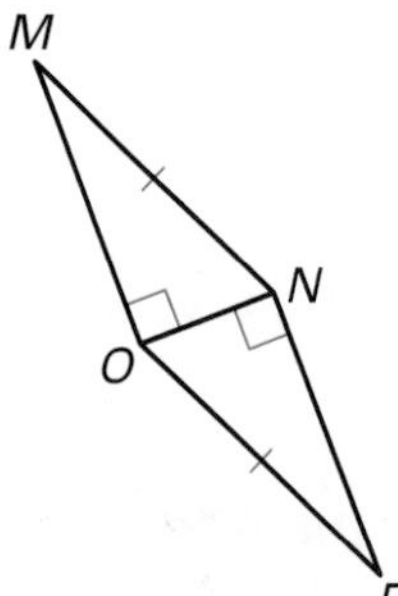

12. $\triangle ABC, \triangle ADC$

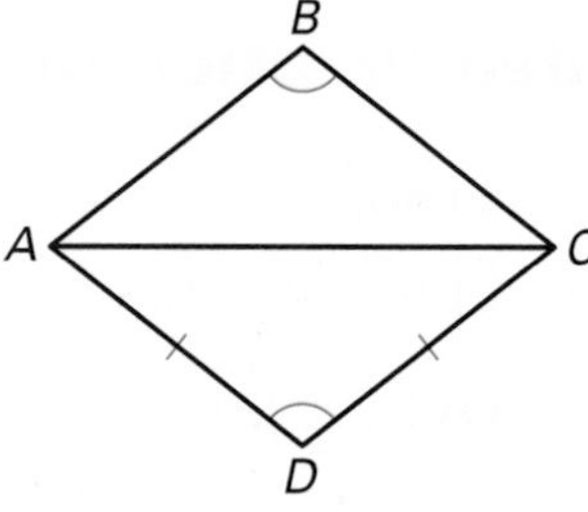

13. **Error Analysis** *Describe* the error in stating that the two triangles are congruent.

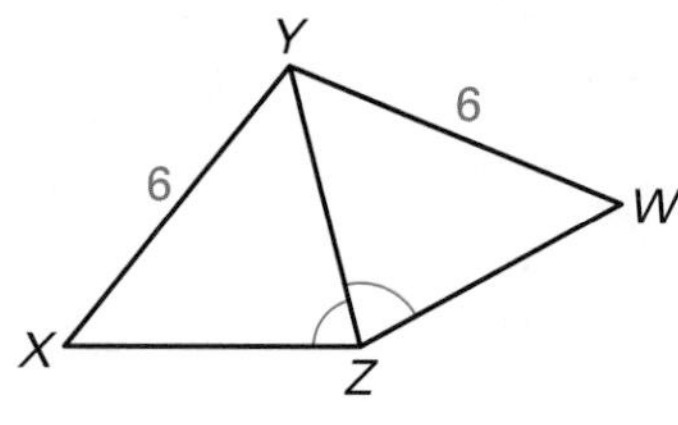

$\triangle XYZ \cong \triangle WYZ$ by the SAS Congruence Postulate.

Exercise Set A *(continued)*

State the third congruence that must be given to prove that $\triangle JRM \cong \triangle DFB$ using the indicated postulate.

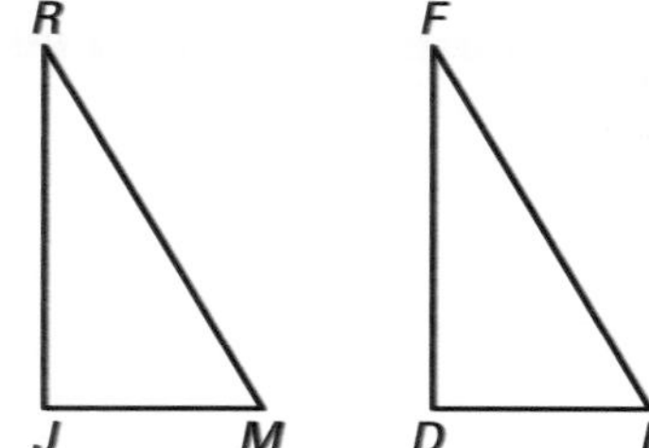

14. GIVEN: $\overline{JR} \cong \overline{DF}$, $\overline{JM} \cong \overline{DB}$, __?__ $\cong$ __?__
Use the SSS Congruence Postulate.

15. GIVEN: $\overline{JR} \cong \overline{DF}$, $\overline{JM} \cong \overline{DB}$, __?__ $\cong$ __?__
Use the SAS Congruence Postulate.

16. GIVEN: $\overline{RM} \cong \overline{FB}$, $\angle J$ is a right angle and $\angle J \cong \angle D$, __?__ $\cong$ __?__
Use the HL Congruence Theorem.

17. Proof Copy and complete the proof.

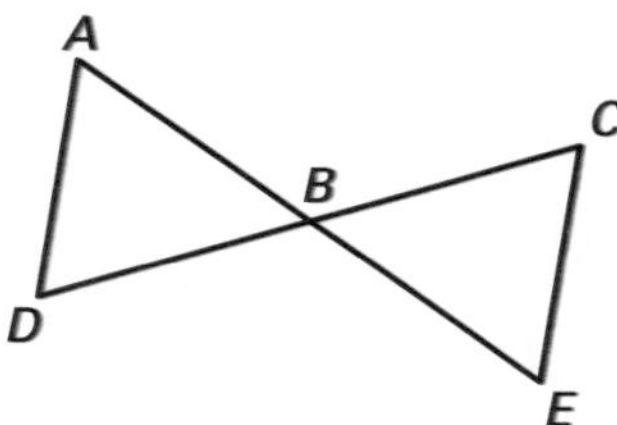

GIVEN: B is the midpoint of $\overline{AE}$.
B is the midpoint of $\overline{CD}$.

PROVE: $\triangle ABD \cong \triangle EBC$

Statements	Reasons
1. B is the midpoint of $\overline{AE}$.	1. __?__
2. __?__	2. Definition of midpoint
3. B is the midpoint of $\overline{CD}$.	3. __?__
4. __?__	4. Definition of midpoint
5. $\angle ABD \cong \angle EBC$	5. __?__
6. $\triangle ABD \cong \triangle EBC$	6. __?__

18. Proof Copy and complete the proof.

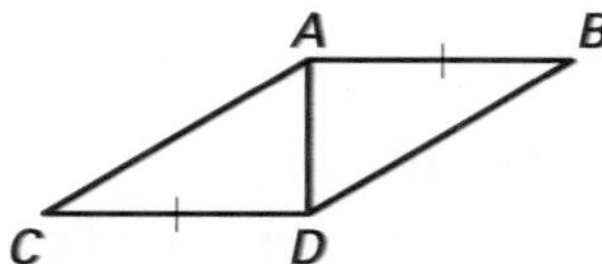

GIVEN: $\overline{AB} \perp \overline{AD}$, $\overline{AD} \perp \overline{CD}$, $\overline{AB} \cong \overline{CD}$

PROVE: $\triangle ABD \cong \triangle DCA$

Statements	Reasons
1. $\overline{AB} \perp \overline{AD}$ and $\overline{AD} \perp \overline{CD}$	1. __?__
2. $\angle BAD$ and $\angle CDA$ are right angles.	2. __?__
3. $\angle BAD \cong \angle CDA$	3. __?__
4. $\overline{AB} \cong \overline{CD}$	4. __?__
5. $\overline{AD} \cong \overline{AD}$	5. __?__
6. $\triangle ABD \cong \triangle DCA$	6. __?__

LESSON 4.9

Exercise Set B

MM1G3c Understand and use congruence postulates and theorems for triangles (SSS, SAS, ASA, AAS, HL).

Decide whether enough information is given to prove that the triangles are congruent. If there is enough information, state the congruence postulate or theorem you would use.

1. $\triangle ABC, \triangle FEC$

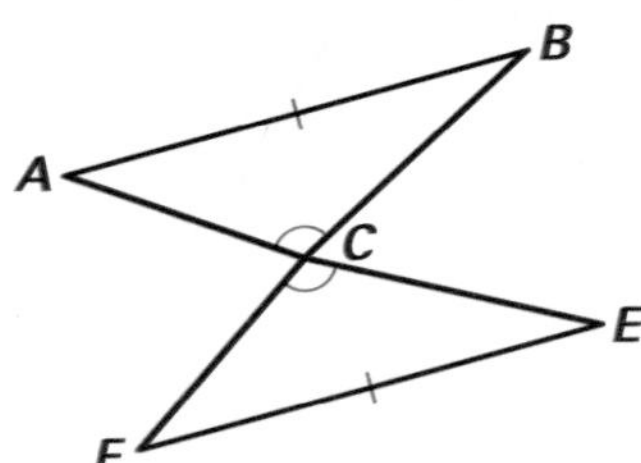

2. $\triangle GHI, \triangle JKL$

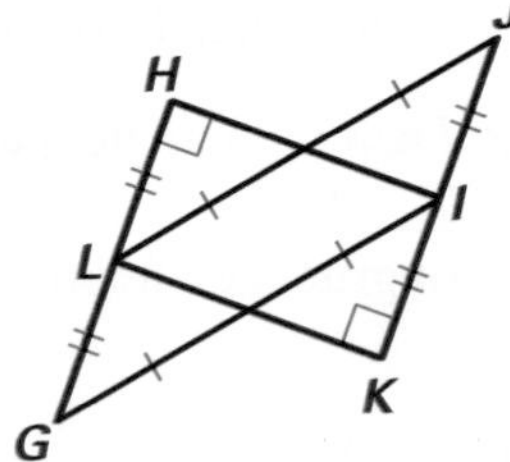

3. $\triangle MNO, \triangle PQR$

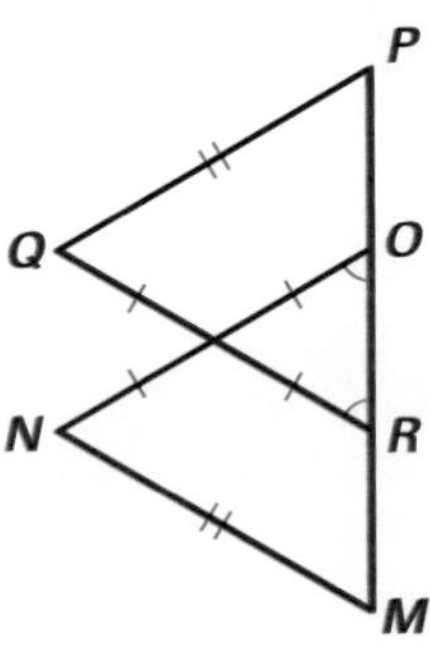

4. $\triangle STX, \triangle VUW$

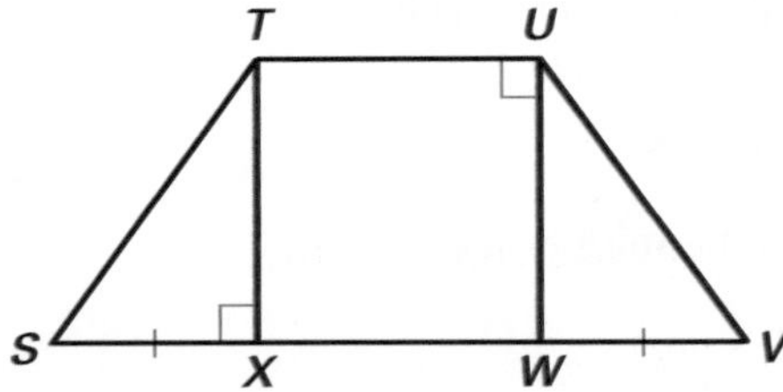

State the third congruence that must be given to prove that $\triangle ABC \cong \triangle FED$ using the indicated postulate or theorem.

5. GIVEN: $\overline{BC} \cong \overline{ED}, \overline{AC} \cong \overline{FD}$, _?_ $\cong$ _?_
   Use the SAS Congruence Postulate.

6. GIVEN: $\overline{AB} \cong \overline{FE}, \overline{AC} \cong \overline{FD}$, _?_ $\cong$ _?_
   Use the SSS Congruence Postulate.

7. GIVEN: $\overline{BC} \cong \overline{ED}$, $\angle B$ is a right angle and $\angle B \cong \angle E$, _?_ $\cong$ _?_
   Use the HL Congruence Theorem.

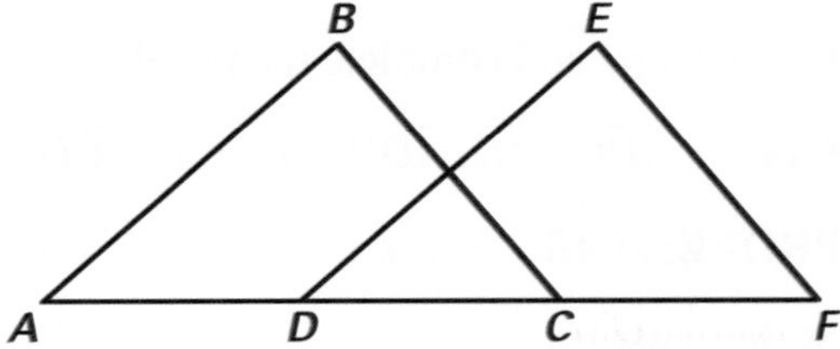

8. Suppose P is the midpoint of $\overline{OQ}$ in $\triangle OQS$. If $\overline{SP} \perp \overline{OQ}$, explain why $\triangle SPO \cong \triangle SPQ$.

Exercise Set B *(continued)*

9. **Proof** Copy and complete the proof.

GIVEN: $\overline{QS} \cong \overline{PR}$, $\overline{PS} \perp \overline{RS}$, $\overline{QR} \perp \overline{RS}$

PROVE: $\triangle PRS \cong \triangle QSR$

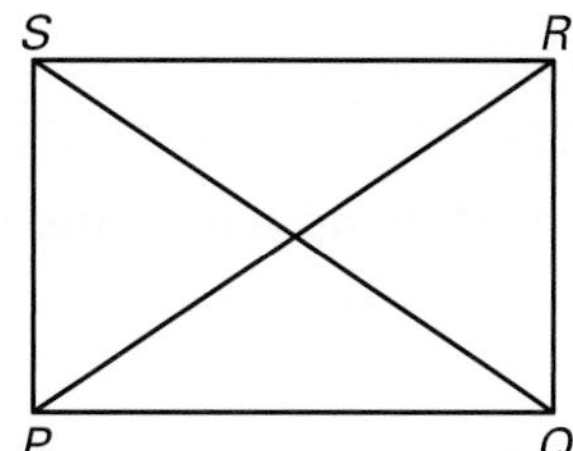

Statements	Reasons
1. $\overline{QS} \cong \overline{PR}$	1. Given
2. $\overline{PS} \perp \overline{RS}$, $\overline{QR} \perp \overline{RS}$	2. Given
3. $\angle S$ and $\angle R$ are right angles.	3. ?
4. ?	4. Definition of a right triangle
5. $\overline{RS} \cong \overline{SR}$	5. ?
6. $\triangle PRS \cong \triangle QSR$	6. ?

10. **Proof** Copy and complete the proof.

GIVEN: $\overline{OM} \perp \overline{LN}$, $\overline{ML} \cong \overline{MN}$

PROVE: $\triangle OML \cong \triangle OMN$

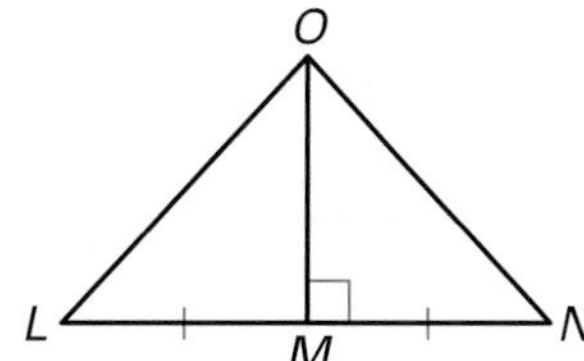

Statements	Reasons
1. $\overline{OM} \perp \overline{LN}$	1. Given
2. ?	2. If 2 lines are $\perp$, then they form 4 right $\angle$s.
3. ?	3. Right Angle Congruence Theorem
4. $\overline{ML} \cong \overline{MN}$	4. ?
5. $\overline{OM} \cong \overline{OM}$	5. ?
6. $\triangle OML \cong \triangle OMN$	6. ?

11. Which two triangles in the figure are congruent? *Explain* your reasoning.

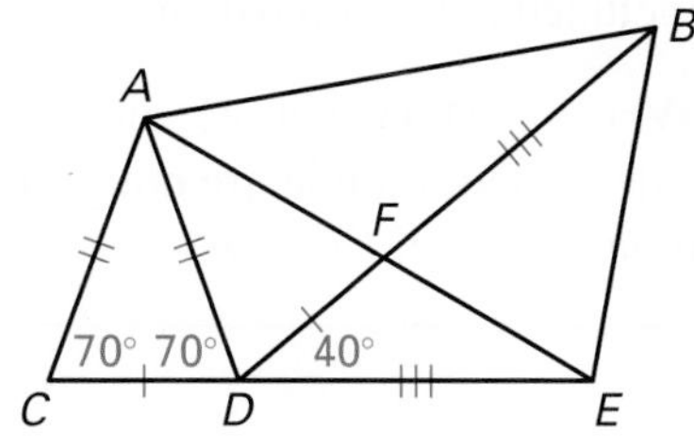

Georgia Performance Standards

MM1G3c Understand and use congruence postulates and theorems for triangles (SSS, SAS, ASA, AAS, HL).

Investigating Math Activity

Discovering ASA Congruence

Use before Lesson 4.10

Materials **tracing paper and straightedge**

Question

Are two triangles congruent if two angles and the included side of one triangle are congruent to two angles and the included side of the other triangle?

Explore

Compare two triangles.

STEP 1 **Draw a triangle**
Use your straightedge to draw a triangle. Label the vertices A, B, and C.

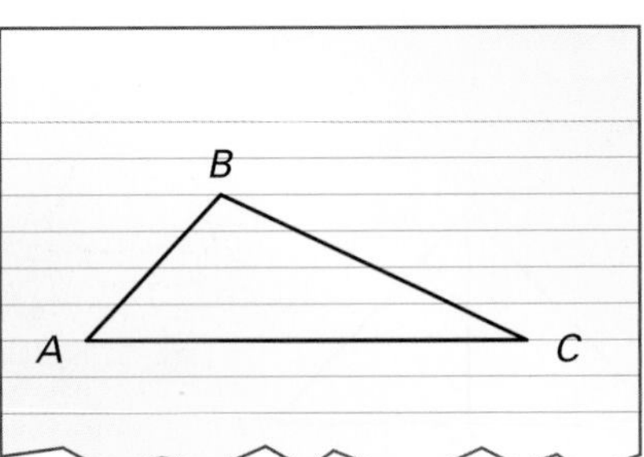

STEP 2 **Copy two angles and one side**
Place a piece of tracing paper over $\triangle ABC$, and trace $\angle A$, side $\overline{AB}$ and $\angle B$.

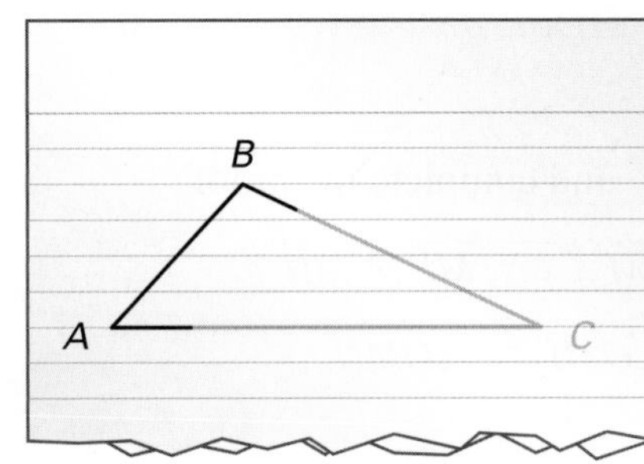

STEP 3 **Make a triangle**
On the tracing paper, extend the other sides of $\angle A$ and $\angle B$ until they intersect. Label the intersection D.

STEP 4 **Compare triangles**
Compare the triangles by laying the tracing paper with $\triangle ABD$ on top of $\triangle ABC$.

Draw Conclusions

1. Is $\triangle ABD$ congruent to $\triangle ABC$? *Explain.*
2. **Reasoning** Can you make two triangles that are different shapes with two angles of one triangle congruent to two angles of the other triangle and their included sides congruent? *Justify* your answer.
3. **Writing** Make a conjecture about two triangles if two angles and the included side of one triangle are congruent to two angles and the included side of the other triangle. *Explain.*

UNIT 4

LESSON 4.10

Prove Triangles Congruent by ASA and AAS

Georgia Performance Standards: MM1G3c

Goal Use two more methods to prove congruences.

Vocabulary

A **flow proof** uses arrows to show the flow of a logical argument.

Angle-Side-Angle (ASA) Congruence Postulate: If two angles and the included side of one triangle are congruent to two angles and the included side of a second triangle, then the two triangles are congruent.

Theorem 4.13 Angle-Angle-Side (AAS) Congruence Theorem: If two angles and a non-included side of one triangle are congruent to two angles and the corresponding non-included side of a second triangle, then the two triangles are congruent.

Example 1 Identify congruent triangles

Can the triangles be proven congruent with the information given in the diagram? If so, state the postulate or theorem you would use.

a. 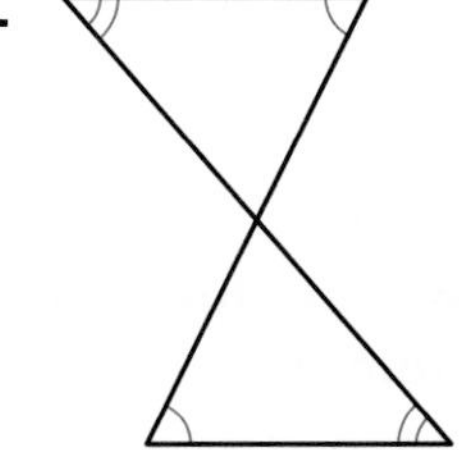

b. 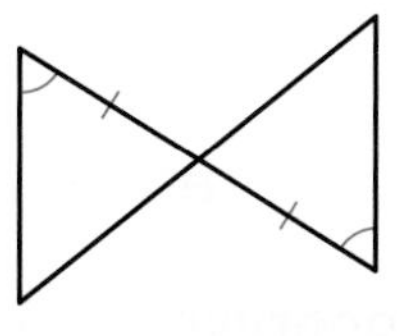

c. 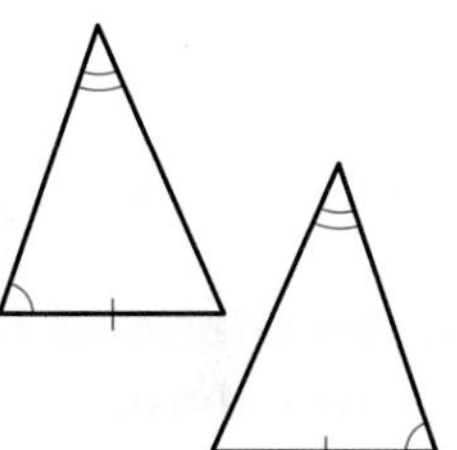

Solution

a. The vertical angles are congruent, so three pairs of angles are congruent. There is not enough information to prove the triangles are congruent, because no sides are known to be congruent.

b. The vertical angles are congruent, so two pairs of angles and their included sides are congruent. The triangles are congruent by the ASA Congruence Postulate.

c. Two pairs of angles and a non-included pair of sides are congruent. The triangles are congruent by the AAS Congruence Theorem.

Theorem 4.14 Alternate Interior Angles Theorem

If two parallel lines are cut by a transversal, then the pairs of alternate interior angles are congruent. In the figure, line t is a transversal, and $\angle 4$ and $\angle 5$ are alternate interior angles.

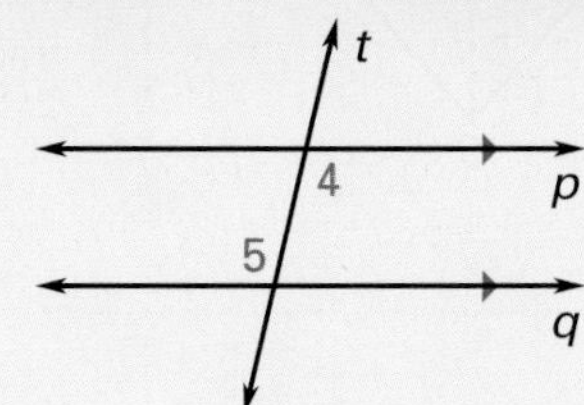

UNIT 4

Georgia Performance Standards

MM1G3c Understand and use congruence postulates and theorems for triangles (SSS, SAS, ASA, AAS, HL).

Example 2 Write a flow proof

In the diagram, $\angle G \cong \angle B$ and $\overline{CB} \parallel \overline{GA}$. Write a flow proof to show $\triangle GCA \cong \triangle BAC$.

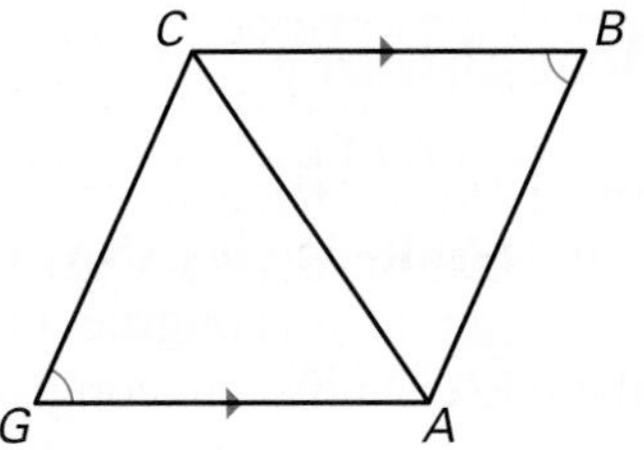

Solution

GIVEN: $\angle G \cong \angle B, \overline{CB} \parallel \overline{GA}$

PROVE: $\triangle GCA \cong \triangle BAC$

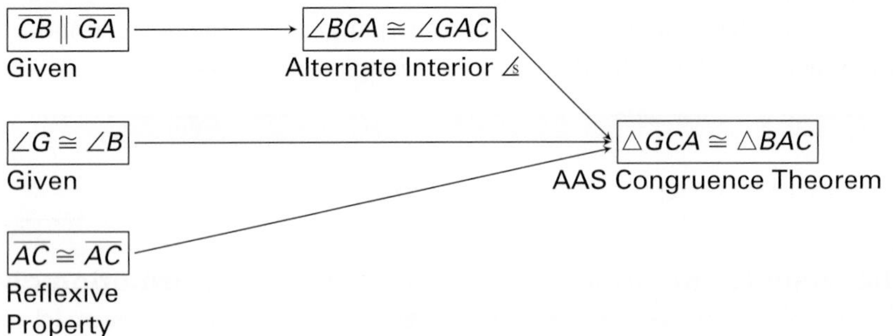

UNIT 4

Guided Practice for Examples 1 and 2

Can the triangles be proven congruent with the information given in the diagram? If so, state the postulate or theorem you would use.

1.

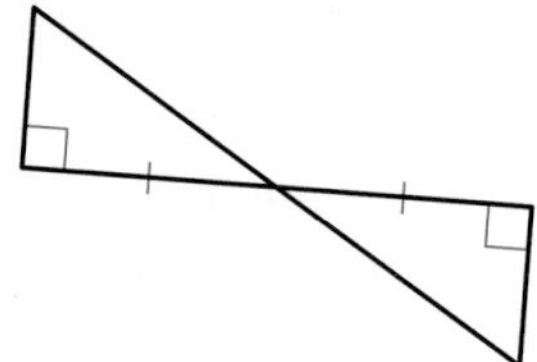

2.

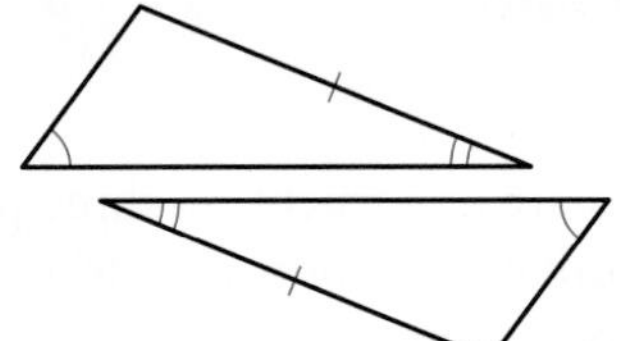

3.

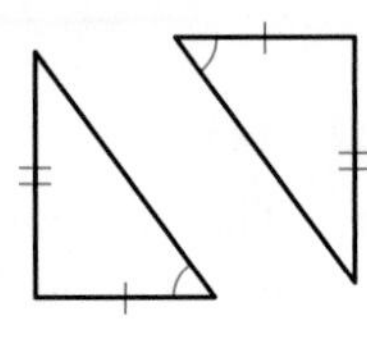

Write a flow proof to show that the triangles are congruent.

4. **GIVEN:** $\angle PQS \cong \angle RQS$
$\angle QSP \cong \angle QSR$
PROVE: $\triangle PQS \cong \triangle RQS$

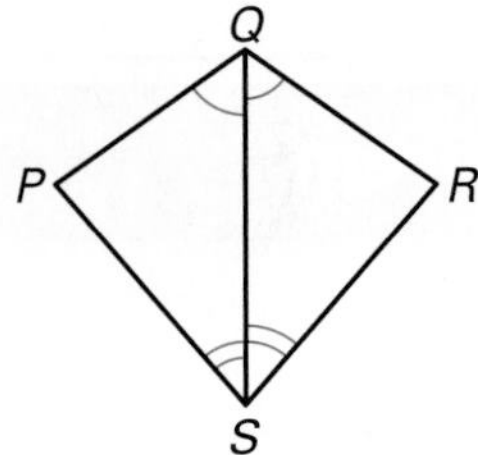

5. **GIVEN:** $\angle OMN \cong \angle ONM$
$\angle LMO \cong \angle JNO$
PROVE: $\triangle MJN \cong \triangle NLM$

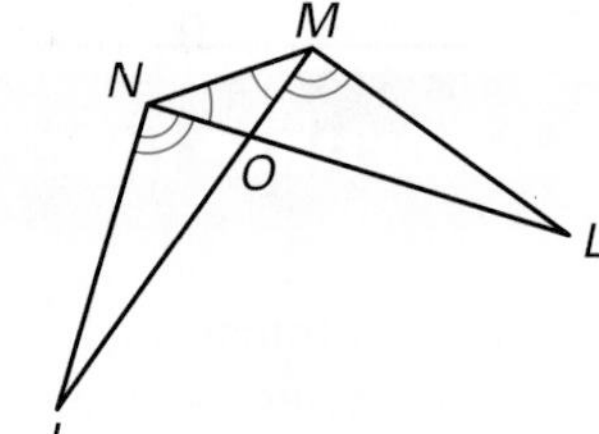

LESSON 4.10

Exercise Set A

MM1G3c Understand and use congruence postulates and theorems for triangles (SSS, SAS, ASA, AAS, HL).

State the third congruence that is needed to prove that $\triangle DEF \cong \triangle MNO$ using the given postulate or theorem.

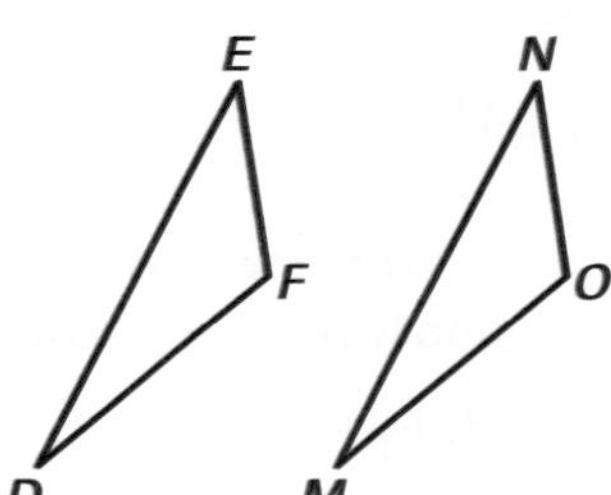

1. **GIVEN:** $\overline{DE} \cong \overline{MN}$, $\angle M \cong \angle D$, __?__ $\cong$ __?__
   Use the SAS Congruence Postulate.

2. **GIVEN:** $\overline{FE} \cong \overline{ON}$, $\angle F \cong \angle O$, __?__ $\cong$ __?__
   Use the AAS Congruence Theorem.

3. **GIVEN:** $\overline{DF} \cong \overline{MO}$, $\angle F \cong \angle O$, __?__ $\cong$ __?__
   Use the ASA Congruence Postulate.

State the third congruence that is needed to prove that $\triangle ABC \cong \triangle XYZ$ using the given postulate or theorem.

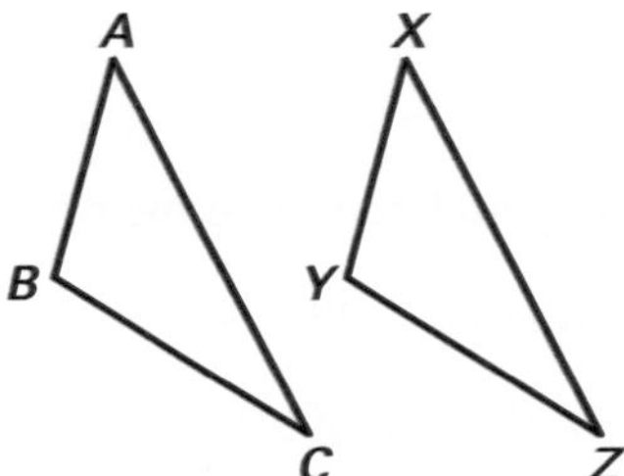

4. **GIVEN:** $\angle A \cong \angle X$, $\angle B \cong \angle Y$, __?__ $\cong$ __?__
   Use the AAS Congruence Theorem.

5. **GIVEN:** $\angle A \cong \angle X$, $\overline{AB} \cong \overline{XY}$, __?__ $\cong$ __?__
   Use the ASA Congruence Postulate.

6. **GIVEN:** $\overline{BC} \cong \overline{YZ}$, $\angle C \cong \angle Z$, __?__ $\cong$ __?__
   Use the AAS Congruence Theorem.

Is it possible to prove that the triangles are congruent? If so, state the postulate(s) or theorem(s) you would use.

7. 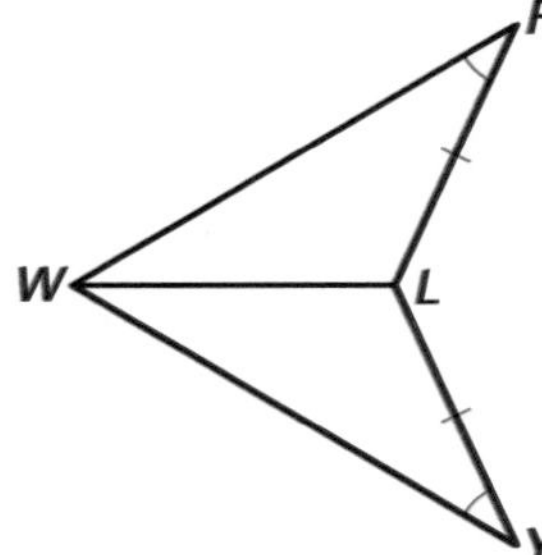

8. 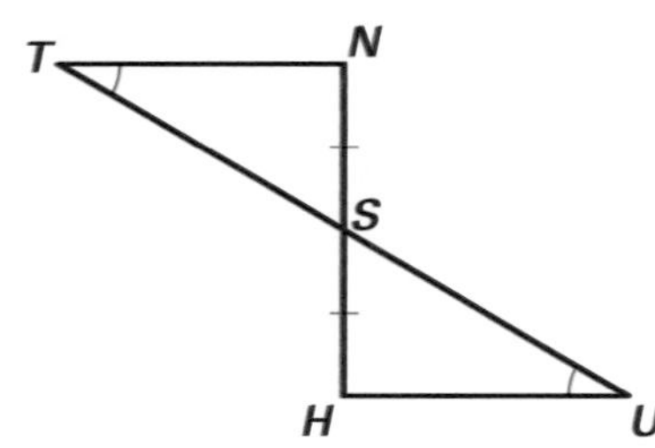

9. 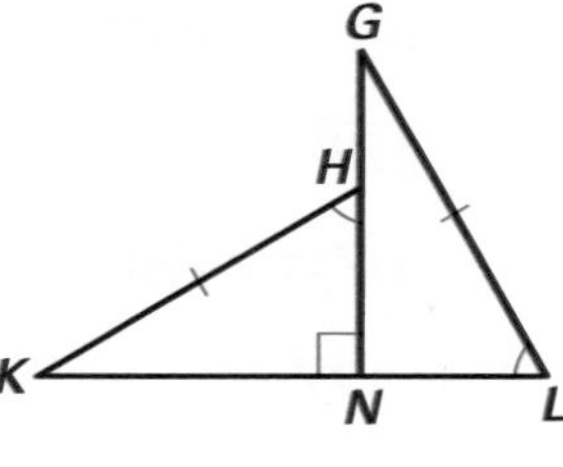

10. Error Analysis *Describe* the error in concluding that $\triangle DEF \cong \triangle PQR$.

By AAA, $\triangle DEF \cong \triangle PQR$.

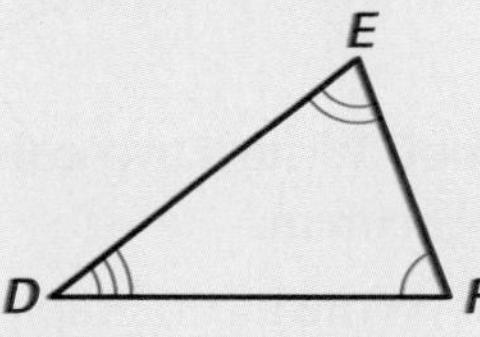

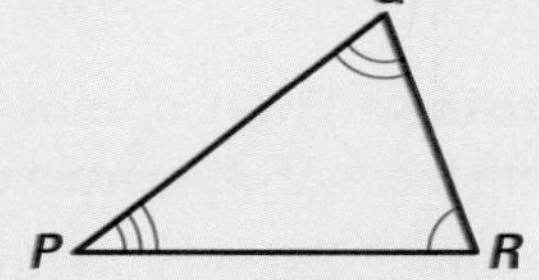

UNIT 4

Exercise Set A *(continued)*

Tell whether you can use the given information to determine whether $\triangle JRM \cong \triangle XYZ$. *Explain* your reasoning.

11. $\overline{JM} \cong \overline{XZ}, \angle M \cong \angle Z, \angle R \cong \angle Y$

12. $\overline{JM} \cong \overline{XZ}, \overline{JR} \cong \overline{XY}, \angle J \cong \angle X$

13. $\angle J \cong \angle X, \angle M \cong \angle Z, \angle R \cong \angle Y$

14. $\angle M \cong \angle Z, \overline{JR} \cong \overline{XY}, \overline{RM} \cong \overline{YZ}$

***Explain* how you can prove that the indicated triangles are congruent using the given postulate or theorem.**

15. $\triangle BEF \cong \triangle BED$ by SAS

16. $\triangle ADB \cong \triangle CFB$ by ASA

17. $\triangle AFB \cong \triangle CDB$ by AAS

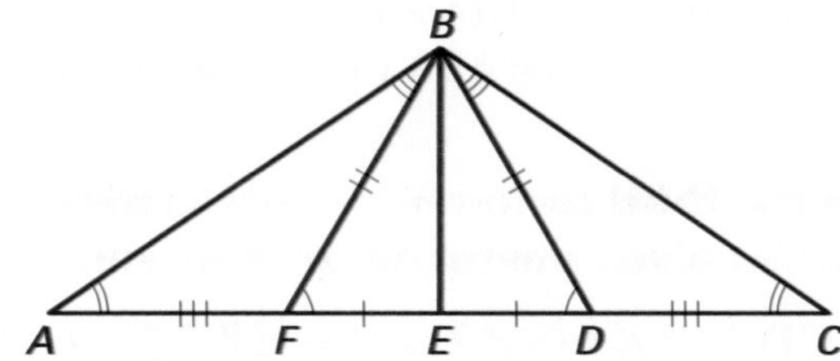

18. Proof Copy and complete the proof.

GIVEN: $\overline{WU} \parallel \overline{YV}, \overline{XU} \parallel \overline{ZV}, \overline{WX} \cong \overline{YZ}$

PROVE: $\triangle WXU \cong \triangle YZV$

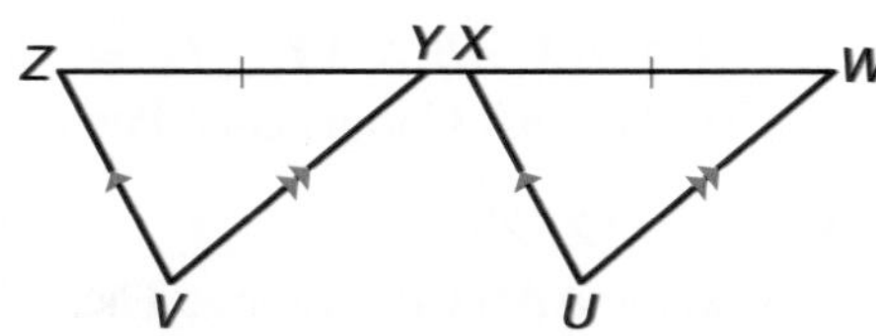

Statements	Reasons
1. $\overline{WU} \parallel \overline{YV}$	1. ?
2. $\angle UWX \cong \angle VYZ$	2. ?
3. $\overline{XU} \parallel \overline{ZV}$	3. ?
4. $\angle UXW \cong \angle VZY$	4. ?
5. $\overline{WX} \cong \overline{YZ}$	5. ?
6. $\triangle WXU \cong \triangle YZV$	6. ?

19. Multiple Representations Use the figure at the right.

GIVEN: $\angle B \cong \angle D, \overline{DA} \cong \overline{BE}, \triangle ACE$ is equilateral.

PROVE: $\triangle ABC \cong \triangle EDC$

a. Writing a Two-Column Proof Write a two-column proof using the AAS Congruence Theorem.

b. Writing a Paragraph Proof Write a paragraph proof using the ASA Congruence Postulate.

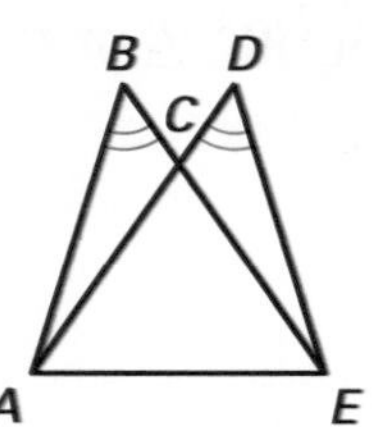

UNIT 4

LESSON 4.10

Exercise Set B

MM1G3c Understand and use congruence postulates and theorems for triangles (SSS, SAS, ASA, AAS, HL).

State the third congruence that is needed to prove that $\triangle DEF \cong \triangle QRT$ using the given postulate or theorem.

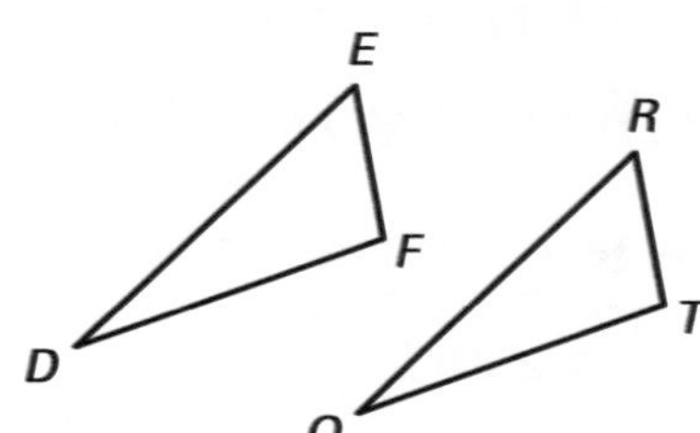

1. GIVEN: $\angle D \cong \angle Q$, $\angle F \cong \angle T$, _?_ $\cong$ _?_
   Use the AAS Congruence Theorem.

2. GIVEN: $\angle E \cong \angle R$, $\overline{EF} \cong \overline{RT}$, _?_ $\cong$ _?_
   Use the ASA Congruence Postulate.

3. GIVEN: $\overline{DE} \cong \overline{QR}$, $\angle D \cong \angle Q$, _?_ $\cong$ _?_
   Use the SAS Congruence Postulate.

Is it possible to prove that the triangles are congruent? If so, state the postulate(s) or theorem(s) you would use.

4. $\triangle TNS \cong \triangle UHS$

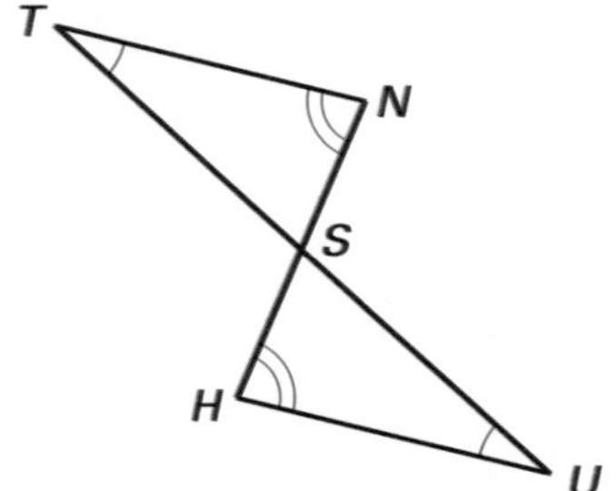

5. $\triangle KLN \cong \triangle MNL$

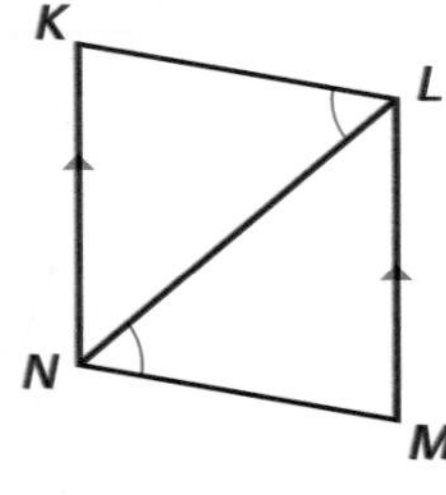

6. $\triangle TXZ \cong \triangle VYW$

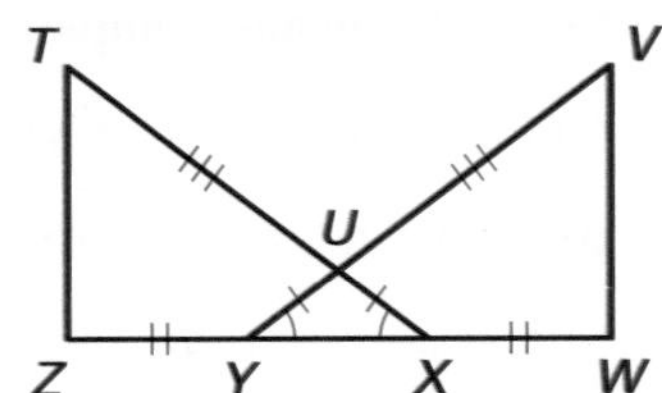

Tell whether you can use the given information to determine whether $\triangle JRM \cong \triangle XYZ$. *Explain* your reasoning.

7. $\overline{JM} \cong \overline{XZ}$, $\angle M \cong \angle Y$, $\angle J \cong \angle X$

8. $\overline{JM} \cong \overline{XZ}$, $\overline{JR} \cong \overline{YZ}$, $\angle J \cong \angle X$

9. $\angle J \cong \angle X$, $\angle M \cong \angle Z$, $\overline{RM} \cong \overline{YZ}$

10. $\overline{JR} \cong \overline{YZ}$, $\overline{RM} \cong \overline{ZX}$, $\overline{MJ} \cong \overline{XY}$

***Explain* how you can prove that the indicated triangles are congruent using the given postulate or theorem.**

11. $\triangle AFD \cong \triangle BFC$ by SAS

12. $\triangle ACE \cong \triangle DBA$ by AAS

13. $\triangle ACD \cong \triangle BDC$ by SAS

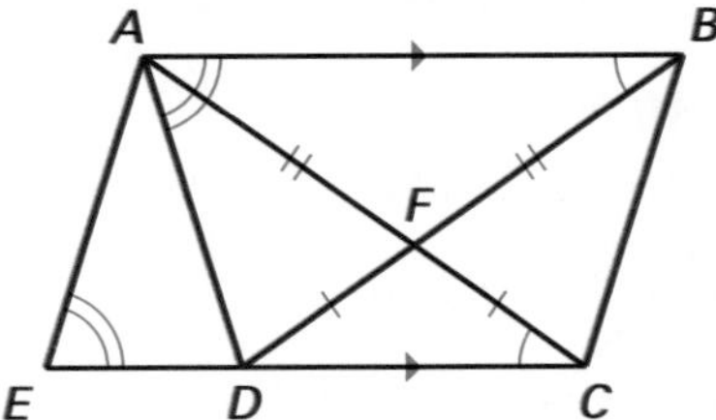

14. **Proof** Write a proof.

    GIVEN: $\overline{AB} \parallel \overline{DC}$, $\angle ADB \cong \angle CBD$

    PROVE: $\triangle ABD \cong \triangle CDB$

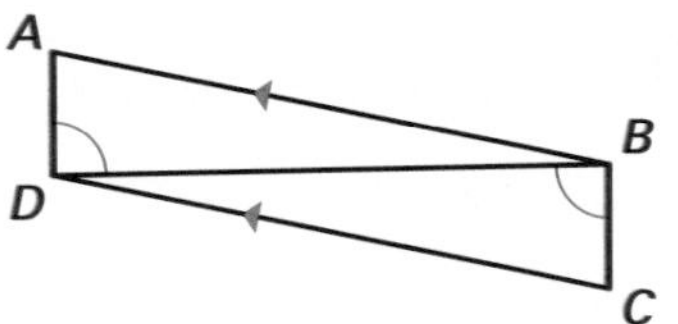

Exercise Set B *(continued)*

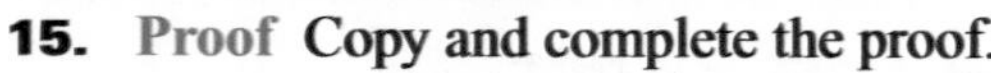

15. Proof Copy and complete the proof.

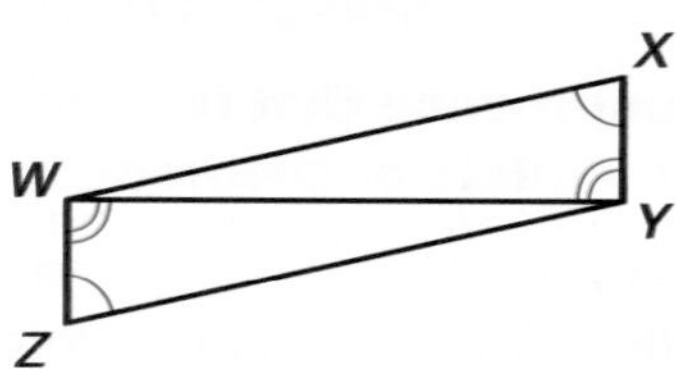

GIVEN: $\angle XYW \cong \angle ZWY$,
$\angle WXY \cong \angle YZW$

PROVE: $\triangle XYW \cong \triangle ZWY$

Statements	Reasons
1. $\angle XYW \cong \angle ZWY$	1. ?
2. $\angle WXY \cong \angle YZW$	2. ?
3. $\overline{WY} \cong \overline{WY}$	3. ?
4. $\triangle XYW \cong \triangle ZWY$	4. ?

16. Proof Copy and complete the proof.

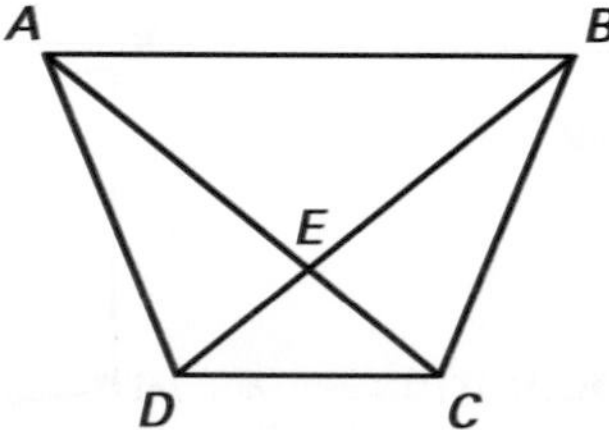

GIVEN: $\overline{DE} \cong \overline{CE}$, $\angle ADE \cong \angle BCE$

PROVE: $\triangle AED \cong \triangle BEC$

Statements	Reasons
1. $\overline{DE} \cong \overline{CE}$	1. ?
2. $\angle ADE \cong \angle BCE$	2. ?
3. $\angle AED \cong \angle BEC$	3. ?
4. $\triangle AED \cong \triangle BEC$	4. ?

17. Proof Write a proof.

GIVEN: $\overline{ML} \cong \overline{LK}$, $\angle MLJ \cong \angle KLJ$

PROVE: $\triangle MLN \cong \triangle KLN$

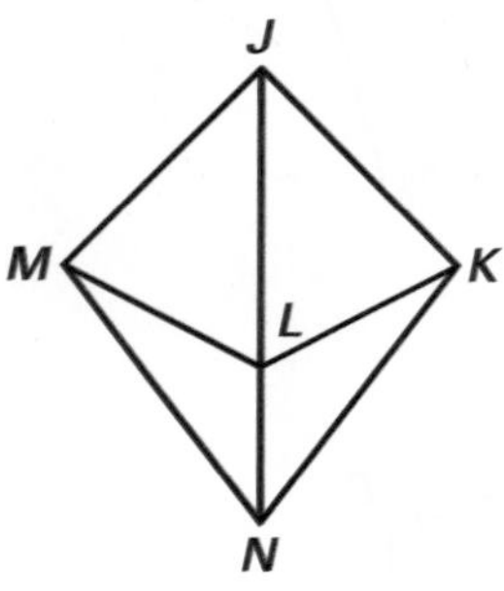

18. Proof Write a proof.

GIVEN: $\angle CAD \cong \angle BDA$, $\angle B \cong \angle C$

PROVE: $\triangle CDA \cong \triangle BAD$

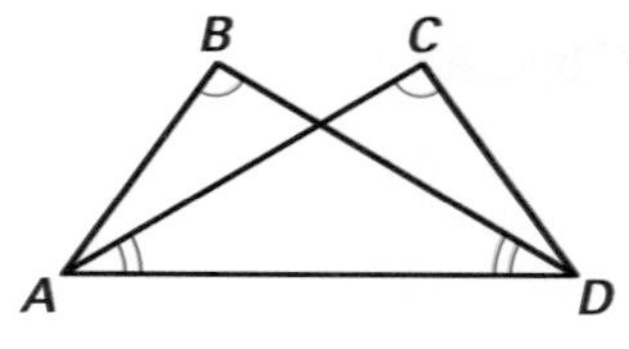

TEST | for Unit 4

Find the distance between the given points. Then find the midpoint of the line segment whose endpoints are the given points.

1. (6, 6), (9, 10) **2.** (−8, 7), (4, 3) **3.** $\left(5, -\frac{3}{2}\right), \left(-2, \frac{9}{2}\right)$

Describe **a pattern in the sequence of numbers. Write the next number.**

4. −6, −1, 4, 9, . . . **5.** 100, −50, 25, −12.5, . . .

Write the if-then form, the converse, the inverse, and the contrapositive for the given statement. Tell whether each statement is *true* or *false*.

6. All 90° angles are right angles. **7.** Frogs are amphibians.

8. $5x + 4 = -6$, because $x = -2$. **9.** An octagon has eight sides.

10. If you decide to go to a movie, then you will miss soccer practice. Tonight, you go to a movie. Using the Law of Detachment, what statement can you make?

Name the property illustrated by the statement.

11. If $\angle 1 \cong \angle 2$, then $\angle 2 \cong \angle 1$. **12.** $\angle QRS \cong \angle SRQ$

13. If $\overline{UV} \cong \overline{WX}$ and $\overline{WX} \cong \overline{YZ}$, then $\overline{UV} \cong \overline{YZ}$.

Find the value of the variables and the measure of each angle in the diagram.

14.

$3(2x + 6)°$, $12y°$, $(14y - 12)°$, $(7x + 3)°$

15.

$(9y + 5)°$, $(11y - 5)°$, $(13x + 3)°$, $2(7x - 6)°$

16. Graph the line $y = \frac{3}{2}x + 4$. Which point on the line is the shortest distance from the point (5, 5)? What is the distance? Round your answer to the nearest tenth.

Decide whether the congruence statement is true. *Explain* your reasoning.

17. $\triangle ABC \cong \triangle EDC$ **18.**  $\triangle PQR \cong \triangle STU$ **19.**  $\triangle MNP \cong \triangle PQM$

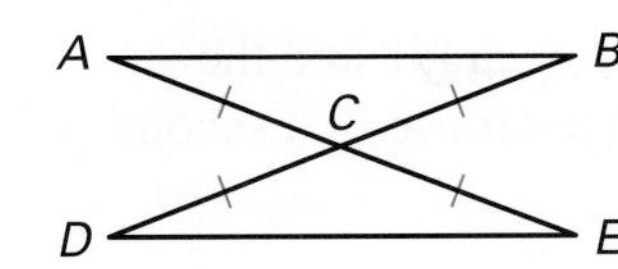

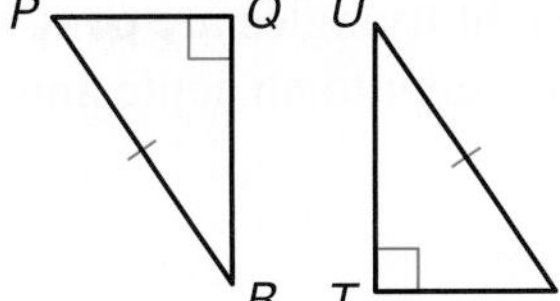

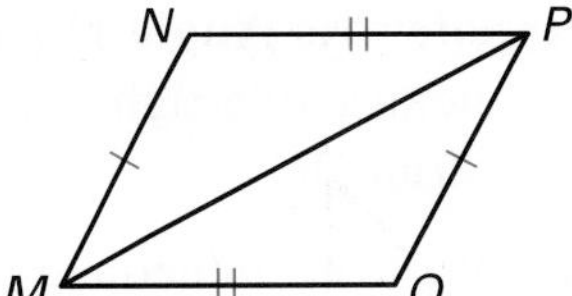

20. **Proof** Write a proof.

GIVEN: $\overline{BE} \cong \overline{BC}$, $\angle A \cong \angle D$

PROVE: $\triangle ABE \cong \triangle DBC$

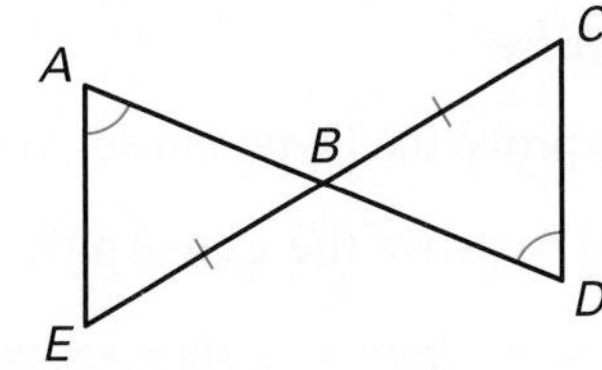

UNIT 4

TEST | for Unit 4 *(continued)*

21. Lacrosse Two lacrosse players are playing on a field as shown. The distance between consecutive grid lines represents 1 foot.

a. How far is each player from the ball? Round your answer to the nearest tenth of a foot.

b. Both players start running toward the ball. Player A runs at a rate of 20 feet per second. Player B runs at a rate of 23 feet per second. Who will reach the ball first?

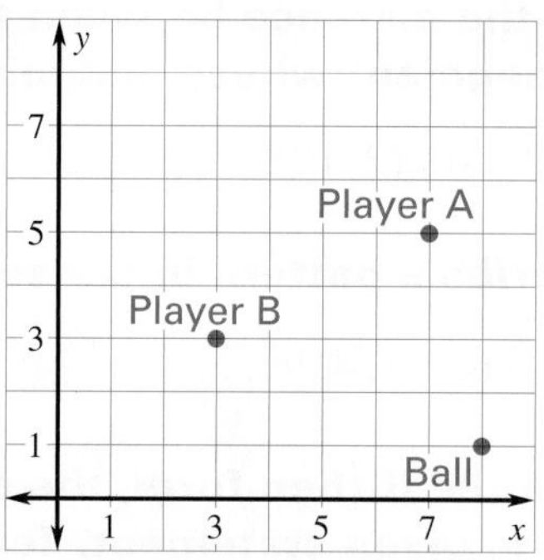

22. Musicians The Venn diagram represents all of the musicians at a high school. Write an if-then statement that describes a relationship between the various groups of musicians.

Musicians

Chorus

Marching band

Jazz band

23. Structural Support The back view of a bench is shown. Use the SSS Congruence Postulate to determine whether the bench is stable. *Explain* your reasoning.

24. Weaving If two people construct wooden frames for a triangle weaving loom using the instructions at the right, will the frames be congruent triangles? *Explain* your reasoning.

Instructions

Construct the frame so that the loom has a 90° angle at the bottom and one of the two upper corners is a 45° angle. The piece of wood at the top should measure 72 inches.

Performance Task

Right Triangles

In Lesson 4.9, you learned the Hypotenuse-Leg Theorem for right triangles. Below are two more theorems about right triangles.

Leg-Angle Theorem: Two right triangles are congruent if an acute angle and a leg of a right triangle are congruent to an acute angle and a leg of a second right triangle.

Hypotenuse-Angle Theorem: Two right triangles are congruent if an acute angle and the hypotenuse of a right triangle are congruent to an acute angle and the hypotenuse of a second right triangle.

a. Write each theorem in if-then form.

b. Write the converse, the inverse, and the contrapositive of each theorem. Decide whether each statement is *true* or *false*.

c. Write a paragraph proof to prove the Hypotenuse-Angle Theorem. Use a diagram in your proof.

d. Write a two-column proof to prove the Leg-Angle Theorem. Use a diagram in your proof.

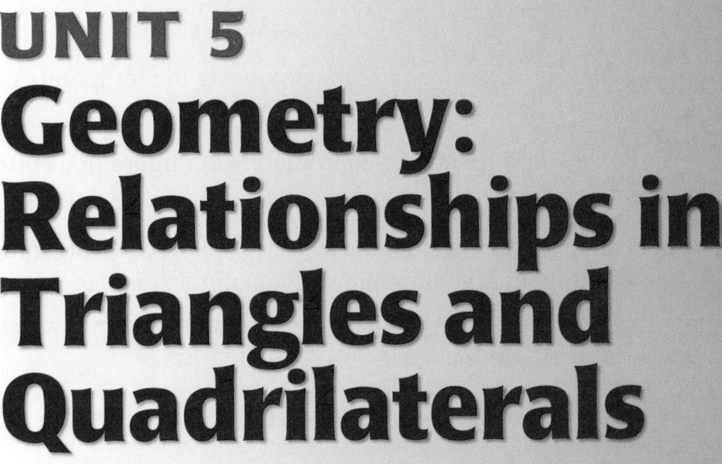

UNIT 5
Geometry: Relationships in Triangles and Quadrilaterals

LESSON 5.1

Midsegment Theorem and Coordinate Proof

Georgia Performance Standards: MM1G1c, MM1G1e

Goal Use properties of midsegments and write coordinate proofs.

Vocabulary

A **midsegment of a triangle** is a segment that connects the midpoints of two sides of the triangle.

When you use variables to represent the coordinates of a figure in a *coordinate proof*, the results are true for all figures of that type.

Theorem 5.1 Midsegment Theorem: The segment connecting the midpoints of two sides of a triangle is parallel to the third side and is half as long as that side.

Example 1 Use the Midsegment Theorem to find lengths

In the diagram, $\overline{ST}$ and $\overline{TU}$ are midsegments of $\triangle PQR$. Find PR and TU.

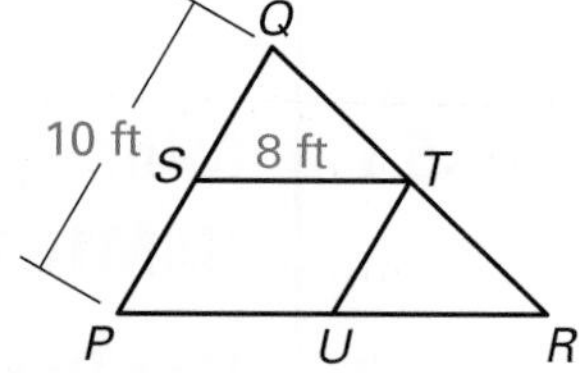

Solution

$PR = 2 \cdot ST = 2(8 \text{ ft})$

$= 16 \text{ ft}$

$TU = \frac{1}{2} \cdot QP = \frac{1}{2}(10 \text{ ft})$

$= 5 \text{ ft}$

Guided Practice for Example 1

1. In the diagram, $\overline{XZ}$ and $\overline{ZY}$ are midsegments of $\triangle LMN$. Find MN and ZY.

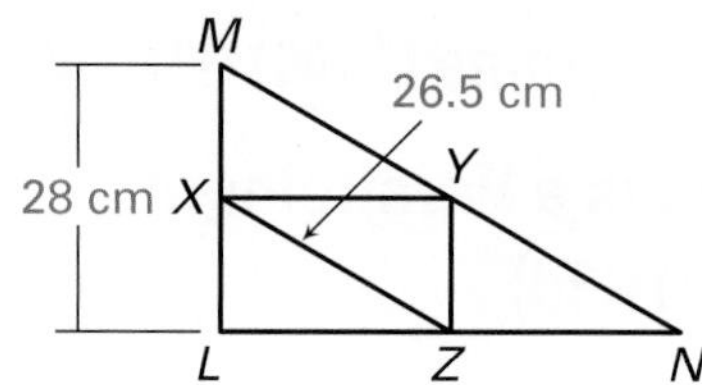

2. In the diagram, $\overline{ED}$ and $\overline{DF}$ are midsegments of $\triangle ABC$. Find DF and BC.

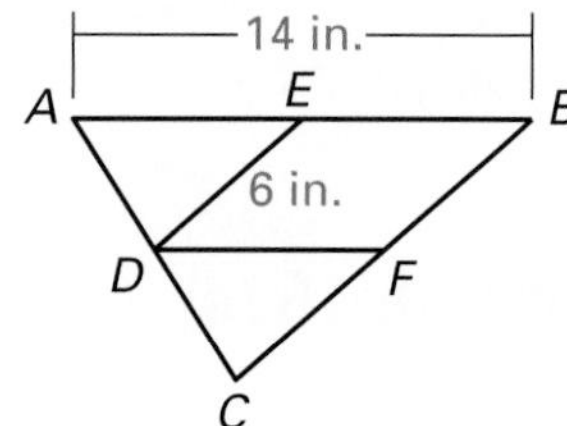

UNIT 5

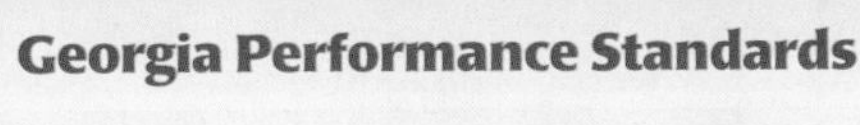

Georgia Performance Standards

MM1G1c Determine the midpoint of a segment. 

MM1G1e Use the coordinate plane to investigate properties of and verify conjectures related to triangles and quadrilaterals. 

Example 2 Use the Midsegment Theorem

In the diagram at the right, $\overline{SB} \cong \overline{SC}$, $\overline{RS} \parallel \overline{AC}$, and $RS = \frac{1}{2}AC$. Show that R is the midpoint of $\overline{BA}$.

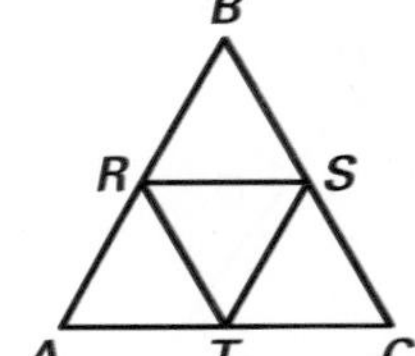

Solution

Because $\overline{SB} \cong \overline{SC}$, S is the midpoint of $\overline{BC}$. Because $\overline{RS} \parallel \overline{AC}$ and $RS = \frac{1}{2}AC$, $\overline{RS}$ is a midsegment of $\triangle ABC$ by definition. By the Midsegment Theorem, R is the midpoint of $\overline{BA}$.

Example 3 Place a figure in a coordinate plane

Place each figure in a coordinate plane in a way that is convenient for finding side lengths. Assign coordinates to each vertex.

a. An isosceles triangle **b.** A square

Solution

It is easy to find lengths of horizontal and vertical segments and distances from (0, 0), so place one vertex at the origin and one or more sides on an axis.

a. Let $2m$ represent the length of the base of the isosceles triangle. The coordinates of the vertex opposite the base are (m, n), which makes each of the legs congruent.

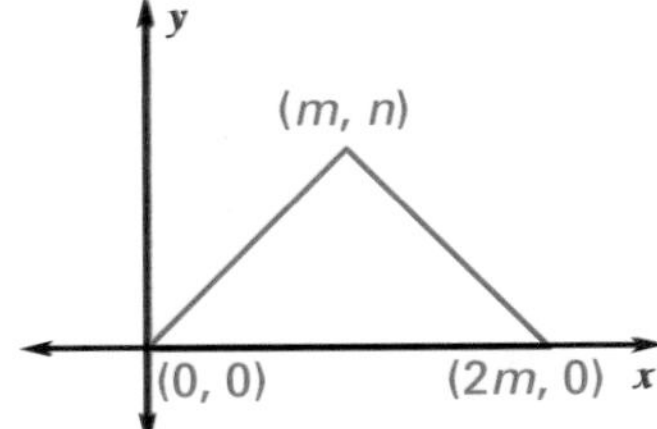

b. Let a represent the side length of the square.

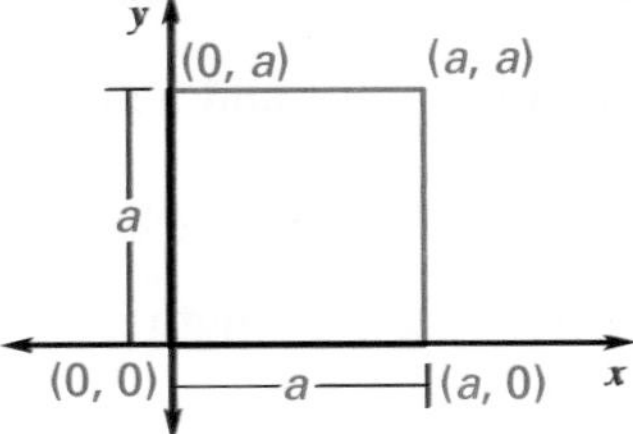

Guided Practice for Examples 2 and 3

3. In Example 2, if T is the midpoint of $\overline{AC}$, what do you know about $\overline{ST}$?

4. A rectangle has vertices at $(0, 0)$, $(j, 0)$, and (j, k). Find the coordinates of the fourth vertex.

UNIT 5

LESSON 5.1

Exercise Set A

MM1G1c Determine the midpoint of a segment.

MM1G1e Use the coordinate plane to investigate properties of and verify conjectures related to triangles and quadrilaterals.

$\overline{DE}$ is a midsegment of $\triangle ABC$. Find the value of x.

1.

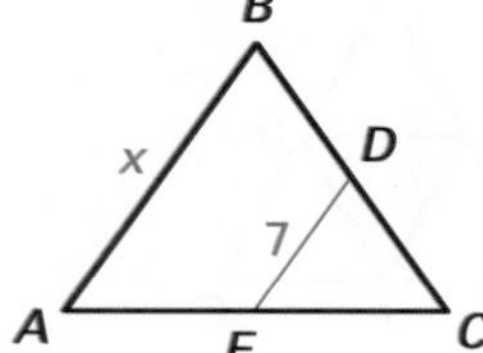

2.

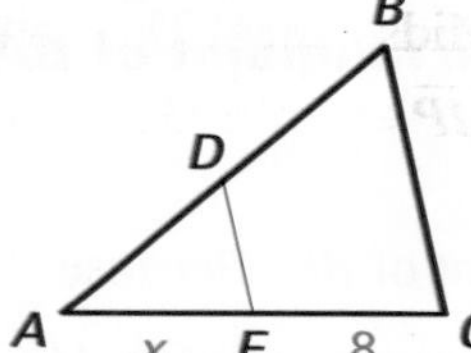

3.

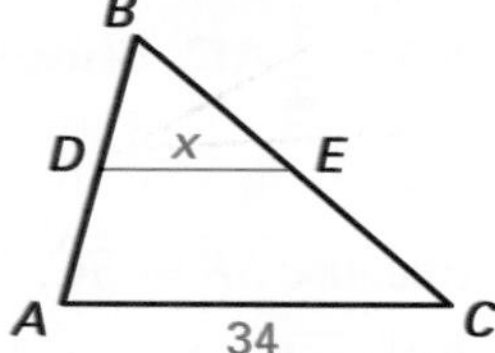

In $\triangle JKL$, $\overline{JR} \cong \overline{RK}$, $\overline{KS} \cong \overline{SL}$, and $\overline{JT} \cong \overline{TL}$. Copy and complete the statement.

4. $\overline{RS} \parallel$ _?_

5. $\overline{ST} \parallel$ _?_

6. $\overline{KL} \parallel$ _?_

7. $\overline{SL} \cong$ _?_ $\cong$ _?_

8. $\overline{JR} \cong$ _?_ $\cong$ _?_

9. $\overline{JT} \cong$ _?_ $\cong$ _?_

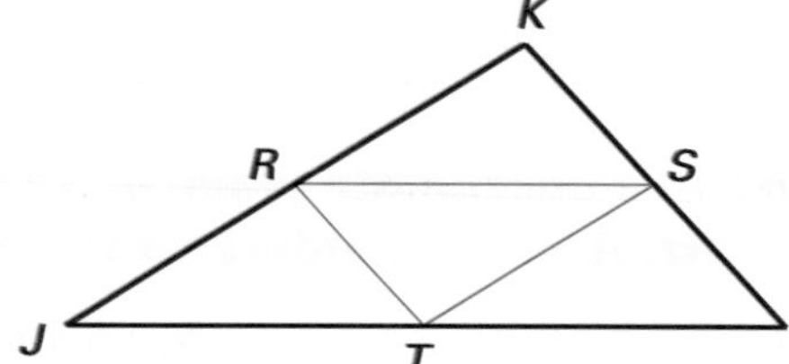

Place the figure in a coordinate plane in a convenient way. Assign coordinates to each vertex.

10. Right triangle: leg lengths are 5 units and 3 units

11. Rectangle: length is 7 units and width is 4 units

12. Square: side length is 6 units

13. Isosceles right triangle: leg length is 12 units

Use $\triangle GHJ$, where D, E, and F are midpoints of the sides.

14. If $DE = 4x + 5$ and $GJ = 3x + 25$, what is DE?

15. If $EF = 3x - 1$ and $GH = 5x + 3$, what is EF?

16. If $HJ = 8x - 2$ and $DF = 2x + 11$, what is HJ?

17. Find the perimeter of $\triangle DEF$.

18. Find the perimeter of $\triangle GHJ$.

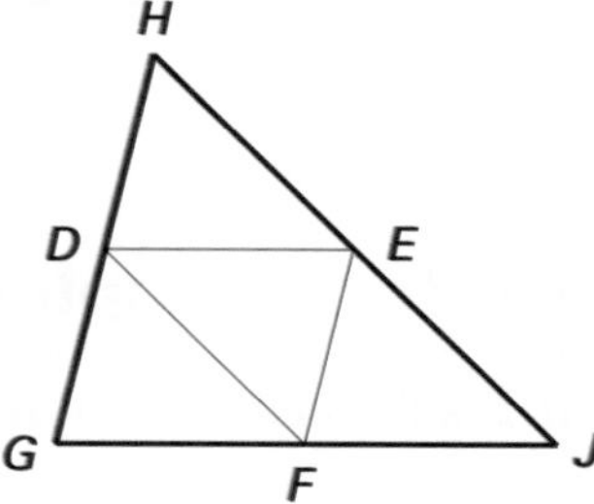

UNIT 5

Exercise Set A *(continued)*

19. Error Analysis *Explain* why the conclusion is incorrect.

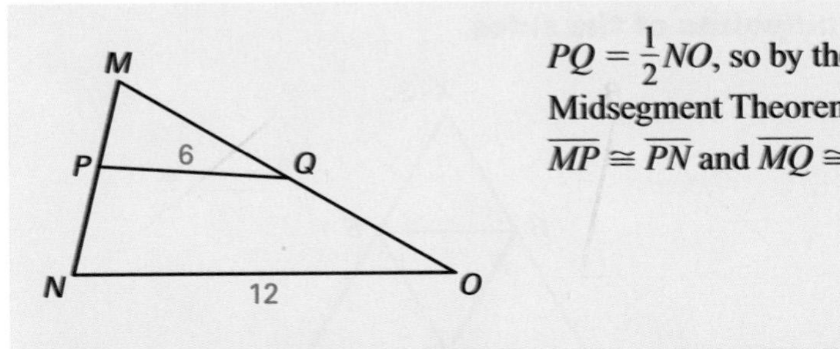

Find the unknown coordinates of the point(s) in the figure. Then show that the given statement is true.

20. $\triangle ABC \cong \triangle DEC$

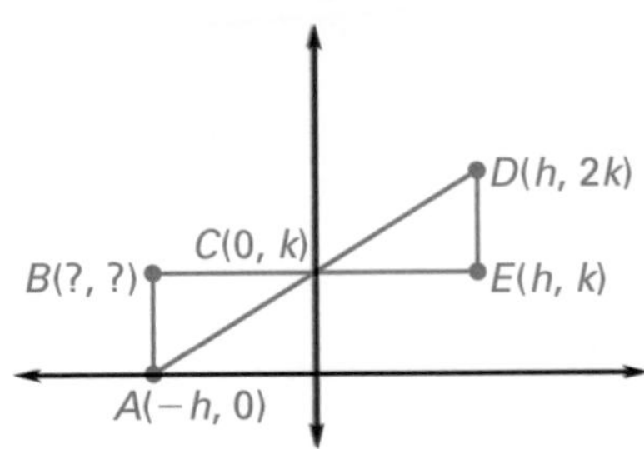

21. $\overline{PT} \cong \overline{SR}$

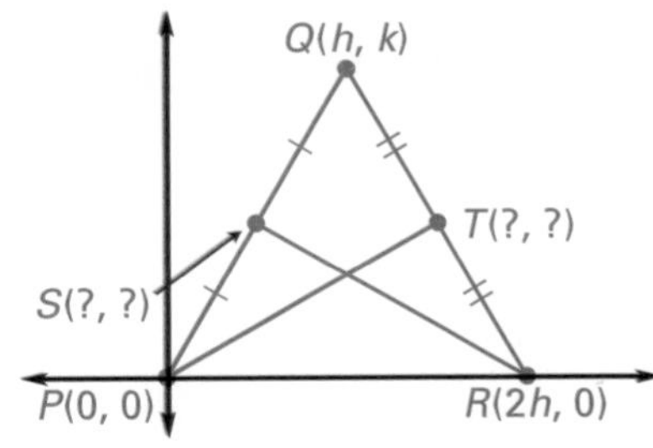

22. The coordinates of $\triangle ABC$ are $A(0, 5)$, $B(8, 20)$, and $C(0, 26)$. Find the length of each side and the perimeter of $\triangle ABC$. Then find the perimeter of the triangle formed by connecting the three midsegments of $\triangle ABC$.

23. **Swing Set** You are assembling the frame for a swing set. The horizontal crossbars in the kit you purchased are each 36 inches long. You attach the crossbars at the midpoints of the legs. At each end of the frame, how far apart will the bottoms of the legs be when the frame is assembled? *Explain.*

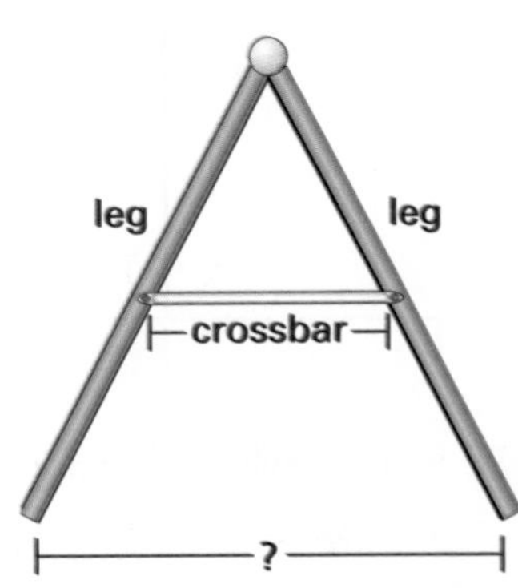

24. **A-Frame House** In an A-frame house, the floor of the second level, labeled $\overline{LM}$, is closer to the first floor, $\overline{NP}$, than midsegment $\overline{JK}$. If $\overline{JK}$ is 14 feet long, can $\overline{LM}$ be 12 feet long? 14 feet long? 20 feet long? 24 feet long? 30 feet long? *Explain.*

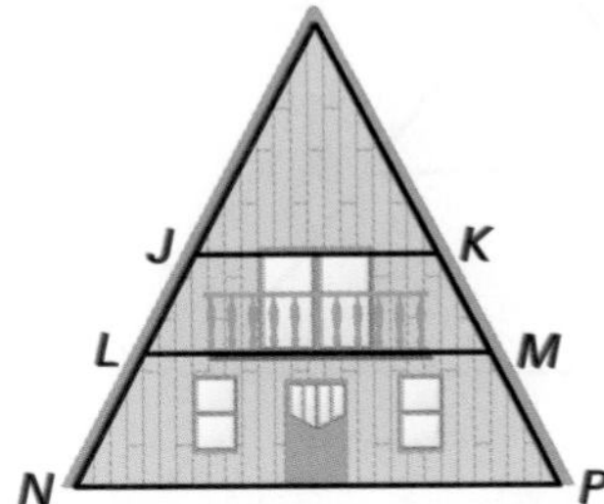

LESSON 5.1 **Exercise Set B**

MM1G1c Determine the midpoint of a segment.

MM1G1e Use the coordinate plane to investigate properties of and verify conjectures related to triangles and quadrilaterals.

Use △*WXY*, where *R*, *S*, and *T* are midpoints of the sides.

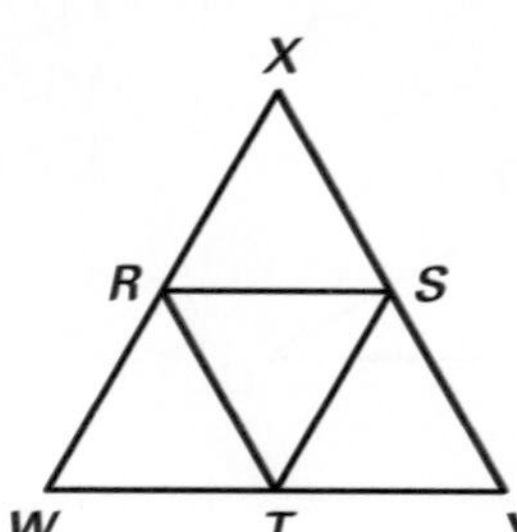

1. $\overline{RS} \parallel$ __?__
2. $\overline{ST} \parallel$ __?__
3. If $TY = 4$, then $RS =$ __?__.
4. If $RT = 7$, then $XY =$ __?__.

Use the diagram of △*ABC* where *D*, *E*, and *F* are the midpoints of the sides.

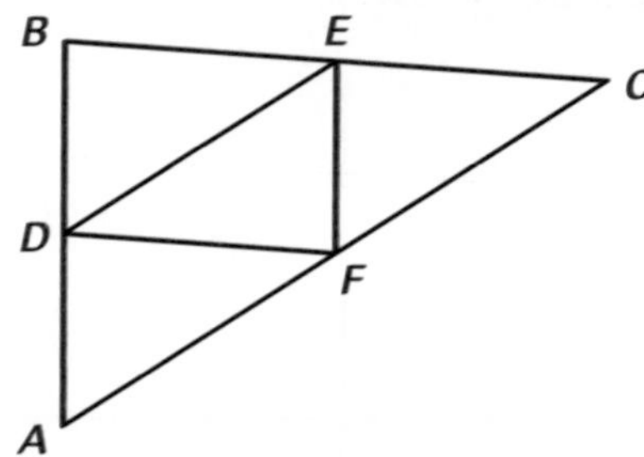

5. If $FE = 6.5x - 10$ and $AB = 3x + 20$, then $AB =$ __?__.
6. If $DF = 3.5x + 6$ and $BC = 3x + 36$, then $DF =$ __?__.

Find the unknown coordinates of the points in the figure.

7\.

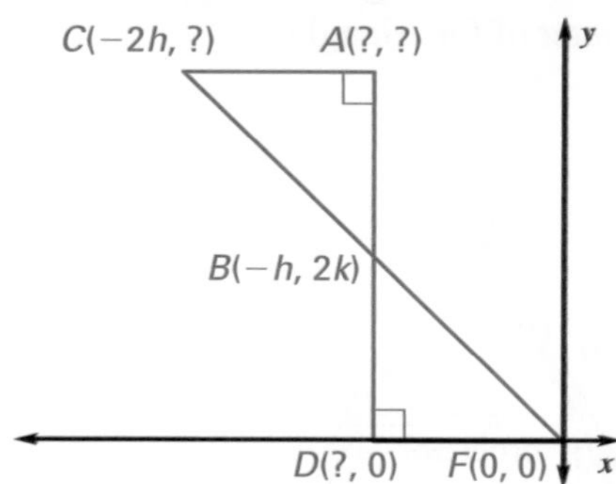

8\.

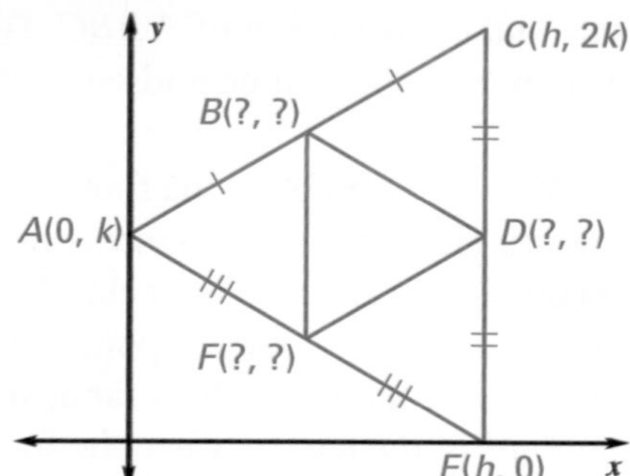

9. **Error Analysis** *Explain* why $\overline{BD}$ is not a midsegment of △*ACE*.

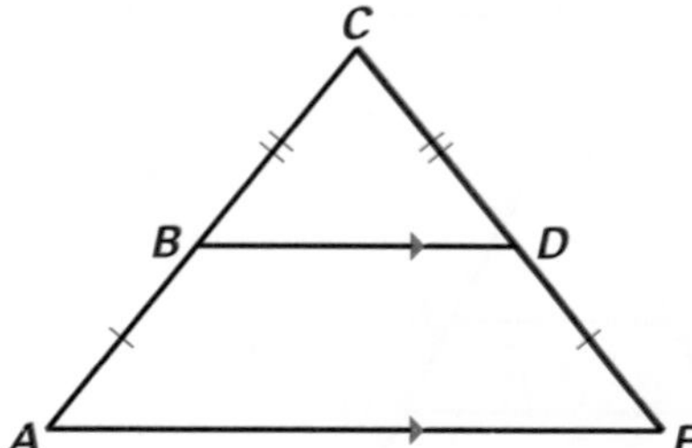

Exercise Set B *(continued)*

In Exercises 10 and 11, write a coordinate proof.

10. **GIVEN:** Coordinates of $\triangle DEF$
G is the midpoint of $\overline{DE}$.
H is the midpoint of $\overline{EF}$.

PROVE: $GH = \frac{1}{2}DF$

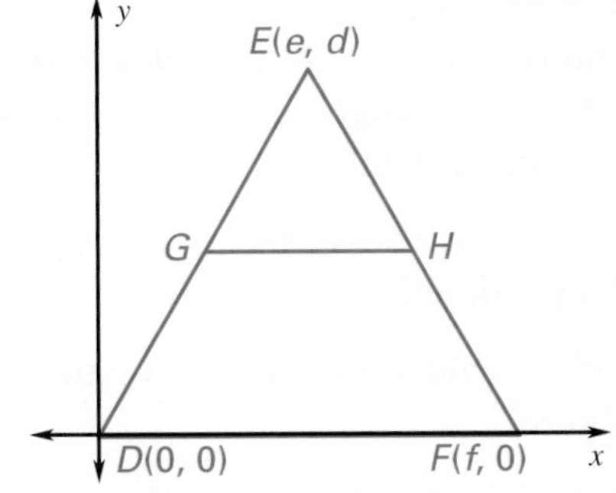

11. **GIVEN:** $\overline{DB}$ bisects $\angle ABC$.

PROVE: $\triangle ABD \cong \triangle CBD$

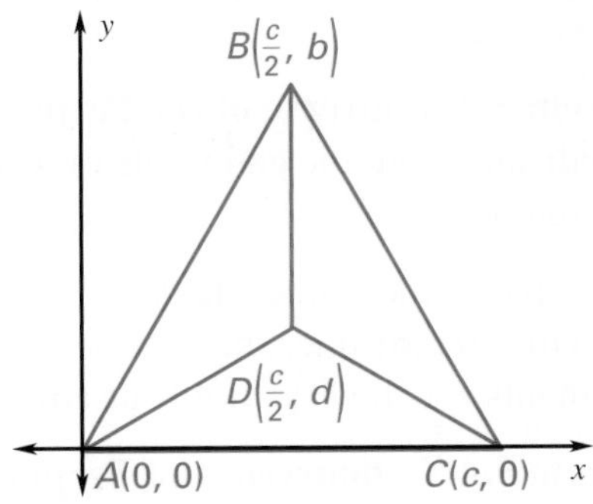

12. **Roof Trusses** An attic truss provides storage space within the roof of a house. The midsegment of the truss is the ceiling of the storage space. If the base of the truss is 30 feet, find the width x of the storage space. *Explain.*

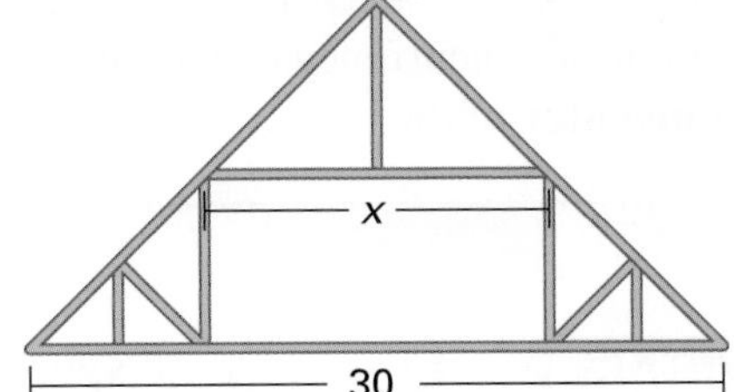

13. Use the information in the diagram at the right. What is the length of $\overline{AC}$ of $\triangle ABC$? *Explain* your reasoning.

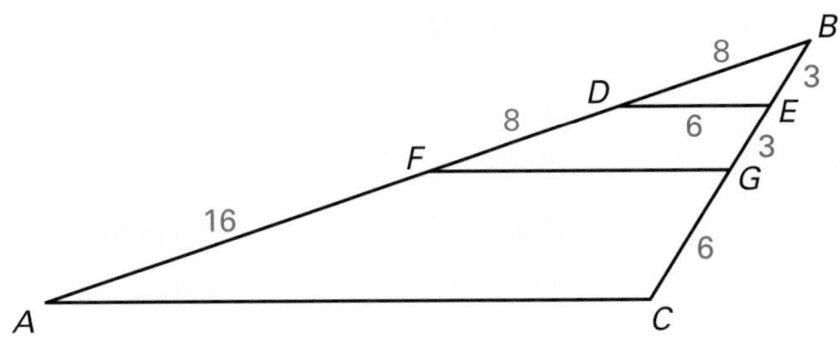

LESSON 5.2

Use Perpendicular Bisectors

Georgia Performance Standards: MM1G3e

Goal Use perpendicular bisectors to solve problems.

Vocabulary

By definition, congruent triangles have congruent corresponding parts. So, if you can prove that two triangles are congruent, you know that their corresponding parts must be congruent as well.

A segment, ray, line, or plane that is perpendicular to a segment at its midpoint is called a **perpendicular bisector.**

A point is **equidistant** from two figures if the point is the *same distance* from each figure.

Theorem 5.2 Perpendicular Bisector Theorem: In a plane, if a point is on the perpendicular bisector of a segment, then it is equidistant from the endpoints of the segment.

Theorem 5.3 Converse of the Perpendicular Bisector Theorem: In a plane, if a point is equidistant from the endpoints of a segment, then it is on the perpendicular bisector of the segment.

When three or more lines, rays, or segments intersect in the same point, they are called **concurrent** lines, rays, or segments. The point of intersection of the lines, rays, or segments is called the **point of concurrency.**

Theorem 5.4 Concurrency of Perpendicular Bisectors of a Triangle: The perpendicular bisectors of a triangle intersect at a point that is equidistant from the vertices of the triangle.

The point of concurrency of the three perpendicular bisectors of a triangle is called the **circumcenter** of the triangle.

Example 1 Use the Perpendicular Bisector Theorem

$\overleftrightarrow{KM}$ is the perpendicular bisector of $\overline{JL}$. Find ML.

M
7x
3x + 16
J
K
L

Solution

Find x.

$JM = ML$	Perpendicular Bisector Theorem
$7x = 3x + 16$	Substitute.
$x = 4$	Solve for x.

Find ML.

$ML = 3(4) + 16$

$= 28$

UNIT 5

Georgia Performance Standards

MM1G3e Find and use points of concurrency in triangles: incenter, orthocenter, circumcenter, and centroid.

Example 2 Use perpendicular bisectors

In the diagram shown, $\overleftrightarrow{DC}$ is the perpendicular bisector of $\overline{AB}$ and $\overline{AE} \cong \overline{BE}$.

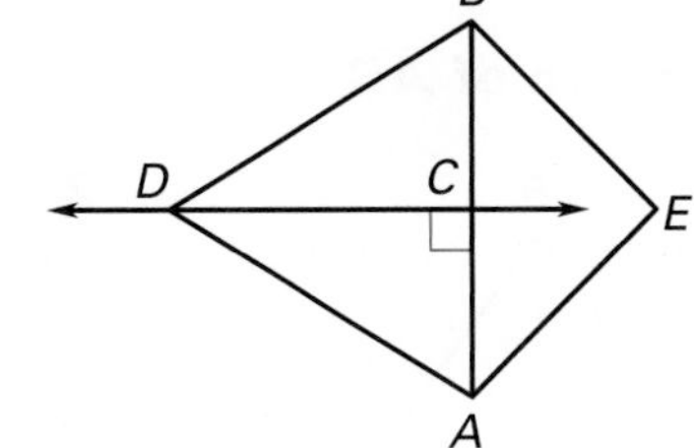

a. What segment lengths in the diagram are equal?

b. Is E on $\overleftrightarrow{DC}$?

Solution

a. $\overleftrightarrow{DC}$ bisects $\overline{AB}$, so $CA = CB$. Because D is on the perpendicular bisector of $\overline{AB}$, $DA = DB$ by Theorem 5.2. Because $\overline{AE} \cong \overline{BE}$, $AE = BE$ by definition of congruence.

b. Because $AE = BE$, E is equidistant from A and B. So, by the Converse of the Perpendicular Bisector Theorem, E is on the perpendicular bisector of $\overline{AB}$, which is $\overleftrightarrow{DC}$.

Guided Practice for Examples 1 and 2

In the diagram, $\overleftrightarrow{PQ}$ is the perpendicular bisector of $\overline{RS}$.

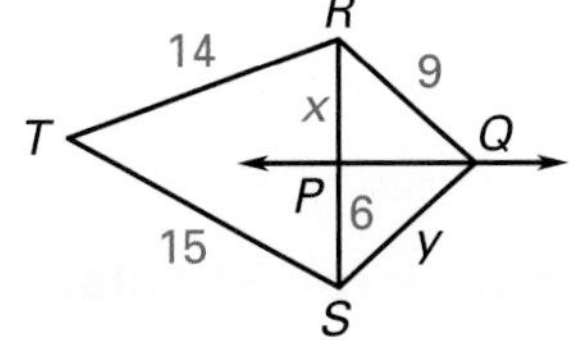

1. What segment lengths in the diagram are equal? *Explain* your reasoning.

2. Is T on $\overleftrightarrow{PQ}$? *Explain.*

Example 3 Use the concurrency of perpendicular bisectors

The perpendicular bisectors of $\triangle ABC$ meet at point G. Find GB.

Solution

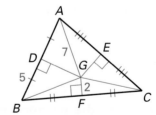

Using Theorem 5.4, you know that point G is equidistant from the vertices of the triangle. So, $GA = GB = GC$.

$GB = GA$ Theorem 5.4

$GB = 7$ Substitute.

Guided Practice for Example 3

3. The perpendicular bisectors of $\triangle RST$ meet at point D. Find DR.

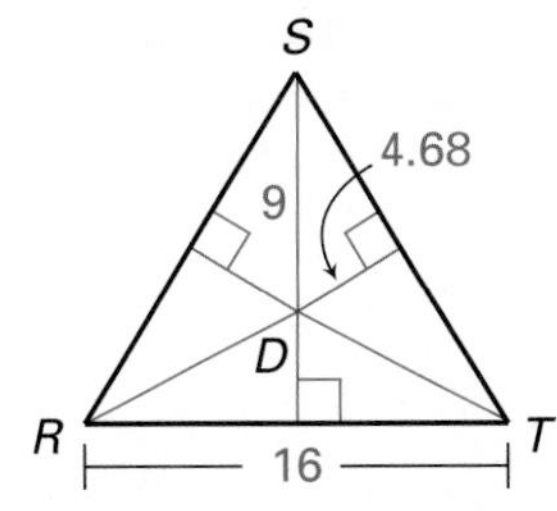

LESSON 5.2 **Exercise Set A**

MM1G3e Find and use points of concurrency in triangles: incenter, orthocenter, circumcenter, and centroid.

Find the length of $\overline{AB}$.

1.

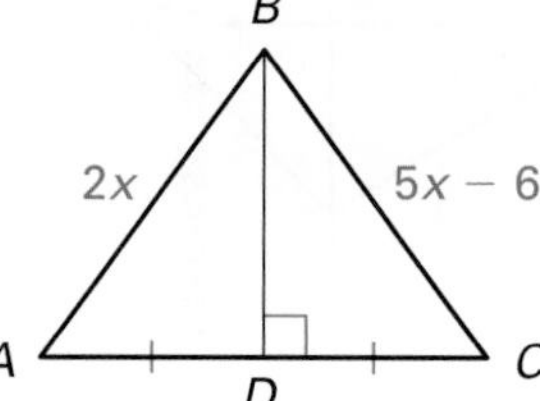

2.

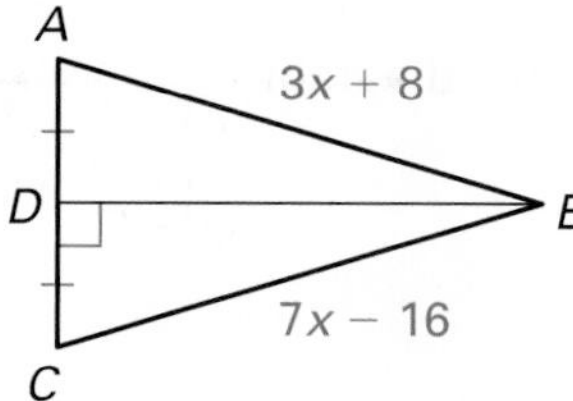

3.

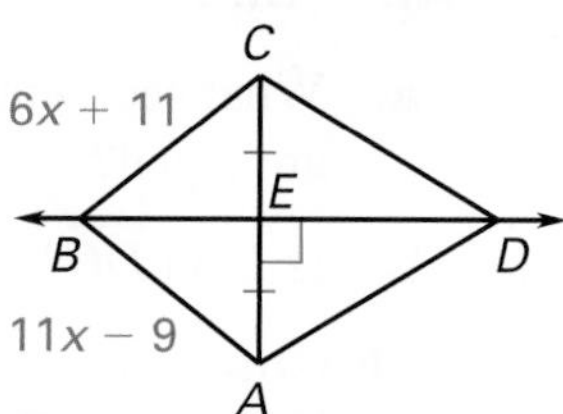

Tell whether the information in the diagram allows you to conclude that *C* is on the perpendicular bisector of $\overline{AB}$.

4.

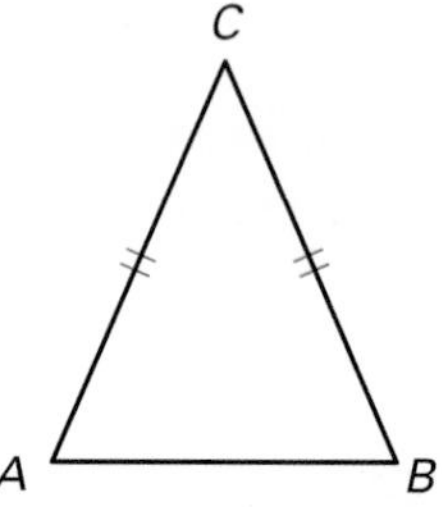

5.

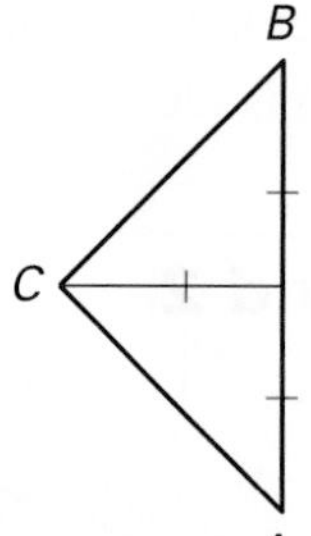

6.

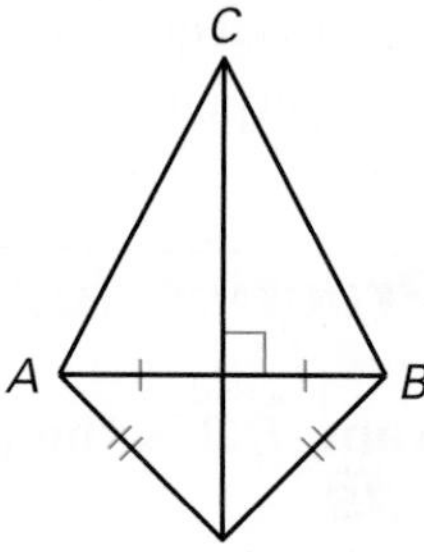

Use the diagram. $\overline{EH}$ is the perpendicular bisector of $\overline{DF}$. Find the indicated measure.

7. Find *EF*.

8. Find *DE*.

9. Find *FG*.

10. Find *DG*.

11. Find *FH*.

12. Find *DF*.

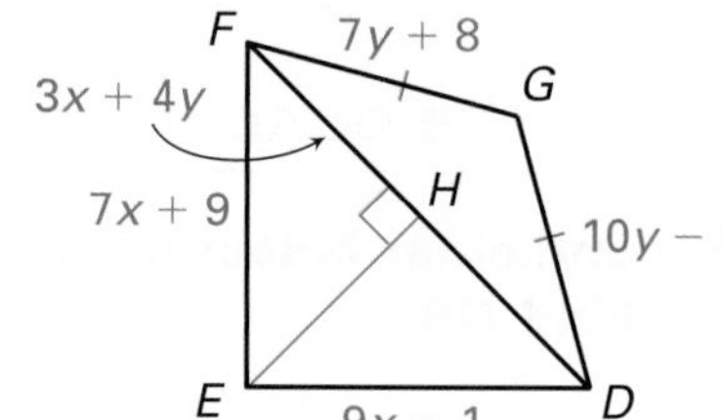

In the diagram, the perpendicular bisectors of $\triangle ABC$ meet at point *G* and are shown dashed. Find the indicated measure.

13. Find *AG*.

14. Find *BD*.

15. Find *CF*.

16. Find *BG*.

17. Find *CE*.

18. Find *AC*.

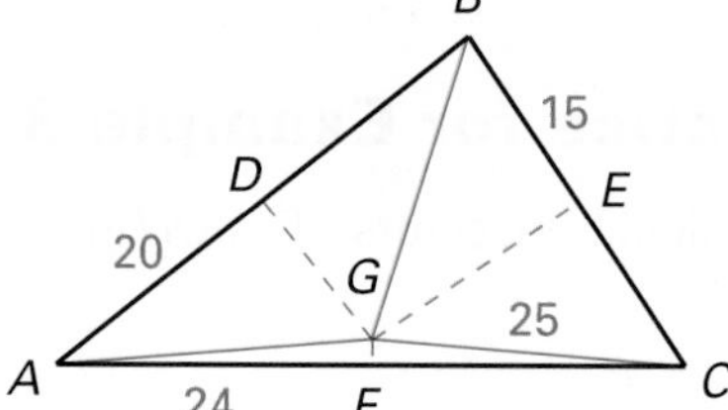

Exercise Set A *(continued)*

19. Error Analysis *Explain* why the conclusion is not correct given the information in the diagram.

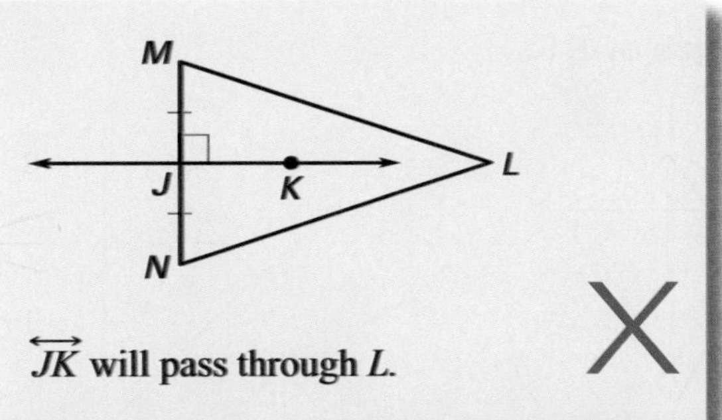

Draw $\overline{AB}$ with the given length. Construct the perpendicular bisector and choose point C on the perpendicular bisector so that the distance between C and $\overline{AB}$ is 1 inch. Measure $\overline{AC}$ and $\overline{BC}$.

20. $AB = 0.5$ inch

21. $AB = 1$ inch

22. $AB = 2$ inches

Write a two-column or a paragraph proof.

23. **GIVEN:** C is on the perpendicular bisector of $\overline{AB}$.

PROVE: $\triangle ACD \cong \triangle BCD$

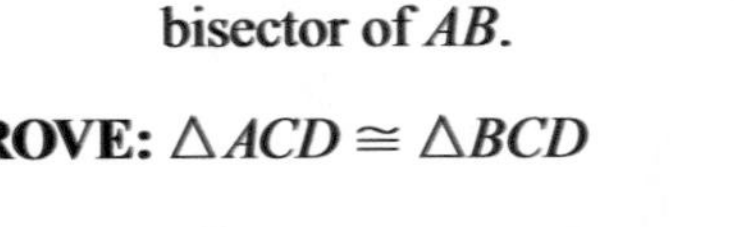

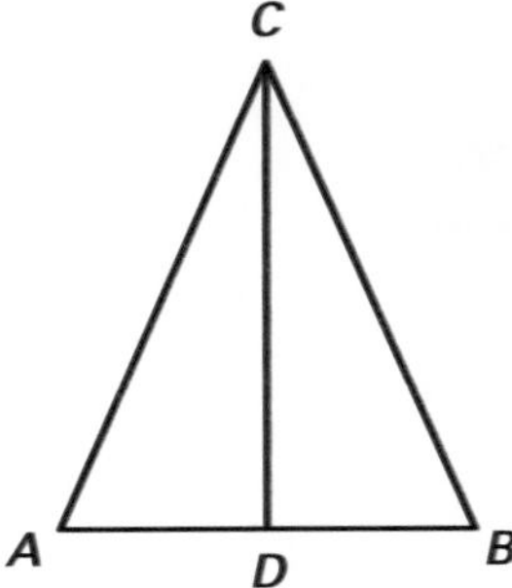

24. **GIVEN:** $\triangle GHJ \cong \triangle FHJ$

PROVE: $\overline{EF} \cong \overline{EG}$

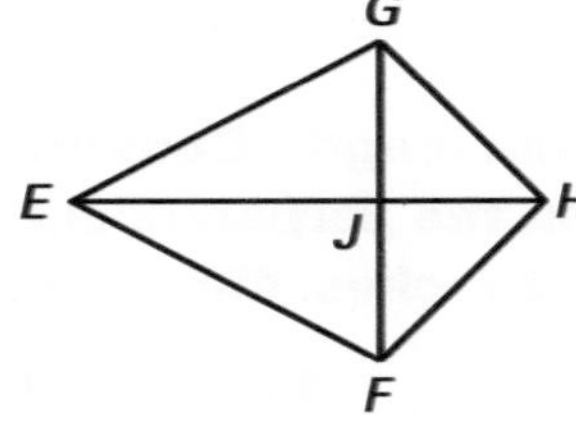

25. **Early Aircraft Set** On many of the earliest airplanes, wires connected vertical posts to the edges of the wings, which were wooden frames covered with cloth. The lengths of the wires from the top of a post to the edges of the frame are the same and distances from the bottom of the post to the ends of the two wires are the same. What does that tell you about the post and the section of frame between the ends of the wires?

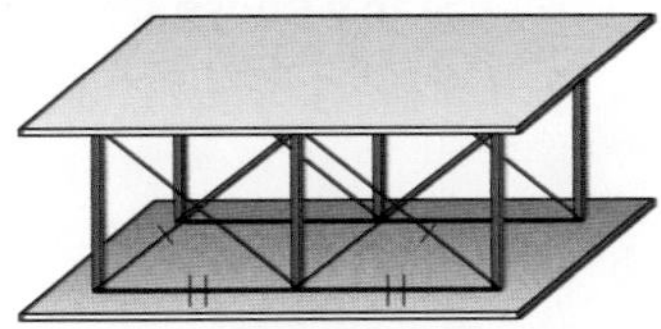

LESSON 5.2 **Exercise Set B**

MM1G3e Find and use points of concurrency in triangles: incenter, orthocenter, circumcenter, and centroid.

Find the length of $\overline{RS}$.

1.

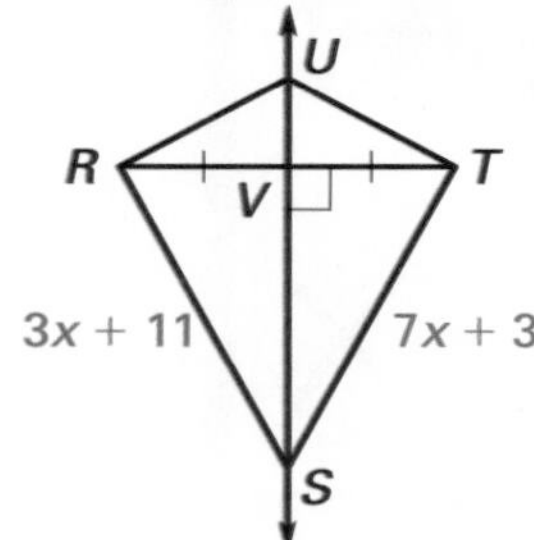

2.

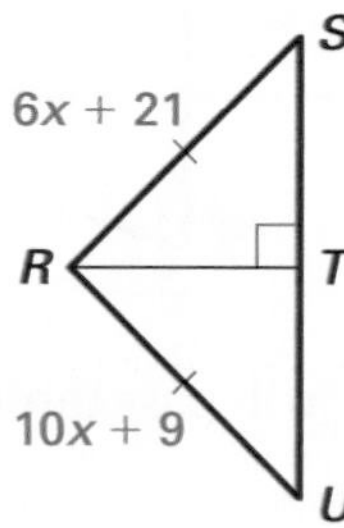

3.

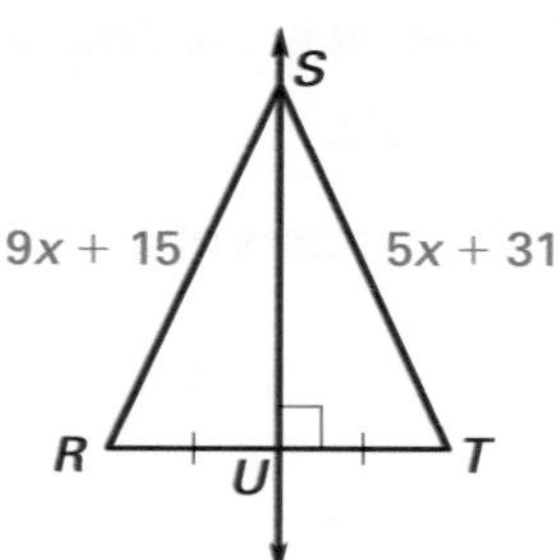

Use the diagram. $\overline{DE}$ is the perpendicular bisector of $\overline{AC}$. Find the indicated measure.

4. Find AB.

5. Find AE.

6. Find AD.

7. Find BC.

8. Find AC.

9. Find CD.

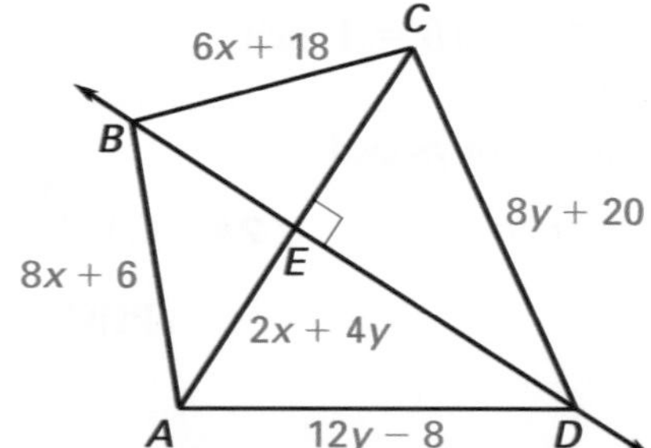

Draw $\overline{AB}$ with the given length. Construct the perpendicular bisector and choose point D on the perpendicular bisector so that the distance between D and $\overline{AB}$ is 2 inches. Measure $\overline{AD}$ and $\overline{BD}$.

10. $AB = 2$ inches

11. $AB = 1.5$ inches

12. $AB = 1$ inch

13. The perpendicular bisectors of $\triangle ABC$ meet at point G and are shown as dashed lines. Find BG.

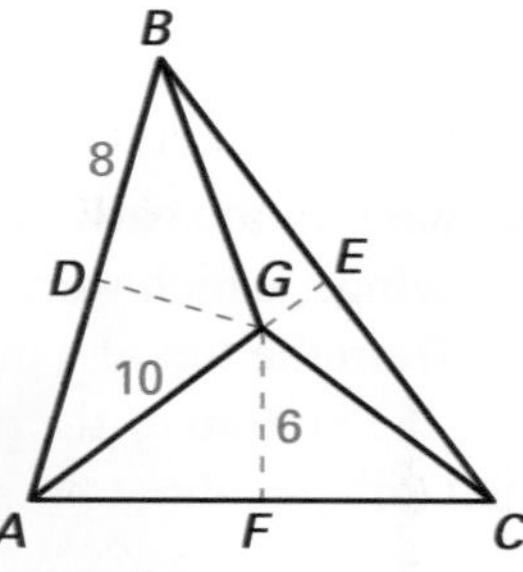

14. **Exercising** You and two friends plan to exercise together. You want your meeting place to be the same distance from each person's house. *Explain* how you can use the diagram to locate the meeting place.

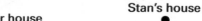

your house

Stan's house

Maria's house

Exercise Set B *(continued)*

In Exercises 15 and 16, copy and complete the statement using *always, sometimes,* or *never.*

15. A perpendicular bisector of a triangle __?__ passes through the midpoint of a side of the triangle.

16. Angle bisectors of a triangle __?__ intersect at a single point.

In Exercises 17 and 18, write a two-column or a paragraph proof.

17. **GIVEN:** $\overline{NP}$ is a perpendicular bisector of $\overline{MO}$.

PROVE: $\triangle NMR \cong \triangle NOR$

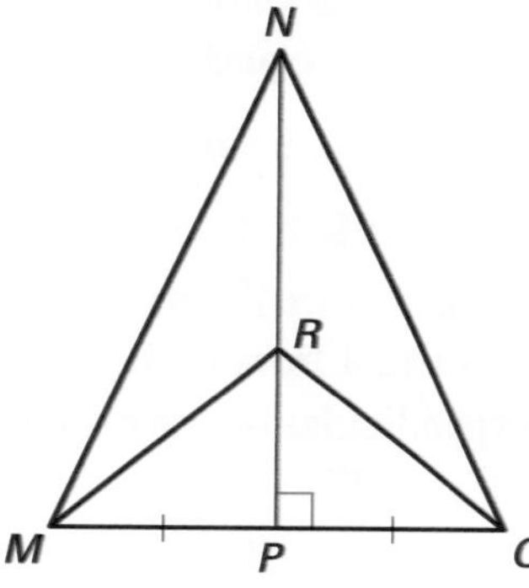

18. **GIVEN:** $\triangle FJG \cong \triangle FJI$

PROVE: $\overline{HI} \cong \overline{HG}$

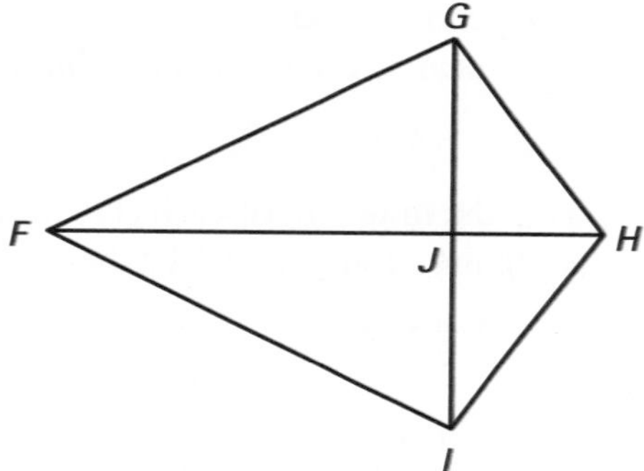

19. **Bridge** In the diagram, the road is perpendicular to the support beam and $\overline{AB} \cong \overline{CB}$. What theorem allows you to conclude that $\overline{AD} \cong \overline{CD}$? *Explain.*

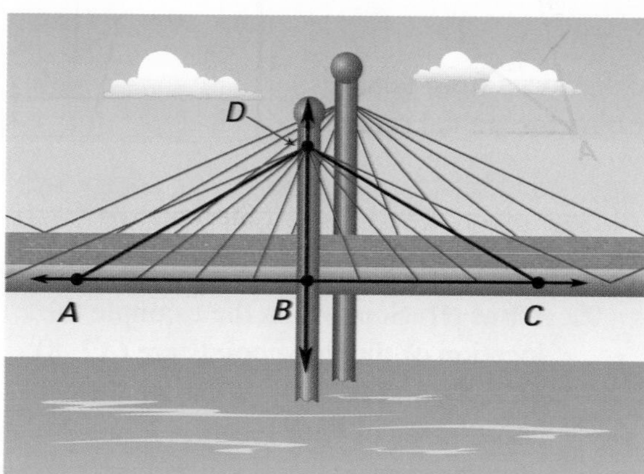

Georgia Performance Standards

MM1G1e Use the coordinate plane to investigate properties of and verify conjectures related to triangles and quadrilaterals. ☑

MM1G3e Find and use points of concurrency in triangles: incenter, orthocenter, circumcenter, and centroid. ☑

LESSON 5.2

Problem Solving Workshop

Problem You are equidistant from cliff C, mountain M, and waterfall W. The points are marked in the graph at the right where distances are measured in miles. What are the coordinates of your position P?

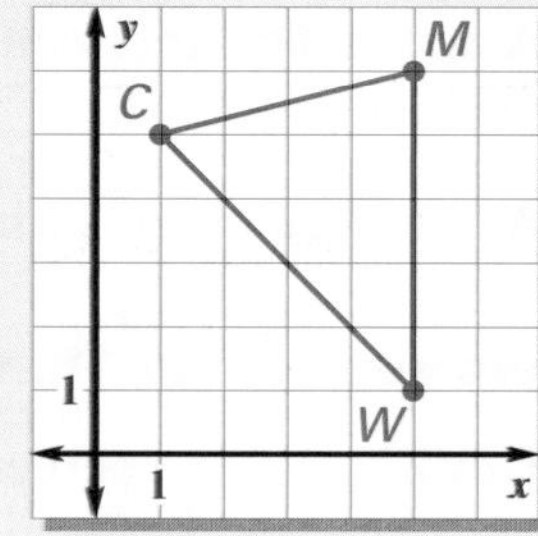

STEP 1 **Read and Understand**

What do you know? The coordinates of three points that you are equidistant from

What do you want to find out? The coordinates of your position

STEP 2 **Make a Plan** Use what you know to solve the problem.

STEP 3 **Solve the Problem** The three points form a triangle. Because you are equidistant from each point, you are located at the intersection of the perpendicular bisectors of the triangle. Label $\overline{CM}$ as 1, $\overline{MW}$ as 2, and $\overline{CW}$ as 3. Find the slope of each side of the triangle.

$$m_1 = \frac{6-5}{5-1} = \frac{1}{4}, m_2 = \frac{6-1}{5-5} = \text{undefined}, m_3 = \frac{1-5}{5-1} = -1$$

The perpendicular bisectors of each side have a slope that is the negative reciprocal of each side. Find this slope.

$$m_{1\perp} = -4, m_{2\perp} = 0, m_{3\perp} = 1$$

Find the midpoint of each side. Let J be the midpoint of $\overline{CM}$, K be the midpoint of $\overline{MW}$, and L be the midpoint of $\overline{CW}$.

$$J = \left(\frac{1+5}{2}, \frac{5+6}{2}\right) = (3.\ 5.5), K = \left(\frac{5+5}{2}, \frac{6+1}{2}\right) = (5, 3.5),$$

$$L = \left(\frac{1+5}{2}, \frac{5+1}{2}\right) = (3, 3)$$

Use the midpoint of each side and the slope of the perpendicular bisectors to find where the perpendicular bisectors intersect. From the graph, your position is $P(3.5, 3.5)$.

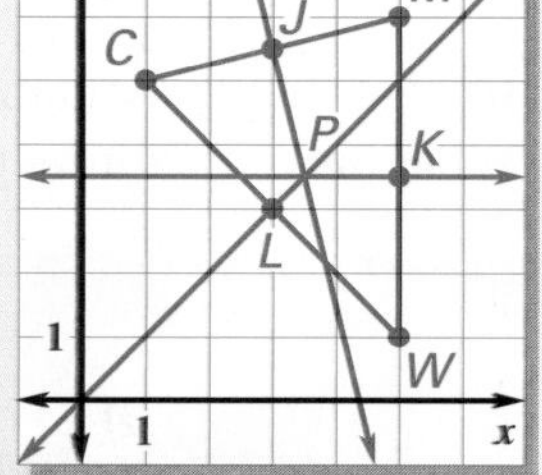

STEP 4 **Look Back** Check to see that the distances from your location along each perpendicular bisector are the same.

Practice

1. **What If?** Suppose in the example above that cliff C is located at (2, 3). What are the coordinates of your position P now?

2. **What If?** Suppose in the example the location of the three points are $C(2, 8)$, $M(7, 8)$, and $W(5, 3)$. What are the coordinates of your location P now?

UNIT 5

Georgia Performance Standards

MM1G3e Find and use points of concurrency in triangles: incenter, orthocenter, circumcenter, and centroid. 

Investigating Math Activity

Exploring the Incenter

Use before Lesson 5.3

Materials **tracing paper, straightedge, and compass**

Question

What is the relationship between the incenter and the sides of a triangle?
The point of concurrency of the three angle bisectors of a triangle is called the *incenter* of the triangle. The incenter always lies inside the triangle.

Explore

STEP 1 **Draw Triangle** Use your straightedge to draw a large acute scalene triangle on a piece of tracing paper. Label the vertices of the triangle, J, K, and L.

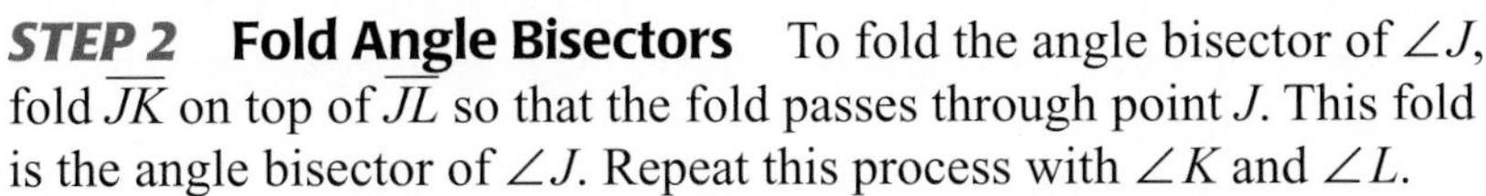

STEP 2 **Fold Angle Bisectors** To fold the angle bisector of $\angle J$, fold $\overline{JK}$ on top of $\overline{JL}$ so that the fold passes through point J. This fold is the angle bisector of $\angle J$. Repeat this process with $\angle K$ and $\angle L$.

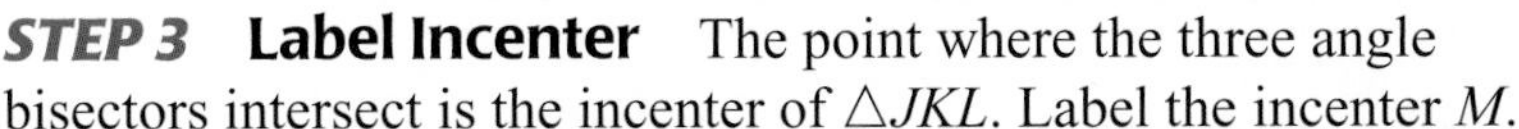

STEP 3 **Label Incenter** The point where the three angle bisectors intersect is the incenter of $\triangle JKL$. Label the incenter M.

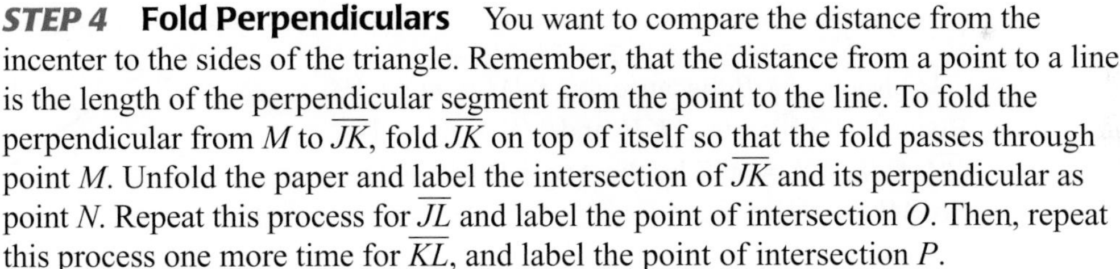

STEP 4 **Fold Perpendiculars** You want to compare the distance from the incenter to the sides of the triangle. Remember, that the distance from a point to a line is the length of the perpendicular segment from the point to the line. To fold the perpendicular from M to $\overline{JK}$, fold $\overline{JK}$ on top of itself so that the fold passes through point M. Unfold the paper and label the intersection of $\overline{JK}$ and its perpendicular as point N. Repeat this process for $\overline{JL}$ and label the point of intersection O. Then, repeat this process one more time for $\overline{KL}$, and label the point of intersection P.

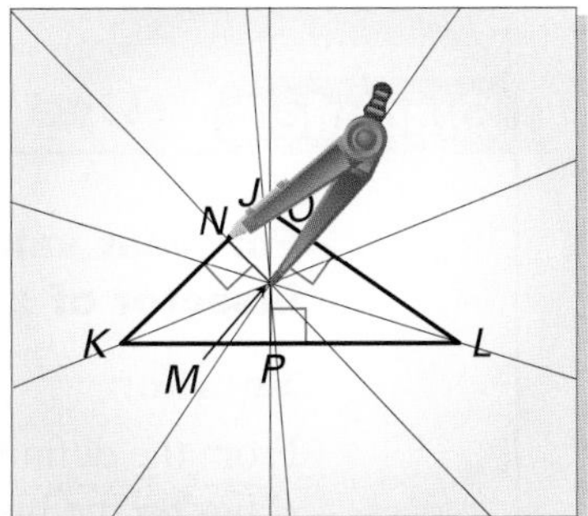

STEP 5 **Compare Distances** Use the compass to compare the distances between point M and points N, O, and P. Place the point of the compass on point M and the compass pencil on point N. Leave the point of the compass on M and move the compass pencil to point O. Now, move the compass pencil to point P. Did you have to adjust your compass?

Draw Conclusions

1. How do the distances MN, MO, and MP compare?
2. **Reasoning** Compare your results to Exercise 1 with your classmates. *Describe* the relationship between the incenter and the sides of a triangle.
3. Complete the statement: The angle bisectors of a triangle intersect at a point that is __?__.

UNIT 5

LESSON 5.3

Use Angle Bisectors of Triangles

Georgia Performance Standards: MM1G3e

Goal Use angle bisectors to find distance relationships.

Vocabulary

An **angle bisector** is a ray that divides an angle into two congruent adjacent angles.

The point of concurrency of the three angle bisectors of a triangle is called the **incenter** of the triangle.

Theorem 5.5 Angle Bisector Theorem: If a point is on the bisector of an angle, then it is equidistant from the two sides of the angle.

Theorem 5.6 Converse of the Angle Bisector Theorem: If a point is in the interior of an angle and is equidistant from the sides of the angle, then it lies on the bisector of the angle.

Theorem 5.7 Concurrency of Angle Bisectors of a Triangle: The angle bisectors of a triangle intersect at a point that is equidistant from the sides of the triangle.

UNIT 5

Example 1 Use the Angle Bisector Theorem

Find the length of $\overline{LM}$.

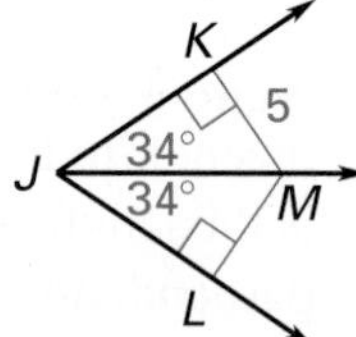

Solution

$\overrightarrow{JM}$ bisects $\angle KJL$ because $m\angle KJM = m\angle LJM$. Because $\overrightarrow{JM}$ bisects $\angle KJL$ and $\overline{MK} \perp \overline{JK}$ and $\overline{ML} \perp \overline{JL}$, $ML = MK$ by the Angle Bisector Theorem. So, $ML = MK = 5$.

Example 2 Use algebra to solve a problem

For what value of *x* does *P* lie on the bisector of $\angle GFH$?

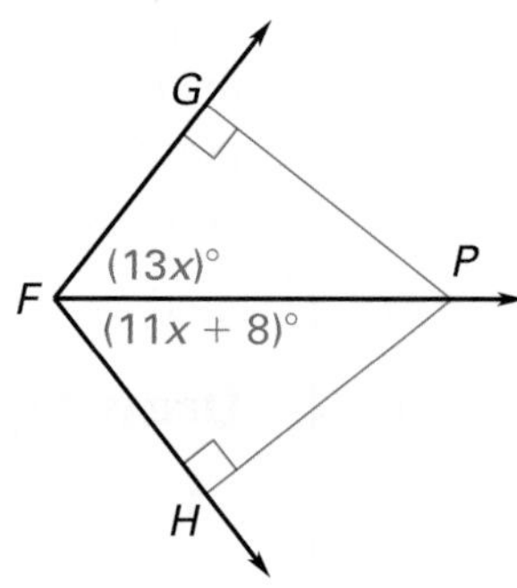

Solution

From the definition of an angle bisector, you know that P lies on the bisector of $\angle GFH$ if $m\angle GFP = m\angle HFP$.

$m\angle GFP = m\angle HFP$	Set angle measures equal.
$13x = 11x + 8$	Substitute.
$x = 4$	Solve for x.

Point P lies on the bisector of $\angle GFH$ when $x = 4$.

Georgia Performance Standards

MM1G3e Find and use points of concurrency in triangles: incenter, orthocenter, circumcenter, and centroid.

Guided Practice for Examples 1 and 2

Find the value of *x*.

1.

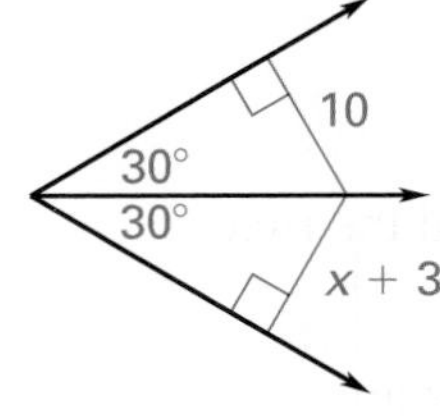

2.

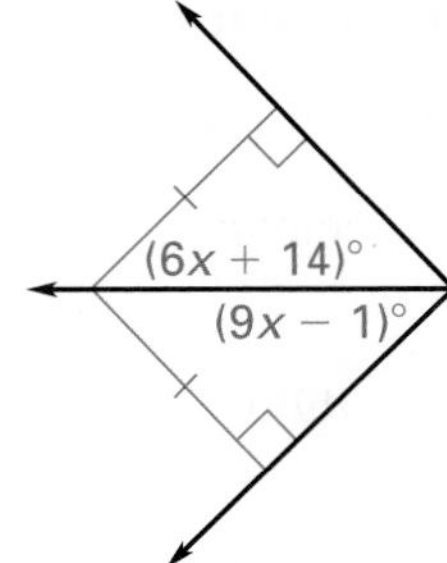

3.

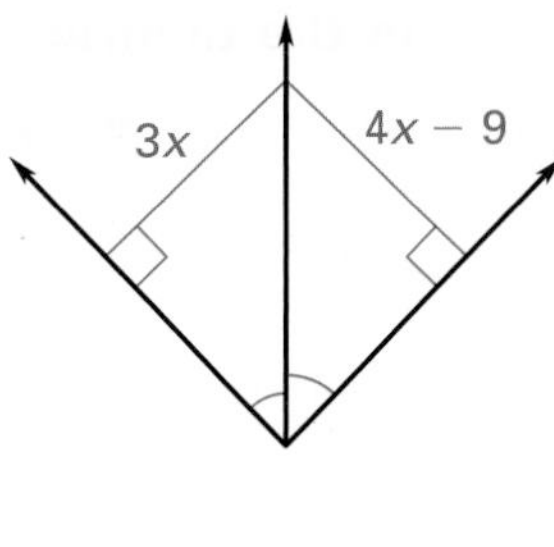

Example 3 Use the concurrency of angle bisectors

In the diagram, *V* is the incenter of $\triangle PQR$. Find *VS*.

Solution

By the Concurrency of Angle Bisectors of a Triangle Theorem, the incenter V is equidistant from the sides of $\triangle PQR$. So, to find VS, you can find VT in $\triangle PQR$ by using the Pythagorean Theorem.

$c^2 = a^2 + b^2$	Pythagorean Theorem
$17^2 = VT^2 + 15^2$	Substitute known values.
$289 = VT^2 + 225$	Multiply.
$64 = VT^2$	Subtract 225 from each side.
$8 = VT$	Take the positive square root of each side.

Because $VT = VS$, $VS = 8$.

Guided Practice for Example 3

4. In Example 3, suppose you are not given QV or QT, but you are given that $RU = 24$ and $RV = 25$. Find VS.

5. In the diagram, D is the incenter of $\triangle ABC$. Find DF.

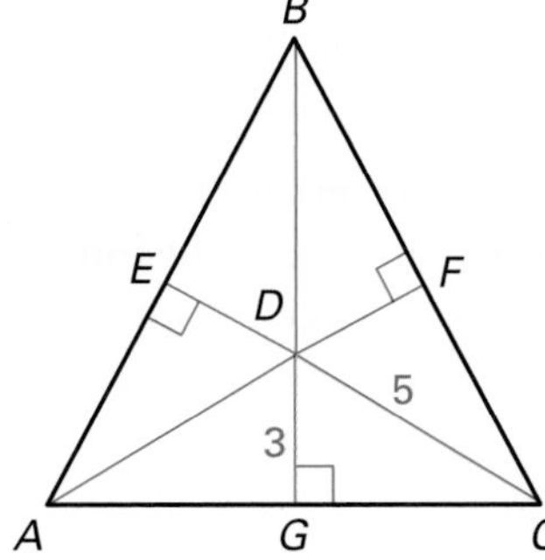

LESSON 5.3

Exercise Set A

MM1G3e Find and use points of concurrency in triangles: incenter, orthocenter, circumcenter, and centroid.

Use the information in the diagram to find the measure.

1. Find AD.

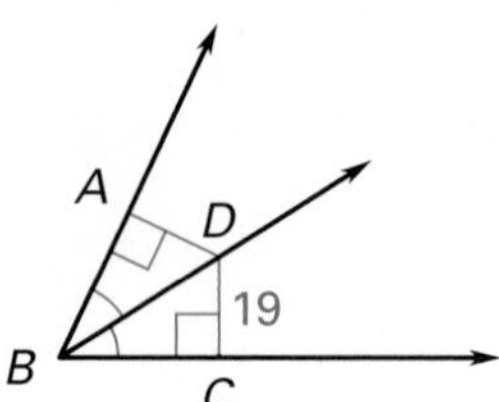

2. Find $m\angle EFH$.

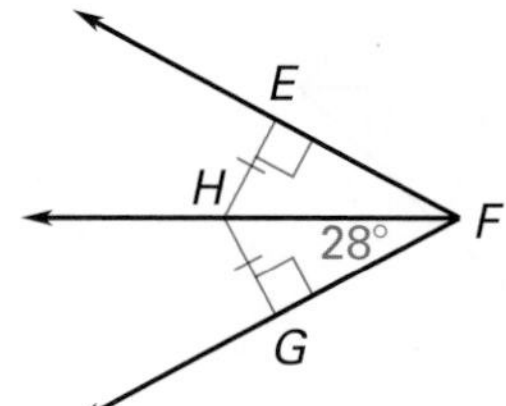

3. Find $m\angle JKL$.

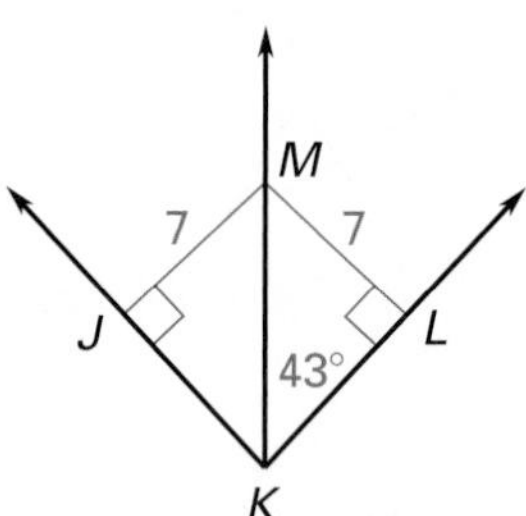

Can you conclude that $\overrightarrow{BD}$ bisects $\angle ABC$? *Explain.*

4.

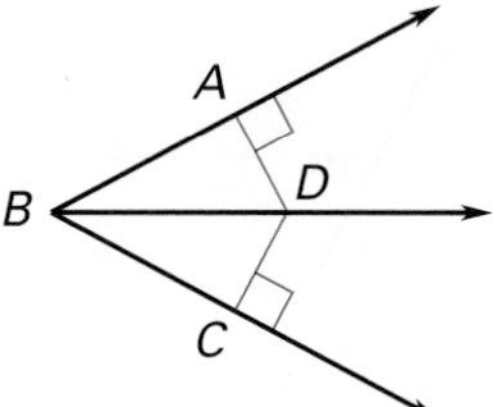

5.

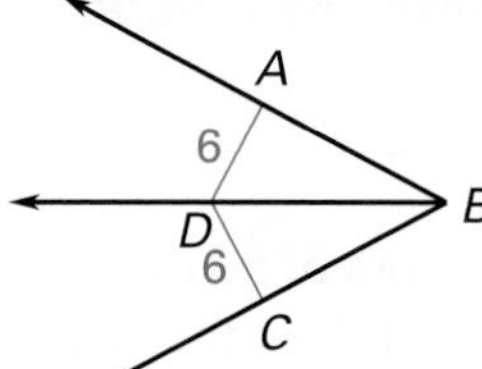

6.

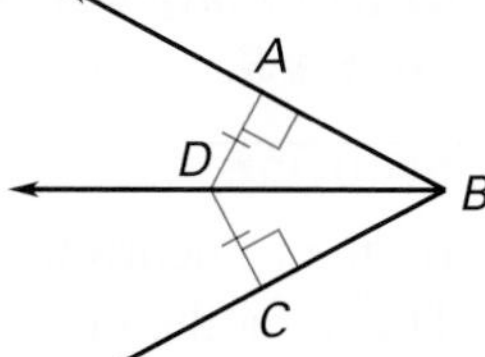

Find the value of *x*.

7.

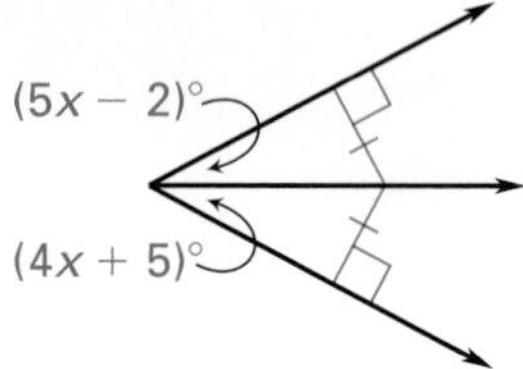

8.

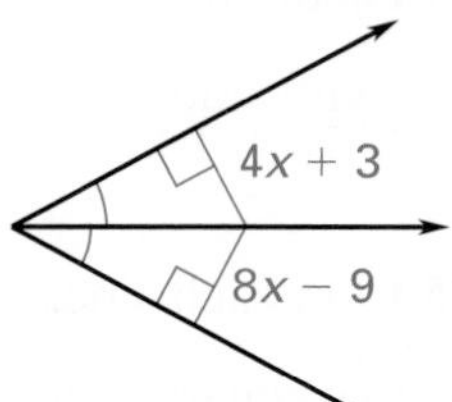

9.

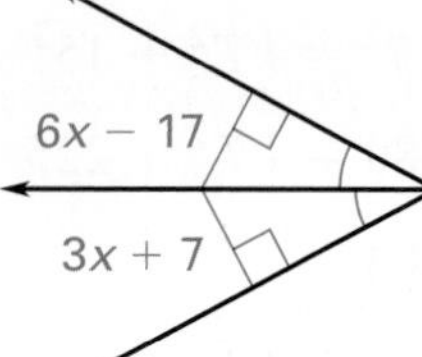

Can you find the value of *x*? *Explain.*

10.

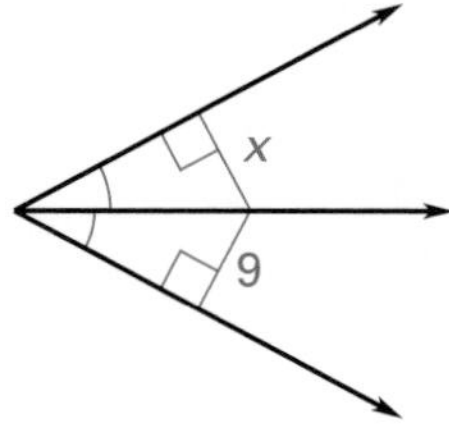

11.

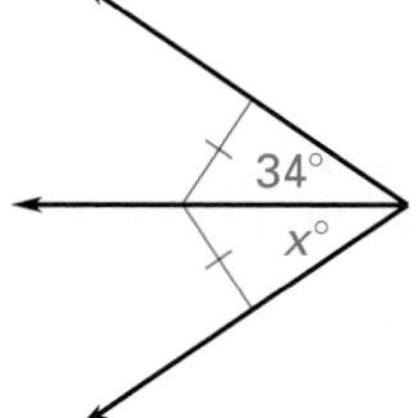

12.

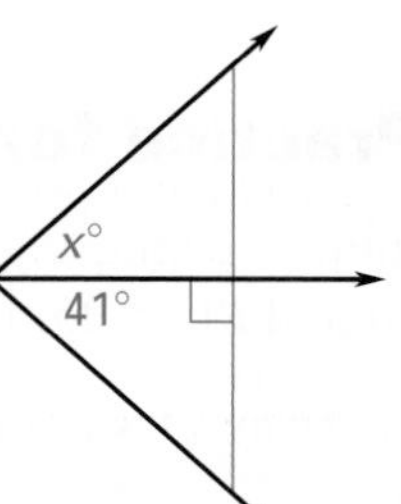

13. Error Analysis *Describe* the error in reasoning. Then state the correct conclusion about distances that can be deduced from the diagram.

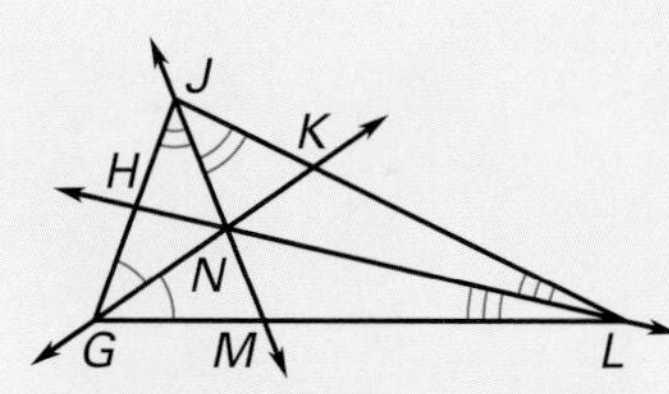

UNIT 5

Exercise Set A *(continued)*

Find the indicated measure.

14. Point G is the incenter of $\triangle ACE$. Find BG.

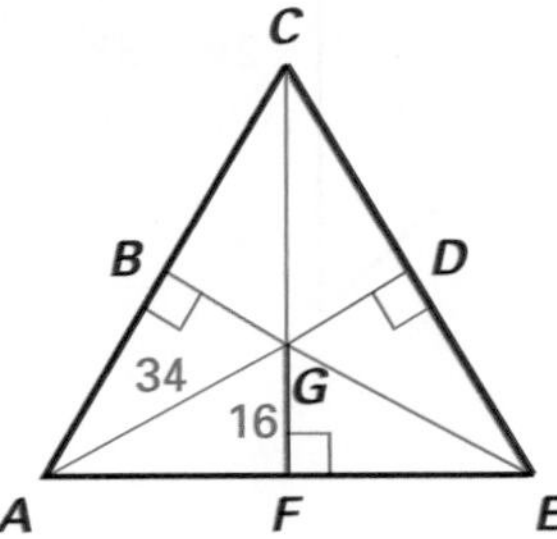

15. Point P is the incenter of $\triangle HKM$. Find JP.

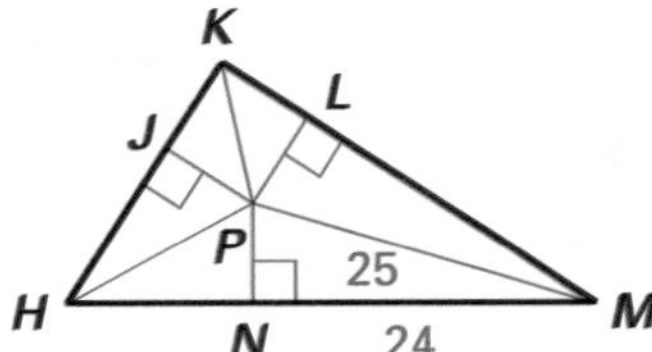

Find the value of *x* that makes *N* the incenter of the triangle.

16.

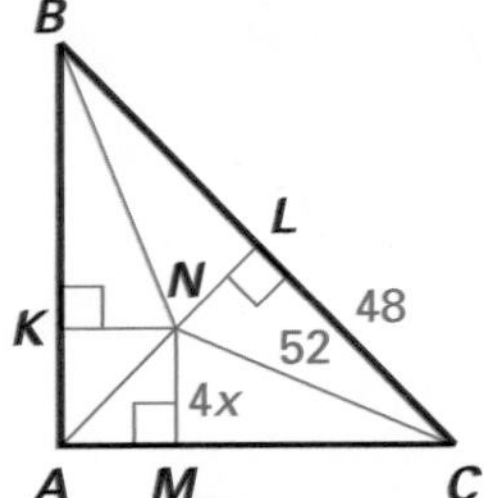

17.

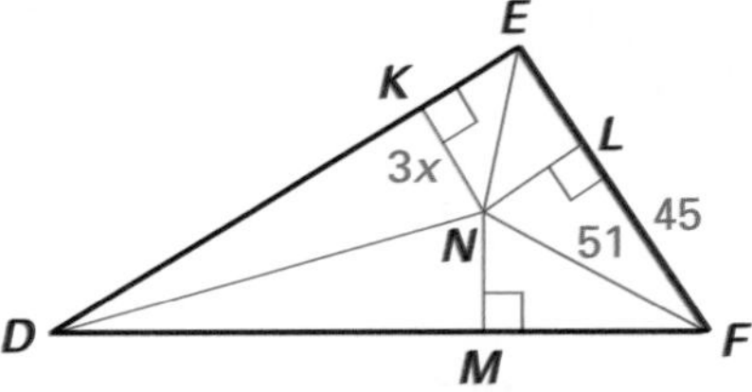

18. **Hockey** You and a friend are playing hockey in your driveway. You are the goalie, and your friend is going to shoot the puck from point S. The goal extends from left goal post L to right goal post R. Where should you position yourself (point G) to have the best chance to prevent your friend from scoring a goal? *Explain.*

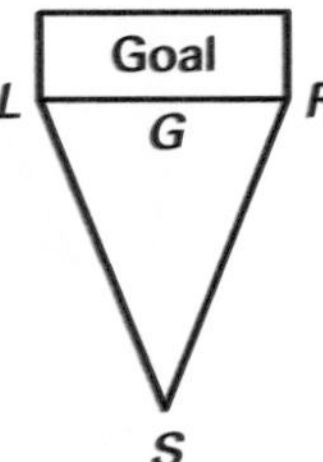

19. **Monument** You are building a monument in a triangular park. You want the monument to be the same distance from each edge of the park. Use the figure with incenter G to determine how far from point D you should build the monument.

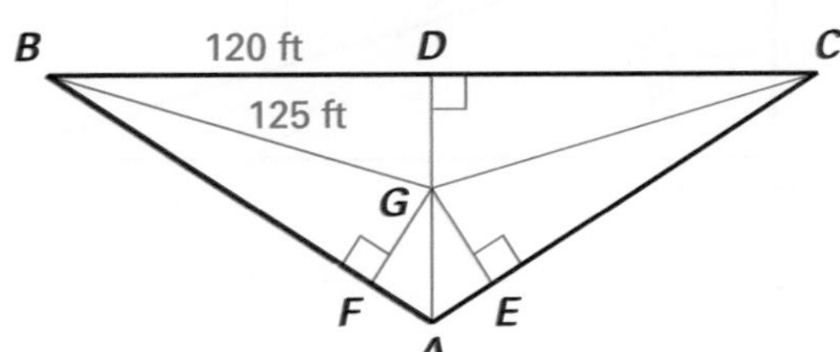

UNIT 5

LESSON 5.3 **Exercise Set B**

MM1G3e Find and use points of concurrency in triangles: incenter, orthocenter, circumcenter, and centroid.

Find the value of *x*.

1.

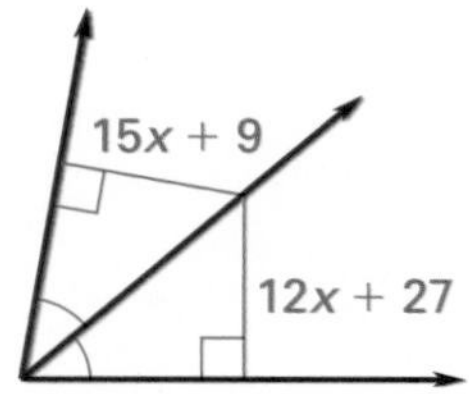

2.

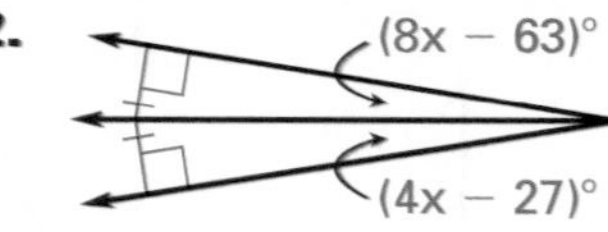

3.

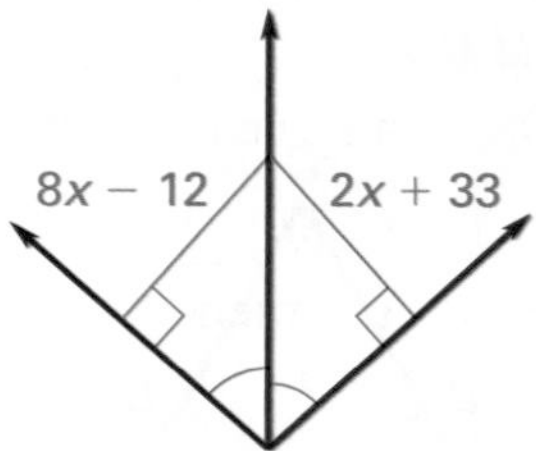

Can you conclude that $\overrightarrow{EH}$ bisects $\angle FEG$? *Explain.*

4.

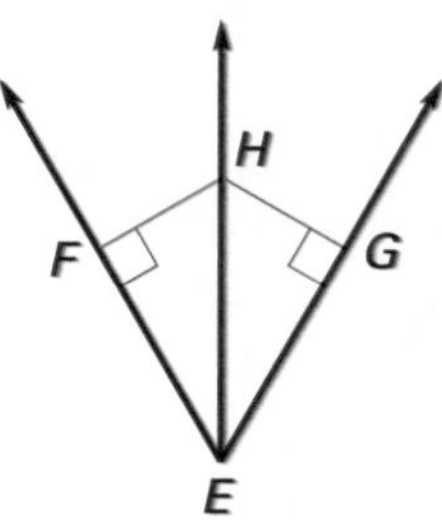

5.

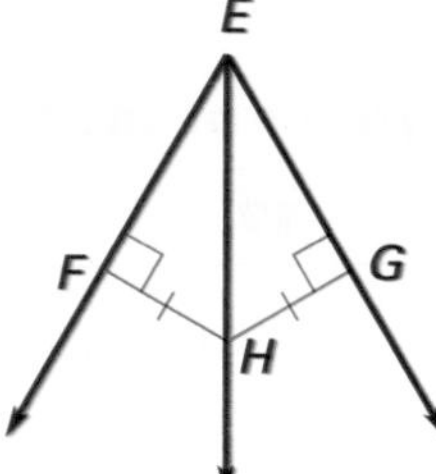

6.

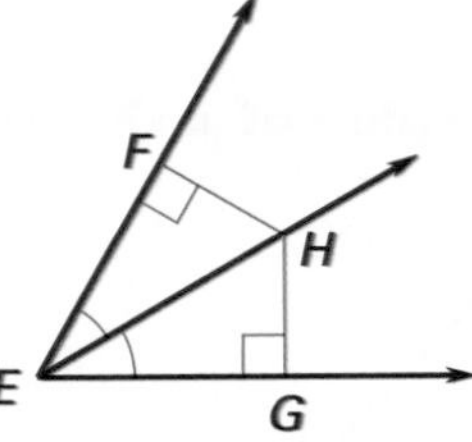

Can you find the value of *x*?

7.

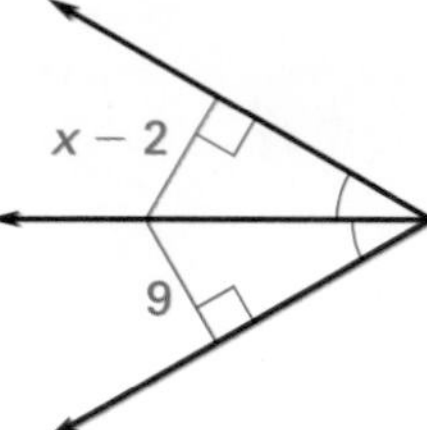

8.

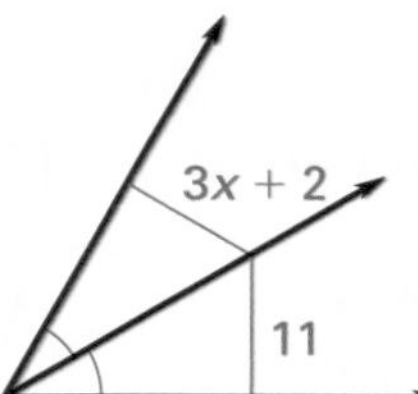

9.

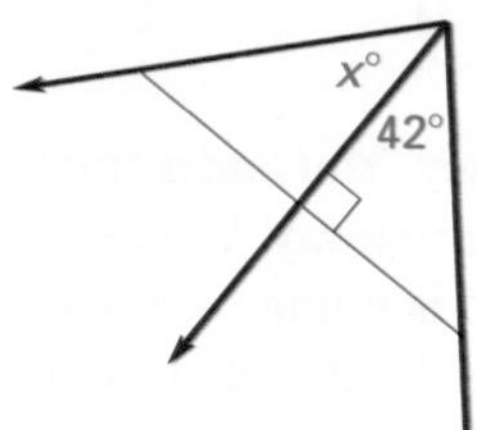

Find the indicated measure.

10. Find DG.

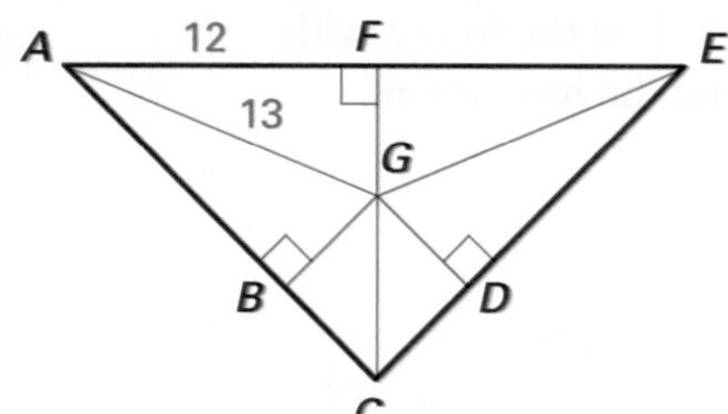

11. Find BG.

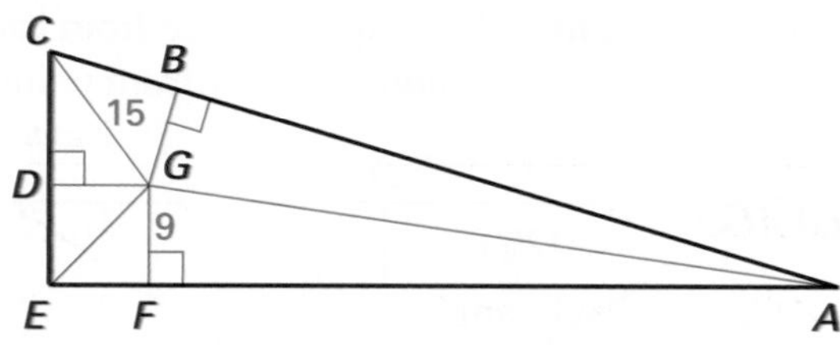

UNIT 5

Exercise Set B *(continued)*

12. **Error Analysis** *Explain* why the conclusion is not correct given the information in the diagram.

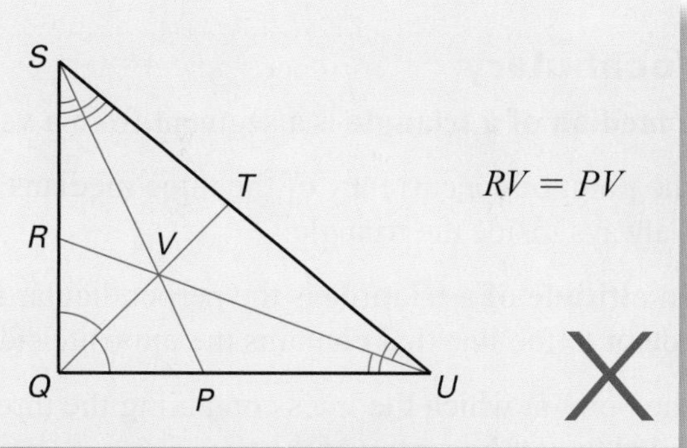

Find the value of *x* that makes *N* the incenter of the triangle.

13.

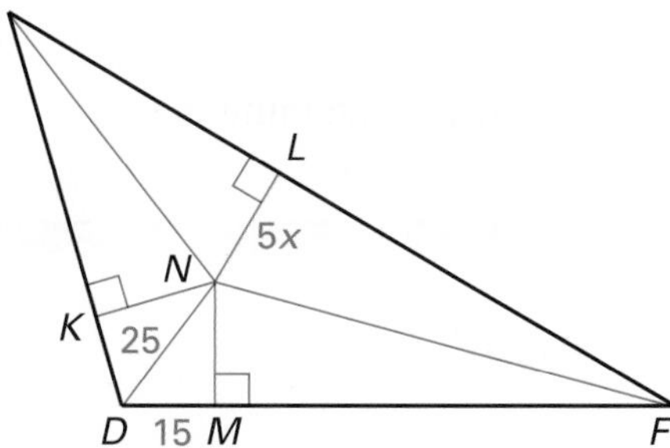

14.

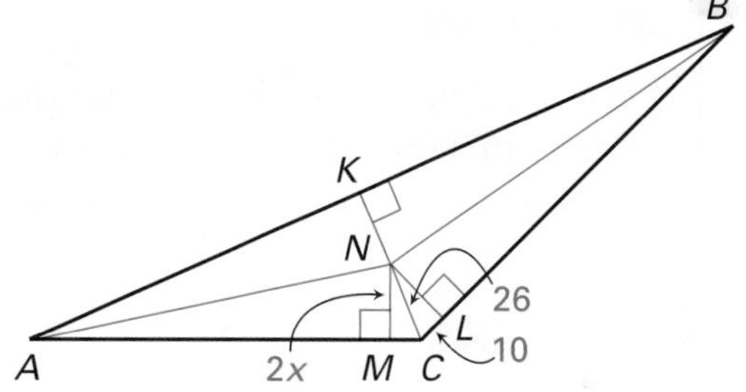

15. **Window** You are hanging a sun catcher in a triangular window. Use the diagram to explain how to find the correct length of string ($\overline{BD}$) needed to display the ornament at the incenter of the window.

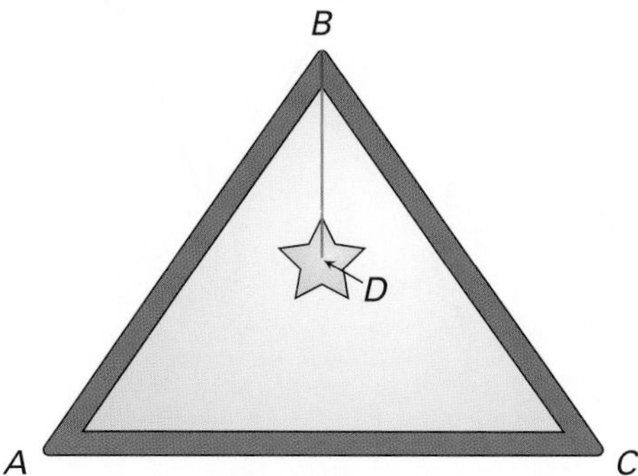

16. **Proof** Write a two-column or paragraph proof.

GIVEN: D is on the bisector of $\angle BAC$.
$\overline{DB} \perp \overline{AB}, \overline{DC} \perp \overline{AC}$

PROVE: $\overline{DB} \cong \overline{DC}$

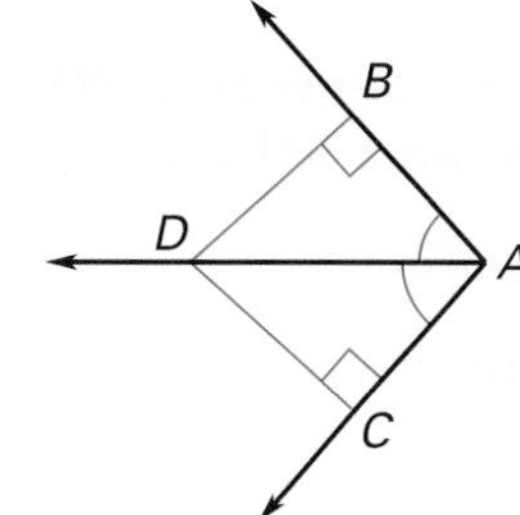

UNIT 5

LESSON 5.4

Use Medians and Altitudes

Georgia Performance Standards: MM1G1c, MM1G1e, MM1G3e

Goal Use medians and altitudes of triangles.

Vocabulary

A **median of a triangle** is a segment from a vertex to the midpoint of the opposite side.

The point of concurrency of the three medians of a triangle is called the **centroid,** and is always inside the triangle.

An **altitude of a triangle** is the perpendicular segment from a vertex to the opposite side or to the line that contains the opposite side.

The point at which the lines containing the three altitudes of a triangle intersect is called the **orthocenter** of the triangle.

Theorem 5.8 Concurrency of Medians of a Triangle: The medians of a triangle intersect at a point that is two thirds of the distance from each vertex to the midpoint of the opposite side.

Theorem 5.9 Concurrency of Altitudes of a Triangle: The lines containing the altitudes of a triangle are concurrent.

UNIT 5

Example 1 Use the centroid of a triangle

In $\triangle ABC$, D is the centroid and $BD = 12$. Find DG and BG.

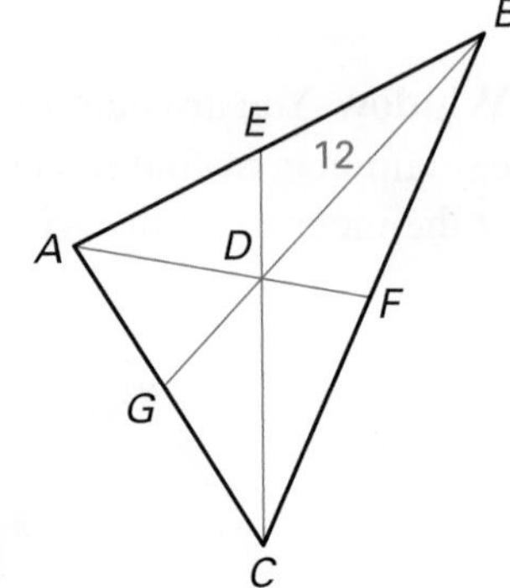

Solution

$BD = \frac{2}{3}BG$ Concurrency of Medians of a Triangle Theorem

$12 = \frac{2}{3}BG$ Substitute 12 for BD.

$18 = BG$ Multiply each side by the reciprocal, $\frac{3}{2}$.

Then $DG = BG - BD = 18 - 12 = 6$.

So, $DG = 6$ and $BG = 18$.

Guided Practice for Example 1

In $\triangle PQR$, S is the centroid, $UQ = 5$, $TR = 3$, $RV = 5$, and $SU = 2$.

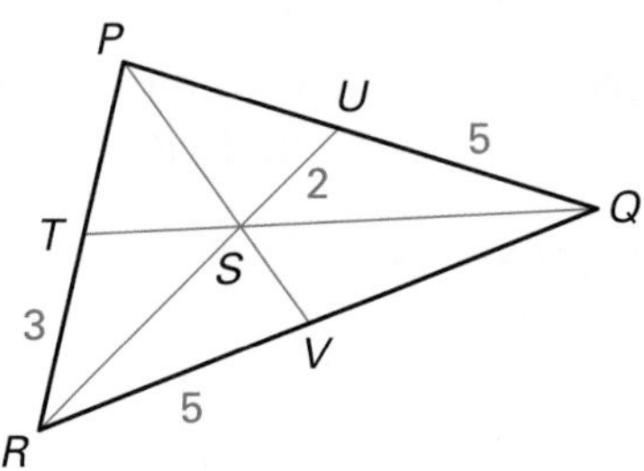

1. Find RU and RS.

2. Find the perimeter of $\triangle PQR$.

Georgia Performance Standards

MM1G1c Determine the midpoint of a segment. 

MM1G1e Use the coordinate plane to investigate properties of and verify conjectures related to triangles and quadrilaterals. 

MM1G3e Find and use points of concurrency in triangles: incenter, orthocenter, circumcenter, and centroid. 

Example 2 Find the centroid of a triangle

The vertices of $\triangle ABC$ are $A(0, 0)$, $B(4, 10)$, and $C(8, 2)$. Find the coordinates of the centroid P of $\triangle ABC$.

Sketch $\triangle ABC$. Then use the Midpoint Formula to find the midpoint D of $\overline{AC}$ and sketch median $\overline{BD}$.

$$D\left(\frac{0+8}{2}, \frac{0+2}{2}\right) = D(4, 1)$$

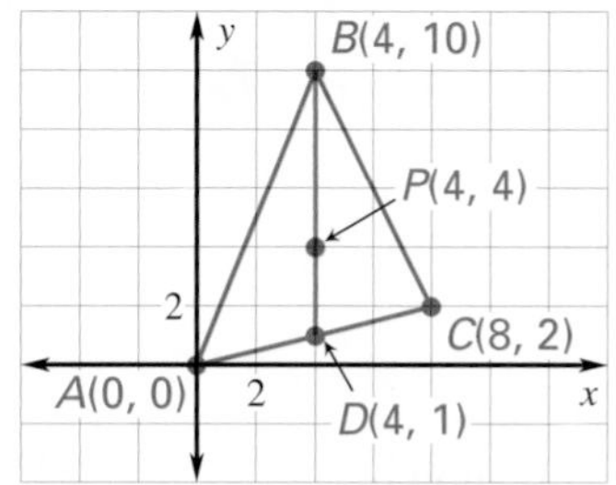

The centroid is two thirds of the distance from each vertex to the midpoint of the opposite side.

The distance from vertex $B(4, 10)$ to $D(4, 1)$ is $10 - 1 = 9$ units. So, the centroid is $\frac{2}{3}(9) = 6$ units down from B on $\overline{BD}$.

The coordinates of the centroid P are $(4, 10 - 6)$ or $(4, 4)$.

Example 3 Find the orthocenter

Determine whether the orthocenter P lies inside, outside, or on an (a) acute triangle, (b) right triangle, and (c) obtuse triangle.

a.

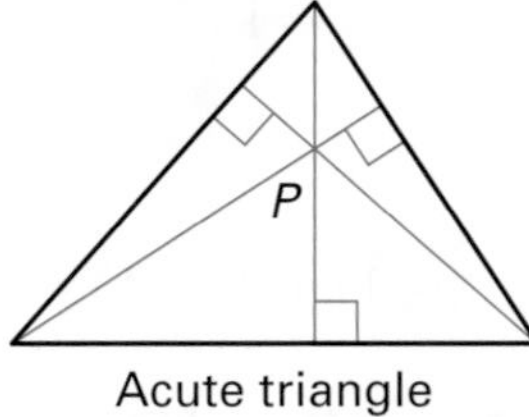

Acute triangle
P is inside triangle.

b.

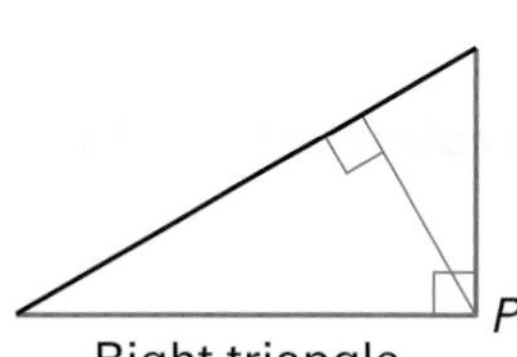

Right triangle
P is on triangle.

c.

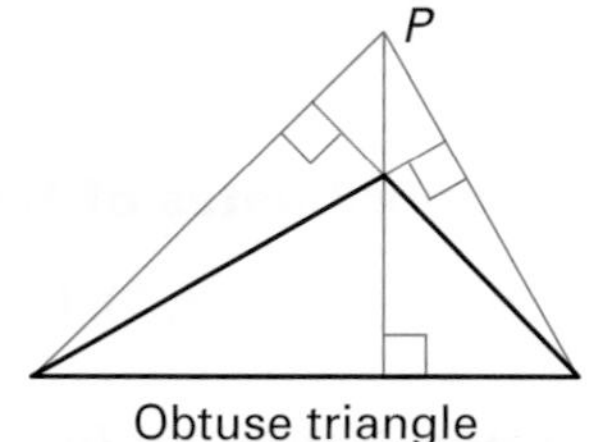

Obtuse triangle
P is outside triangle.

Guided Practice for Examples 2 and 3

Find the coordinates of the centroid of the triangle with the given vertices.

3.

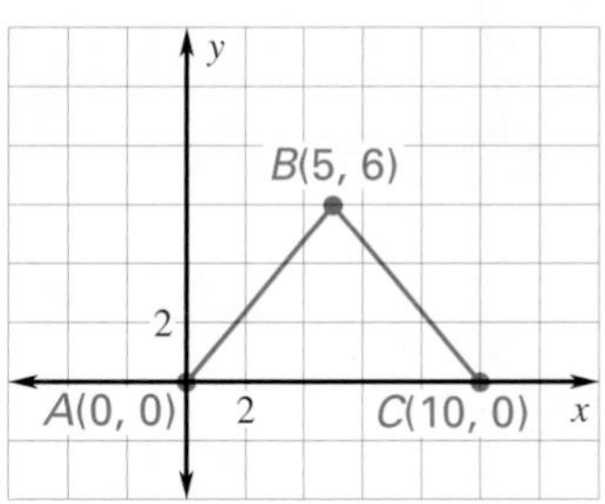

4.

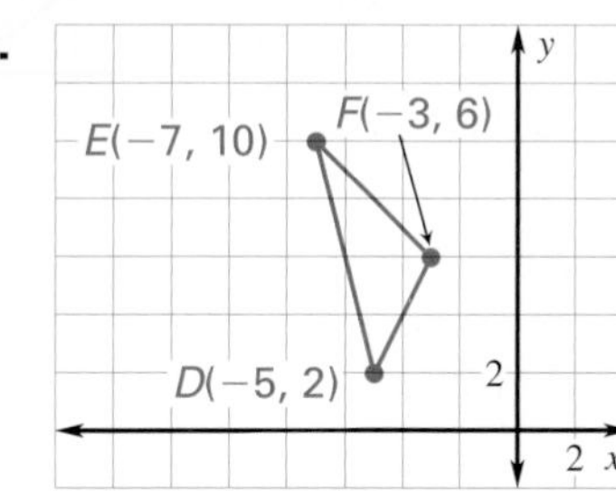

5. Sketch an isosceles triangle. Find and label its orthocenter P.

LESSON 5.4

Exercise Set A

MM1G1c Determine the midpoint of a segment.

MM1G1e Use the coordinate plane to investigate properties of and verify conjectures related to triangles and quadrilaterals.

MM1G3e Find and use points of concurrency in triangles: incenter, orthocenter, circumcenter, and centroid.

G is the centroid of $\triangle ABC$, $AD = 8$, $AG = 10$, and $CD = 18$. Find the length of the segment.

1. $\overline{BD}$
2. $\overline{AB}$
3. $\overline{EG}$
4. $\overline{AE}$
5. $\overline{CG}$
6. $\overline{DG}$

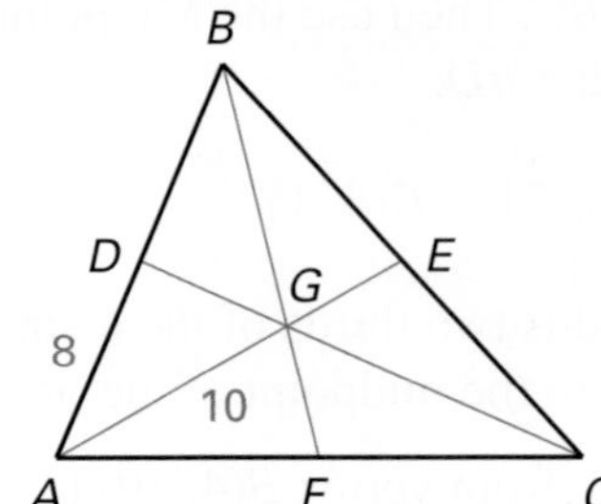

7. Use the graph shown.

   a. Find the coordinates of M, the midpoint of $\overline{JK}$. Use the median $\overline{LM}$ to find the coordinates of the centroid P.

   b. Find the coordinates of N, the midpoint of $\overline{JL}$. Verify that $KP = \frac{2}{3}KN$.

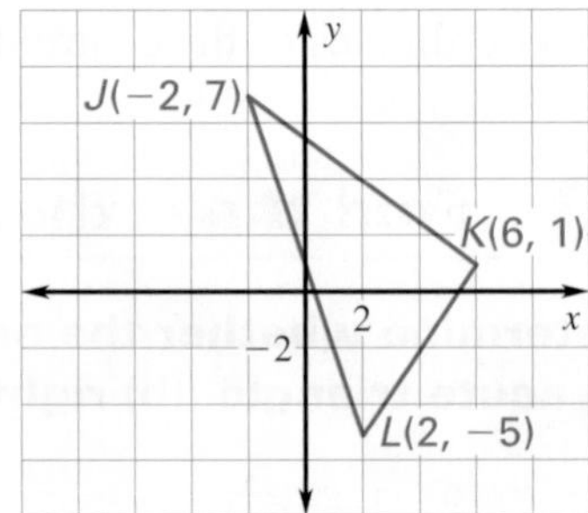

Find the coordinates of the centroid P of $\triangle ABC$.

8. $A(-7, -4), B(-3, 5), C(1, -4)$
9. $A(0, -2), B(6, 1), C(9, -5)$

Is $\overline{BD}$ a *perpendicular bisector* of $\triangle ABC$? Is $\overline{BD}$ a *median*? an *altitude*?

10.

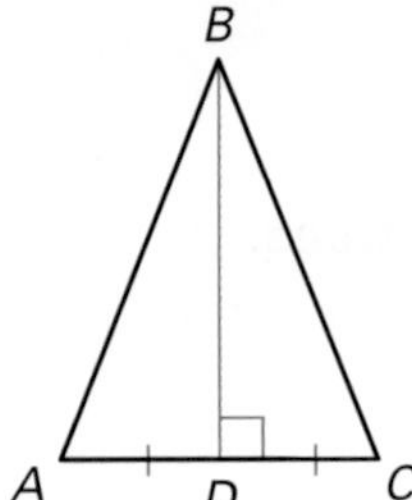

11.

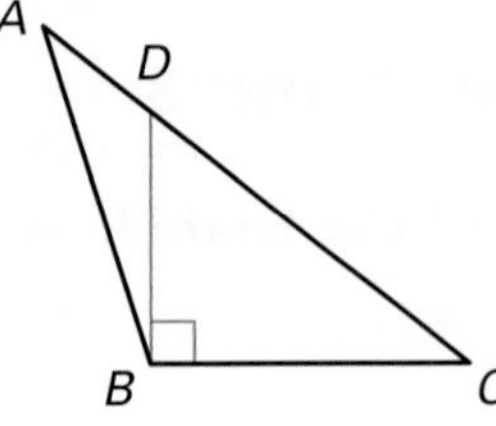

12.

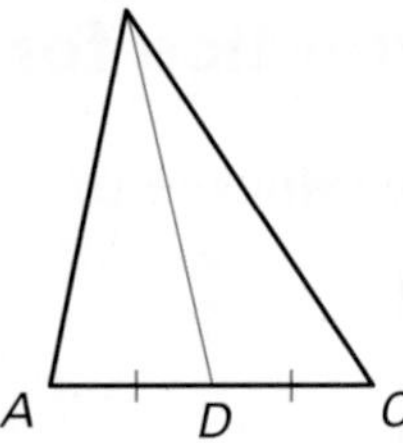

Exercise Set A *(continued)*

Find the measurements.

13. Given that $AB = BC$, find AD and $m\angle ABC$.

14. Given that G is the centroid of $\triangle ABC$, find FG and BD.

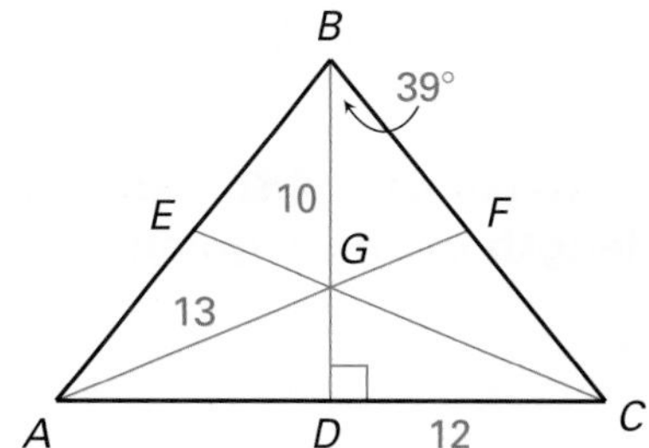

Copy and complete the statement for $\triangle HJK$ with medians $\overline{HN}$, $\overline{JL}$, and $\overline{KM}$, and centroid P.

15. $PN =$ __?__ HN

16. $PL =$ __?__ JP

17. $KP =$ __?__ KM

Point G is the centroid of $\triangle ABC$. Use the given information to find the value of x.

18. $CG = 3x + 7$ and $CE = 6x$

19. $FG = x + 8$ and $AF = 9x - 6$

20. $BG = 5x - 1$ and $DG = 4x - 5$

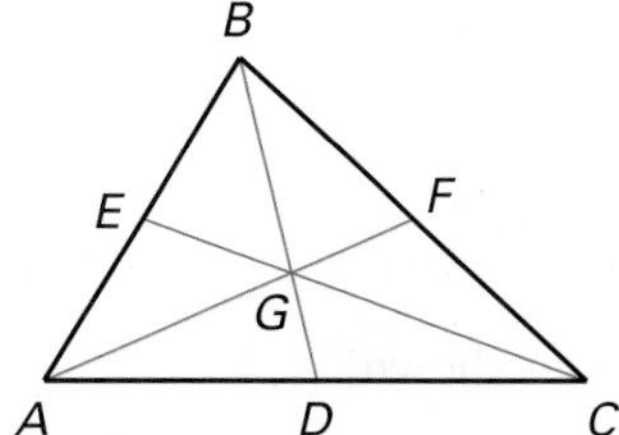

Complete the sentence with *always, sometimes,* or *never*.

21. The median of a triangle is __?__ the perpendicular bisector.

22. The altitude of a triangle is __?__ the perpendicular bisector.

23. The medians of a triangle __?__ intersect inside the triangle.

24. The altitudes of a triangle __?__ intersect inside the triangle.

25. **House Decoration** You are going to put a decoration on your house in the triangular area above the front door. You want to place the decoration on the centroid of the triangle. You measure the distance from point A to point B (see figure). How far down from point A should you place the decoration? *Explain.*

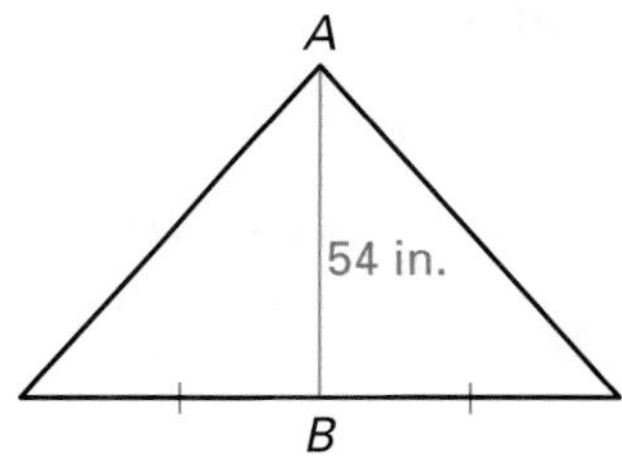

26. **Art Project** You are making an art piece which consists of different items of all shapes and sizes. You want to insert an isosceles triangle with the dimensions shown. In order for the triangle to fit, the height (altitude) must be less than 8.5 millimeters. Find the altitude. Will the triangle fit in your art piece?

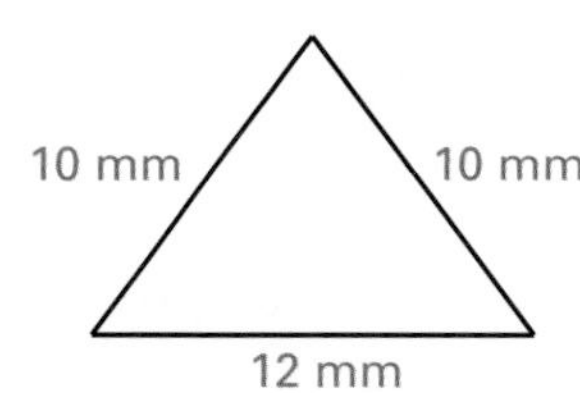

UNIT 5

LESSON 5.4

Exercise Set B

MM1G1c Determine the midpoint of a segment.

MM1G1e Use the coordinate plane to investigate properties of and verify conjectures related to triangles and quadrilaterals.

MM1G3e Find and use points of concurrency in triangles: incenter, orthocenter, circumcenter, and centroid.

***G* is the centroid of $\triangle ABC$, $AD = 15$, $CG = 13$, and $\overline{AD} \perp \overline{CB}$. Find the length of the segment.**

1. $\overline{AG}$
2. $\overline{GD}$
3. $\overline{CD}$
4. $\overline{GE}$
5. $\overline{GB}$

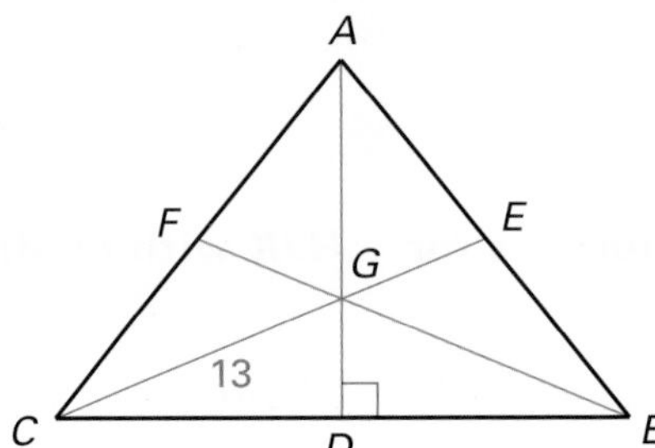

Copy and complete the statement for $\triangle LMN$ with medians $\overline{LQ}$, $\overline{NP}$, and $\overline{MO}$, and centroid *R*.

6. $MR =$ _?_ MO
7. $RQ =$ _?_ LQ
8. Use the graph shown.
   a. Find the coordinates of *D*, the midpoint of $\overline{AB}$.
   b. Use the median $\overline{CD}$ to find the coordinates of the centroid *G*.
   c. Find the coordinates of *E*, the midpoint of $\overline{AC}$. Verify that $BG = \frac{2}{3}BE$.

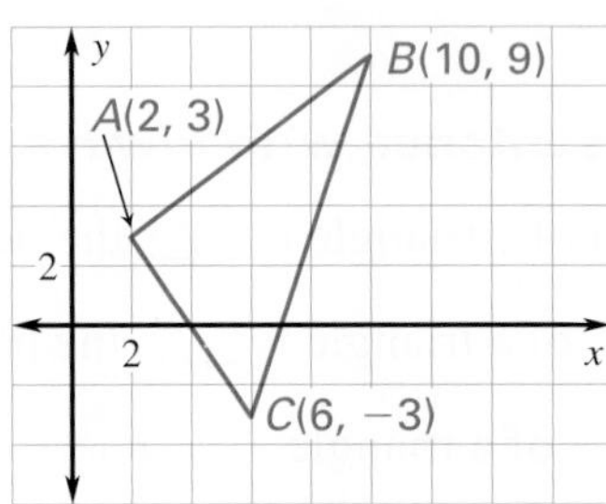

Point *L* is the centroid of $\triangle NOM$. Use the given information to find the value of *x*.

9. $OL = 8x$ and $OQ = 9x + 6$
10. $NL = x + 4$ and $NP = 3x + 3$
11. $ML = 10x - 4$ and $MR = 12x + 18$

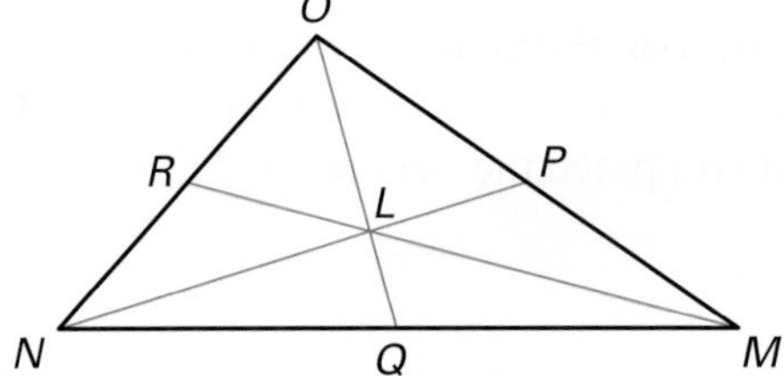

UNIT 5

Exercise Set B *(continued)*

12. **Multiple Representations** Find the orthocenter of the triangle shown.

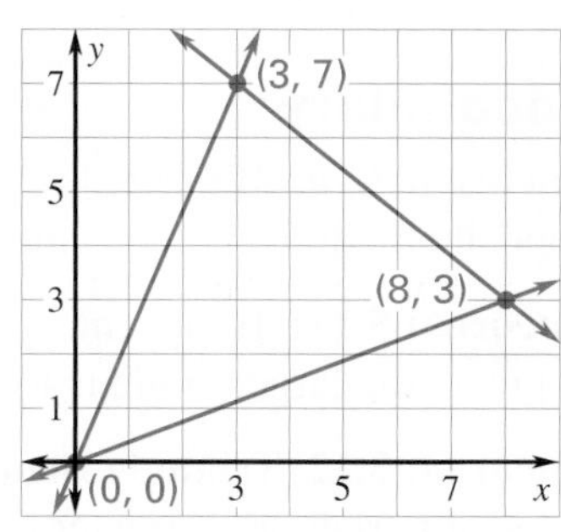

a. **Estimating the Orthocenter** Copy the triangle and draw the altitudes. Estimate the coordinates of the orthocenter.

b. **Solving a System of Equations** Find the equation of each altitude of the triangle. Solve the system of equations to find the orthocenter.

Find the coordinates of the centroid *D* of $\triangle ABC$.

13. $A(0, 0)$, $B(10, 0)$, $C(5, 6)$

14. $A(-5, 2)$, $B(-3, 6)$, $C(-7, 10)$

Copy and complete the sentence with *always, sometimes,* or *never*.

15. The altitude from the vertex angle of an isosceles triangle is __?__ the median.

16. The median to any side of an equilateral triangle is __?__ the angle bisector.

17. **Chess** A badge is awarded to each new member of the chess club. Find the area of the unshaded triangular portion of the badge. Which special segment of the triangle did you use?

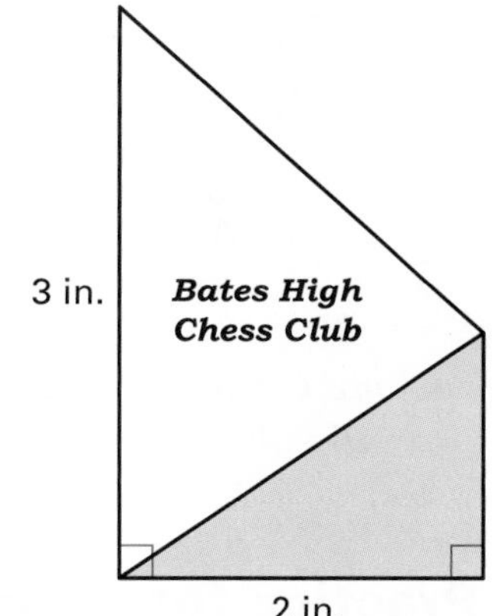

18. **Proof** Write a two-column or paragraph proof.

GIVEN: $\triangle ABC$ is isosceles.
$\overline{BD}$ is the median to base $\overline{AC}$.

PROVE: $\overline{BD}$ is also an altitude.

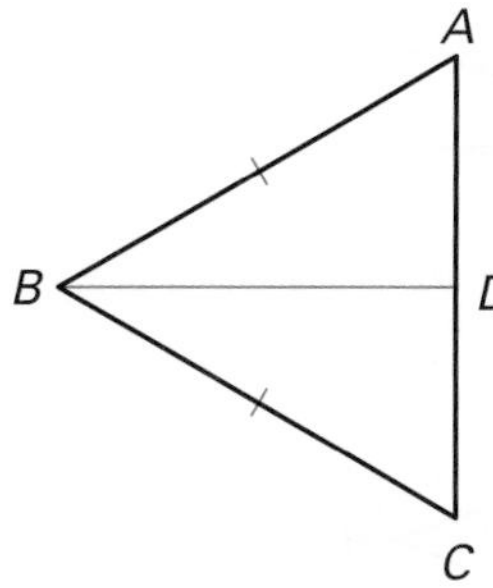

LESSON 5.5

Use Inequalities in a Triangle

Georgia Performance Standards: MM1G3b

Goal Find possible side lengths of a triangle.

Vocabulary

Theorem 5.10: If one side of a triangle is longer than another side, then the angle opposite the longer side is larger than the angle opposite the shorter side.

Theorem 5.11: If one angle of a triangle is larger than another angle, then the side opposite the larger angle is longer than the side opposite the smaller angle.

Theorem 5.12 Triangle Inequality Theorem: The sum of the lengths of any two sides of a triangle is greater than the length of the third side.

Theorem 5.13 Exterior Angle Inequality Theorem: The measure of an exterior angle of a triangle is greater than the measure of either of the nonadjacent interior angles.

UNIT 5

Example 1 Write measurements in order from least to greatest

Write the measurements of the triangle in order from least to greatest.

a. B 55° C 37° A 88°

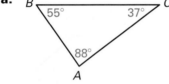

b. E D F; DE = 21, EF = 12, DF = 11

Solution

a. $m\angle C < m\angle B < m\angle A$
$AB < AC < BC$

b. $m\angle E < m\angle D < m\angle F$
$DF < EF < DE$

Guided Practice for Example 1

Write the measurements of the triangle in order from least to greatest.

1.

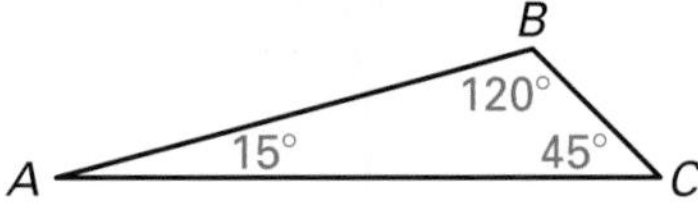

2.

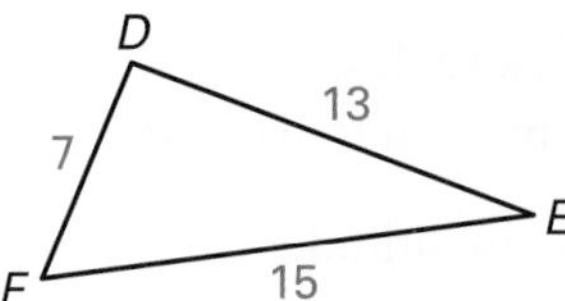

3.

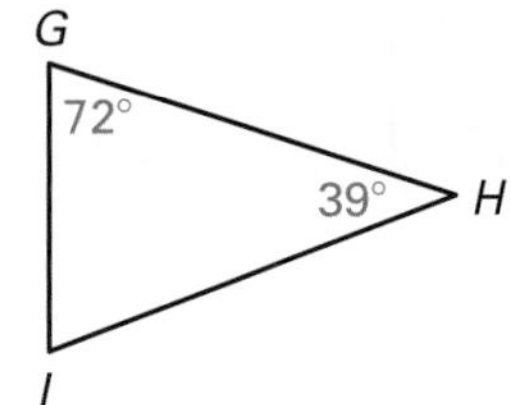

4.

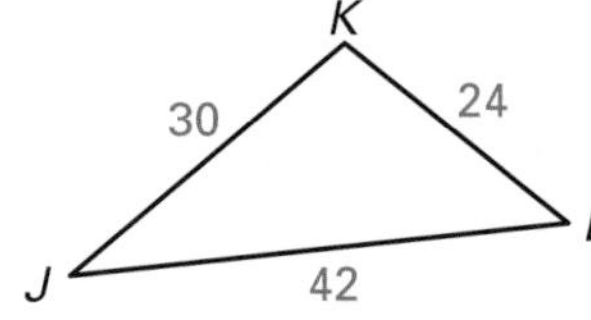

Georgia Performance Standards

MM1G3b Understand and use the triangle inequality, the side-angle inequality, and the exterior-angle inequality.

Guided Practice for Example 1 *(continued)*

5. A right triangle has sides that are about 2, 2, and 3 inches long and angles of 45°, 45°, and 90°. Sketch and label a diagram with the longest side on the bottom and the right angle at the top.

6. A triangle has sides that are about 33, 18, and 24 centimeters long and angles of about 32°, 103°, and 45°. Sketch and label a diagram with the shortest side on the bottom and the largest angle at the left.

7. A right triangle has sides that are 16, 34, and 30 inches long and angles of 90°, about 28°, and about 62°. Sketch and label a diagram with the shortest side on the bottom and the right angle at the left.

Example 2 Use the Triangle Inequality Theorem

Is it possible to construct a triangle with the given side lengths? Explain.

a. 3, 5, 9 **b.** 3, 5, 8 **c.** 3, 5, 7

Solution

Using the Triangle Inequality Theorem, you can show that a triangle can be constructed with side lengths x, y, z if $x + y > z$, $x + z > y$, and $y + z > x$.

a. These lengths do not form a triangle because $3 + 5 < 9$.

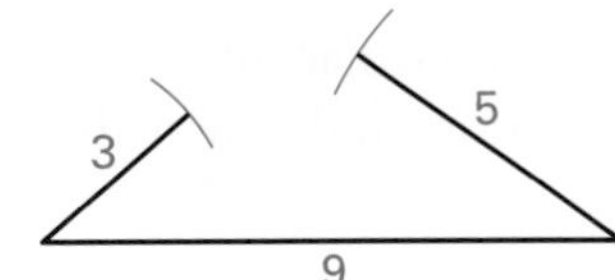

b. These lengths do not form a triangle because $3 + 5 = 8$.

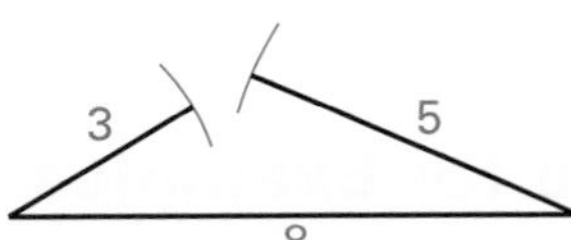

c. These lengths do form a triangle because $3 + 5 > 7$, $3 + 7 > 5$, and $5 + 7 > 3$.

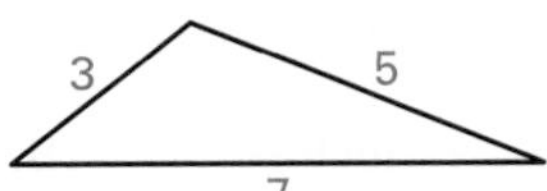

Guided Practice for Example 2

Is it possible to construct a triangle with the given side lengths? If not, explain why not.

8. 5, 7, 13 **9.** 6, 9, 12 **10.** 10, 15, 25

11. 4, 7, 12 **12.** 6, 15, 18 **13.** 6, 8, 10

UNIT 5

Example 3 Find possible side lengths

A triangle has one side of length 13 and another side of length 16. Describe the possible lengths of the third side.

Solution

Let x represent the length of the third side. Draw diagrams to help visualize the small and large values of x. Then use the Triangle Inequality Theorem to write and solve the inequalities.

Small values of x

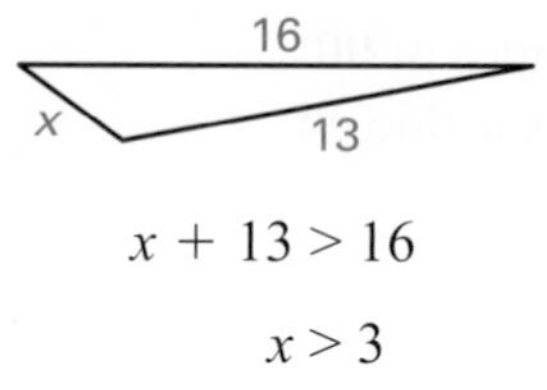

$x + 13 > 16$

$x > 3$

Large values of x

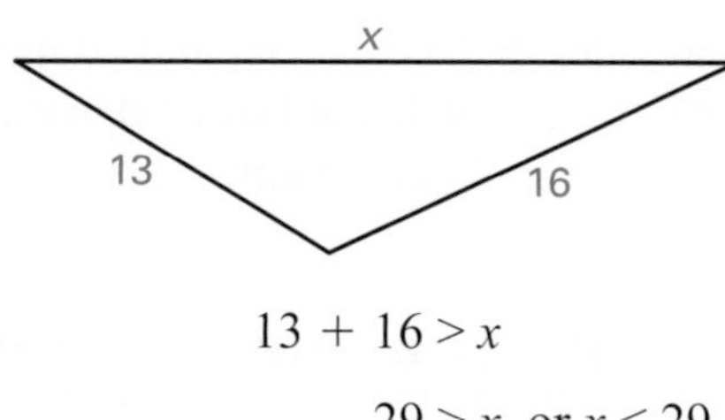

$13 + 16 > x$

$29 > x$, or $x < 29$

The length of the third side must be greater than 3 and less than 29.

Example 4 Relate exterior and interior angles

Write an inequality that relates $m\angle 1$ to $m\angle 2$ and $m\angle 1$ to $m\angle 3$.

Solution

$\angle 2$ and $\angle 3$ are nonadjacent interior angles to $\angle 1$. So, by the Exterior Angle Inequality Theorem, $m\angle 1 > m\angle 2$ and $m\angle 1 > m\angle 3$.

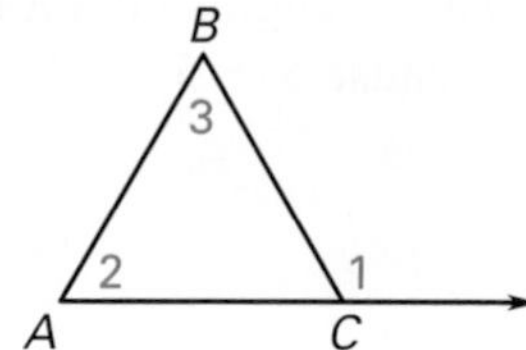

Guided Practice for Examples 3 and 4

Two sides of a triangle are given. *Describe* the possible lengths of the third side.

14. 2 centimeters and 5 centimeters

15. 7 inches and 12 inches

16. 4 feet and 10 feet

17. 11 meters and 10 meters

18. 9 inches and 25 inches

19. 1 mile and 8 miles

20. Write an inequality that relates $m\angle 1$ to $m\angle 2$ and $m\angle 1$ to $m\angle 3$.

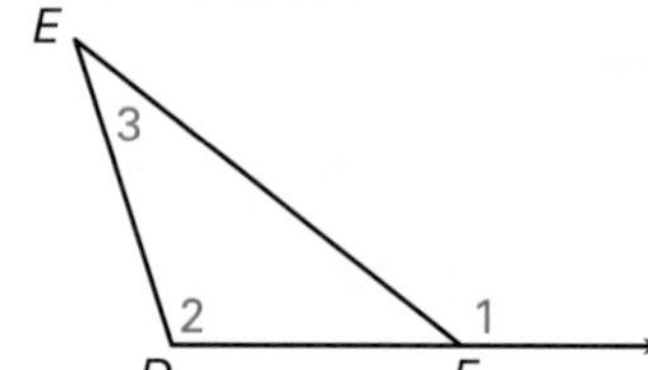

LESSON 5.5

Exercise Set A

MM1G3b Understand and use the triangle inequality, the side-angle inequality, and the exterior-angle inequality.

Use a ruler and protractor to draw the given type of triangle. Mark the largest angle and longest side in red and the smallest angle and shortest side in blue. What do you notice?

1. Obtuse scalene

2. Acute isosceles

3. Right isosceles

List the sides and the angles in order from least to greatest.

4.

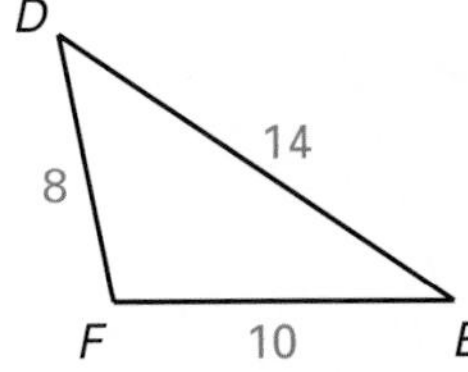

5.

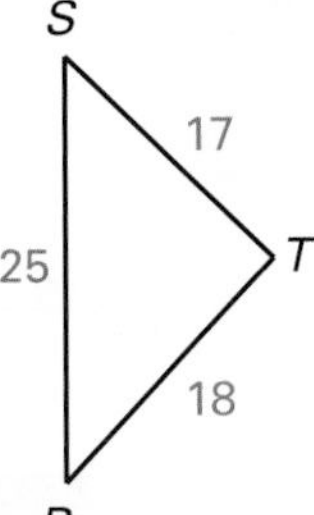

6.

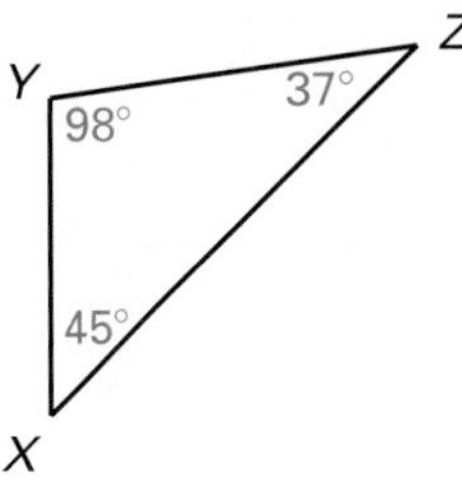

7.

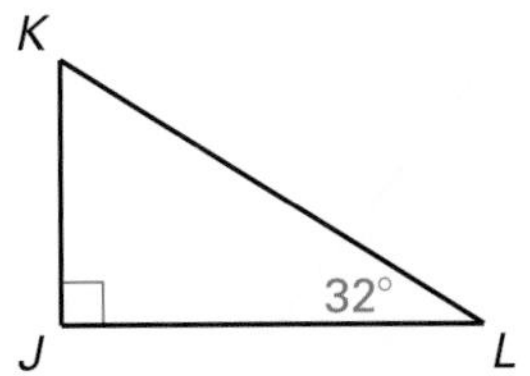

8.

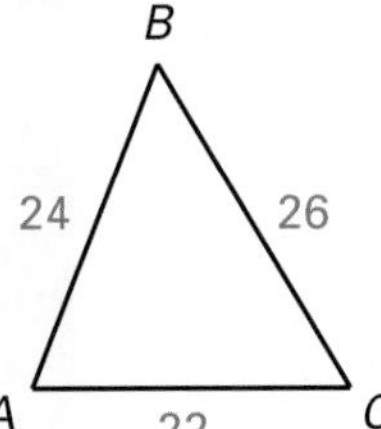

9.

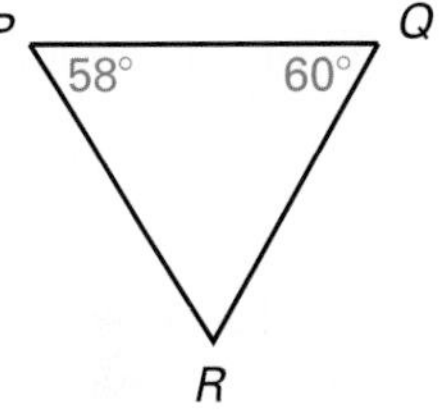

Sketch and label the triangle described.

10. Side lengths: 14, 17, and 19, with longest side on the bottom
Angle measures: 45°, 60°, and 75°, with smallest angle at the right

11. Side lengths: 11, 18, and 24, with shortest side on the bottom
Angle measures: 25°, 44°, and 111°, with largest angle at the left

12. Side lengths: 32, 34, and 48, with shortest side arranged vertically at the right.
Angle measures: 42°, 45°, and 93°, with largest angle at the top.

Is it possible to construct a triangle with the given side lengths? If not, explain why not.

13. 3, 4, 5

14. 1, 4, 6

15. 17, 17, 33

16. 22, 26, 65

17. 6, 43, 39

18. 7, 54, 45

***Describe* the possible lengths of the third side of the triangle given the lengths of the other two sides.**

19. 6 in., 9 in.

20. 4 ft, 12 ft

21. 9 m, 18 m

22. 21 yd, 16 yd

23. 22 in., 2 ft

24. 24 in., 1 yd

Exercise Set A *(continued)*

25. Write an inequality that relates $m\angle 1$ to $m\angle 2$ and $m\angle 1$ to $m\angle 3$.

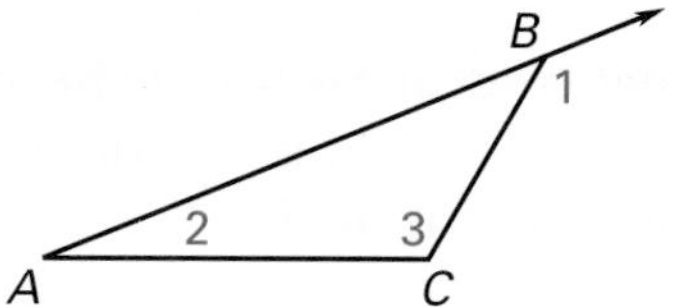

Describe **the possible values of *x*.**

26.

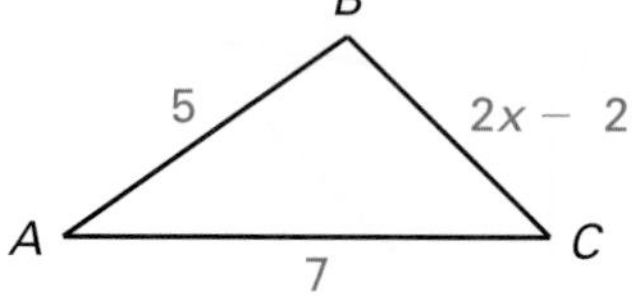

27.

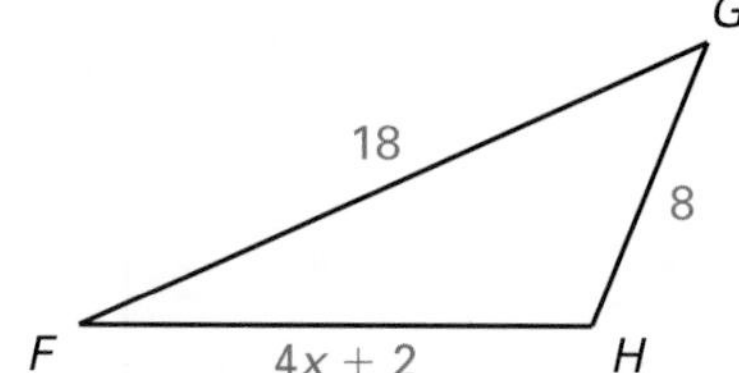

28. **Building** You are standing 200 feet from a tall building. The angle of elevation from your feet to the top of the building is 51° (as shown in the figure). What can you say about the height of the building?

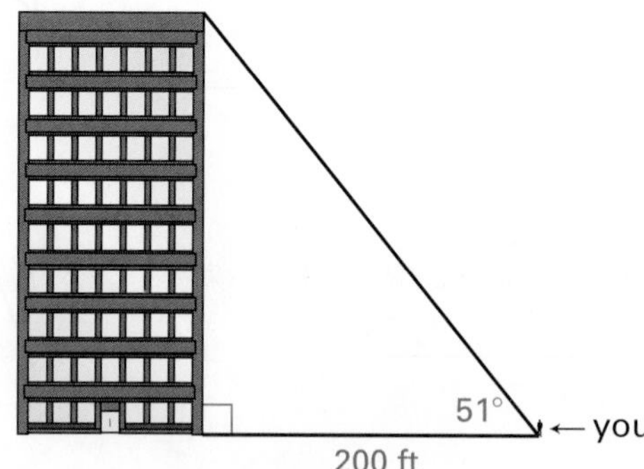

29. **Sea Rescue** The figure shows the relative positions of two rescue boats and two people in the water. Talking by radio, the captains use certain angle relationships to conclude that boat *A* is the closest to person *C* and boat *B* is the closest to person *D*. *Describe* the angle relationships that would lead to this conclusion.

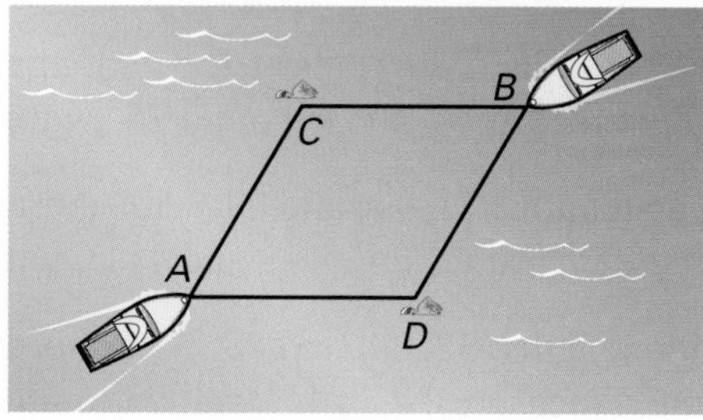

30. **Airplanes** Two airplanes leave the same airport heading in different directions. After 2 hours, one airplane has traveled 710 miles and the other has traveled 640 miles. *Describe* the range of distances that represents how far apart the two airplanes can be at this time.

31. **Baseball** A pitcher throws a baseball 60 feet from the pitcher's mound to home plate. A batter pops the ball up and it comes down just 24 feet from home plate. What can you determine about how far the ball lands from pitcher's mound? *Explain* why the Triangle Inequality Theorem can be used to describe all but the shortest and longest possible distances.

UNIT 5

LESSON 5.5

Exercise Set B

MM1G3b Understand and use the triangle inequality, the side-angle inequality, and the exterior-angle inequality.

Name the smallest and largest angles of the triangle.

1.

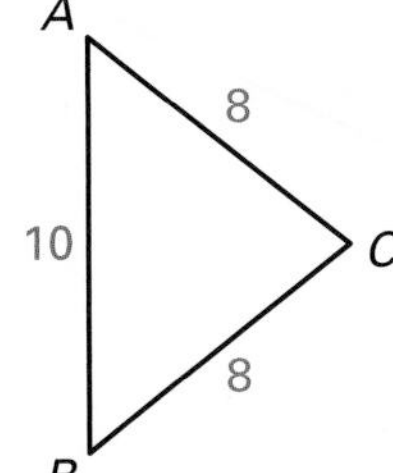

2.

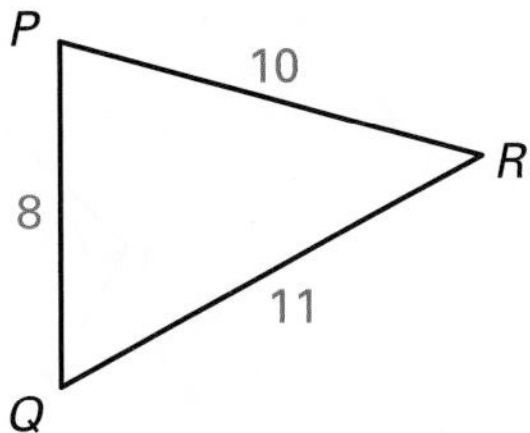

3.

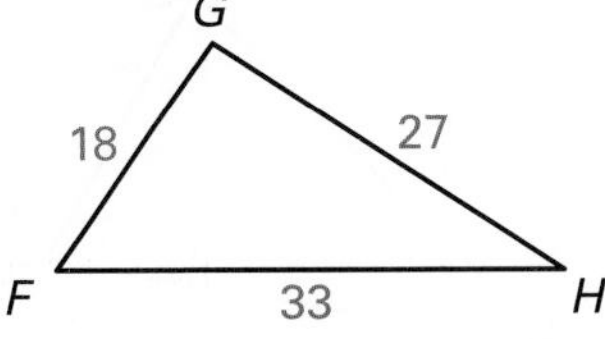

Name the shortest and longest sides of the triangle.

4.

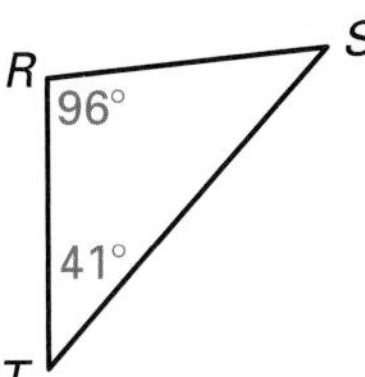

5.

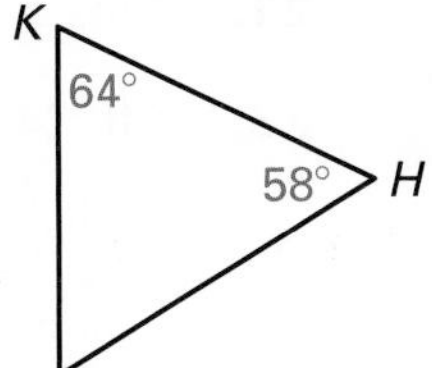

6.

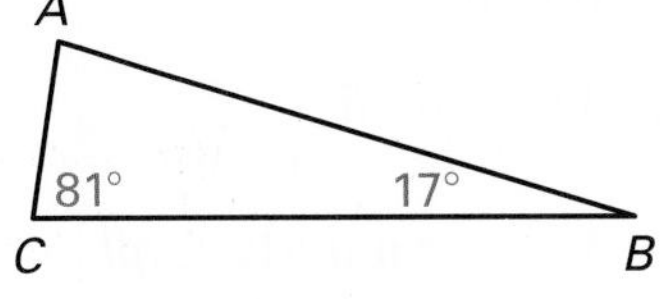

Solve the inequality $AB + AC > BC$ for x.

7.

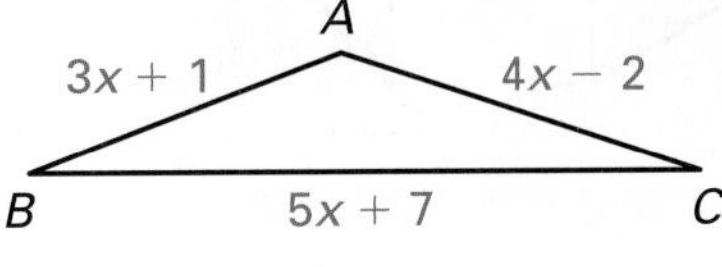

8.

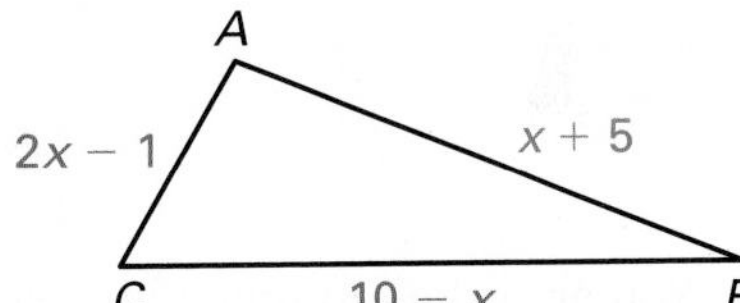

In Exercises 9 and 10, $m\angle J < m\angle K < m\angle L$. Find all possible values of x.

9.

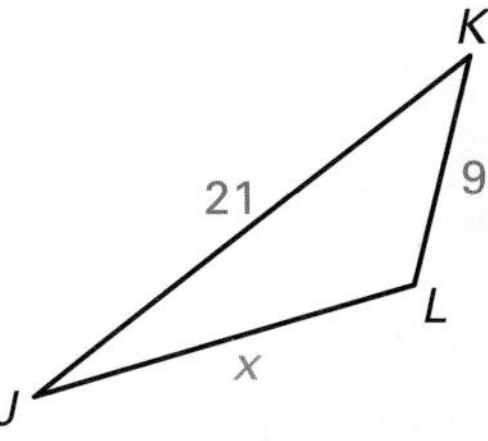

10.

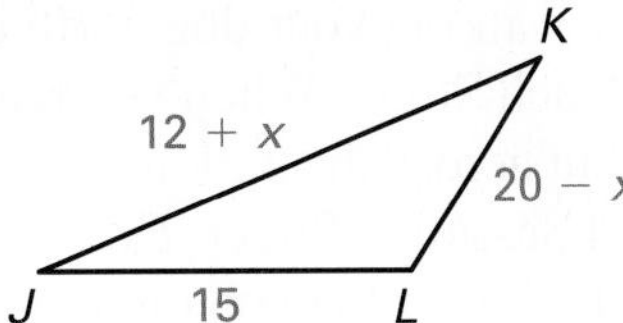

11. A triangle has sides that are 32, 48, and 61 units long and angles of 31°, 52°, and 97°. Sketch and label a diagram with the longest side on the top and the smallest angle at the right.

Is it possible to construct a triangle with the given side lengths? If not, explain why not.

12. 10, 11, 20 **13.** 13, 14, 15 **14.** 14, 20, 38

15. 21, 34, 13 **16.** 49, 25, 23 **17.** 17, 51, 36

UNIT 5

Exercise Set B *(continued)*

List the sides in order from shortest to longest.

18.

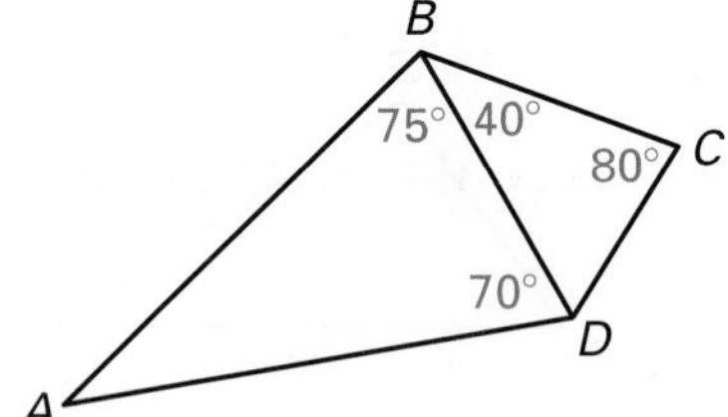

19.

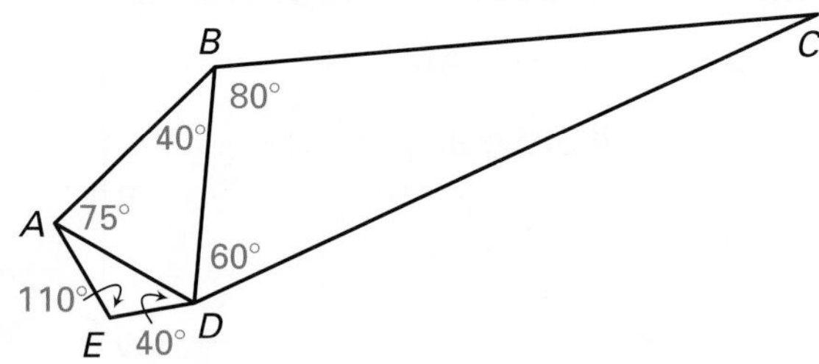

Describe **the possible lengths of the third side of the triangle given the lengths of the other two sides.**

20. 6 ft, 6 ft

21. 9 in., 5 in.

22. 11 yd, 6 yd

23. 7 ft, 24 in.

24. Error Analysis *Explain* why the diagram must be incorrect.

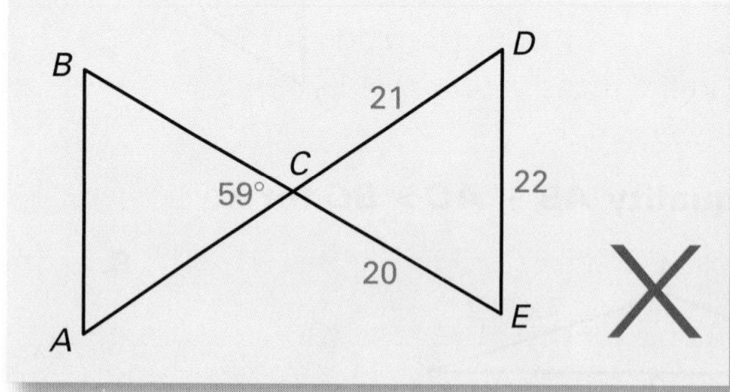

25. **Playground** You are asked to fence in a triangular playground. Two sides of the playground have lengths of 100 feet and 200 feet. What is the maximum total length of fence you could possibly need?

26. **Shortcut** You are walking your dog north on the sidewalk of Peach Street. When you reach 14th Street, you cut across the park to the corner of 13th Street and Sassafras Street. *Explain* why taking this route is shorter than continuing to walk to 13th Street and then to Sassafras Street.

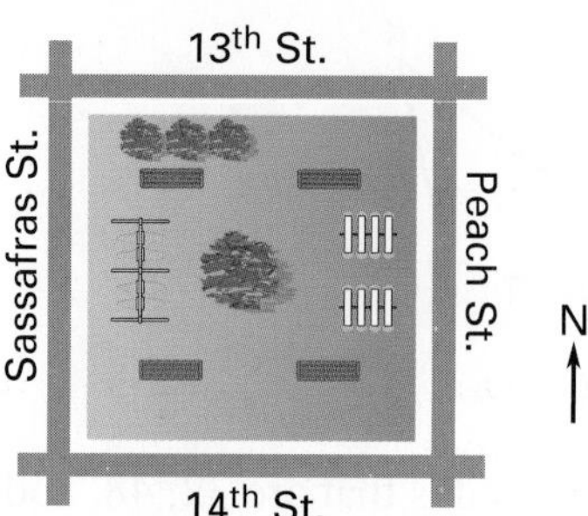

27. Proof Write a paragraph proof.

GIVEN: $\overline{RT} \perp \overline{TS}$

PROVE: $RS > RT$

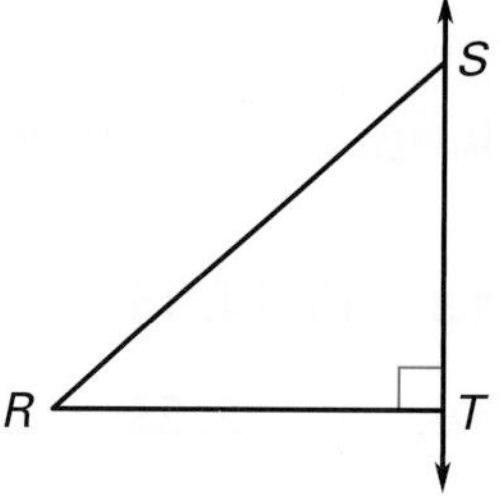

Georgia Performance Standards

MM1G3b Understand and use the triangle inequality, the side-angle inequality, and the exterior-angle inequality. 

Technology Activity

Side Lengths and Angle Measures

Use after Lesson 5.5

Question

How can you use geometry drawing software to decide which sides and angles are the least and greatest in a triangle?

Example

Construct a triangle using geometry drawing software.

STEP 1 **Draw a triangle**
Draw a scalene triangle. Label the vertices A, B, and C.

STEP 2 **Find angle measures**
Find the measure of each angle of the triangle.

STEP 3 **Find side lengths**
Find the length of each side of the triangle.

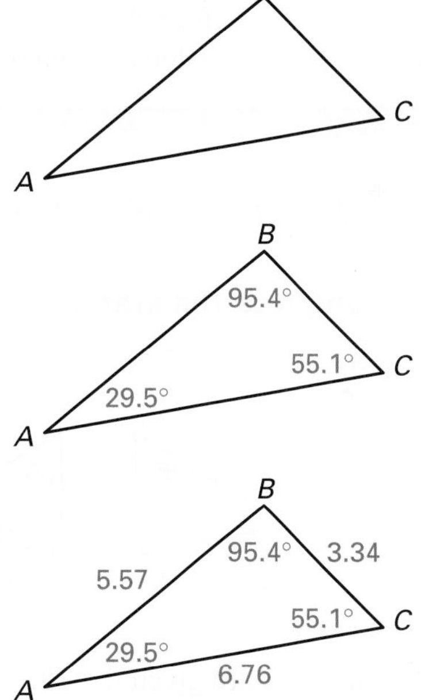

Practice

1. In $\triangle ABC$, is the longest side *adjacent to* or *opposite* the largest angle?

2. In $\triangle ABC$, is the shortest side *adjacent to* or *opposite* the smallest angle?

3. Drag point A to change the shape and size of $\triangle ABC$. Answer the questions from Exercises 1 and 2 for the new triangle.

4. Make a conjecture about how the positions of sides of different lengths in a triangle are related to the positions of the angles of different measures.

UNIT 5

LESSON 5.6

Inequalities in Two Triangles and Indirect Proof

Georgia Performance Standards: MM1G2a

Goal Use inequalities to make comparisons in two triangles.

Vocabulary

Theorem 5.14 Hinge Theorem: If two sides of one triangle are congruent to two sides of another triangle, and the included angle of the first is larger than the included angle of the second, then the third side of the first is longer than the third side of the second.

Theorem 5.15 Converse of the Hinge Theorem: If two sides of one triangle are congruent to two sides of another triangle, and the third side of the first is longer than the third side of the second, then the included angle of the first is larger than the included angle of the second.

In an **indirect proof,** you start by making the temporary assumption that the desired conclusion is false. By then showing that this assumption leads to a logical impossibility, you prove the original statement true by contradiction.

UNIT 5

Example 1 Use the Hinge Theorem and its converse

Complete the statement with <, >, or =. Explain.

a. JL ___?___ ST

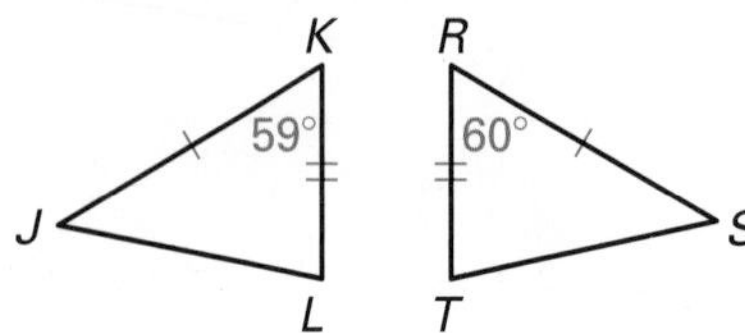

b. $m\angle DEG$ ___?___ $m\angle FEG$

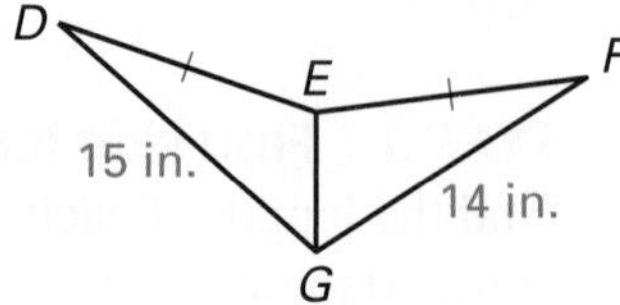

Solution

a. You are given that $\overline{JK} \cong \overline{SR}$ and $\overline{KL} \cong \overline{RT}$. Because $59° < 60°$, by the Hinge Theorem, $JL < ST$.

b. You are given that $\overline{DE} \cong \overline{FE}$ and you know that $\overline{EG} \cong \overline{EG}$ by the Reflexive Property. Because 15 inches > 14 inches, $DG > FG$. So, by the Converse of the Hinge Theorem, $m\angle DEG > m\angle FEG$.

Guided Practice for Example 1

Copy and complete the statement with <, >, or =. *Explain.*

1. $m\angle 1$ ___?___ $m\angle 2$

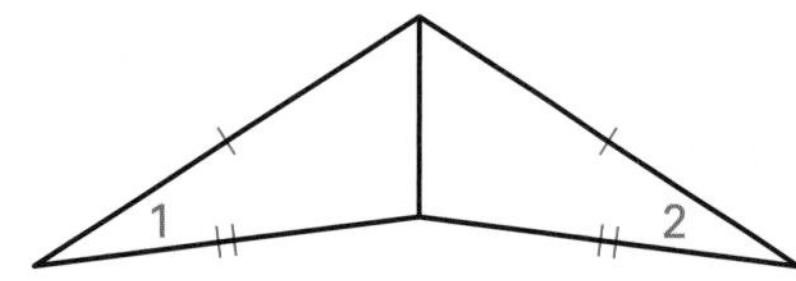

2. AB ___?___ CD

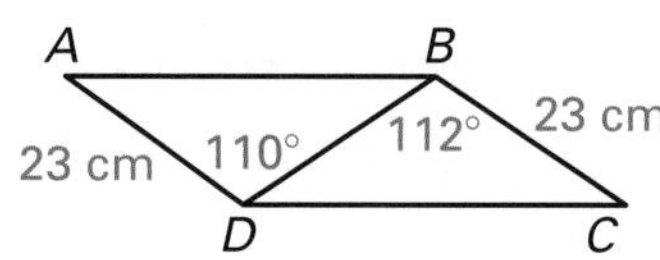

Georgia Performance Standards

MM1G2a Use conjecture, inductive reasoning, deductive reasoning, counterexamples, and indirect proof as appropriate.

Example 2 Solve a multi-step problem

Tree You and a friend walk away from a tree in opposite directions. You both walk 20 yards, then change direction and walk 5 yards. You start due east and then turn 45° toward north. Your friend starts due west and then turns 40° toward south. Who is farther from the tree?

Draw a diagram as shown below. Use linear pairs to find and mark the included angles of 135° and 140°.

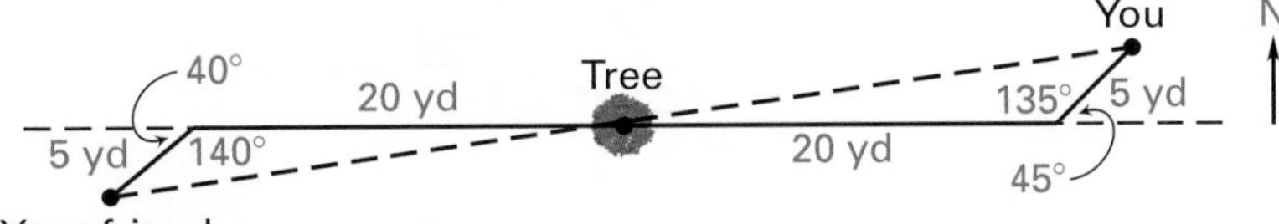

Because 140° > 135°, your friend is farther from the tree by the Hinge Theorem.

Example 3 Write an indirect proof

Write an indirect proof to show that the sum of an odd number and 2 is also an odd number.

GIVEN: x is an odd number.

PROVE: $x + 2$ is an odd number.

STEP 1 Assume temporarily that $x + 2$ is an even number. This means that $\frac{x+2}{2} = n$ for some whole number n. So, solving for x gives $x = 2(n - 1)$.

STEP 2 If x is odd, then, by definition, x cannot be divided evenly by 2. However, $x = 2(n - 1)$ so $\frac{x}{2} = \frac{2(n-1)}{2} = n - 1$. We know that $n - 1$ is a whole number because n is a whole number, so x *can* be divided evenly by 2. This contradicts the given statement that x is odd.

STEP 3 Therefore, the assumption that $x + 2$ is an even number must be false, which proves that $x + 2$ is an odd number.

Guided Practice for Examples 2 and 3

3. In Example 2, suppose you walk 20 yards away from the tree due south and then turn 40° toward east and walk 5 yards. *Compare* your distance from the tree to your friend's distance from the tree.

Write a temporary assumption that you could make to prove the conclusion indirectly.

4. If $xy < 0$ and $x > 0$, then $y < 0$.

5. If $\triangle ABC$ is isosceles and $m\angle A = 100°$, then $m\angle B = m\angle C$.

UNIT 5

LESSON 5.6

Exercise Set A

MM1G2a Use conjecture, inductive reasoning, deductive reasoning, counterexamples, and indirect proof as appropriate.

Copy and complete the statement with $<$, $>$, or $=$. *Explain.*

1. ST __?__ VW

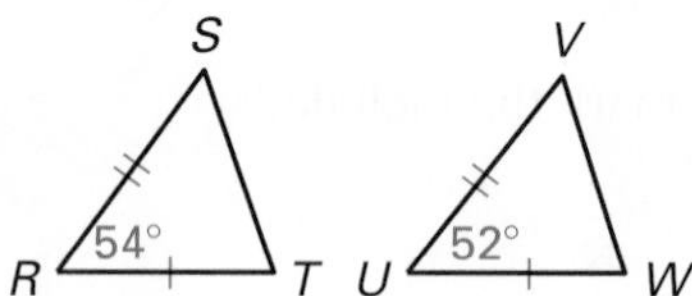

2. DE __?__ EF

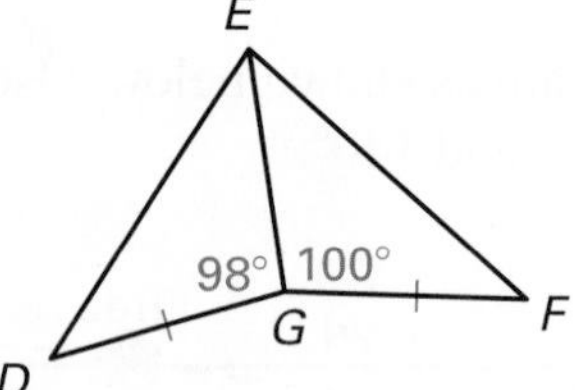

3. JK __?__ LM

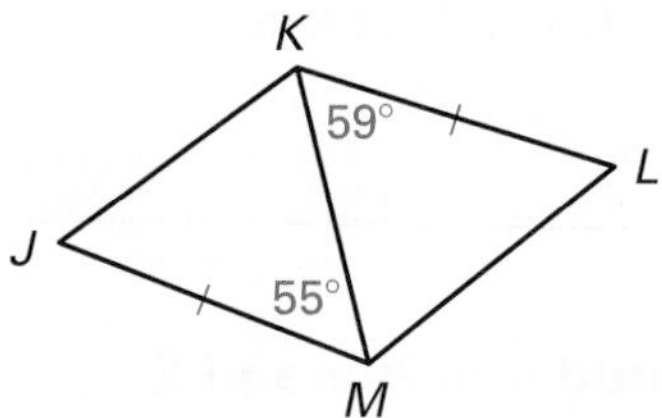

4. $m\angle 1$ __?__ $m\angle 2$

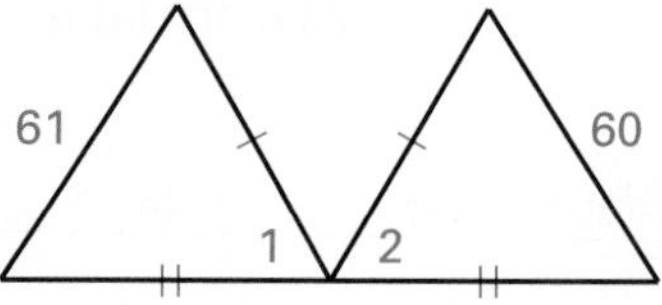

5. $m\angle 1$ __?__ $m\angle 2$

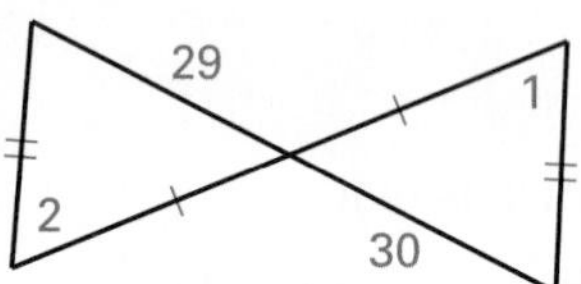

6. $m\angle 1$ __?__ $m\angle 2$

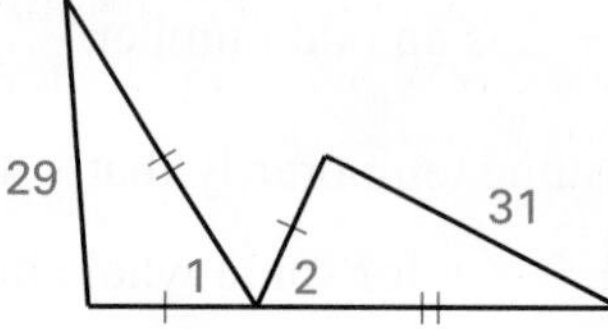

7. $m\angle 1$ __?__ $m\angle 2$

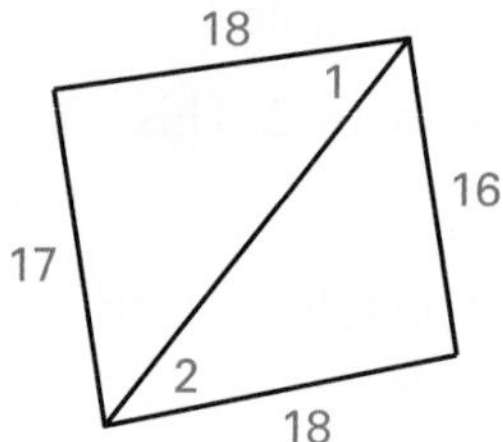

8. AB __?__ CD

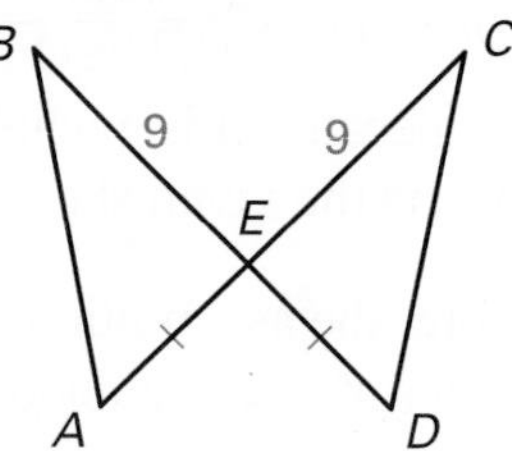

Use the Hinge Theorem or its converse and properties of triangles to write and solve an inequality to describe a restriction on the value of x.

9.

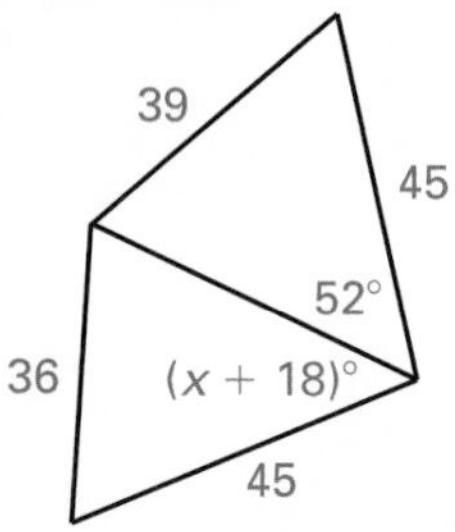

10.

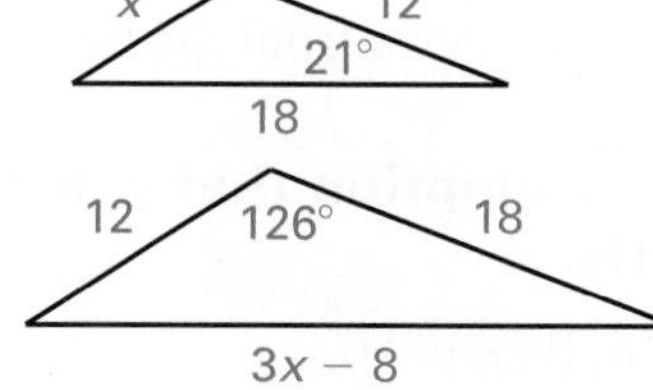

Exercise Set A *(continued)*

Write a temporary assumption you could make to prove the conclusion indirectly.

11. If two lines in a plane are parallel, then the two lines do not contain two sides of a triangle.

12. In $\triangle ABC$, if $m\angle A > 90°$, then $m\angle B < 90°$.

13. If x and y are even integers, then xy is even.

14. **Multiple Representations** All four legs of the table shown have identical measurements, but they are attached to the table top so that $\angle 3$ is smaller than $\angle 1$.

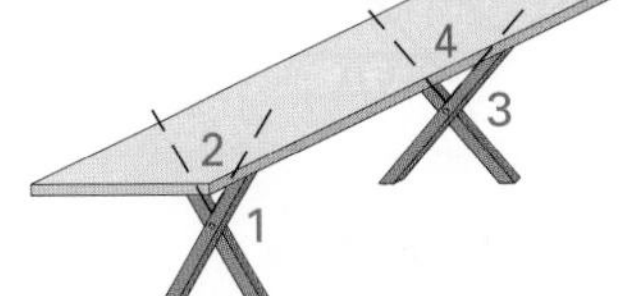

a. Using a Theorem Use the Hinge Theorem to explain why the table top is not level.

b. Using the Converse of a Theorem Use the Converse of the Hinge Theorem to explain how to use a length measure to determine when $\angle 4 \cong \angle 2$ in reattaching the rear pair of legs to make the table level.

15. **Fishing Contest** One contestant in a catch-and-release fishing contest spends the morning at a location 1.8 miles due north of the starting point, then goes 1.2 miles due east for the rest of the day. A second contestant starts out 1.2 miles due east of the starting point, then goes another 1.8 miles in a direction 84° south of due east to spend the rest of the day. Which angler is farther from the starting point at the end of the day? *Explain* how you know.

16. **Indirect Proof** Arrange statements A–F in order to write an indirect proof of Case 1.

GIVEN: $\overline{AD}$ is a median of $\triangle ABC$.
$\angle ADB \cong \angle ADC$

PROVE: $AB = AC$

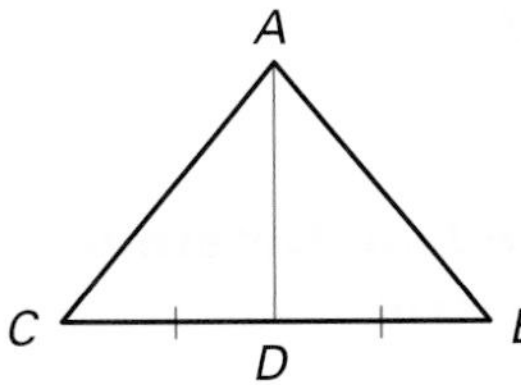

Case 1:

A. Then $m\angle ADB < m\angle ADC$ by the converse of the Hinge Theorem.

B. Then $\overline{BD} \cong \overline{CD}$ by the definition of midpoint. Also, $\overline{AD} \cong \overline{AD}$ by the reflexive property.

C. This contradiction shows that the temporary assumption that $AB < AC$ is false.

D. But this contradicts the given statement that $\angle ADB \cong \angle ADC$.

E. Because $\overline{AD}$ is a median of $\triangle ABC$, D is the midpoint of $\overline{BC}$.

F. Temporarily assume that $AB < AC$.

17. **Indirect Proof** There are two cases to consider for the proof in Exercise 16. Write an indirect proof for Case 2, temporarily assuming $AB > AC$.

UNIT 5

LESSON 5.6

Exercise Set B

MM1G2a Use conjecture, inductive reasoning, deductive reasoning, counterexamples, and indirect proof as appropriate.

Copy and complete the statement with <, >, or =. *Explain.*

1. TP __?__ AG

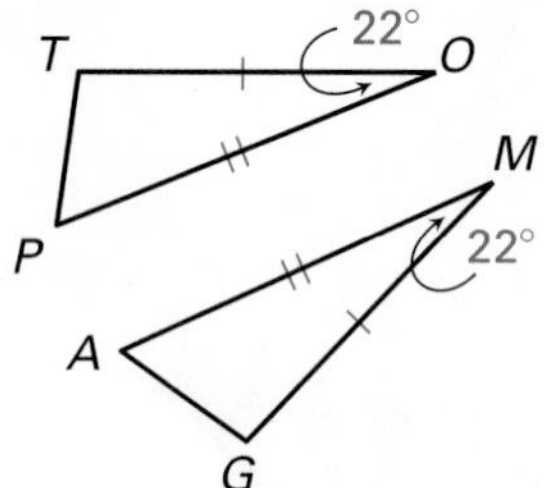

2. KD __?__ CP

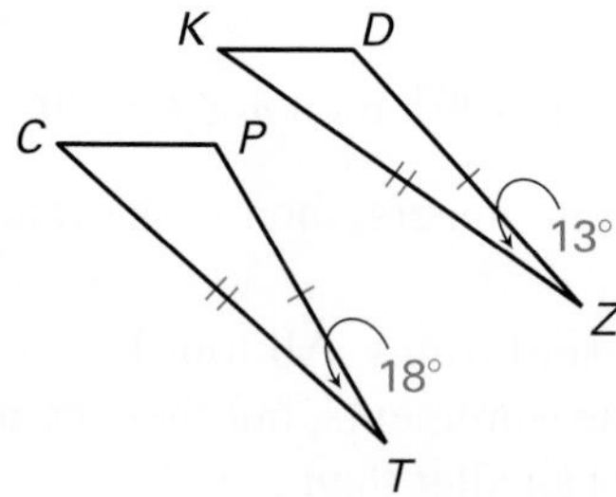

3. $m\angle 1$ __?__ $m\angle 2$

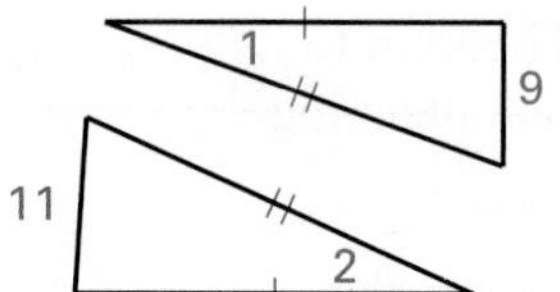

4. $m\angle 1$ __?__ $m\angle 2$

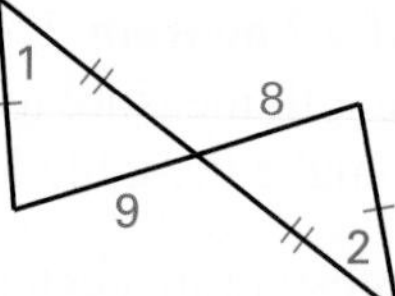

5. AT __?__ BT

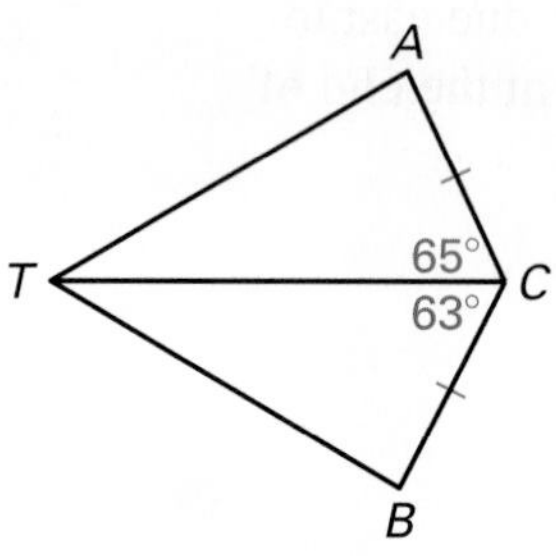

6. $m\angle 1$ __?__ $m\angle 2$

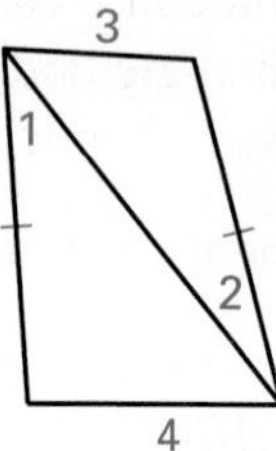

In $\triangle DEF$, $\overline{DM}$ is a median. Determine if each statement is *always*, *sometimes*, or *never* true.

7. If $m\angle 2 > m\angle 1$, then $ED > FD$.

8. If $m\angle E > m\angle F$, then $\angle 1$ is obtuse.

9. If $\angle 2$ is acute, then $m\angle F > m\angle E$.

10. If $m\angle E < m\angle F$, then $m\angle 1 < m\angle 2$.

11. If $m\angle 2 > m\angle 1$, then $ED > FD$.

12. If $m\angle 2 = 90°$, then $FD > ED$.

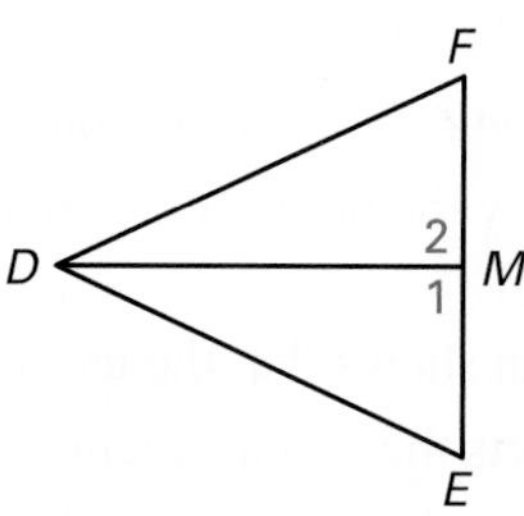

UNIT 5

Exercise Set B *(continued)*

13. Error Analysis *Explain* why the student's reasoning is incorrect.

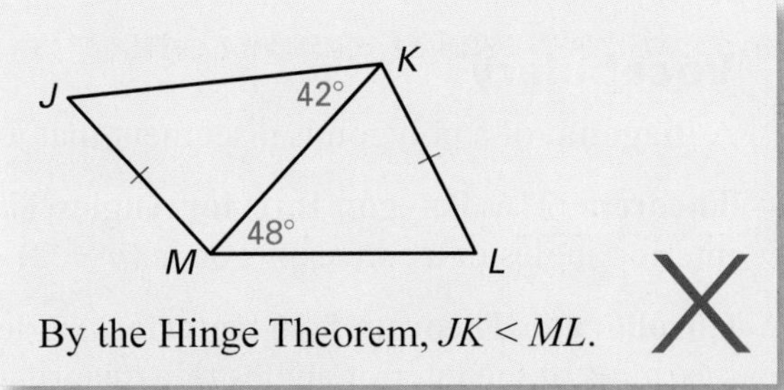

Use the Hinge Theorem or its converse and properties of triangles to write and solve an inequality to describe a restriction on the value of *x*.

14.

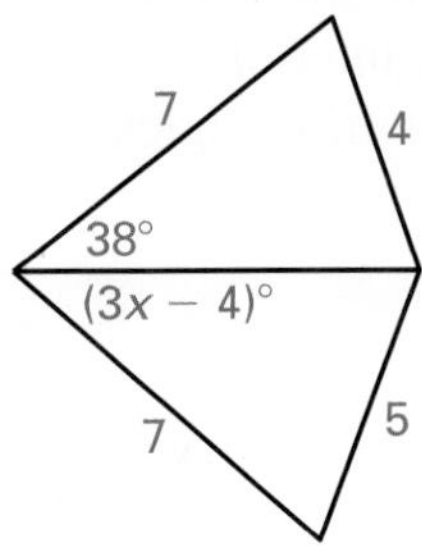

15.

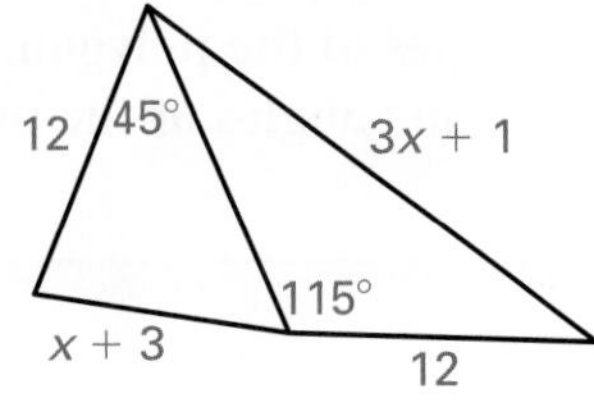

16. **Sailing** Two families are going sailing. Family A leaves the marina and sails 2.3 miles due north, then sails 3 miles due west. Family B leaves the marina and sails 2.3 miles due south, then sails 3 miles in a direction 1° north of due east. Which family is farther from the marina? *Explain* your reasoning.

In Exercises 17–19, write an indirect proof.

17. Prove Theorem 5.11, which is given on page 284.

GIVEN: $m\angle A > m\angle B$

PROVE: $BC > AC$

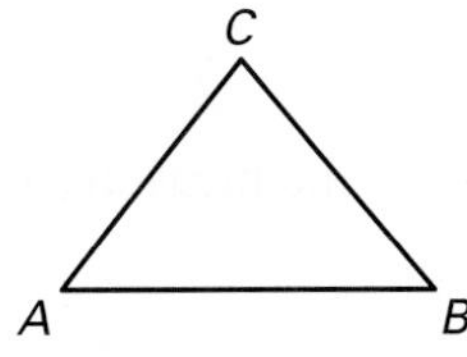

18. **GIVEN:** $\angle ABC \cong \angle DBC$

PROVE: $\overline{BC} \perp \overline{AD}$

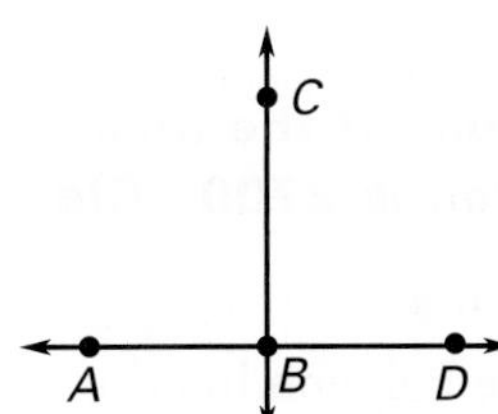

19. **GIVEN:** $\overline{RU}$ is an altitude, $\overrightarrow{RU}$ bisects $\angle SRT$.

PROVE: $\triangle RST$ is isosceles.

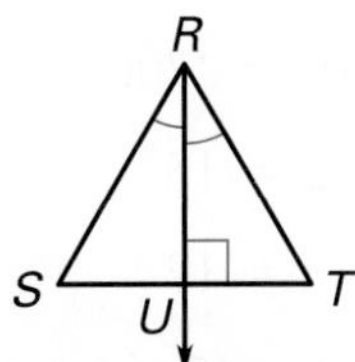

UNIT 5

LESSON 5.7

Find Angle Measures in Polygons

Georgia Performance Standards: MM1G3a

Goal Find angle measures in polygons.

Vocabulary

A **diagonal** of a polygon is a segment that joins two nonconsecutive vertices.

Theorem 5.16 Polygon Interior Angles Theorem: The sum of the measures of the interior angles of a convex n-gon is $(n - 2) \cdot 180°$.

Corollary to Theorem 5.16 Interior Angles of a Quadrilateral: The sum of the measures of the interior angles of a quadrilateral is 360°.

Theorem 5.17 Polygon Exterior Angles Theorem: The sum of the measures of the exterior angles of a convex polygon, one angle at each vertex, is 360°.

When the sides of a polygon are extended, other angles are formed. The original angles are the **interior angles of the polygon.** The angles that are adjacent to the interior angles are the **exterior angles of the polygon.** In a *regular polygon*, the interior angles are congruent.

UNIT 5

Example 1 Find the sum of angle measures in a polygon

Find the sum of the measures of the interior angles of a convex hexagon.

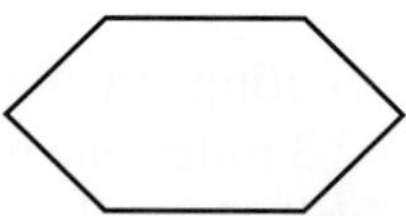

Solution

A hexagon has 6 sides. Use the Polygon Interior Angles Theorem.

$(n - 2) \cdot 180° = (6 - 2) \cdot 180°$	Substitute 6 for n.
$= 4 \cdot 180°$	Subtract.
$= 720°$	Multiply.

The sum of the measures of the interior angles of a hexagon is 720°.

Example 2 Find the number of sides of a polygon

The sum of the measures of the interior angles of a convex polygon is 2700°. Classify the polygon by the number of sides.

Solution

Use the Polygon Interior Angles Theorem to write an equation involving the number of sides n. Then solve the equation to find the number of sides.

$(n - 2) \cdot 180° = 2700°$	Polygon Interior Angles Theorem
$n - 2 = 15$	Divide each side by 180°.
$n = 17$	Add 2 to each side.

The polygon has 17 sides. It is a 17-gon.

Georgia Performance Standards

MM1G3a Determine the sum of interior and exterior angles in a polygon.

Guided Practice for Examples 1 and 2

1. Find the sum of the measures of the interior angles of the polygon shown in the diagram.

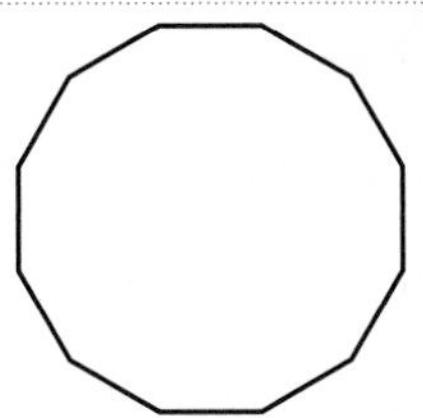

2. The sum of the measures of the interior angles of a convex polygon is 540°. Classify the polygon by the number of sides.

Example 3 Find an unknown interior angle measure

Find the value of x in the diagram.

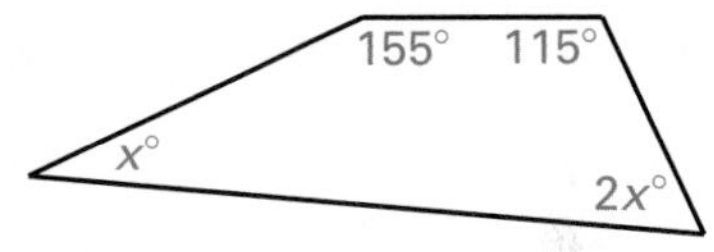

Solution

The polygon is a quadrilateral. Use the Corollary to the Polygon Interior Angles Theorem to write an equation involving x. Then solve the equation.

$x° + 2x° + 155° + 115° = 360°$	Corollary to Theorem 5.16
$3x + 270 = 360$	Combine like terms.
$x = 30$	Solve for x.

Example 4 Find an unknown exterior angle measure

Find the value of x in the diagram.

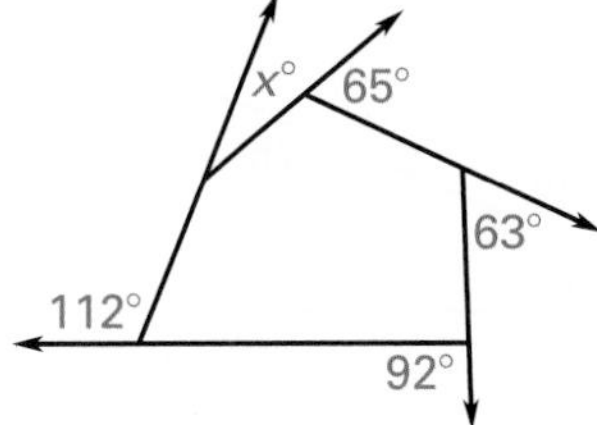

Solution

Use the Polygon Exterior Angles Theorem to write an equation involving x. Then solve the equation.

$x° + 65° + 63° + 92° + 112° = 360°$	Polygon Exterior Angles Theorem
$x + 332 = 360$	Combine like terms.
$x = 28$	Solve for x.

Guided Practice for Examples 3 and 4

3. What is the value of x in the diagram?

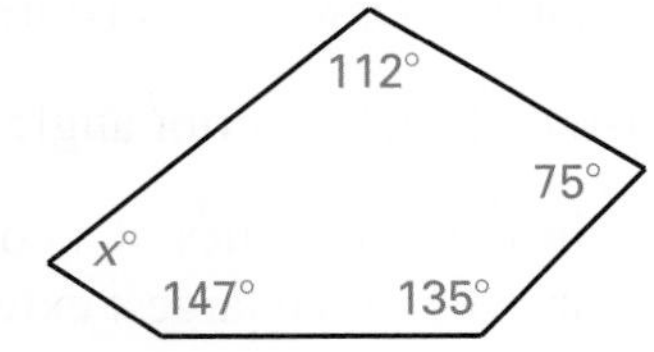

4. A convex heptagon has exterior angles with measures 60°, 51°, 67°, 48°, 32°, and 59°. What is the measure of an exterior angle at the seventh vertex?

LESSON 5.7 **Exercise Set A**

MM1G3a Determine the sum of interior and exterior angles in a polygon.

Find the sum of the measures of the interior angles of the indicated convex polygon.

1. Hexagon
2. Dodecagon
3. 11-gon
4. 15-gon
5. 20-gon
6. 40-gon

The sum of the measures of the interior angles of a convex polygon is given. Classify the polygon by the number of sides.

7. 180°
8. 540°
9. 900°
10. 1800°
11. 2520°
12. 3960°
13. 5040°
14. 5940°
15. 8640°

Find the value of *x*.

16.
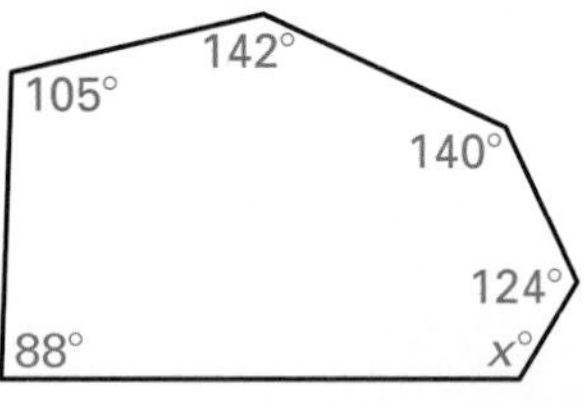

17.
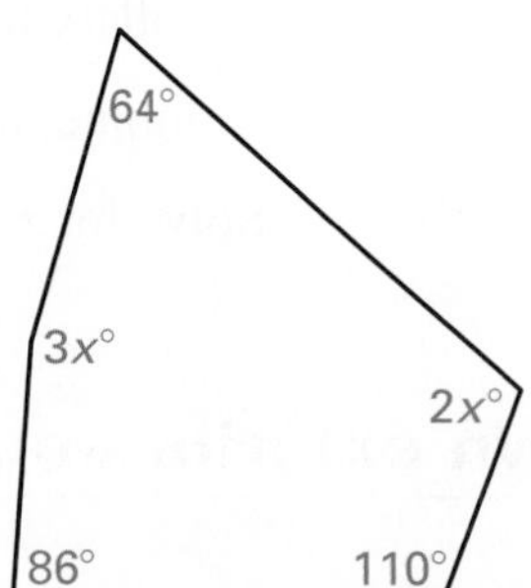

18.
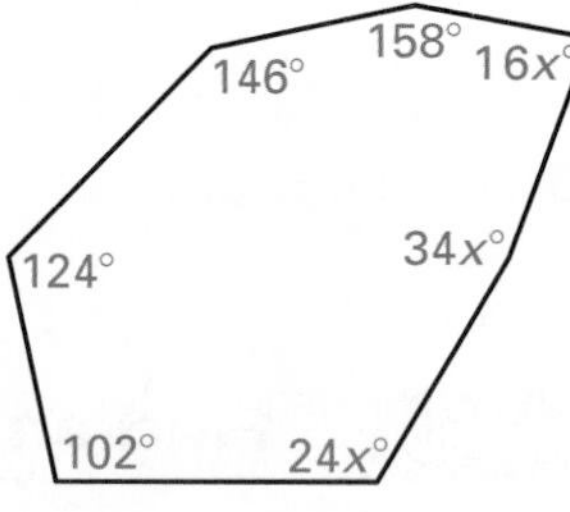

19.
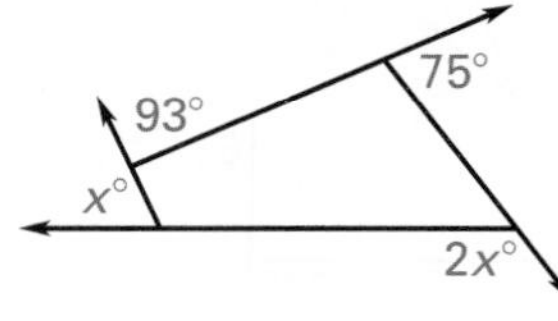

20.
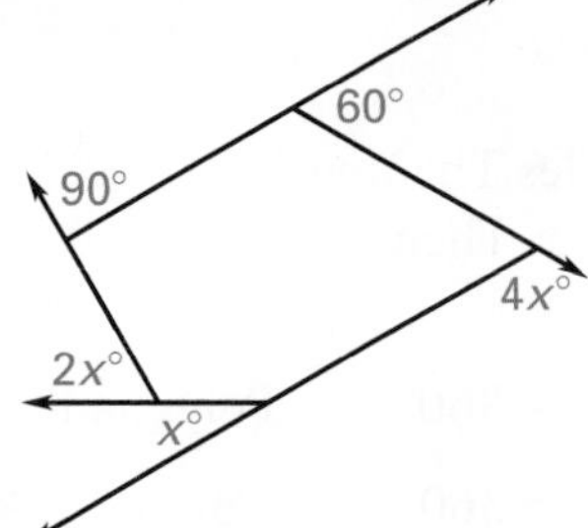

21.
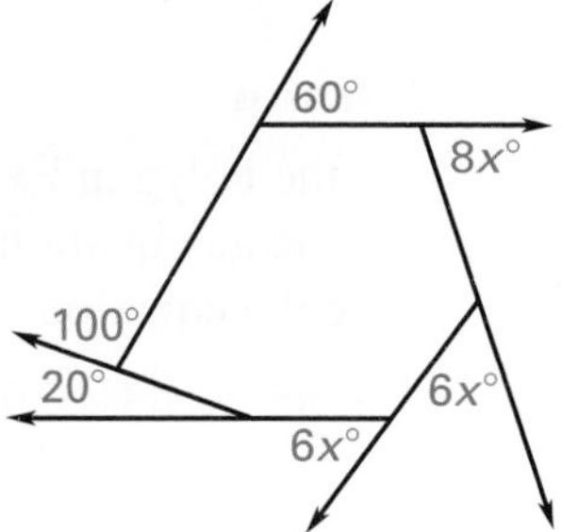

22. **Error Analysis** A student claims that the sum of the measures of the exterior angles of a pentagon is greater than the sum of the measures of the exterior angles of a quadrilateral. The student justifies this claim by saying that a pentagon has one more side than a quadrilateral. *Describe* and correct the student's error.

23. What is the measure of each exterior angle of a regular nonagon?

24. The measures of the exterior angles of a convex quadrilateral are 90°, $10x°$, $5x°$, and 45°. What is the measure of the largest exterior angle?

UNIT 5

Exercise Set A *(continued)*

25. The measures of the interior angles of a convex octagon are $45x°$, $40x°$, 155°, 120°, 155°, $38x°$, 158°, and $41x°$. What is the measure of the smallest interior angle?

Find the measures of an interior angle and an exterior angle of the indicated polygon.

26. Regular triangle

27. Regular octagon

28. Regular 16-gon

29. Regular 45-gon

30. Regular 60-gon

31. Regular 100-gon

In Exercises 32–35, find the value of *n* for each regular *n*-gon described.

32. Each interior angle of the regular n-gon has a measure of 140°.

33. Each interior angle of the regular n-gon has a measure of 175.2°.

34. Each exterior angle of the regular n-gon has a measure of 45°.

35. Each exterior angle of the regular n-gon has a measure of 3°.

36. Storage Shed The side view of a storage shed is shown below. Find the value of x. Then determine the measure of each angle.

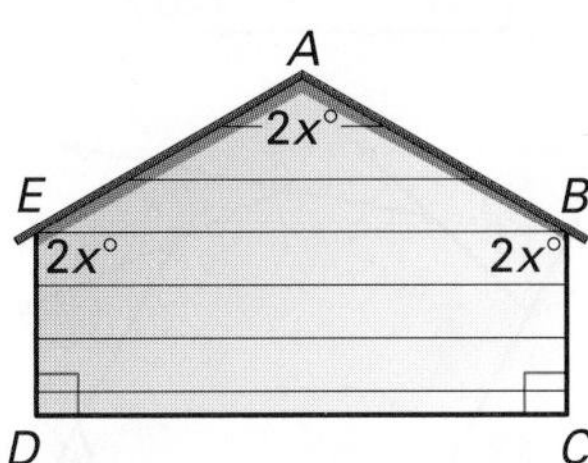

37. Tents The front view of a camping tent is shown below. Find the value of x. Then determine the measure of each angle.

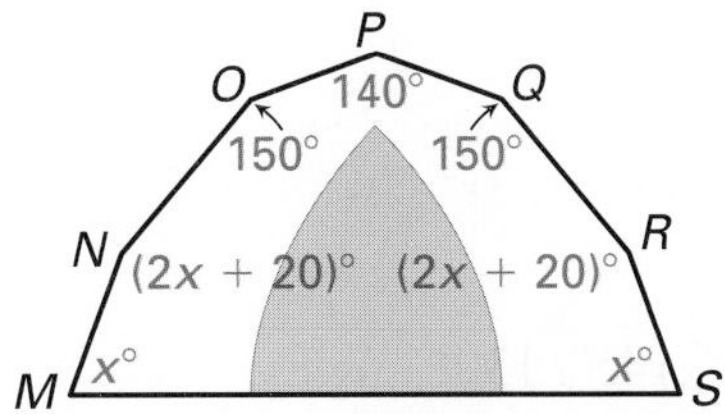

38. Proof Because all the interior angle measures of a regular n-gon are equal, you can find the measure of each individual interior angle. The measure of each interior angle of a regular n-gon is $\frac{(n-2) \cdot 180}{n}$. Write a paragraph proof to prove this statement.

LESSON 5.7

Exercise Set B

MM1G3a Determine the sum of interior and exterior angles in a polygon.

Find the sum of the measures of the interior angles of the indicated convex polygon.

1. 21-gon
2. 35-gon
3. 50-gon

The sum of the measures of the interior angles of a convex polygon is given. Classify the polygon by the number of sides.

4. 1440°
5. 3060°
6. 3780°
7. 6480°
8. 8100°
9. 8820°

Find the value of *x*.

10. 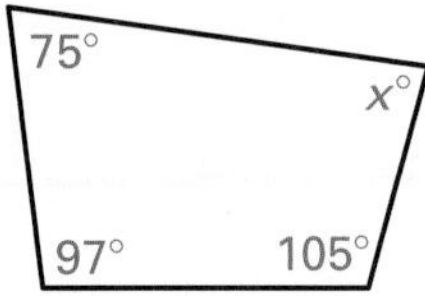

11. 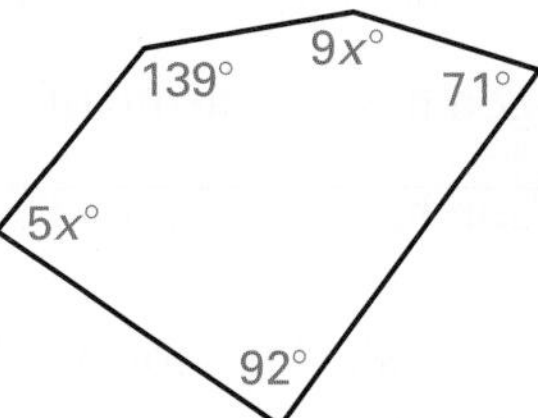

12. 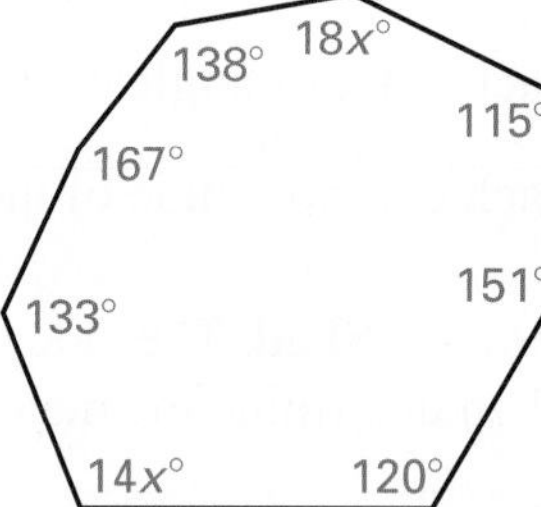

13. 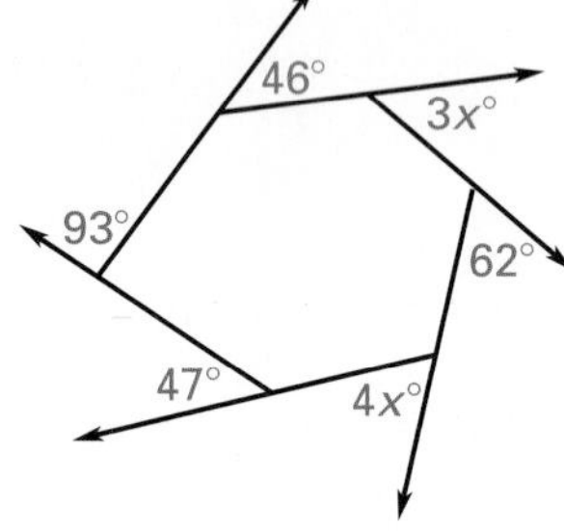

14. 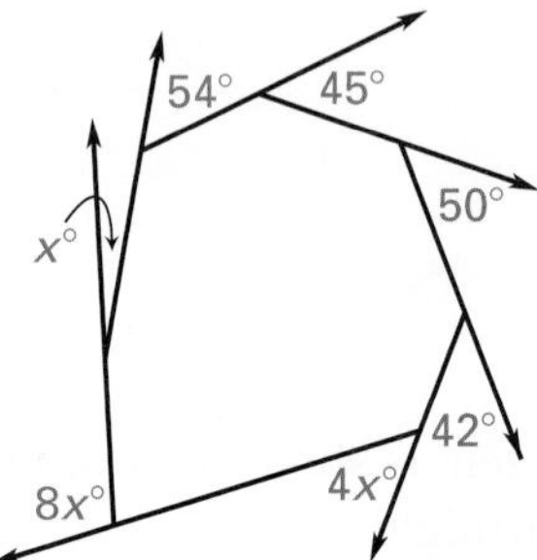

15. 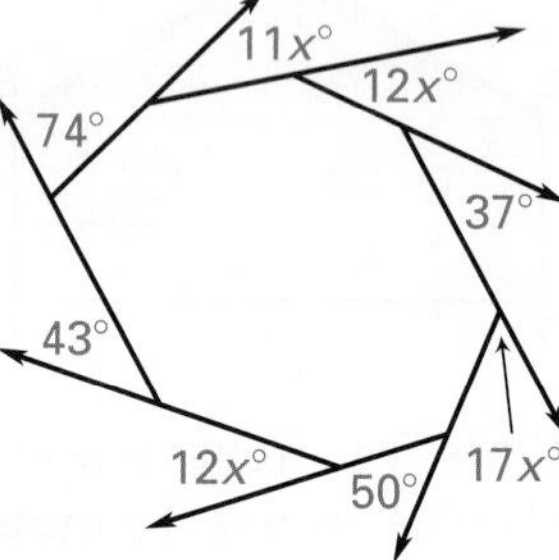

16. What is the measure of each interior angle of a regular nonagon?
17. The measures of the exterior angles of a convex hexagon are 45°, 60°, x°, $3x$°, $7x$°, and 90°. What is the measure of the largest exterior angle?
18. The measures of the interior angles of a convex decagon are 150°, 145°, 130°, $34x$°, $35x$°, 135°, 160°, 120°, $30x$°, and $21x$°. What is the measure of the smallest interior angle?

Find the measures of an interior angle and an exterior angle of the indicated regular polygon.

19. Regular heptagon
20. Regular dodecagon
21. Regular 17-gon
22. Regular 50-gon
23. Regular 70-gon
24. Regular 125-gon

UNIT 5

Exercise Set B *(continued)*

In Exercises 25–28, find the value of *n* for each regular *n*-gon described.

25. Each interior angle of the regular n-gon has a measure of 165°.

26. Each interior angle of the regular n-gon has a measure of 177.6°.

27. Each exterior angle of the regular n-gon has a measure of 5°.

28. Each exterior angle of the regular n-gon has a measure of 12°.

Determine if it is possible for a regular polygon to have an interior angle with the given angle measure. *Explain* your reasoning.

29. 155° **30.** 160° **31.** 175° **32.** 168°

33. Light Fixture The side view of a light fixture is shown below. Find the value of x. Then determine the measure of each angle.

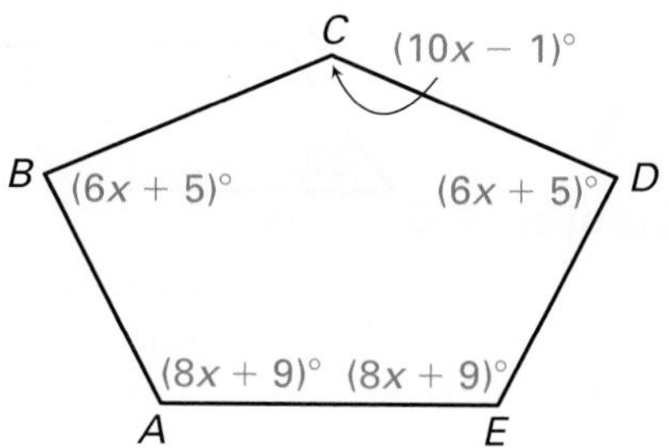

34. Tent The front view of a camping tent is shown below. Find the value of x. Then determine the measure of each angle.

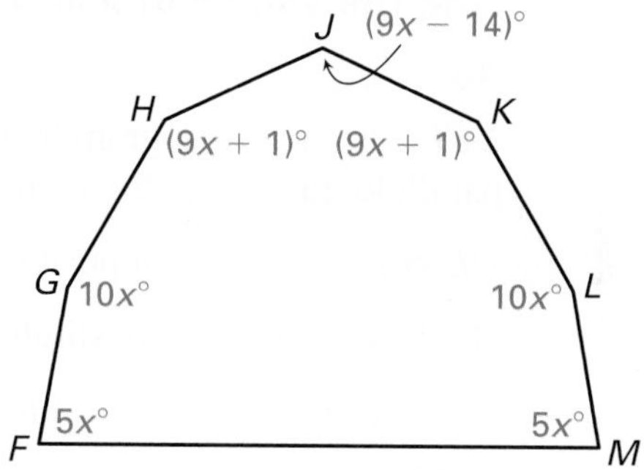

35. Multiple Representations The formula for the measure of each interior angle in a regular polygon can be written in function notation.

a. Writing a Function Write a function $h(n)$, where n is the number of sides in a regular polygon and $h(n)$ is the measure of any interior angle in the regular polygon.

b. Using a Function Use the function from part (a) to find $h(10)$. Then use the function to find n if $h(n) = 156°$.

c. Graphing a Function Graph the function from part (a) for $n = 3, 4, 5, 6, 7, 8$, and 9. Based on your graph, describe what happens to the value of $h(n)$ as n increases. *Explain* your reasoning.

36. Proof Write a paragraph proof to prove the following statement:

If the measure of each interior angle of a regular n-gon is $x°$, then $n = \frac{360}{180 - x}$.

LESSON 5.8

Use Properties of Parallelograms

Georgia Performance Standards: MM1G1e, MM1G3d

Goal Find angle and side measures in parallelograms.

Vocabulary

A **parallelogram** is a quadrilateral with both pairs of opposite sides parallel.

Theorem 5.18: If a quadrilateral is a parallelogram, then its opposite sides are congruent.

Theorem 5.19: If a quadrilateral is a parallelogram, then its opposite angles are congruent.

Theorem 5.20: If a quadrilateral is a parallelogram, then its consecutive angles are supplementary.

Theorem 5.21: If a quadrilateral is a parallelogram, then its diagonals bisect each other.

Example 1 Use properties of parallelograms

Find the values of *x* and *y*.

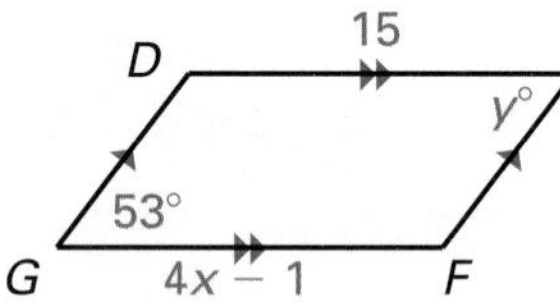

Solution

DEFG is a parallelogram by the definition of a parallelogram. Use Theorem 5.18 to find the value of *x*.

$DE = FG$ Opposite sides of a ▱ are ≅.

$15 = 4x - 1$ Substitute 15 for *DE* and $4x - 1$ for *FG*.

$4 = x$ Solve for *x*.

By Theorem 5.19, $\angle G \cong \angle E$, or $m\angle G = m\angle E$. So, $y° = 53°$.

In ▱*DEFG*, $x = 4$ and $y = 53$.

Guided Practice for Example 1

Find the value of each variable in the parallelogram.

1.

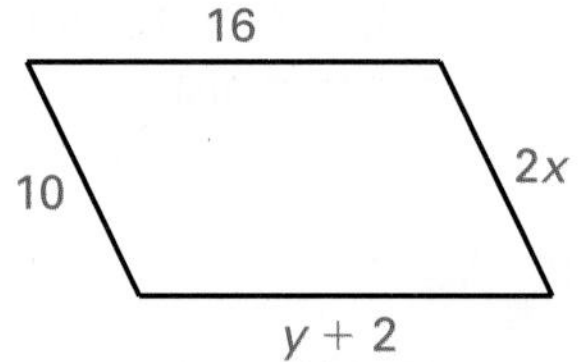

2.

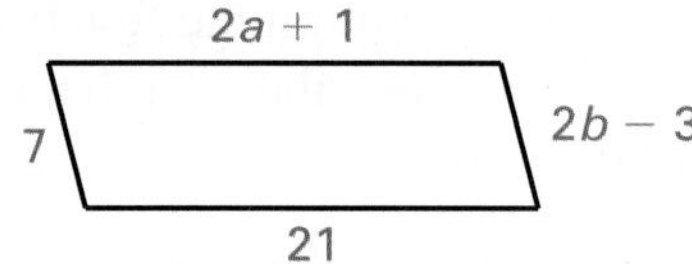

3.

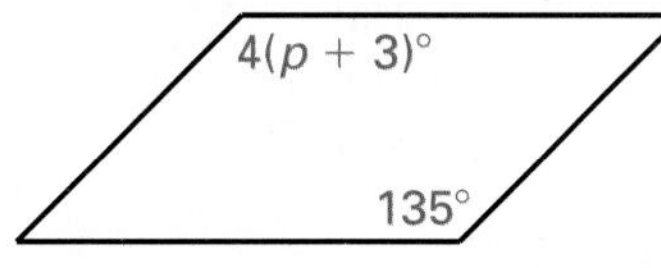

4.

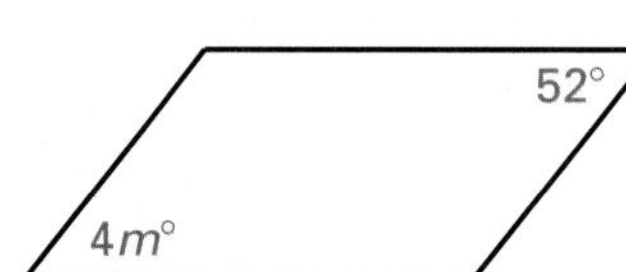

UNIT 5

Georgia Performance Standards

MM1G1e Use the coordinate plane to investigate properties of and verify conjectures related to triangles and quadrilaterals.

MM1G3d Understand, use, and prove properties of and relationships among special quadrilaterals: parallelogram, rectangle, rhombus, square, trapezoid, and kite.

Example 2 Use properties of parallelograms

Find the value of x in $\square WXYZ$.

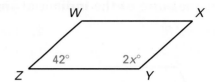

Solution

Use Theorem 5.20 to find the value of x.

$m\angle WZY + m\angle XYZ = 180°$ Consecutive angles in a $\square$ are supplementary.

$42° + 2x° = 180°$ Substitute.

$x = 69$ Solve for x.

Example 3 Find the intersection of diagonals

The vertices of $\square ABCD$ are $A(-1, 6)$, $B(5, 6)$, $C(3, -2)$, and $D(-3, -2)$. The diagonals of $\square ABCD$ intersect at point P. What are the coordinates of P?

Solution

STEP 1 Sketch $\square ABCD$ in the coordinate plane.

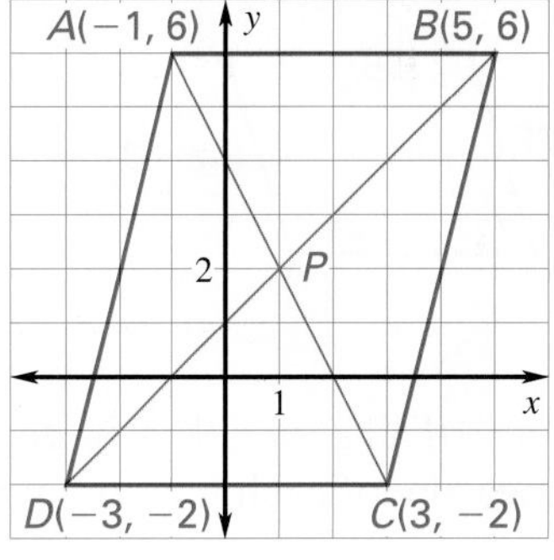

STEP 2 By Theorem 5.21, the diagonals of a parallelogram bisect each other. So, P is the midpoint of diagonals $\overline{AC}$ and $\overline{DB}$. Use the Midpoint Formula to find the midpoint P of $\overline{DB}$.

Midpoint: $\left(\frac{5 + (-3)}{2}, \frac{6 + (-2)}{2}\right) = (1, 2)$

The coordinates of P are $(1, 2)$.

Guided Practice for Examples 2 and 3

Find the indicated measure in $\square PQRS$.

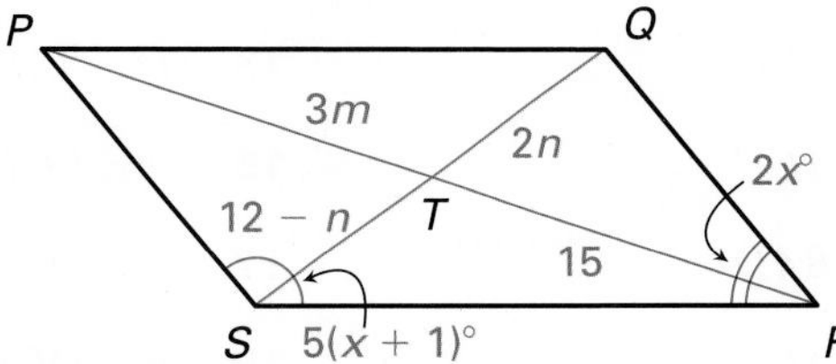

5. PR **6.** ST

7. $m\angle SRQ$ **8.** $m\angle PQR$

9. The vertices of $\square ABCD$ are $A(-4, 2)$, $B(3, 2)$, $C(1, -1)$, and $D(-6, -1)$. The diagonals of $\square ABCD$ intersect at point P. What are the coordinates of P?

10. The vertices of $\square ABCD$ are $A(-5, 6)$, $B(1, 6)$, $C(4, 0)$, and $D(-2, 0)$. The diagonals of $\square ABCD$ intersect at point P. What are the coordinates of P?

LESSON 5.8 **Exercise Set A**

MM1G1e Use the coordinate plane to investigate properties of and verify conjectures related to triangles and quadrilaterals.

MM1G3d Understand, use, and prove properties of and relationships among special quadrilaterals: parallelogram, rectangle, rhombus, square, trapezoid, and kite.

Find the measure of the indicated angle in the parallelogram.

1. Find $m\angle B$.

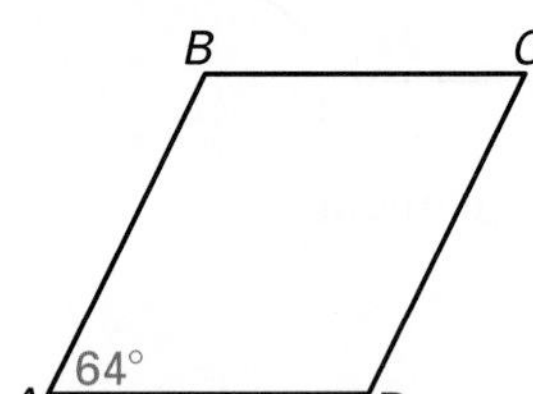

2. Find $m\angle G$.

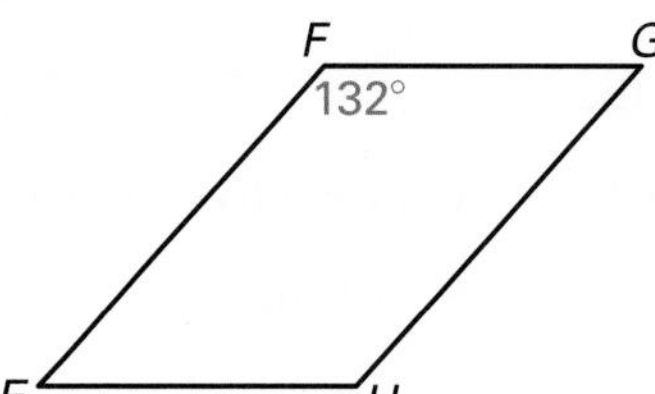

3. Find $m\angle M$.

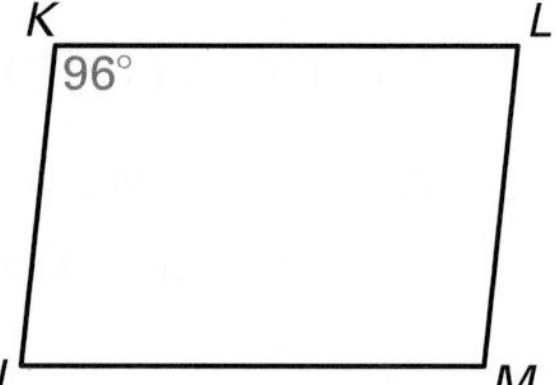

Find the value of each variable in the parallelogram.

4.

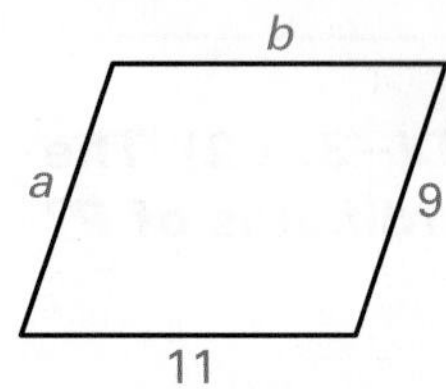

5.

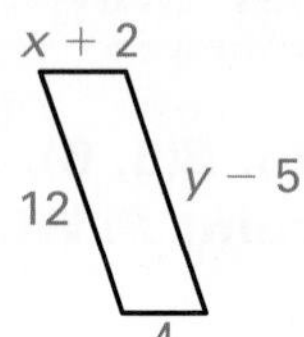

6.

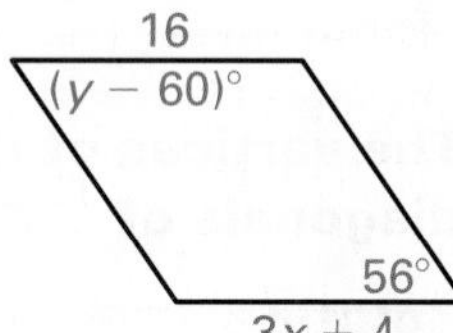

7.

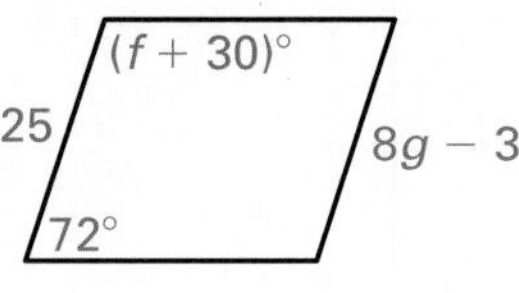

8.

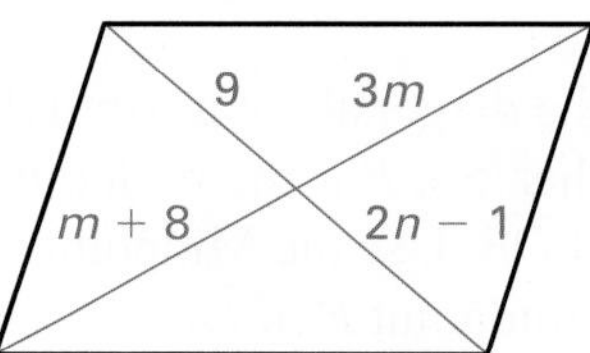

9.

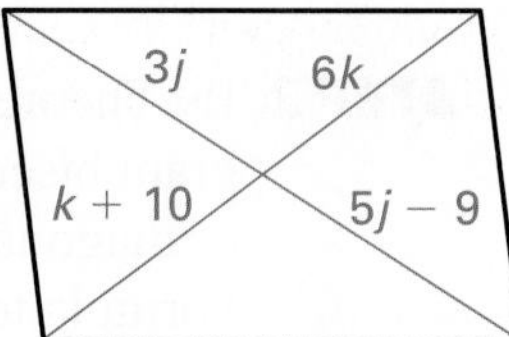

10. In ▱$WXYZ$, $m\angle W$ is 50 degrees more than $m\angle X$. Sketch ▱$WXYZ$. Find the measure of each interior angle. Then label each angle with its measure.

11. In ▱$EFGH$, $m\angle G$ is 25 degrees less than $m\angle H$. Sketch ▱$EFGH$. Find the measure of each interior angle. Then label each angle with its measure.

Find the indicated measure in ▱*ABCD*.

12. $m\angle AEB$

13. $m\angle BAE$

14. $m\angle AED$

15. $m\angle ECB$

16. $m\angle BAD$

17. $m\angle DCE$

18. $m\angle ADC$

19. $m\angle DCB$

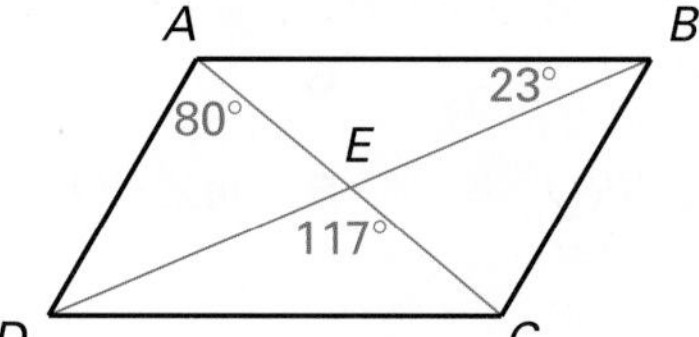

Exercise Set A *(continued)*

Use the diagram of ▱*MNOP*. Points *Q*, *R*, *S*, and *T* are midpoints of $\overline{MX}$, $\overline{NX}$, $\overline{OX}$, and $\overline{PX}$. Find the indicated measure.

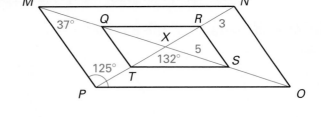

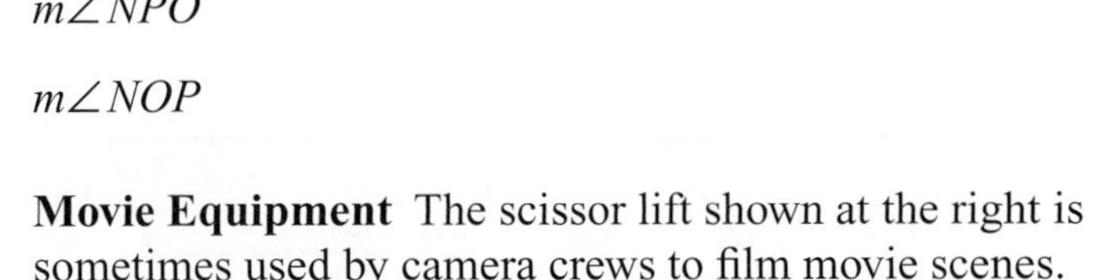

20. PN

21. MQ

22. XO

23. $m\angle NMQ$

24. $m\angle NXO$

25. $m\angle MNP$

26. $m\angle NPO$

27. $m\angle NOP$

28. **Movie Equipment** The scissor lift shown at the right is sometimes used by camera crews to film movie scenes. The lift can be raised or lowered so that the camera can get a variety of views of one scene. In the figure, points E, F, G, and H are the vertices of a parallelogram.

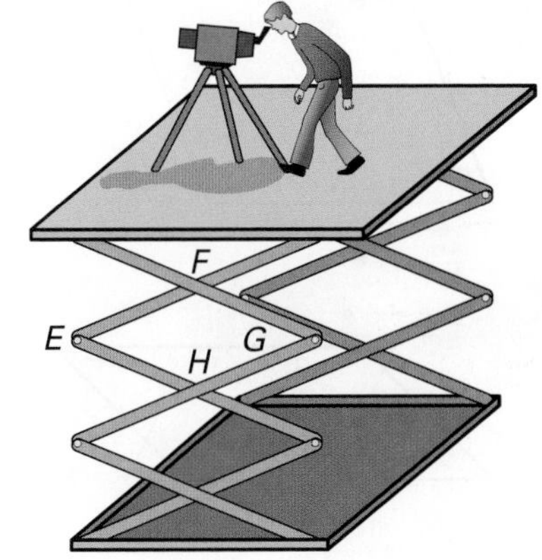

a. If $m\angle E = 45°$, find $m\angle F$.

b. What happens to $\angle E$ and $\angle F$ when the lift is raised? *Explain.*

29. In parallelogram $RSTU$, the ratio of RS to ST is $5:3$. Find RS if the perimeter of ▱$RSTU$ is 64.

30. Parallelogram $MNOP$ and parallelogram $PQRO$ share a common side, as shown. Using a two-column proof, prove that segment MN is congruent to segment QR.

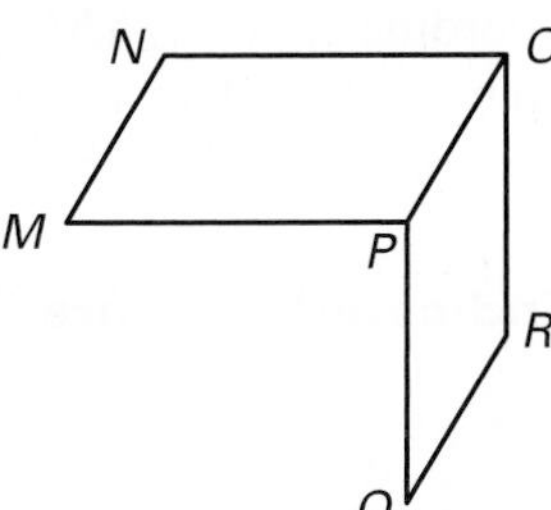

GIVEN: $MNOP$ and $PQRO$ are parallelograms.

PROVE: $\overline{MN} \cong \overline{QR}$

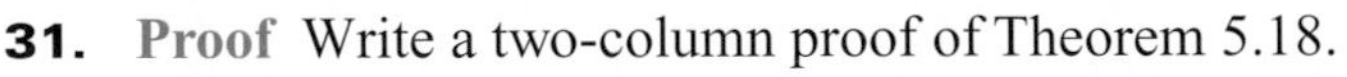

31. **Proof** Write a two-column proof of Theorem 5.18.

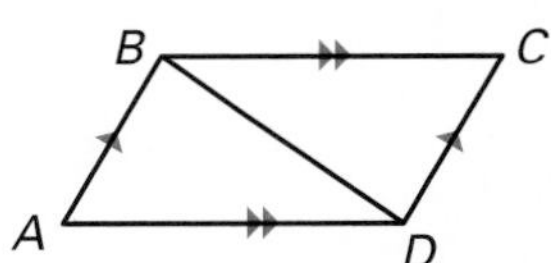

GIVEN: $ABCD$ is a parallelogram.

PROVE: $\overline{AB} \cong \overline{CD}$, $\overline{BC} \cong \overline{AD}$

LESSON 5.8

Exercise Set B

MM1G1e Use the coordinate plane to investigate properties of and verify conjectures related to triangles and quadrilaterals.

MM1G3d Understand, use, and prove properties of and relationships among special quadrilaterals: parallelogram, rectangle, rhombus, square, trapezoid, and kite.

Find the value of each variable in the parallelogram.

1.

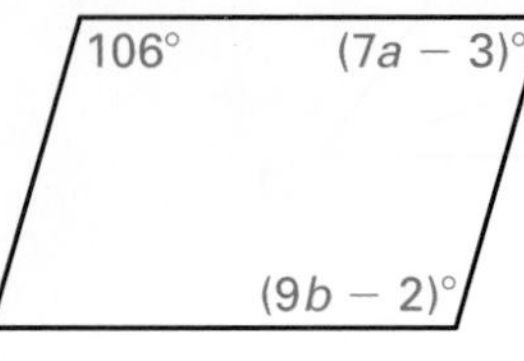

2.

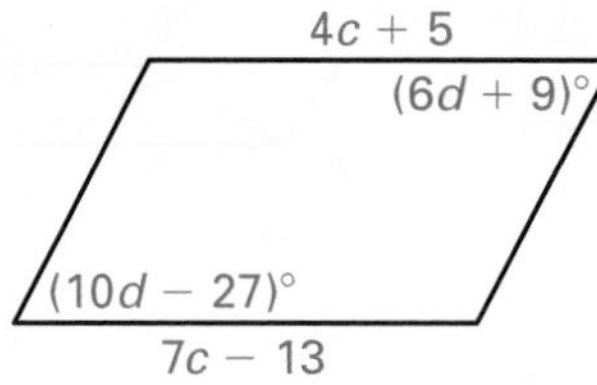

3.

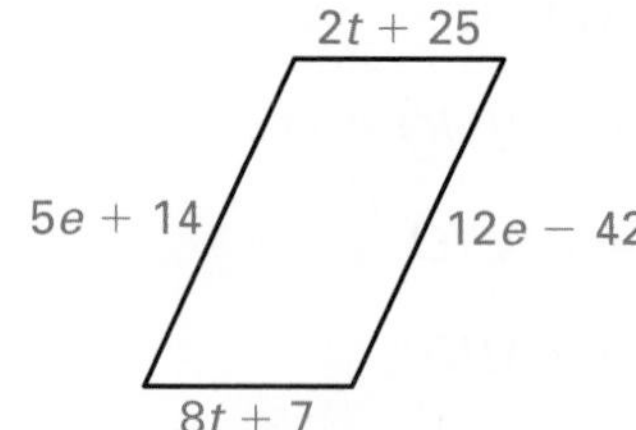

4.

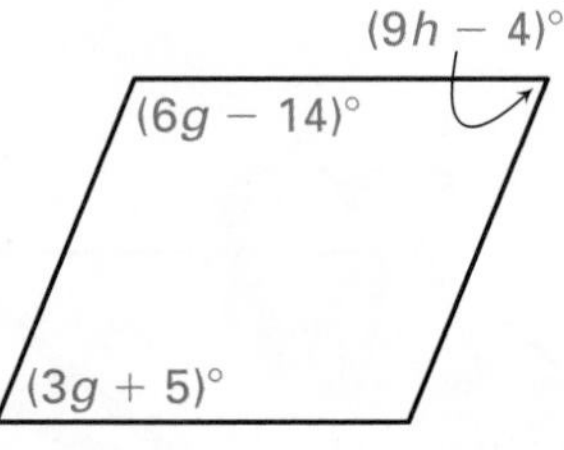

5.

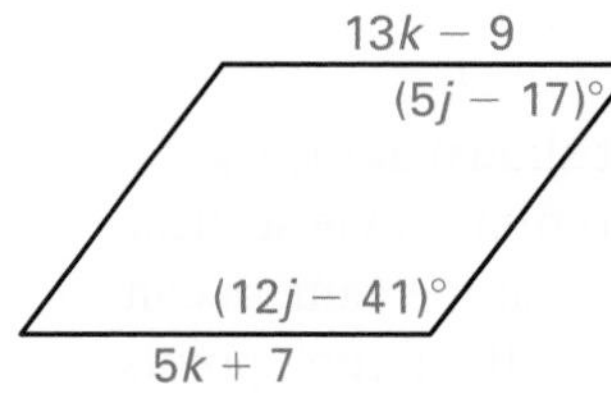

6.

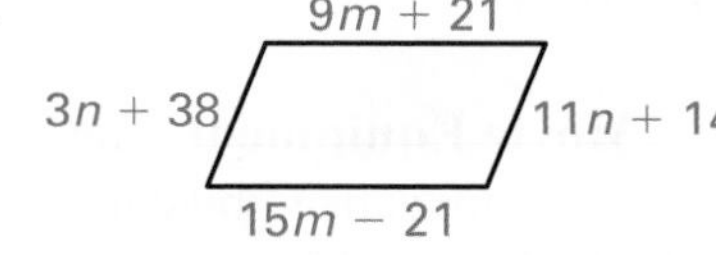

7.

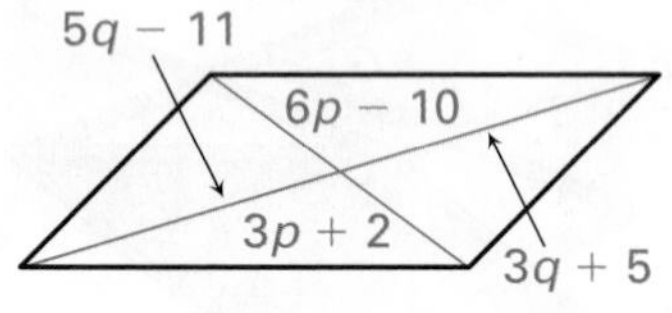

8.

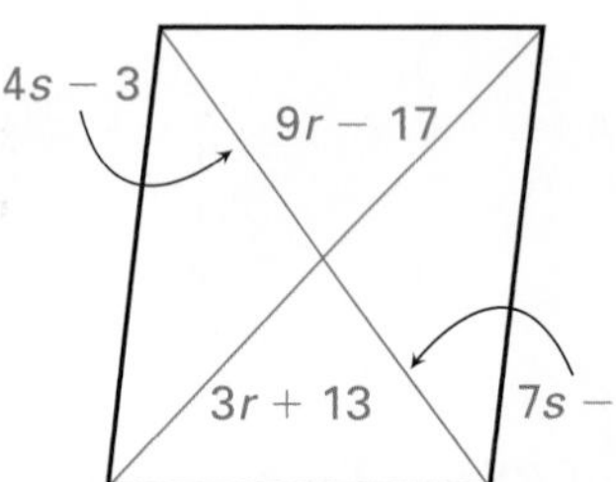

9.

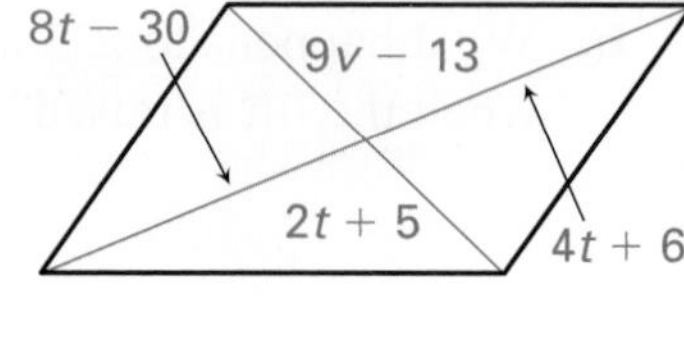

10. The coordinates for ▱*ABCD* are $A(-1, 3)$, $B(4, 2)$, $C(2, -1)$, and $D(-3, 0)$. Plot the points and draw ▱*ABCD* on a coordinate plane. Then draw the diagonals $\overline{AC}$ and $\overline{BD}$. Label the intersection of the diagonals as point *E*. What are the coordinates of point *E*?

Find the indicated measure in ▱*ABCD*. *Explain.*

11. *AE* **12.** *AD*

13. *EB* **14.** *DB*

15. *AB* **16.** Perimeter of △*AEB*

17. $m\angle DBA$ **18.** $m\angle DEC$

19. $m\angle ACD$ **20.** $m\angle CAB$

21. Perimeter of ▱*ABCD*

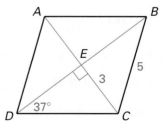

A B E 5 3 D 37° C

UNIT 5

Exercise Set B *(continued)*

22. The measure of one interior angle of a parallelogram is 2.6 times the measure of another angle. Find the measure of each angle.

23. The measure of one interior angle of a parallelogram is 57.8 degrees more than the measure of another angle. Find the measure of each angle.

Use the diagram of ▱*MNOP* at the right.

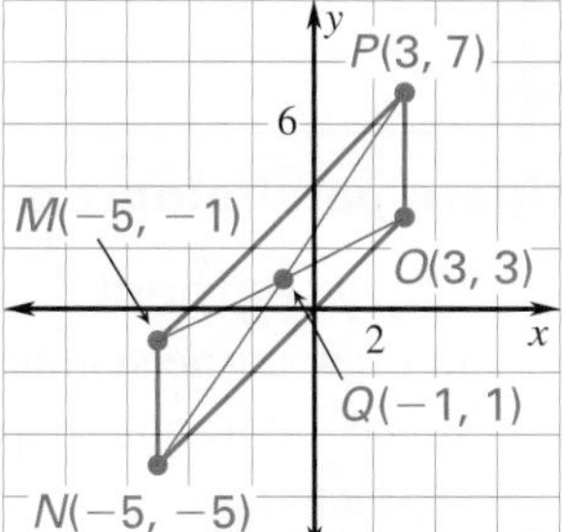

24. Use the Distance Formula to show $\overline{MP} \cong \overline{NO}$.

25. Use the Distance Formula to show $\overline{MN} \cong \overline{PO}$.

26. Find the slope of $\overline{MP}$ and $\overline{NO}$.

27. How do the slopes found in Exercise 26 show that $\overline{MP}$ and $\overline{NO}$ are parallel?

28. Use the Distance Formula to show that the diagonals $\overline{MO}$ and $\overline{NP}$ bisect each other.

29. Copy and complete the proof.

GIVEN: *MATH* is a ▱.
$m\angle MHN = 56°$
$\angle MNT \cong \angle ATN$

PROVE: $m\angle MNH = 56°$

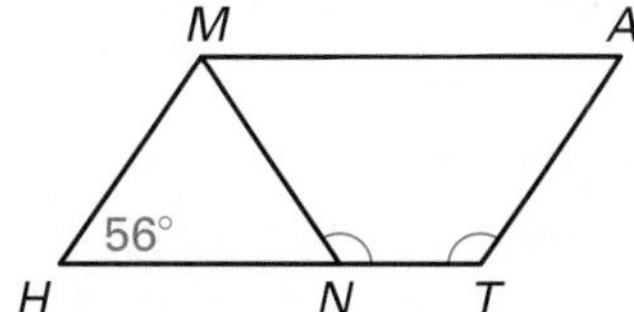

Statements	Reasons
1. *MATH* is a ▱.	1. ?
2. $\angle MHN$ and $\angle ATN$ are supplementary.	2. ?
3. ?	3. Definition of supplementary angles
4. $m\angle MHN = 56°$	4. ?
5. ?	5. Substitution property of equality
6. $m\angle ATN = 124°$	6. ?
7. ?	7. Given
8. $m\angle MNT = m\angle ATN$	8. ?
9. ?	9. Transitive property of equality
10. $m\angle MNT + m\angle MNH = 180°$	10. ?
11. ?	11. Substitution property of equality
12. $m\angle MNH = 56°$	12. ?

Georgia Performance Standards

MM1G3d Understand, use, and prove properties of and relationships among special quadrilaterals: parallelogram, rectangle, rhombus, square, trapezoid, and kite.

Investigating Math Activity

Exploring Parallelograms

Use before Lesson 5.9

Materials **tracing paper and straightedge**

Question

How can you show that a quadrilateral is a parallelogram?

Explore

Investigate parallelograms.

STEP 1 **Copy segment** Use your straightedge to draw a line segment on your paper. Place the tracing paper over the line segment and copy it. Label this segment $\overline{AB}$. Move the tracing paper up and to the right and copy the segment again. Label this segment $\overline{DC}$.

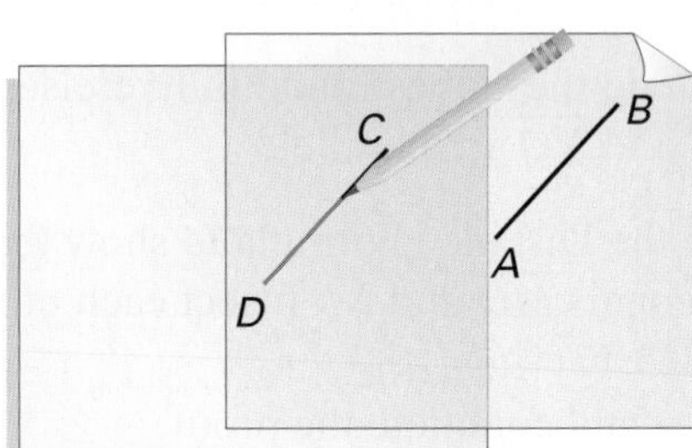

STEP 2 **Complete quadrilateral** Use your straightedge to connect points A and D and points B and C to create a quadrilateral.

STEP 3 **Compare sides** Place a second piece of tracing paper over quadrilateral $ABCD$, and copy $\overline{AD}$. To compare $\overline{AD}$ and $\overline{BC}$, slide the second piece of tracing paper so that $\overline{AD}$ is on top of $\overline{BC}$.

STEP 4 **Compare angles** To compare $\angle A$ and $\angle C$, fold the tracing paper with quadrilateral $ABCD$ so that $\angle A$ is on top of $\angle C$. Unfold the tracing paper. To compare $\angle B$ and $\angle D$, fold the tracing paper so that $\angle B$ is on top of $\angle D$.

STEP 5 **Draw diagonals** Use your straightedge to draw in the diagonals of quadrilateral $ABCD$. Label the point of intersection E.

STEP 6 **Analyze diagonals** To determine whether the diagonals bisect each other, place a third piece of tracing paper on top of quadrilateral $ABCD$ and copy $\overline{BE}$. Slide the third piece of tracing paper so that the copied segment is on top of $\overline{ED}$ and compare their lengths. Repeat this process with the other diagonal.

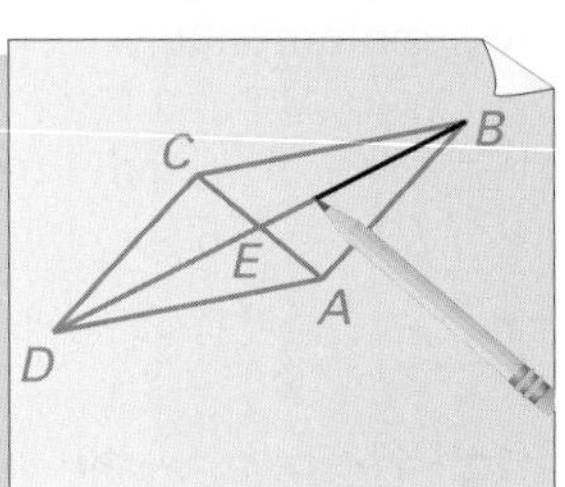

Draw Conclusions

1. **Writing** Is quadrilateral $ABCD$ a parallelogram? *Explain.*
2. **Reasoning** If a quadrilateral has two pairs of opposite congruent sides, is it a parallelogram? *Explain* your answer.
3. Do the diagonals of quadrilateral $ABCD$ bisect each other? *Explain* your answer.

LESSON 5.9

Show That a Quadrilateral is a Parallelogram

Georgia Performance Standards: MM1G1a, MM1G1e, MM1G3d

Goal Use properties to identify parallelograms.

Vocabulary

Theorem 5.22: If both pairs of opposite sides of a quadrilateral are congruent, then the quadrilateral is a parallelogram.

Theorem 5.23: If both pairs of opposite angles of a quadrilateral are congruent, then the quadrilateral is a parallelogram.

Theorem 5.24: If one pair of opposite sides of a quadrilateral are congruent and parallel, then the quadrilateral is a parallelogram.

Theorem 5.25: If the diagonals of a quadrilateral bisect each other, then the quadrilateral is a parallelogram.

Example 1 Identify parallelograms

Explain how you know that quadrilateral *QRST* is a parallelogram.

a. 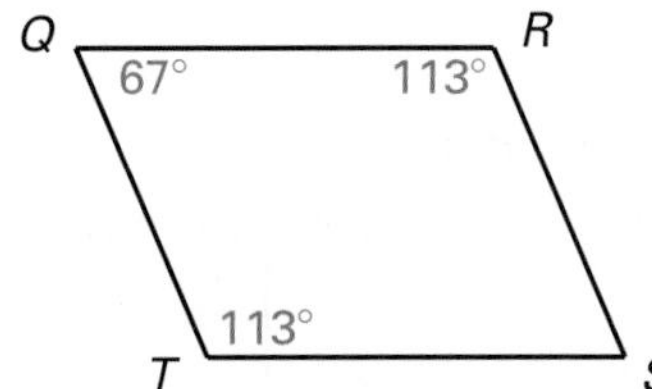

b. 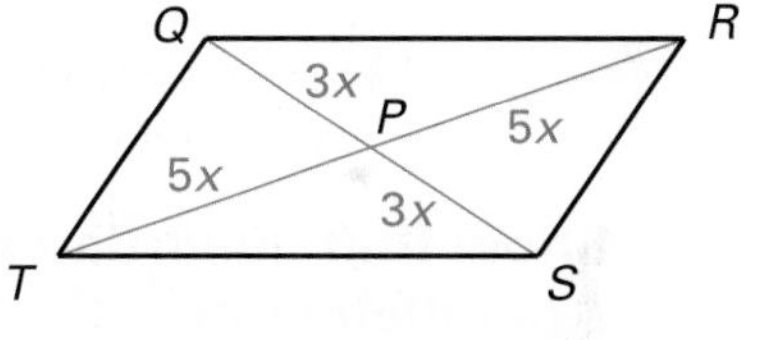

Solution

a. By the Corollary to Theorem 5.16 you know that $m\angle Q + m\angle R + m\angle S + m\angle T = 360°$, so $m\angle S = 67°$. Because both pairs of opposite angles are congruent, then *QRST* is a parallelogram by Theorem 5.23.

b. In the diagram, $QP = PS$ and $RP = PT$. So, the diagonals bisect each other, and *QRST* is a parallelogram by Theorem 5.25.

Guided Practice for Example 1

Which theorem can be used to show that the quadrilateral is a parallelogram?

1. 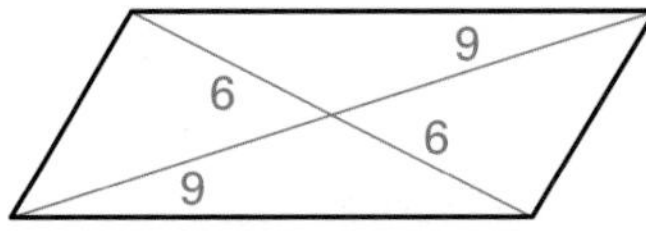

2. 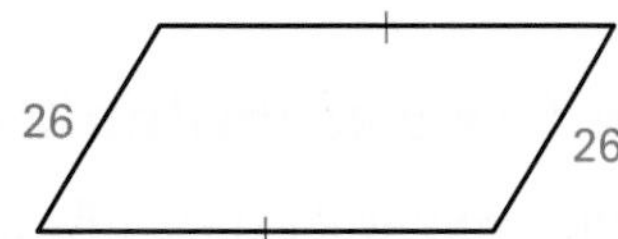

3. 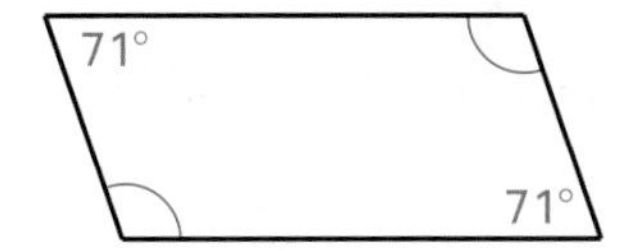

4. 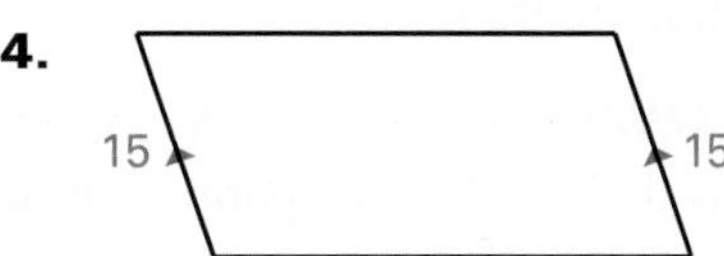

UNIT 5

Georgia Performance Standards

MM1G1a Determine the distance between two points.

MM1G1e Use the coordinate plane to investigate properties of and verify conjectures related to triangles and quadrilaterals.

MM1G3d Understand, use, and prove properties of and relationships among special quadrilaterals: parallelogram, rectangle, rhombus, square, trapezoid, and kite. 

Example 2 Use algebra with parallelograms

For what value of *x* is quadrilateral *FGHJ* a parallelogram?

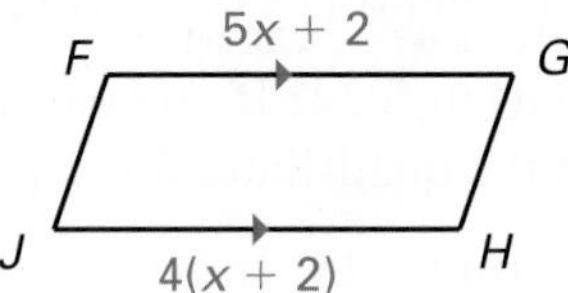

From the diagram, $\overline{FG} \parallel \overline{JH}$. Find x so that $\overline{FG} \cong \overline{JH}$. Then *FGHJ* is a parallelogram by Theorem 5.24.

$FG = JH$	Set the segment lengths equal.
$5x + 2 = 4(x + 2)$	Substitute.
$x = 6$	Solve for x.

When $x = 6$, $FG = 5(6) + 2 = 32$ and $JH = 4(6 + 2) = 32$. So, *FGHJ* is a parallelogram when $x = 6$.

Example 3 Use coordinate geometry

Show that quadrilateral *WXYZ* is a parallelogram.

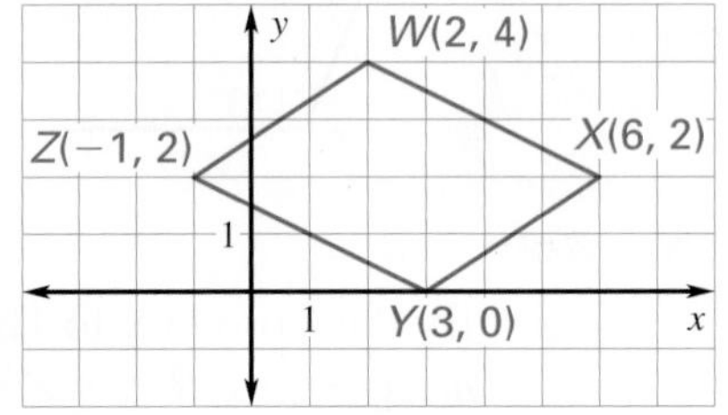

Solution

STEP 1 Use the Distance Formula to show that $\overline{WX}$ and $\overline{YZ}$ are congruent.

$WX = \sqrt{(6 - 2)^2 + (2 - 4)^2} = 2\sqrt{5}$ $\quad YZ = \sqrt{(-1 - 3)^2 + (2 - 0)^2} = 2\sqrt{5}$

Because $WX = YZ = 2\sqrt{5}$, $\overline{WX} \cong \overline{YZ}$.

STEP 2 Use the slope formula to show that $\overline{WX} \parallel \overline{YZ}$.

Slope of $\overline{WX} = \dfrac{2 - 4}{6 - 2} = -\dfrac{1}{2}$ $\quad$ Slope of $\overline{YZ} = \dfrac{2 - 0}{-1 - 3} = -\dfrac{1}{2}$

Because $\overline{WX}$ and $\overline{YZ}$ have the same slope, they are parallel.

$\overline{WX}$ and $\overline{YZ}$ are congruent and parallel. So, *WXYZ* is a parallelogram by Theorem 5.24.

Guided Practice for Examples 2 and 3

5. In the diagram at the right, what value of x makes the quadrilateral a parallelogram?

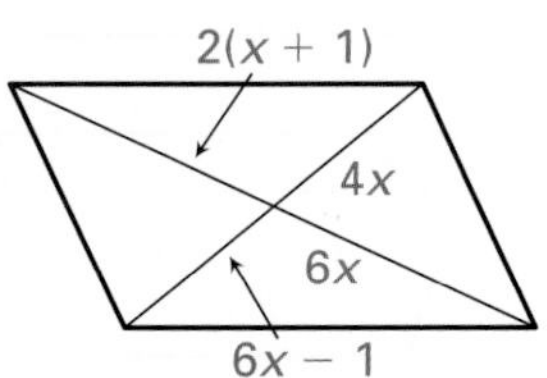

6. The vertices of *LMNO* are $L(-4, 2)$, $M(-5, -2)$, $N(-1, -4)$, and $O(0, 0)$. Show that *LMNO* is a parallelogram.

LESSON 5.9 Exercise Set A

MM1G1a Determine the distance between two points.

MM1G1e Use the coordinate plane to investigate properties of and verify conjectures related to triangles and quadrilaterals.

MM1G3d Understand, use, and prove properties of and relationships among special quadrilaterals: parallelogram, rectangle, rhombus, square, trapezoid, and kite.

What theorem can you use to show that the quadrilateral is a parallelogram?

1.

2.

73
98
98
73

3.

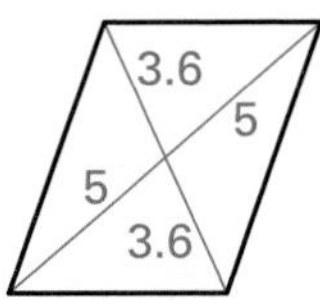

4.

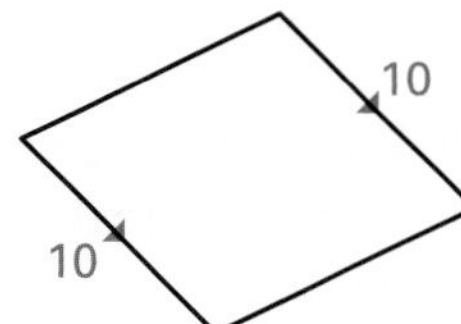

For what value of *x* is the quadrilateral a parallelogram?

5.

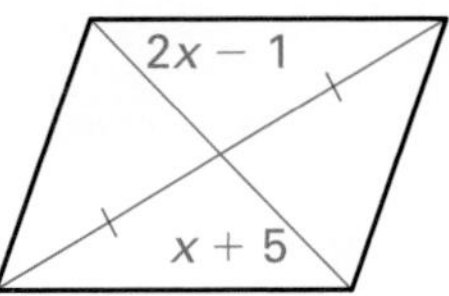

6.

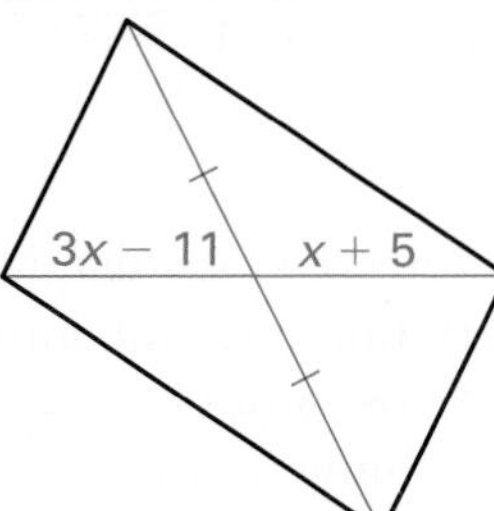

7.

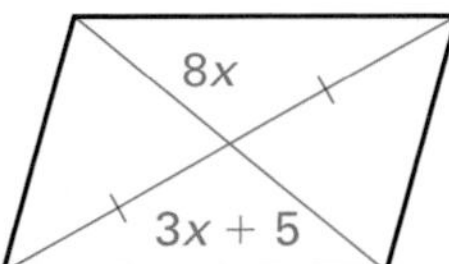

8.

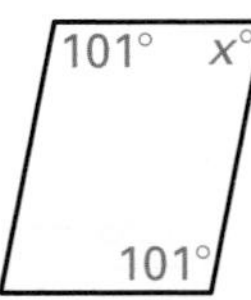

9.

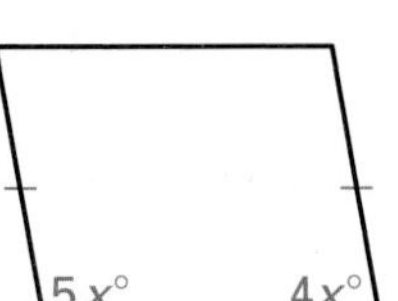

10.

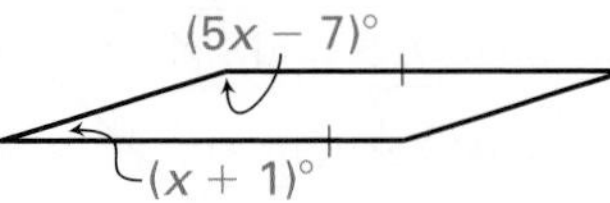

11.

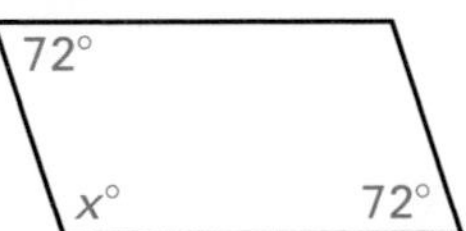

12.

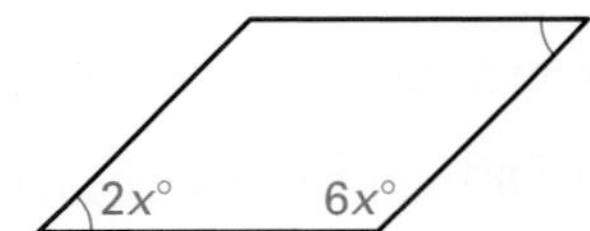

Exercise Set A *(continued)*

The vertices of quadrilateral *ABCD* are given. Draw *ABCD* in a coordinate plane and show that it is a parallelogram.

13. $A(-2, -3)$, $B(0, 4)$, $C(6, 4)$, $D(4, -3)$

14. $A(-3, -4)$, $B(-1, 2)$, $C(7, 0)$, $D(5, -6)$

Describe **how to prove that *ABCD* is a parallelogram.**

15.

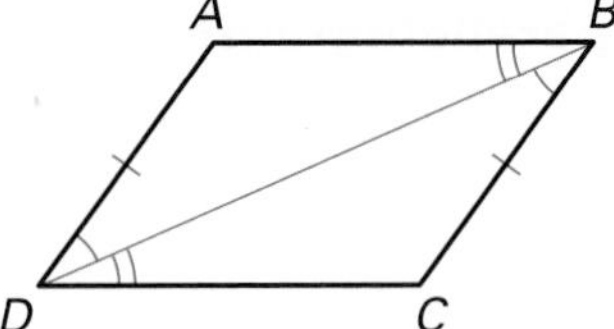

16.

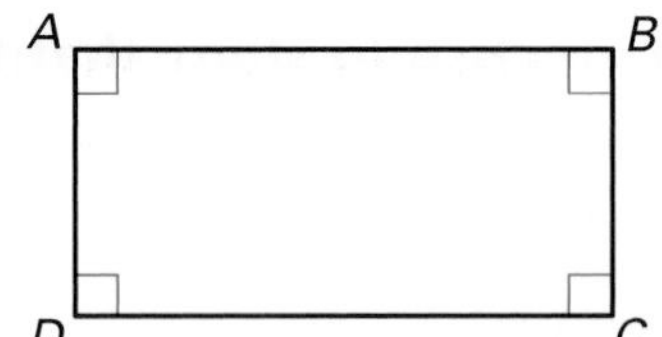

17. Three vertices of $\square ABCD$ are $A(-1, 4)$, $B(4, 4)$, and $C(11, -3)$. Find the coordinates of point D.

18. **History** The diagram shows a battering ram which was used in ancient times to break through walls. A log is suspended on ropes of equal length ($\overline{GF}$ and $\overline{HJ}$). The log swings, causing quadrilateral $FGHJ$ to shift. In the diagram, $\overline{GH} \cong \overline{FJ}$ and $\overline{GH}$ is parallel to the ground. Identify $FGHJ$. *Explain.*

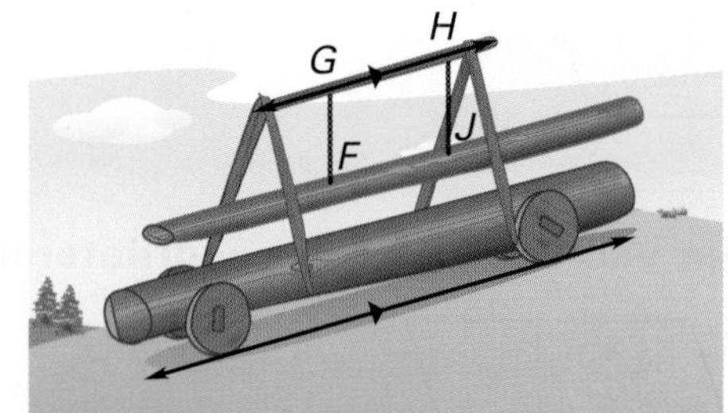

19. **Multiple Representations** Use the diagram of $PQRS$ with the auxiliary line segment drawn. Copy and complete the flow proof of Theorem 5.24. Then write it as a two-column proof.

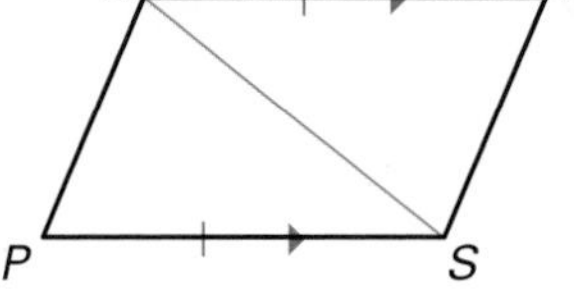

GIVEN: $\overline{QR} \parallel \overline{PS}$, $\overline{QR} \cong \overline{PS}$

PROVE: $PQRS$ is a parallelogram.

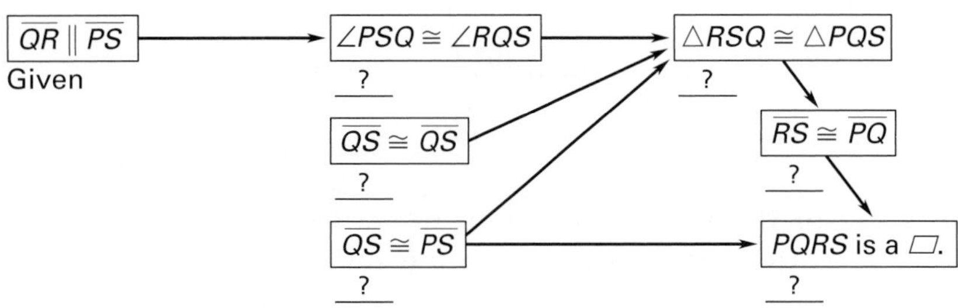

20. **Proof** Prove Theorem 5.25.

GIVEN: Diagonals $\overline{AC}$ and $\overline{CD}$ bisect each other.

PROVE: $ABCD$ is a parallelogram.

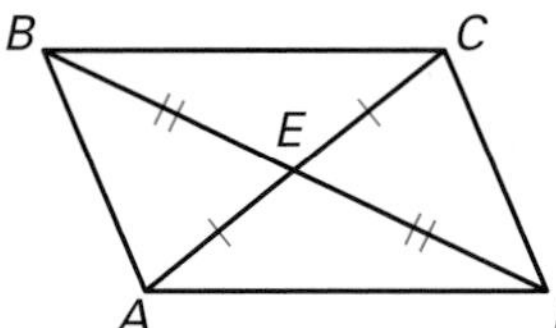

UNIT 5

LESSON 5.9

Exercise Set B

MM1G1a Determine the distance between two points.

MM1G1e Use the coordinate plane to investigate properties of and verify conjectures related to triangles and quadrilaterals.

MM1G3d Understand, use, and prove properties of and relationships among special quadrilaterals: parallelogram, rectangle, rhombus, square, trapezoid, and kite.

For what value of *x* is the quadrilateral a parallelogram?

1. 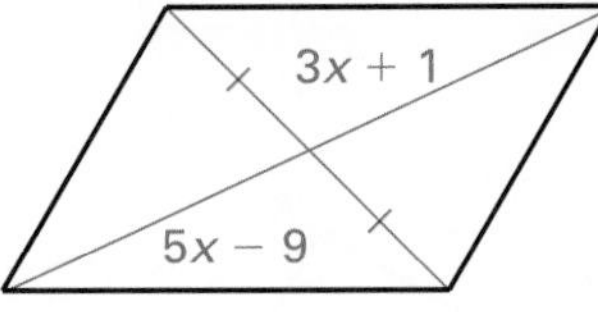

2. 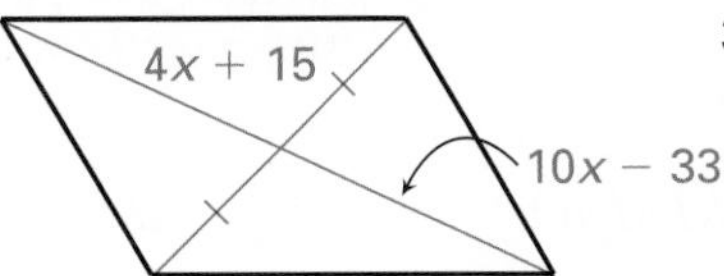

3. 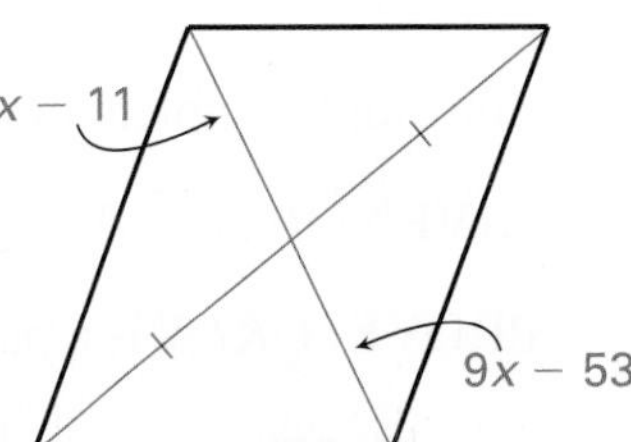

4. 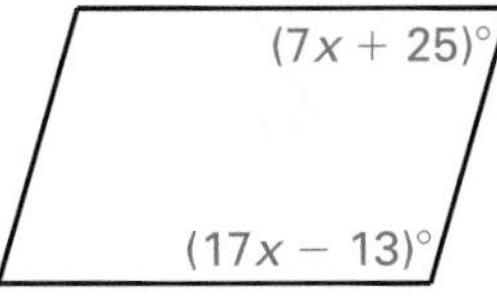

5. 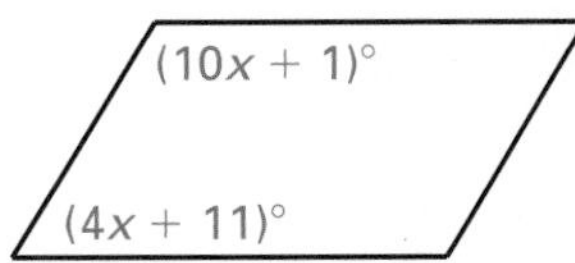

6. 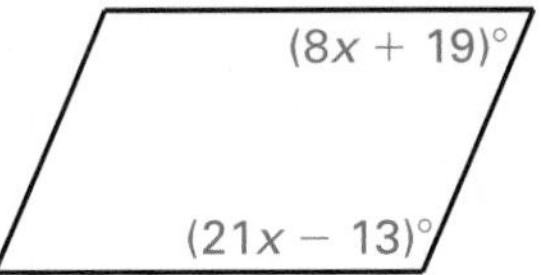

Decide whether you are given enough information to determine that the quadrilateral is a parallelogram.

7. Opposite sides are parallel.
8. Opposite sides are congruent.
9. Two pairs of consecutive sides are congruent.
10. Two pairs of consecutive angles are congruent.
11. Diagonals are congruent.
12. Diagonals bisect each other.
13. All four sides are congruent.
14. Consecutive angles are supplementary.

Prove that the points represent the vertices of a parallelogram. Use the method indicated.

15. $A(-4, 7)$, $B(3, 0)$, $C(2, -5)$, $D(-5, 2)$; Both pairs of opposite sides are parallel.
16. $A(-2, 8)$, $B(2, 7)$, $C(5, 1)$, $D(1, 2)$; Both pairs of opposite sides are congruent.

Find all the possible coordinates for the fourth vertex of a parallelogram with the given vertices. Then draw the parallelogram on a graph.

17. $(4, -1)$, $(-4, 1)$, $(0, 8)$
18. $(3, -4)$, $(-2, -1)$, $(1, 2)$

UNIT 5

Exercise Set B *(continued)*

19. **Error Analysis** A student claims that because two pairs of sides are congruent, quadrilateral *JKLM* shown at the right is a parallelogram. *Describe* the student's error.

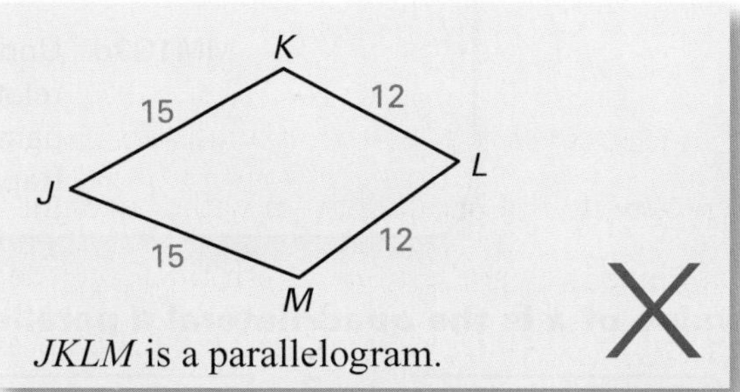

20. Copy and complete the proof.

GIVEN: Regular hexagon *JKLMNO*

PROVE: *OKLN* is a parallelogram.

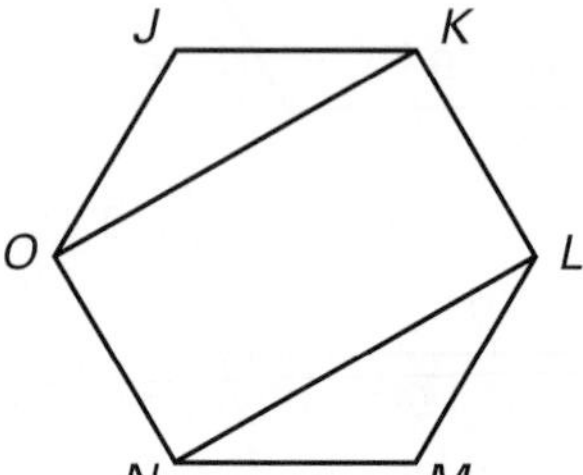

Statements	Reasons
1. ?	1. Given
2. $\overline{JO} \cong \overline{NM}$ $\overline{JK} \cong \overline{ML}$ $\angle J \cong \angle M$	2. ?
3. ?	3. SAS Congruence Postulate
4. $\overline{OK} \cong \overline{NL}$	4. ?
5. ?	5. Definition of regular polygon
6. *OKLN* is a ▱.	6. ?

21. **Proof** Write a two-column proof.

GIVEN: *VWKJ* and *SJRU* are parallelograms.

PROVE: $\angle W \cong \angle U$

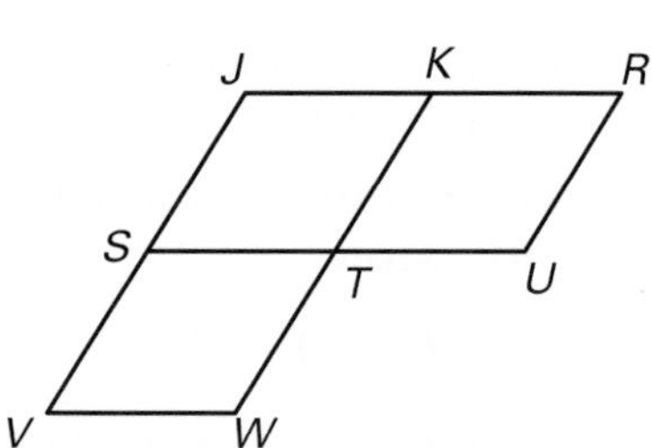

22. **Proof** Write a paragraph proof.

GIVEN: *ABCD* is a ▱.
E is the midpoint of $\overline{AD}$.
F is the midpoint of $\overline{BC}$.

PROVE: Quadrilateral *ABFE* is a parallelogram.

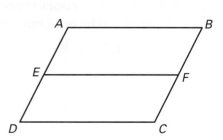

A B E F D C

UNIT 5

LESSON 5.10

Properties of Rhombuses, Rectangles, and Squares

Georgia Performance Standards: MM1G3d

Goal Use properties of rhombuses, rectangles, and squares.

Vocabulary

A **rhombus** is a parallelogram with four congruent sides.

A **rectangle** is a parallelogram with four right angles.

A **square** is a parallelogram with four congruent sides and four right angles.

Rhombus Corollary: A quadrilateral is a rhombus if and only if it has four congruent sides.

Rectangle Corollary: A quadrilateral is a rectangle if and only if it has four right angles.

Square Corollary: A quadrilateral is a square if and only if it is a rhombus and a rectangle.

Theorem 5.26: A parallelogram is a rhombus if and only if its diagonals are perpendicular.

Theorem 5.27: A parallelogram is a rhombus if and only if each diagonal bisects a pair of opposite angles.

Theorem 5.28: A parallelogram is a rectangle if and only if its diagonals are congruent.

UNIT 5

Example 1 Use properties of special quadrilaterals

For any rhombus *ABCD*, decide whether the statement is *always*, *sometimes*, or *never* true. Draw a sketch and explain your reasoning.

a. $AB > BC$

b. $m\angle A > m\angle B$

Solution

a. By definition, a rhombus is a parallelogram with four congruent sides. So, $AB = BC$. The statement is *never* true.

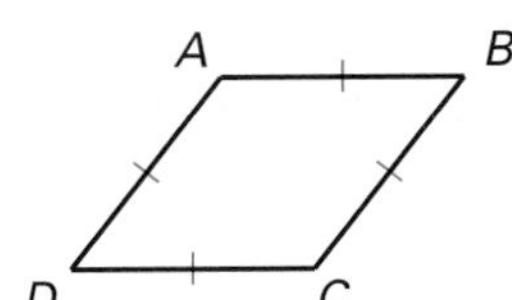

b. By definition, a rhombus is a parallelogram. By Theorem 5.19, opposite angles of a parallelogram are congruent. Because $\angle A$ and $\angle B$ are not opposite angles, they are not necessarily congruent, and $m\angle A$ could be greater than $m\angle B$. If rhombus $ABCD$ is a square, then $m\angle A = m\angle B = 90°$. So, the statement is *sometimes* true.

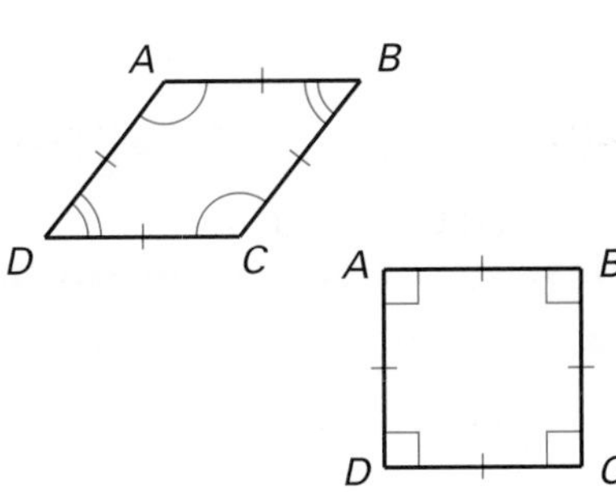

Georgia Performance Standards

MM1G3d Understand, use, and prove properties of and relationships among special quadrilaterals: parallelogram, rectangle, rhombus, square, trapezoid, and kite.

Guided Practice for Example 1

For any rhombus *DEFG*, decide whether the statement is *always*, *sometimes*, or *never* true. Draw a sketch and explain your reasoning.

1. $\angle DEG \cong \angle FEG$ **2.** $\angle DEG \cong \angle EFD$ **3.** $\overline{DG} \cong \overline{GF}$

Example 2 Classify special quadrilaterals

Classify the special quadrilateral. Explain your reasoning.

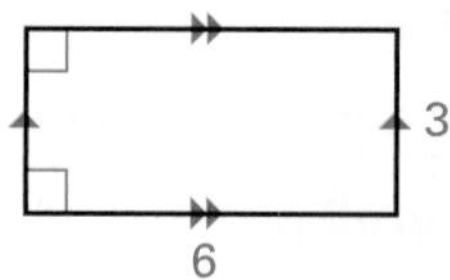

Solution

The quadrilateral is a parallelogram. By Theorem 5.19, opposite angles of a parallelogram are congruent, so all four angles of the quadrilateral are right angles. By the Rectangle Corollary, the quadrilateral is a rectangle. Because the four sides are not congruent, the rectangle is not a square.

Example 3 List properties of special parallelograms

Sketch rhombus *ABCD*. List everything you know about it.

Solution

By definition, you need to draw a figure with the following properties:

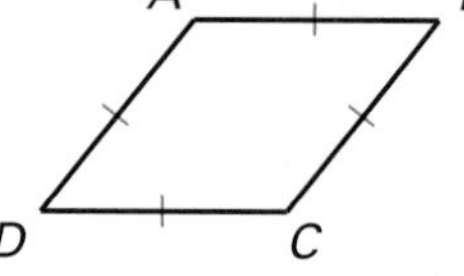

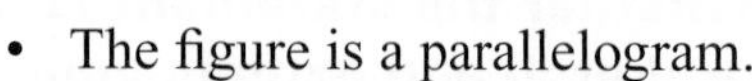

- The figure is a parallelogram.

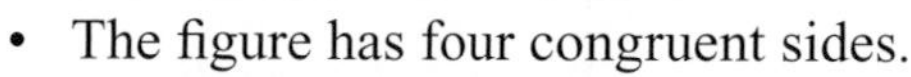

- The figure has four congruent sides.

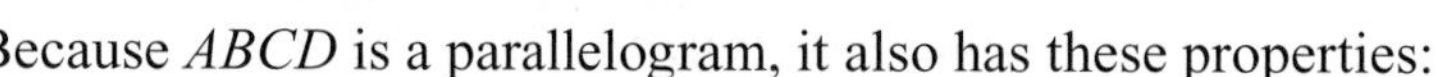

Because *ABCD* is a parallelogram, it also has these properties:

- Opposite sides are parallel and congruent.
- Opposite angles are congruent.
- Consecutive angles are supplementary.
- Diagonals bisect each other.

By Theorem 5.26, the diagonals of *ABCD* are also perpendicular.

Guided Practice for Examples 2 and 3

Classify the special quadrilateral. *Explain* your reasoning.

4.

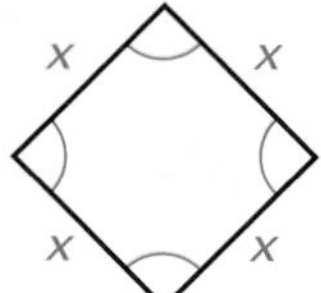

5.

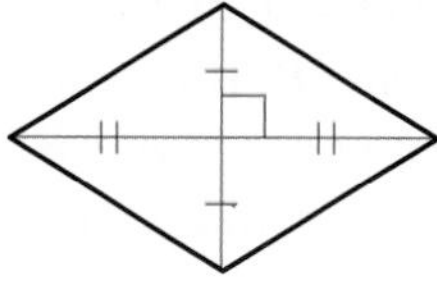

6. Sketch square *ABCD*. List everything you know about it.

LESSON 5.10 **Exercise Set A**

MM1G3d Understand, use, and prove properties of and relationships among special quadrilaterals: parallelogram, rectangle, rhombus, square, trapezoid, and kite.

For any rhombus *ABCD*, decide whether the statement is *always* or *sometimes* true. Draw a diagram and explain your reasoning.

1. $\angle ABC \cong \angle CDA$

2. $\overline{CA} \cong \overline{DB}$

For any rectangle *FGHJ*, decide whether the statement is *always* or *sometimes* true. Draw a diagram and explain your reasoning.

3. $\angle F \cong \angle H$

4. $\overline{GH} \cong \overline{HJ}$

Classify the quadrilateral. *Explain* your reasoning.

5.

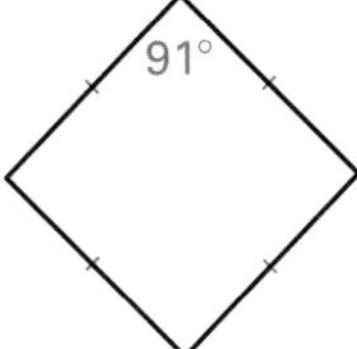

6.

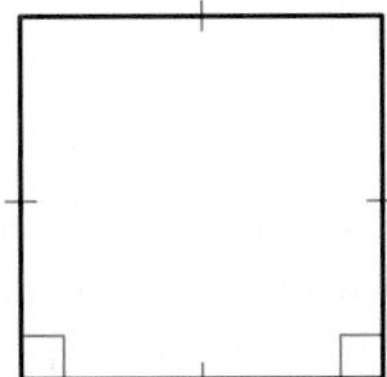

Name each quadrilateral—*parallelogram, rectangle, rhombus,* and *square*—for which the statement is true.

7. It is equilateral.

8. The diagonals are congruent.

9. It can contain obtuse angles.

10. It contains no acute angles.

11. It is equiangular.

12. The diagonals are perpendicular.

13. The diagonals bisect each other.

14. It is equiangular and equilateral.

Classify the special quadrilateral. *Explain* your reasoning. Then find the values of *x* and *y*.

15.

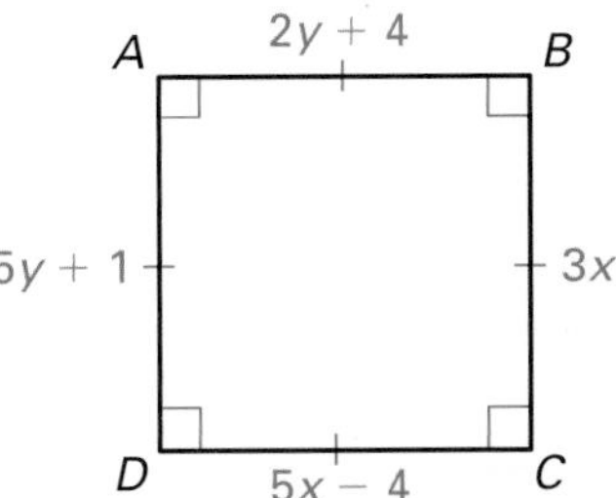

16.

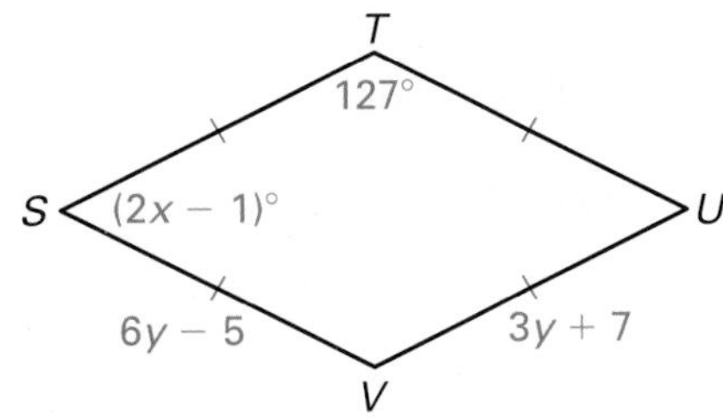

The diagonals of rhombus *PQRS* intersect at *T*. Given that $m\angle RPS = 30°$ and $RT = 6$, find the indicated measure.

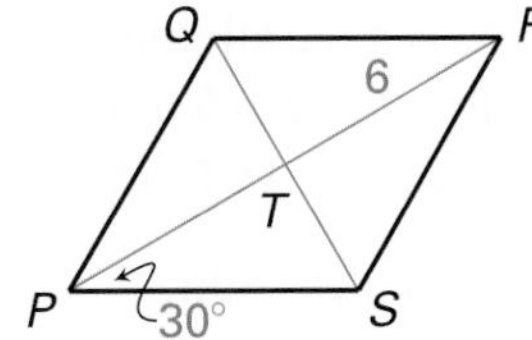

17. $m\angle QPR$

18. $m\angle QTP$

19. RP

20. QT

UNIT 5

Exercise Set A *(continued)*

The diagonals of rectangle *WXYZ* intersect at *P*. Given that m∠ *YXZ* = 50° and *XZ* = 12, find the indicated measure.

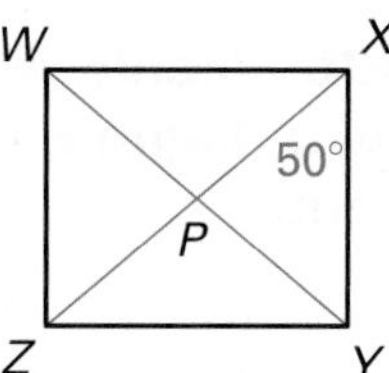

21. $m\angle WXZ$ **22.** $m\angle WPX$

23. PY **24.** WX

The diagonals of square *DEFG* intersect at *H*. Given that *EH* = 5, find the indicated measure.

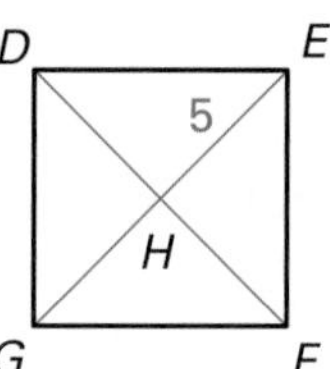

25. $m\angle GHF$ **26.** $m\angle DGH$

27. HF **28.** DE

29. **Windows** In preparation for a storm, a window is protected by nailing boards along its diagonals. The lengths of the boards are the same. Can you conclude that the window is square? *Explain.*

30. **Clothing** The side view of a wooden clothes dryer is shown at the right. Measurements shown are in inches.

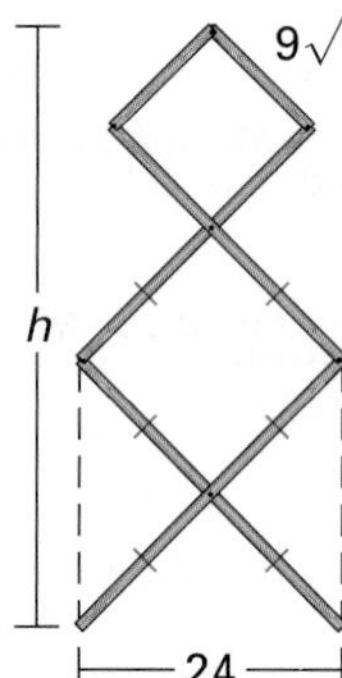

a. The uppermost quadrilateral is a square. Classify the quadrilateral below the square. *Explain* your reasoning.

b. Find the height *h* of the clothes dryer.

31. **Proof** The diagonals of rhombus *ABCD* form several triangles. Using a two-column proof, prove that $\triangle BFA \cong \triangle DFC$.

GIVEN: *ABCD* is a rhombus.

PROVE: $\triangle BFA \cong \triangle DFC$

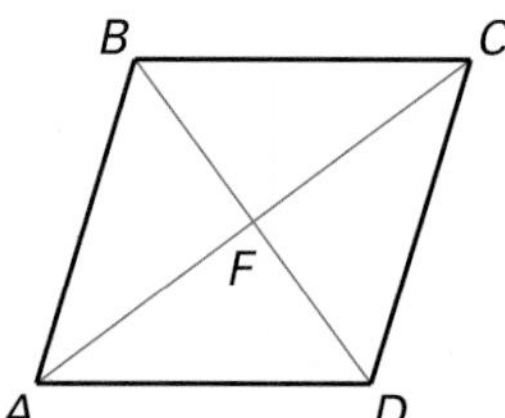

32. **Proof** Write a two-column proof for one part of Theorem 5.27.

GIVEN: *ABCD* is a parallelogram.
$\overline{AC}$ bisects $\angle DAB$ and $\angle BCD$.
$\overline{DB}$ bisects $\angle ADC$ and $\angle CBA$.

PROVE: *ABCD* is a rhombus.

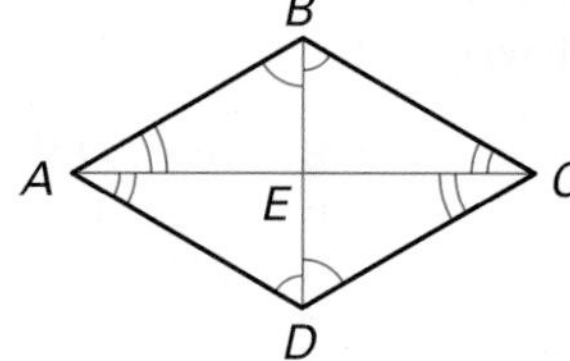

LESSON 5.10 **Exercise Set B**

MM1G3d Understand, use, and prove properties of and relationships among special quadrilaterals: parallelogram, rectangle, rhombus, square, trapezoid, and kite.

Decide whether the statement is *true* or *false*. Decide whether the converse is *true* or *false*. If both statements are *true*, write a biconditional statement.

1. If a quadrilateral is a rectangle, then it is a parallelogram.
2. If a quadrilateral is a parallelogram, then it is a rhombus.
3. If a quadrilateral is a square, then it is a rhombus.
4. If a quadrilateral is a rectangle, then it is a rhombus.
5. If a rhombus is a square, then it is a rectangle.

In the diagram shown, *BDEG* is a rectangle and *ABCD* is a rhombus. Find the measure of the indicated angle.

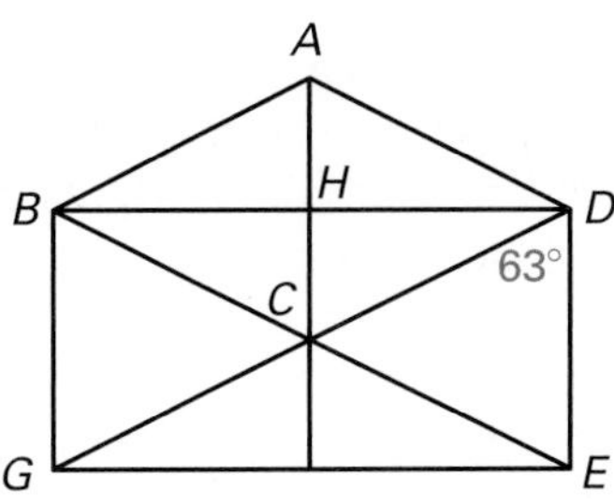

6. $\angle GDB$
7. $\angle ABC$
8. $\angle DAB$
9. $\angle BCG$
10. $\angle GCE$
11. $\angle DEG$
12. $\angle AHB$
13. $\angle DGB$

Find the length or angle measure.

14. *WXYZ* is a square.
$WX = 1 - 10x$
$YZ = 14 + 3x$
$XY = \underline{\ ?\ }$

15. *WXYZ* is a rhombus.
$m\angle X = 24(10 - x)°$
$m\angle Z = 6(x + 15)°$
$m\angle Y = \underline{\ ?\ }$

16. *WXYZ* is a rectangle.
Perimeter of $\triangle XYZ = 24$
$XZ = 13 - x$
$XY + YZ = 5x - 1$
$WY = \underline{\ ?\ }$

Classify the special quadrilateral. *Explain* your reasoning. Then find the values of *x* and *y*.

17.

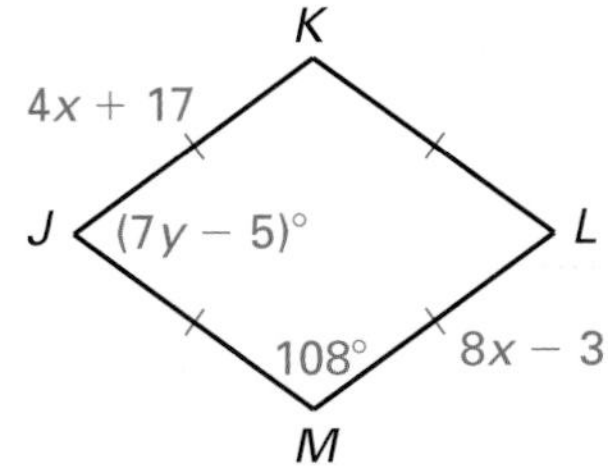

18.

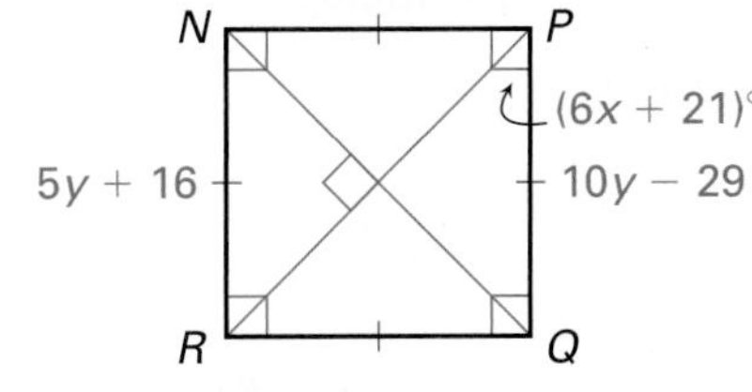

The diagonals of rhombus *RSTV* intersect at *U*. Given that $m\angle URS = 71°$ and $RV = 44$, find the indicated measure.

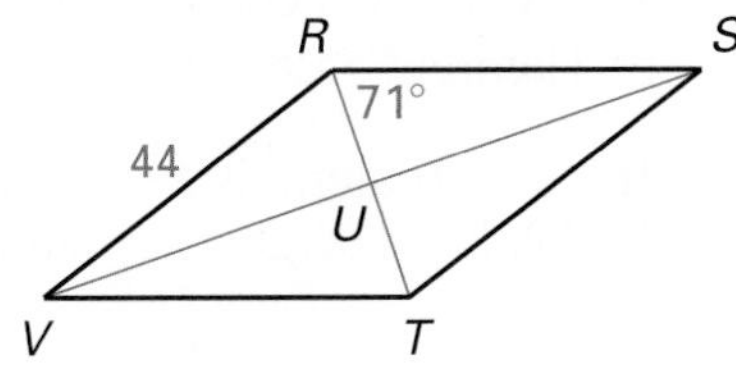

19. $m\angle URV$
20. $m\angle RVT$

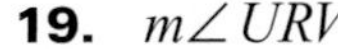

21. RT
22. SU

Exercise Set B *(continued)*

The diagonals of rectangle *WXYZ* intersect at *O*. Given that $m\angle XYW = 56°$ and $WY = 33$, find the indicated measure.

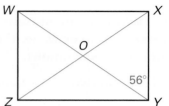

23. $m\angle XWO$ **24.** $m\angle ZOY$

25. XO **26.** WZ

27. Copy and complete the proof.

GIVEN: *WHAT* is a parallelogram.
DART is a rhombus.

PROVE: *WHAT* is a rectangle.

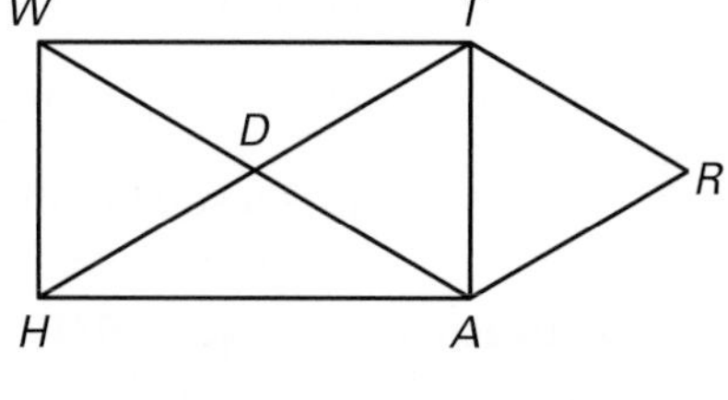

Statements	Reasons
1. *WHAT* is a ▱.	**1.** ?
2. $\overline{WD} \cong \overline{DA}$	**2.** ?
3. ?	**3.** Diagonals of ▱ bisect each other.
4. ?	**4.** Given
5. $\overline{DT} \cong \overline{DA}$	**5.** ?
6. $\overline{WD} \cong \overline{HD} \cong \overline{DA} \cong \overline{DT}$	**6.** ?
7. ?	**7.** Segment Addition Postulate
8. ?	**8.** Substitution
9. *WHAT* is a rectangle.	**9.** ?

28. **Proof** Write a two-column or paragraph proof.

GIVEN: $\triangle GEC \cong \triangle GHX$
GEBH is a parallelogram.

PROVE: *GEBH* is a rhombus.

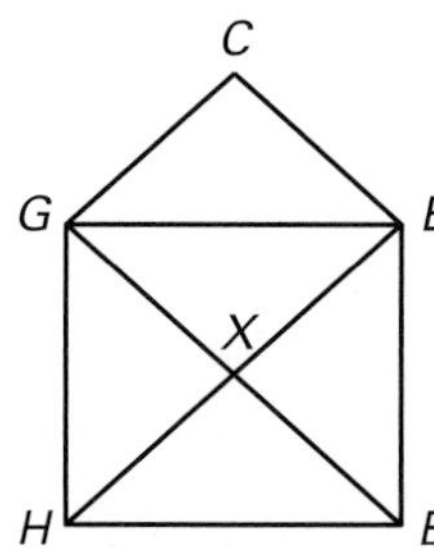

29. **Proof** Write a coordinate proof of the following statement, which is part of Theorem 5.28.

If a quadrilateral is a rectangle, then its diagonals are congruent.

LESSON 5.11

Use Properties of Trapezoids and Kites

Georgia Performance Standards: MM1G1e, MM1G3d

Goal Use properties of trapezoids and kites.

Vocabulary

A **trapezoid** is a quadrilateral with exactly one pair of parallel sides. The parallel sides are the **bases.** For each of the bases of a trapezoid, there is a pair of **base angles,** which are the two angles that have that base as a side.

The nonparallel sides of a trapezoid are the **legs** of the trapezoid. If the legs of a trapezoid are congruent, then the trapezoid is an **isosceles trapezoid.** The **midsegment of a trapezoid** is the segment that connects the midpoints of its legs.

A **kite** is a quadrilateral that has two pairs of consecutive congruent sides, but opposite sides are not congruent.

Theorem 5.29: If a trapezoid is isosceles, then each pair of base angles is congruent.

Theorem 5.30: If a trapezoid has a pair of congruent base angles, then it is an isosceles trapezoid.

Theorem 5.31: A trapezoid is isosceles if and only if its diagonals are congruent.

Theorem 5.32 Midsegment Theorem for Trapezoids: The midsegment of a trapezoid is parallel to each base and its length is one half the sum of the lengths of the bases.

Theorem 5.33: If a quadrilateral is a kite, then its diagonals are perpendicular.

Theorem 5.34: If a quadrilateral is a kite, then exactly one pair of opposite angles are congruent.

Example 1 Use a coordinate plane

Show that *ABCD* is a trapezoid.

Solution

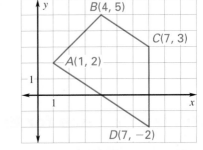

Slope of $\overline{BC} = \frac{3-5}{7-4} = -\frac{2}{3}$

Slope of $\overline{AD} = \frac{-2-2}{7-1} = -\frac{2}{3}$

Slope of $\overline{AB} = \frac{5-2}{4-1} = 1$

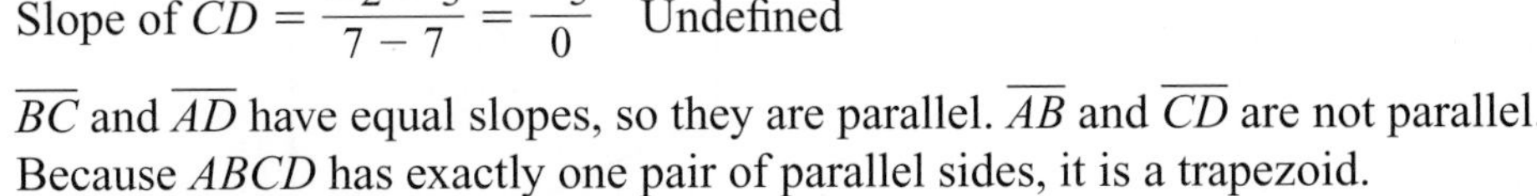

Slope of $\overline{CD} = \frac{-2-3}{7-7} = \frac{-5}{0}$ Undefined

$\overline{BC}$ and $\overline{AD}$ have equal slopes, so they are parallel. $\overline{AB}$ and $\overline{CD}$ are not parallel. Because *ABCD* has exactly one pair of parallel sides, it is a trapezoid.

Guided Practice for Example 1

1. The vertices of *ABCD* are $A(-5, 6)$, $B(1, 3)$, $C(0, 0)$, and $D(-7, 0)$. Show that *ABCD* is a trapezoid.

Georgia Performance Standards

MM1G1e Use the coordinate plane to investigate properties of and verify conjectures related to triangles and quadrilaterals. 

MM1G3d Understand, use, and prove properties of and relationships among special quadrilaterals: parallelogram, rectangle, rhombus, square, trapezoid, and kite. 

Example 2 Use properties of trapezoids

In the diagram, *ABCD* is an isosceles trapezoid and $\overline{PQ}$ is the midsegment.

a. Find $m\angle B$. **b.** Find PQ.

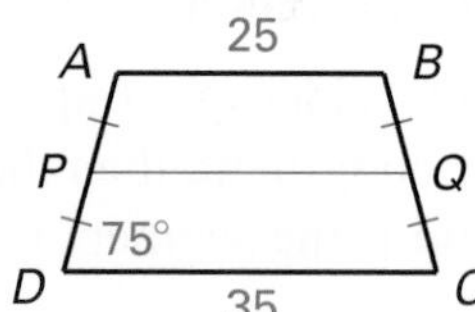

Solution

a. Because $\angle D$ and $\angle A$ are consecutive interior angles formed by $\overleftrightarrow{AD}$ intersecting two parallel lines, they are supplementary. So, $m\angle A = 180° - 75° = 105°$. By Theorem 5.29, $\angle A \cong \angle B$. So, $m\angle B = 105°$.

b. By Theorem 5.32, $PQ = \frac{1}{2}(AB + CD) = \frac{1}{2}(25 + 35) = \frac{1}{2}(60) = 30$.

Example 3 Use properties of kites

In the diagram, *PQRS* is a kite. Find $m\angle Q$.

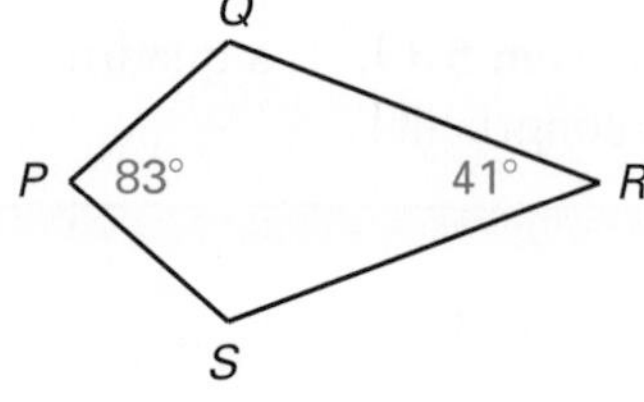

Solution

By Theorem 5.34, *PQRS* has exactly one pair of congruent opposite angles. Because $\angle P \ncong \angle R$, $\angle Q$ and $\angle S$ must be congruent. So, $m\angle Q = m\angle S$.

$m\angle Q + m\angle S + 83° + 41° = 360°$	Corollary to Theorem 5.16
$m\angle Q + m\angle Q + 83° + 41° = 360°$	Substitute $m\angle Q$ for $m\angle S$.
$2(m\angle Q) + 124° = 360°$	Combine like terms.
$m\angle Q = 118°$	Solve for $m\angle Q$.

Guided Practice for Examples 2 and 3

Find the value of *x*.

2.

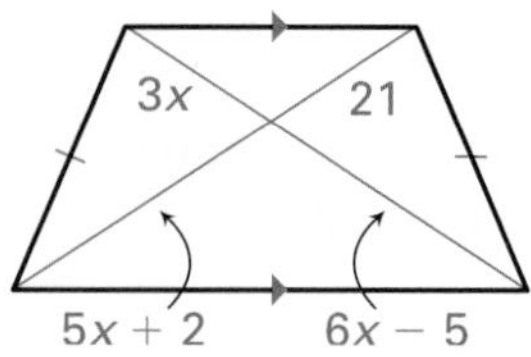

3.

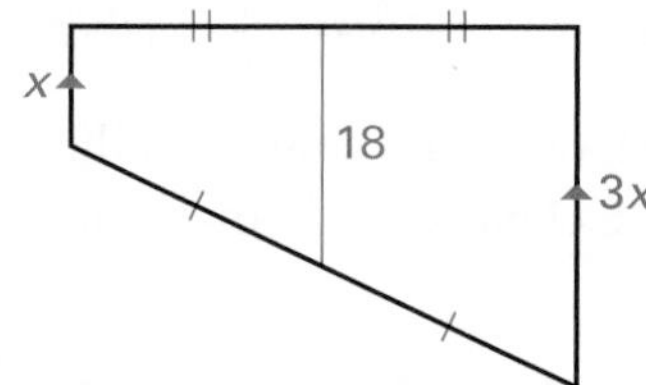

4. In a kite, the measures of the angles are $6x°$, $24°$, $84°$, and $126°$. Find the value of x. What are the measures of the angles that are congruent?

UNIT 5

LESSON 5.11

Exercise Set A

MM1G1e Use the coordinate plane to investigate properties of and verify conjectures related to triangles and quadrilaterals.

MM1G3d Understand, use, and prove properties of and relationships among special quadrilaterals: parallelogram, rectangle, rhombus, square, trapezoid, and kite.

Points *A, B, C,* and *D* are the vertices of a quadrilateral. Determine whether *ABCD* is a trapezoid.

1. $A(-2, 3), B(3, 3), C(-1, -2), D(2, -2)$

2. $A(-3, 2), B(3, 0), C(4, 3), D(-2, 5)$

Find $m\angle F$, $m\angle G$, and $m\angle H$.

3.

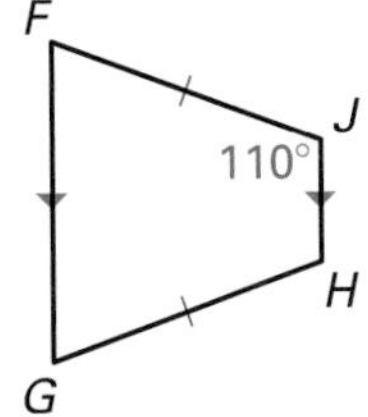

4.

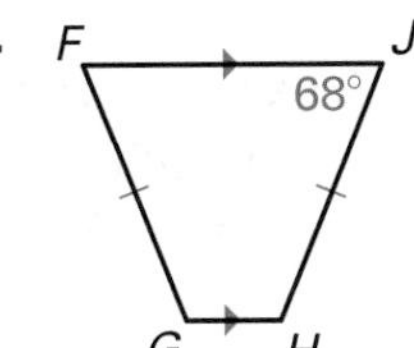

Find the length of the midsegment of the trapezoid.

5.

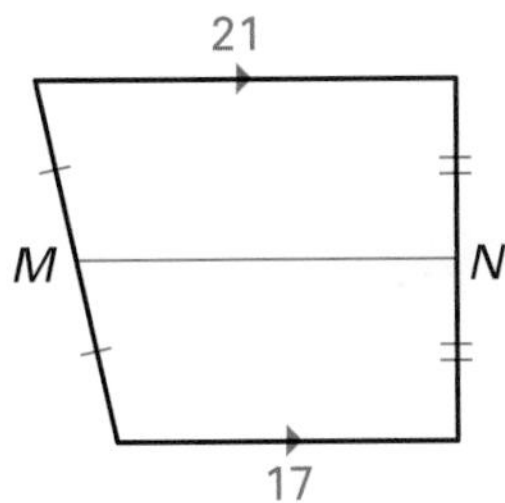

6.

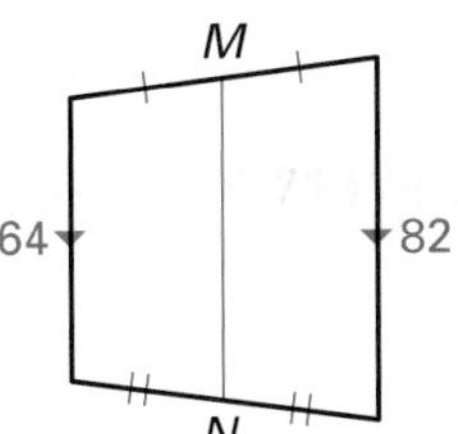

***JKLM* is a kite. Find $m\angle K$.**

7.

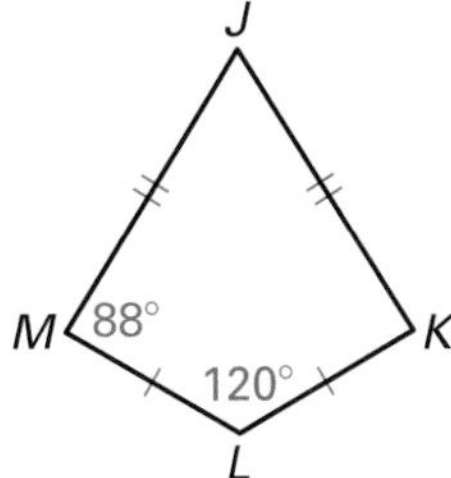

8.

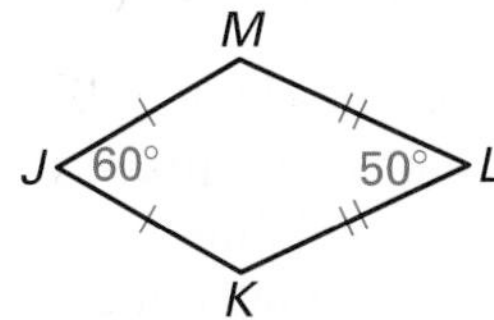

Use Theorem 5.33 and the Pythagorean Theorem to find the side lengths of the kite. Write the lengths in simplest radical form.

9.

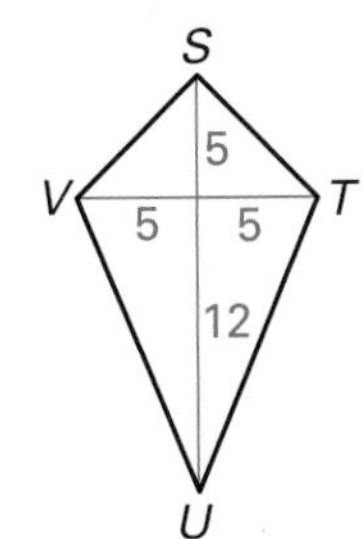

10.

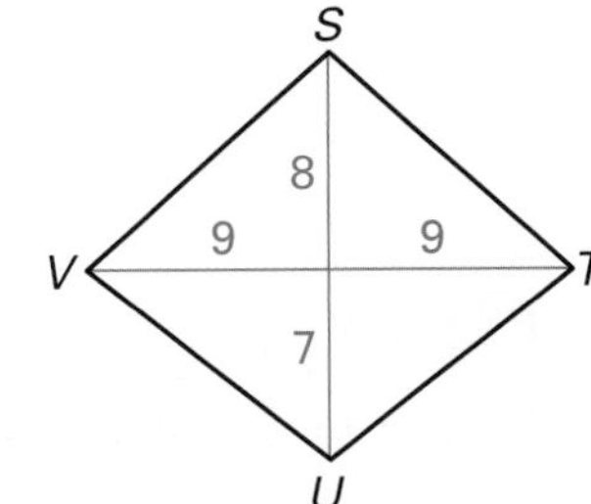

UNIT 5

Exercise Set A *(continued)*

Find the value of *x*.

11.

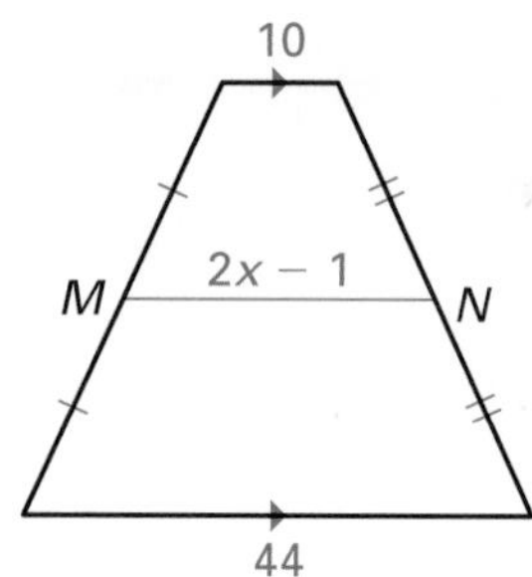

12.

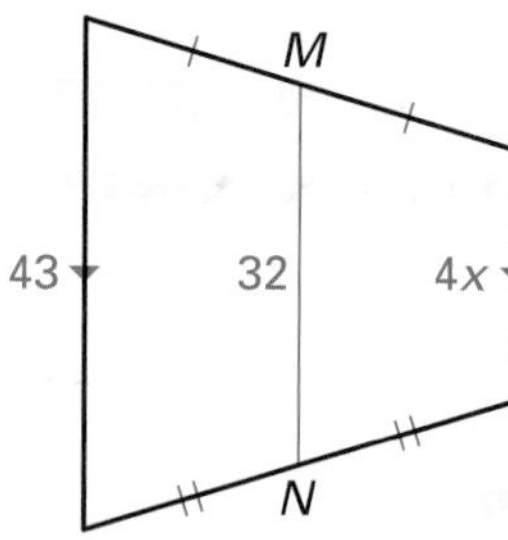

13.

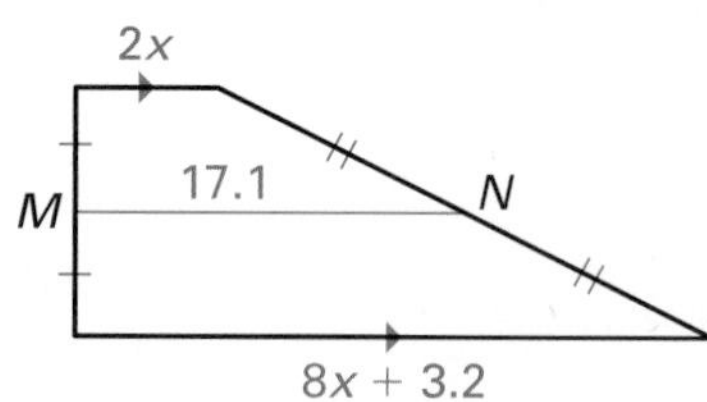

14.

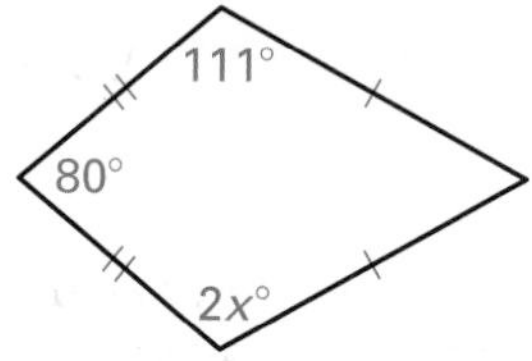

15. Maps Use the map shown at the right. The lines represent a sidewalk connecting the locations on the map.

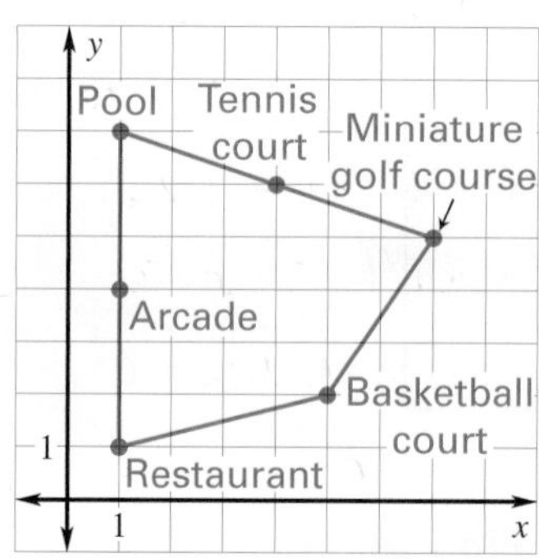

a. Is the sidewalk in the shape of a kite? *Explain.*

b. A sidewalk is built that connects the arcade, tennis court, miniature golf course, and restaurant. What is the shape of the sidewalk?

c. What is the length of the midsegment of the sidewalk in part (b)?

16. Kite You cut out a piece of fabric in the shape of a kite so that the congruent angles of the kite are 100°. Of the remaining two angles, one is 4 times larger than the other. What is the measure of the largest angle in the kite?

17. Proof $\overline{MN}$ is the midsegment of isosceles trapezoid *FGHJ*. Write a paragraph proof to show that *FMNJ* is an isosceles trapezoid.

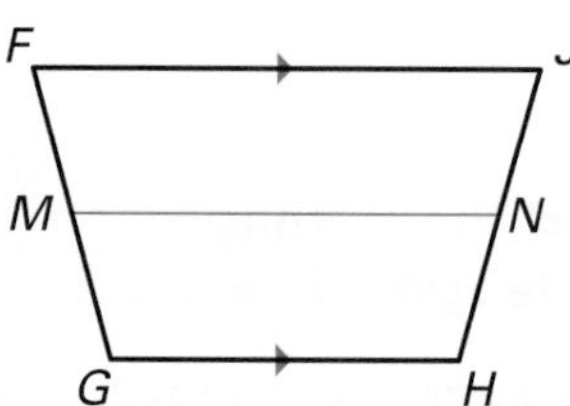

18. Proof Prove Theorem 5.33.

GIVEN: *PQRS* is a kite.
$\overline{PQ} \cong \overline{RQ}, \overline{PS} \cong \overline{RS}$

PROVE: $\overline{PR} \perp \overline{QS}$

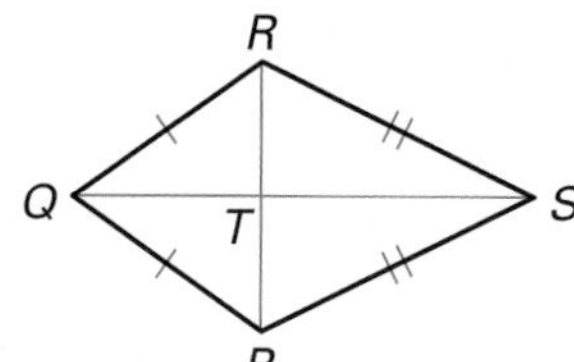

LESSON 5.11

Exercise Set B

MM1G1e Use the coordinate plane to investigate properties of and verify conjectures related to triangles and quadrilaterals.

MM1G3d Understand, use, and prove properties of and relationships among special quadrilaterals: parallelogram, rectangle, rhombus, square, trapezoid, and kite.

Determine whether the quadrilateral is a trapezoid. If it is, is it an isosceles trapezoid?

1.

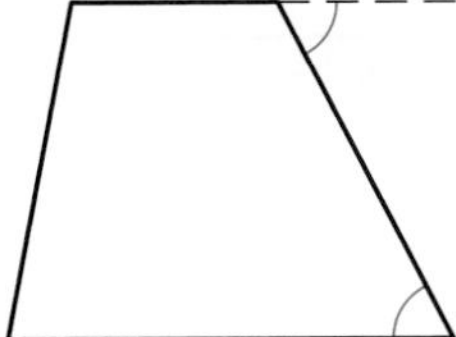

2.

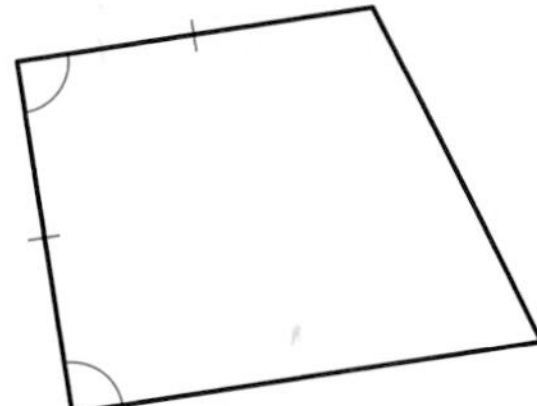

3.

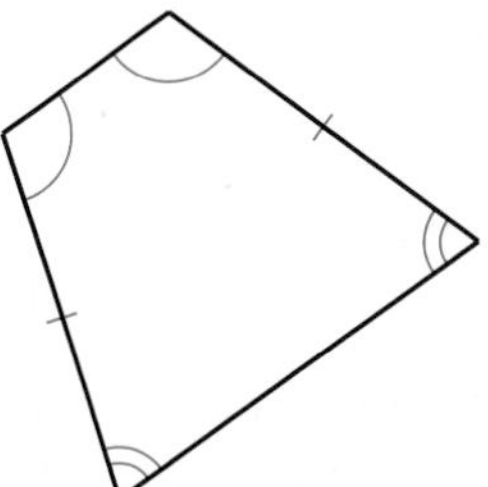

Quadrilateral *ABCD* is a trapezoid with midsegment $\overline{EF}$. Use the given information to answer the following.

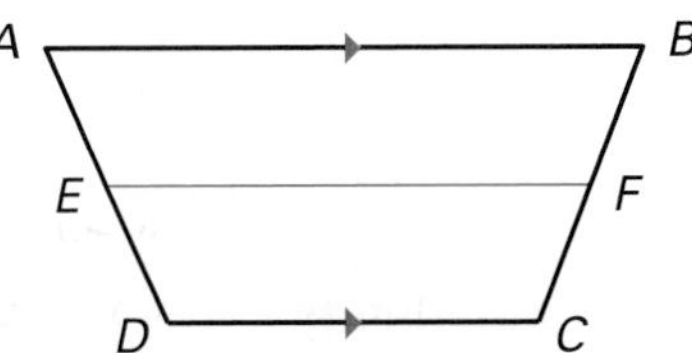

4. If $m\angle B = 73°$, then $m\angle C =$ __?__.

5. If $m\angle A = 51°$ and $m\angle C = 105°$, then $m\angle D =$ __?__.

6. If $m\angle A = 48°$ and $m\angle C = 112°$, then $m\angle CFE =$ __?__.

7. If $AB = 28$ and $DC = 13$, then $EF =$ __?__.

8. If $EF = 13$ and $DC = 6$, then $AB =$ __?__.

9. If $EF = x + 5$ and $DC + AB = 4x + 6$, then $EF =$ __?__.

***WEST* is a kite. Find the measures of the missing angles.**

10.

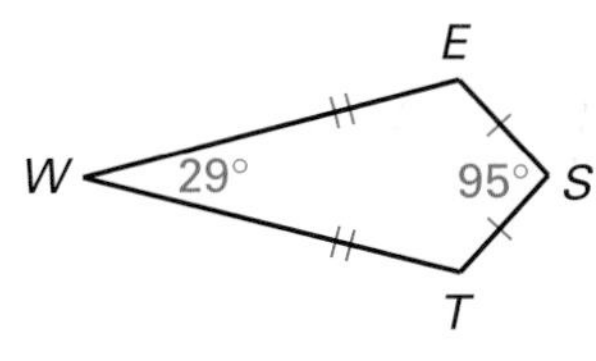

11.

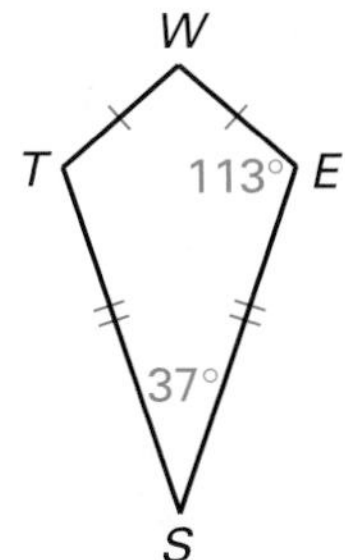

12.

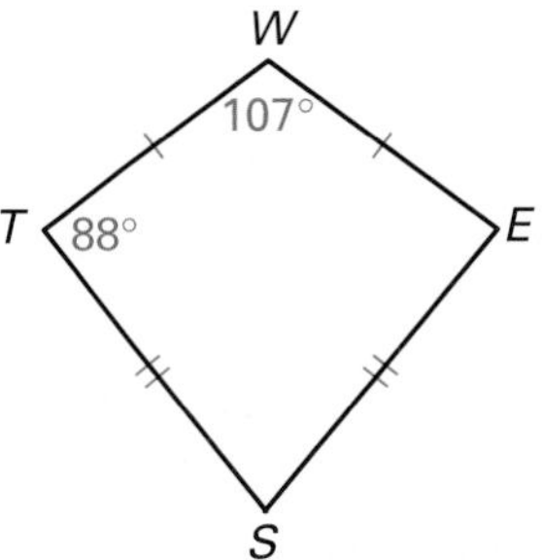

Use Theorem 5.33 and the Pythagorean Theorem to find the side lengths of the kite. Write the lengths in simplest radical form.

13.

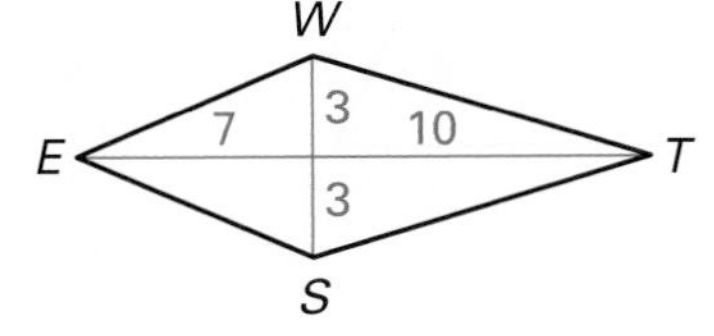

14.

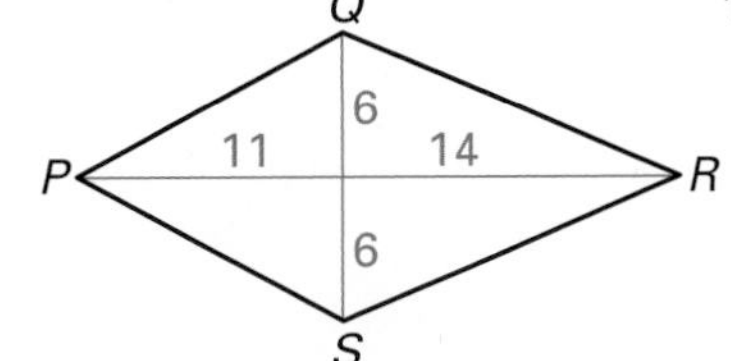

15.

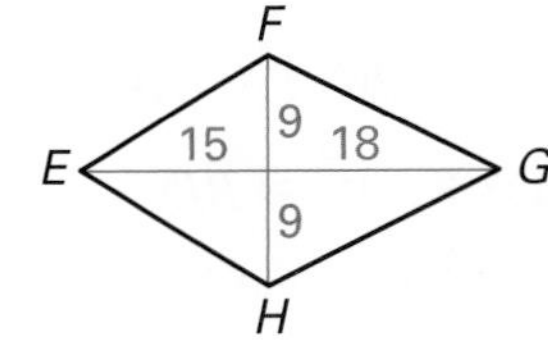

Exercise Set B *(continued)*

Find the value of *x*.

16.

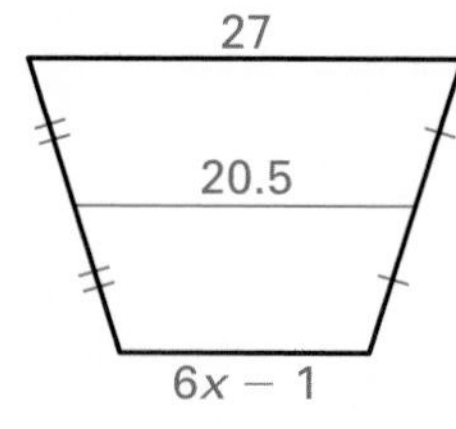

17.

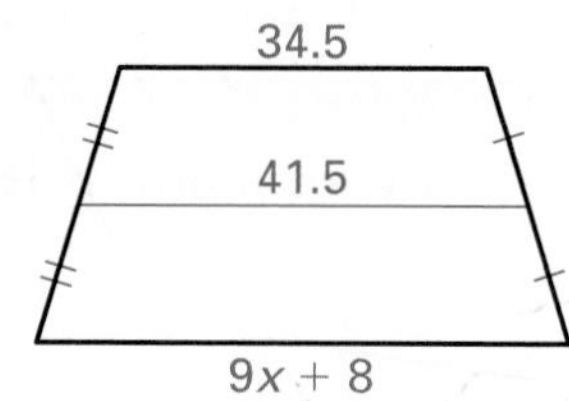

18.

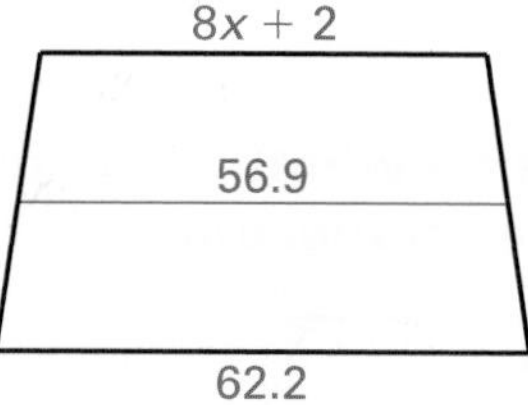

19. In an isosceles trapezoid, if one pair of base angles is twice the measure of the second pair of base angles, what are the measures of the angles?

20. If the midsegment of a trapezoid measures 6 units long, what is true about the lengths of the bases of the trapezoid?

21. Copy and complete the proof.

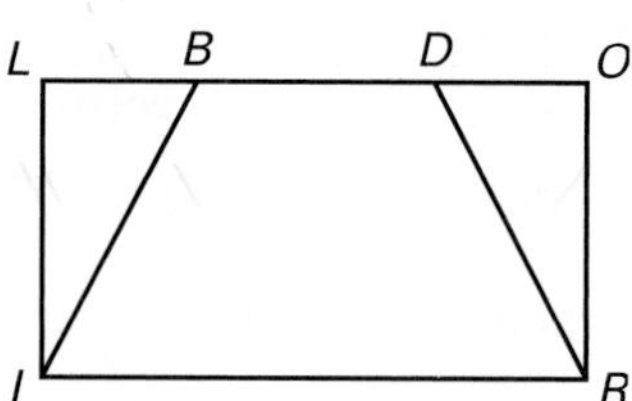

GIVEN: *LORI* is a rectangle.
$\overline{LB} \cong \overline{DO}$

PROVE: *BIRD* is an isosceles trapezoid.

Statements	Reasons
1. *LORI* is a rectangle.	1. ?
2. $\angle ILB$ and $\angle ROB$ are right angles.	2. ?
3. ?	3. All right $\angle$s are $\cong$.
4. $\overline{LI} \cong \overline{OR}$	4. ?
5. ?	5. Given
6. $\triangle LBI \cong \triangle ODR$	6. ?
7. ?	7. Corresponding parts of $\cong$ $\triangle$s are $\cong$.
8. ?	8. Definition of ▱
9. *BIRD* is an isosceles trapezoid.	9. ?

22. Proof Write a two-column proof of part of Theorem 5.31.

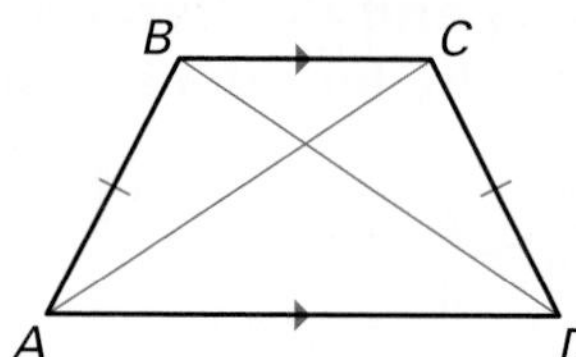

GIVEN: *ABCD* is an isosceles trapezoid.

$\overline{BC} \parallel \overline{AD}$, $\overline{AB} \cong \overline{CD}$

PROVE: $\overline{AC} \cong \overline{BD}$

LESSON 5.12

Identify Special Quadrilaterals

Georgia Performance Standards: MM1G3d

Goal Identify special quadrilaterals.

Vocabulary

Relationships among special quadrilaterals:

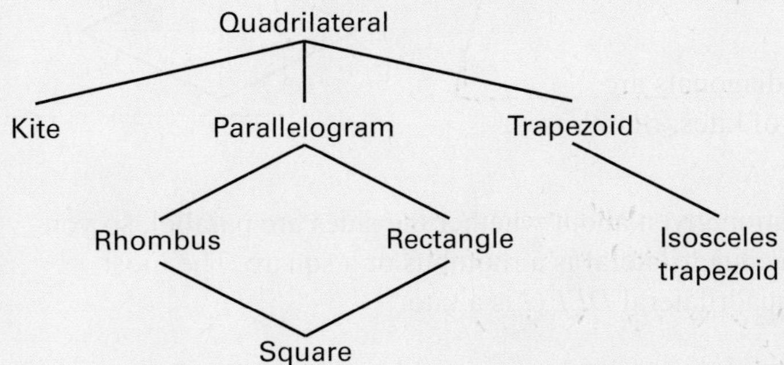

Each shape in the diagram has the properties of the shapes linked above it. For example, a rhombus has the properties of a parallelogram and a quadrilateral.

UNIT 5

Example 1 Identify quadrilaterals

Quadrilateral *WXYZ* has at least one pair of opposite sides that are parallel. What types of quadrilaterals meet this condition?

Solution

There are many possiblities.

Parallelogram Rhombus Rectangle Square Trapezoid Isosceles trapezoid

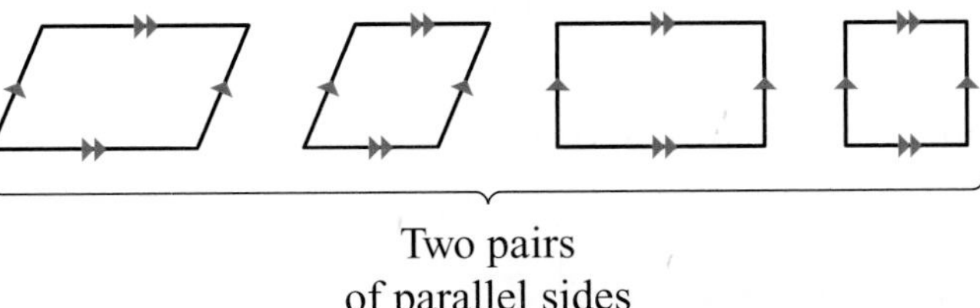

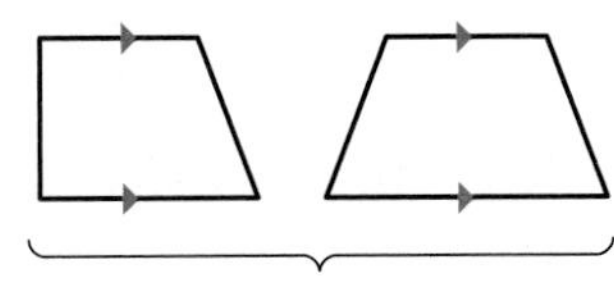

Two pairs of parallel sides

One pair of parallel sides

Guided Practice for Example 1

1. Quadrilateral *ABCD* has congruent diagonals. What types of quadrilaterals meet this condition?

2. Quadrilateral *ABCD* has exactly one pair of opposite angles that are congruent. What types of quadrilaterals meet this condition?

Georgia Performance Standards

MM1G3d Understand, use, and prove properties of and relationships among special quadrilaterals: parallelogram, rectangle, rhombus, square, trapezoid, and kite.

Example 2 Classify a quadrilateral

What is the most specific name for quadrilateral *DEFG*?

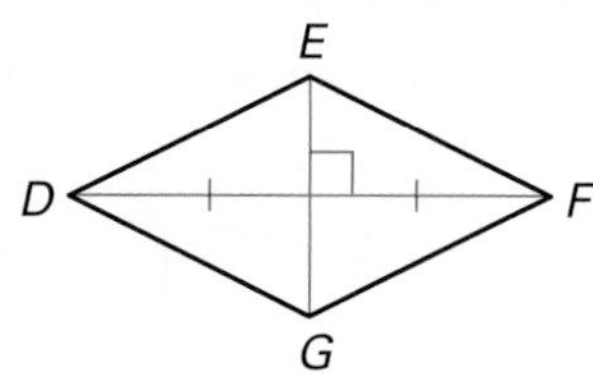

Solution

The diagram shows that the diagonals are perpendicular, which is true of kites, rhombuses, and squares.

However, there is no information given about whether the sides are parallel, so you cannot determine whether the quadrilateral is a rhombus or a square. The most specific name you can give quadrilateral *DEFG* is a kite.

Example 3 Identify a quadrilateral

Is enough information given in the diagram to show that quadrilateral *ABCD* is a rhombus? Explain.

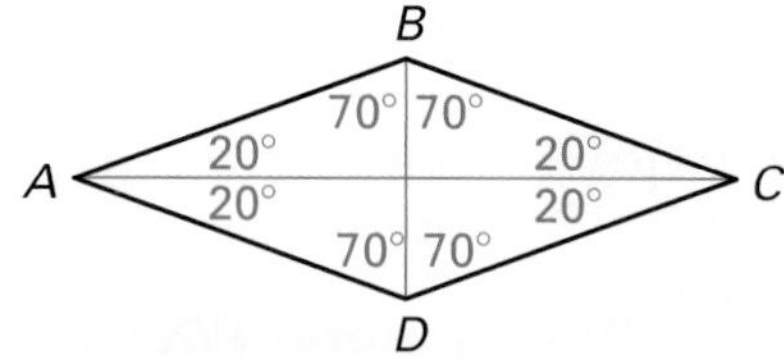

STEP 1 Show that *ABCD* is a parallelogram. From the diagram, $m\angle B = m\angle D = 70° + 70° = 140°$, and $m\angle A = m\angle C = 20° + 20° = 40°$. So, $\angle B \cong \angle D$ and $\angle A \cong \angle C$, and by Theorem 5.23, quadrilateral *ABCD* is a parallelogram.

STEP 2 Show that parallelogram *ABCD* is a rhombus. The diagram shows that each diagonal bisects a pair of opposite angles, so by Theorem 5.27, quadrilateral *ABCD* is a rhombus.

Yes, the diagram is sufficient to show that *ABCD* is a rhombus.

Guided Practice for Examples 2 and 3

Give the most specific name for the quadrilateral. *Explain* your reasoning.

3. 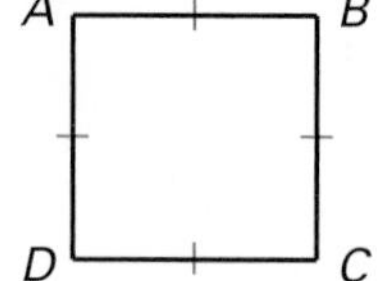

4. 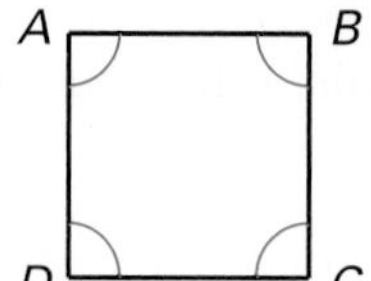

5. 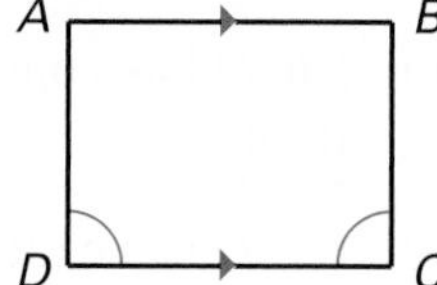

6. You are given the following information about quadrilateral *ABCD*: $AB = 6$, $CD = 12$, $m\angle A = 115°$, and $m\angle D = 65°$. Is enough information given to conclude that quadrilateral *ABCD* is a trapezoid? *Explain* your reasoning.

UNIT 5

LESSON 5.12

Exercise Set A

MM1G3d Understand, use, and prove properties of and relationships among special quadrilaterals: parallelogram, rectangle, rhombus, square, trapezoid, and kite.

Copy and complete the chart. Put an X in the box if the shape *always* has the given property.

	Property	▱	Rectangle	Rhombus	Square	Kite	Trapezoid
1.	Both pairs of opposite sides are congruent.	?	?	?	?	?	?
2.	Both pairs of opposite angles are congruent.	?	?	?	?	?	?
3.	Exactly one pair of opposite sides are congruent.	?	?	?	?	?	?
4.	Exactly one pair of opposite sides are parallel.	?	?	?	?	?	?
5.	Exactly one pair of opposite angles are congruent.	?	?	?	?	?	?
6.	Consecutive angles are supplementary.	?	?	?	?	?	?

Give the most specific name for the quadrilateral. *Explain.*

7.

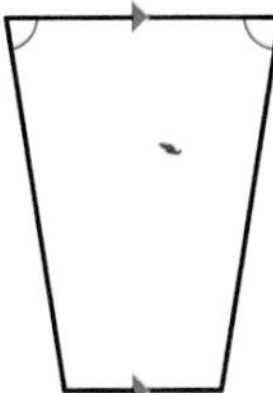

8.

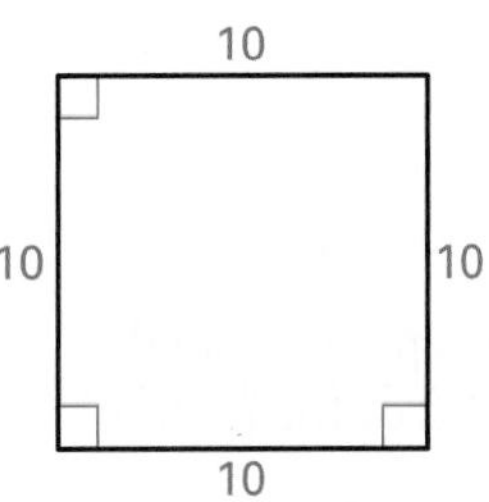

9.

10.

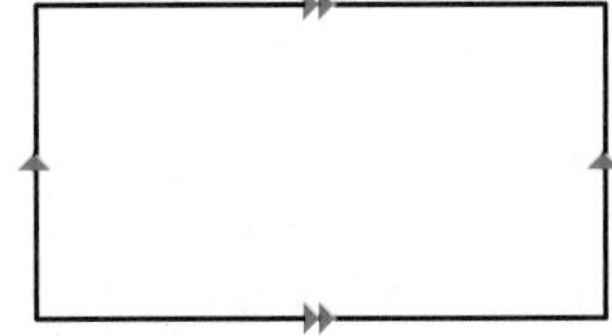

Exercise Set A *(continued)*

Tell whether enough information is given in the diagram to classify the quadrilateral by the indicated name.

11. Rectangle

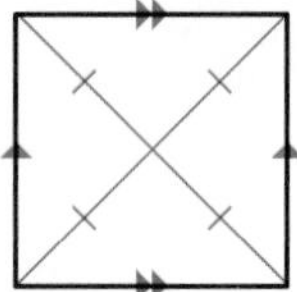

12. Isosceles trapezoid

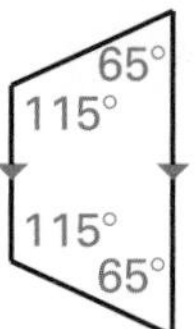

13. Rhombus

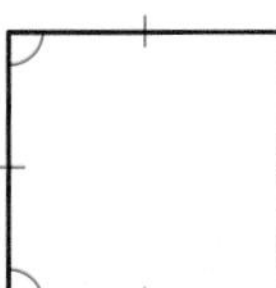

14. Kite

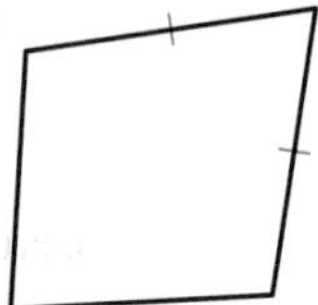

Points *A, B, C,* and *D* are the vertices of a quadrilateral. Give the most specific name for *ABCD*. *Justify* your answer.

15. $A(2, 2), B(4, 6), C(6, 5), D(4, 1)$

16. $A(-5, 1), B(0, -6), C(5, 1), D(0, 3)$

In Exercises 17 and 18, which two segments or angles must be congruent so that you can prove that *FGHJ* is the indicated quadrilateral? There may be more than one right answer.

17. Kite

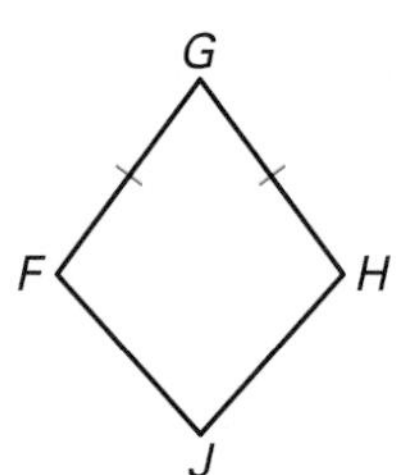

18. Isosceles trapezoid

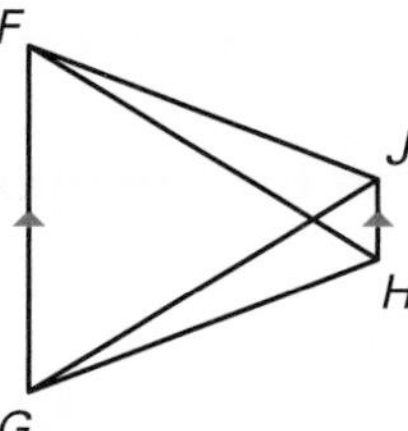

19. Picture Frame What type of special quadrilateral is the stand of the picture frame at the right?

20. Painting A painter uses a quadrilateral shaped piece of canvas. The artist begins by painting lines that represent the diagonals of the canvas. If the lengths of the painted lines are congruent, what types of quadrilaterals could represent the shape of the canvas? If the painted lines are also perpendicular, what type of quadrilateral represents the shape of the canvas?

UNIT 5

LESSON 5.12

Exercise Set B

MM1G3d Understand, use, and prove properties of and relationships among special quadrilaterals: parallelogram, rectangle, rhombus, square, trapezoid, and kite.

Draw the sides or diagonals of *ABCD* as described. What special type of quadrilateral is *ABCD*?

1. $\overline{AC} \cong \overline{BD}$, $\overline{AC}$ and $\overline{BD}$ bisect one another, but $\overline{AC}$ is not perpendicular to $\overline{BD}$.
2. $\overline{AB} \cong \overline{BC}$ and $\overline{CD} \cong \overline{DA}$, but $\overline{BC} \not\cong \overline{CD}$.
3. $\overline{AB} \parallel \overline{CD}$ and $\overline{BC} \cong \overline{DA}$.
4. $\overline{AC} \perp \overline{BD}$, $\overline{AC}$ and $\overline{BD}$ bisect one another, but $\overline{AC} \not\cong \overline{BD}$.
5. $\overline{AC} \perp \overline{BD}$, $\overline{AC}$ and $\overline{BD}$ bisect one another, and $\overline{AC} \cong \overline{BD}$.

Determine whether the statement is *always, sometimes,* or *never* true.

6. Diagonals of a trapezoid are congruent.
7. Opposite sides of a rectangle are congruent.
8. A square is a rectangle.
9. A square is not a rhombus.
10. All angles of a parallelogram are congruent.
11. Opposite angles of an isosceles trapezoid are congruent.
12. The diagonals of a parallelogram are perpendicular.

Tell whether enough information is given in the diagram to classify the quadrilateral by the indicated name. *Explain.*

13. Trapezoid

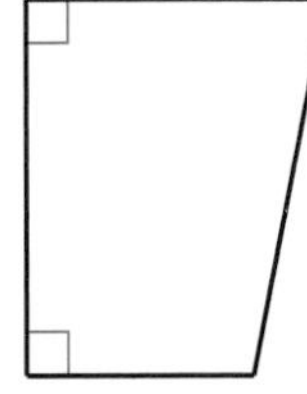

14. Rhombus

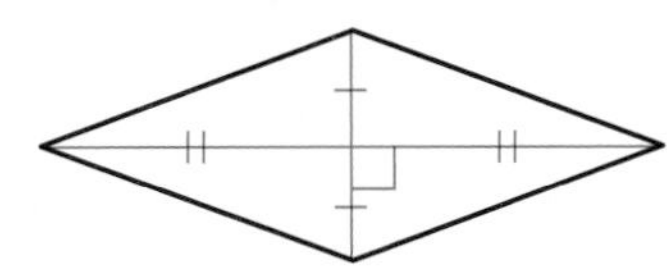

15. Rectangle

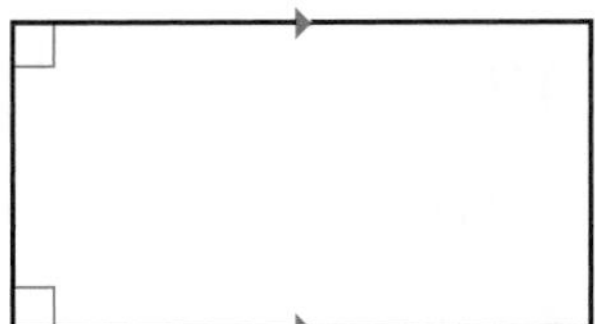

Points *P, Q, R,* and *S* are the vertices of a quadrilateral. Give the most specific name for *PQRS*. *Justify* your answer.

16. $P(-1, 3), Q(4, 2), R(1, -1), S(-4, 0)$
17. $P(-3, 5), Q(-7, 6), R(-9, -2), S(-5, -3)$
18. $P(-2, 9), Q(-2, -1), R(-5, 5), S(-5, 7)$

19. Use the quadrilateral in Exercise 17. Find the midpoint of each side. Connect the midpoints to form a new quadrilateral. What kind of quadrilateral is formed?

UNIT 5

Exercise Set B *(continued)*

Which pairs of segments or angles must be congruent so that you can prove that *ABCD* is the indicated quadrilateral? *Explain.* There may be more than one right answer.

20. Rectangle

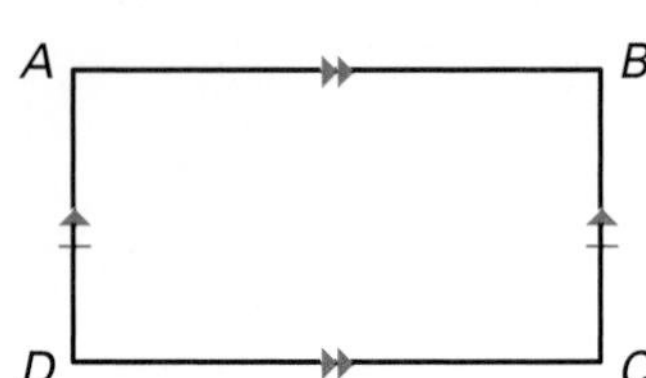

21. Kite

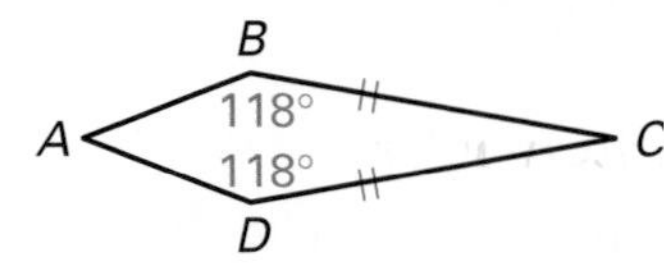

22. Isosceles Trapezoid

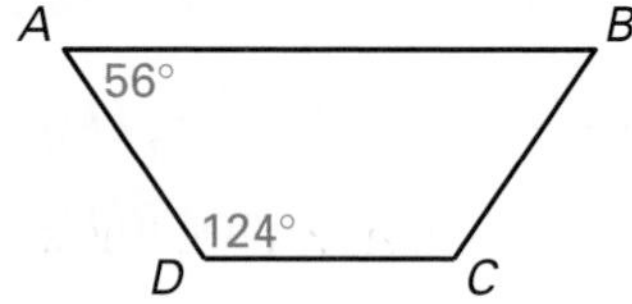

23. *PQRS* is a square. The midpoints of the sides of the square are *E*, *F*, *G*, and *H*. Is quadrilateral *EFGH* a rhombus? Verify your answer by completing the proof.

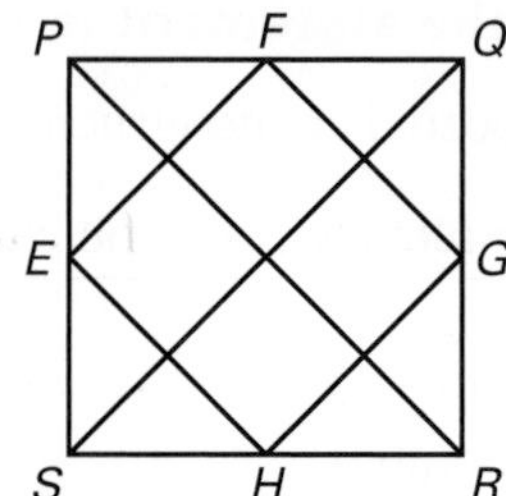

Statements	Reasons
1. *PQRS* is a square.	**1.** ?
2. *E*, *F*, *G*, and *H* are midpoints of the sides of the square.	**2.** ?
3. $\overline{EF}$, $\overline{FG}$, $\overline{GH}$, and $\overline{EH}$ are midsegments of $\triangle PQS$, $\triangle PQR$, $\triangle QRS$, and $\triangle RSP$, respectively.	**3.** ?
4. $EF = \frac{1}{2}QS$, $GH = \frac{1}{2}QS$, $EH = \frac{1}{2}PR$, $FG = \frac{1}{2}PR$	**4.** ?
5. ?	**5.** Diagonals of a square are congruent.
6. ?	**6.** Definition of congruent segments
7. $EF = \frac{1}{2}PR$, $GH = \frac{1}{2}PR$,	**7.** ?
8. $EF = GH = EH = FG$	**8.** ?
9. *EFGH* is a rhombus.	**9.** ?

TEST | for Unit 5

Use the diagram at the right where $\overline{DF}$, $\overline{DE}$, and $\overline{EF}$ are midsegments of $\triangle ABC$.

1. If $DE = 51$, find AC.

2. If $DF = 45$, find EC.

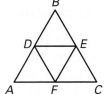

In the diagram, $\overleftrightarrow{BD}$ is the perpendicular bisector of $\overline{AC}$.

3. What segment lengths are equal?

4. What is the value of x?

5. Find AB.

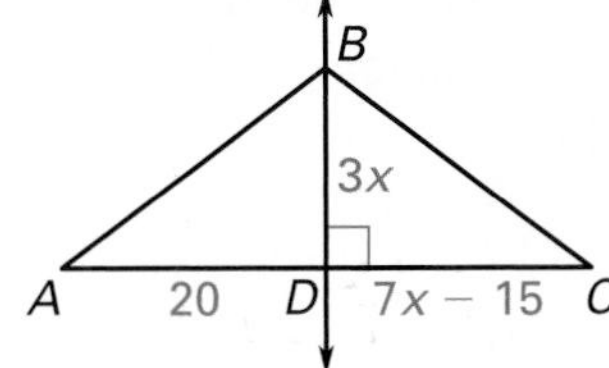

6. In the diagram, D is the incenter of the triangle. Find the value of x.

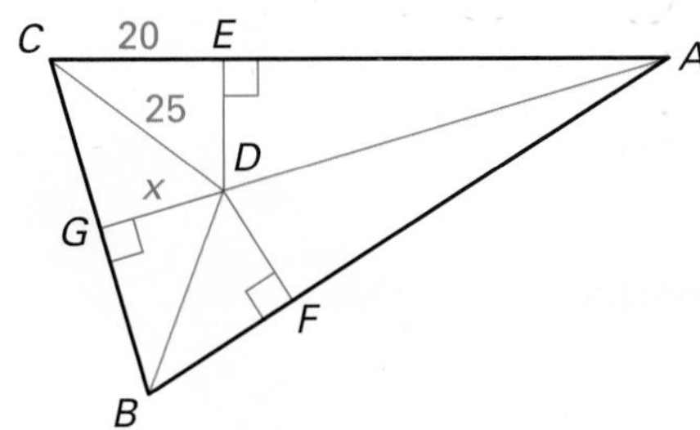

In the diagram at the right, P is the centroid of $\triangle RST$.

7. If $LS = 36$, find PL and PS.

8. If $TP = 20$, find TJ and PJ.

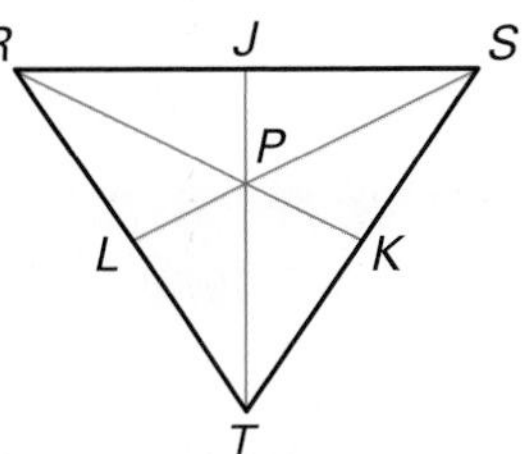

9. Is it possible to construct a triangle with side lengths 4, 8, and 17? If not, explain why not?

10. In $\triangle LMN$, $LM = 9$, $MN = 4$, and $LN = 11$. Sketch and label the triangle. List the angles in order from smallest to largest.

Find the value of x.

11.

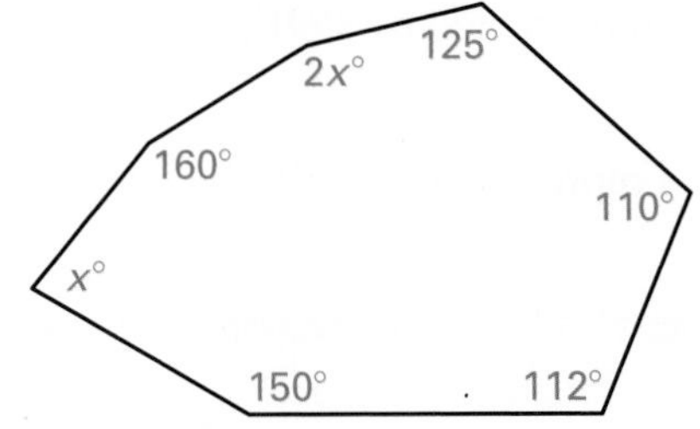

12.

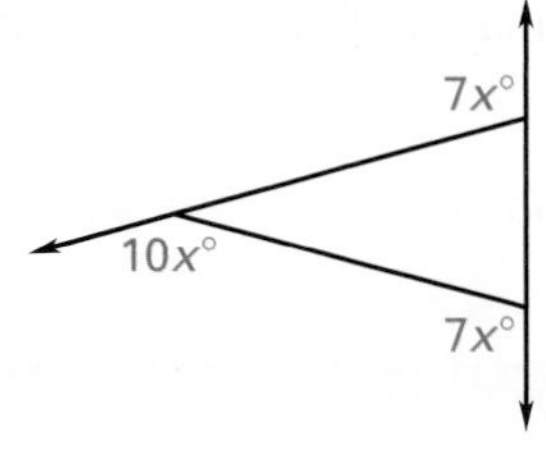

13. In $\square PQRS$, $PQ = 5$ centimeters, $QR = 10$ centimeters, and $m\angle PQR = 36°$. Sketch *PQRS*. Find and label all of its side lengths and interior angle measures.

14. In $\square LMNO$, the ratio of *LM* to *MN* is 4 : 3. Find *LM* if the perimeter of *LMNO* is 42 inches.

15. **Patio** You want to mark off a square region in your yard for a patio. You use a tape measure to mark off a quadrilateral on the ground. Each side of the quadrilateral is 3.5 meters long. *Explain* how you can use the tape measure to make sure that the quadrilateral you drew is a square.

16. **Furniture** In the photograph of a chest of drawers, $\overline{WR}$ is the midsegment of trapezoid *PQSV*, $\overline{VS}$ is the midsegment of trapezoid *WRTU*, $PQ = 12.5$ centimeters, and $VS = 53.9$ centimeters. Find *WR*. Then find *UT*.

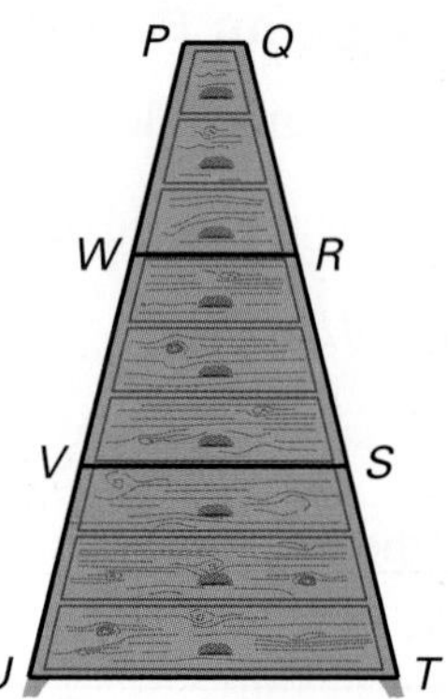

17. **Recycling Container** Quadrilateral *ABCD* represents the front view of a recycling container.

a. *Explain* how you know that the shape of the recycling container is a trapezoid.

b. Do you have enough information to determine that the recycling container is an isosceles trapezoid? *Explain* your reasoning.

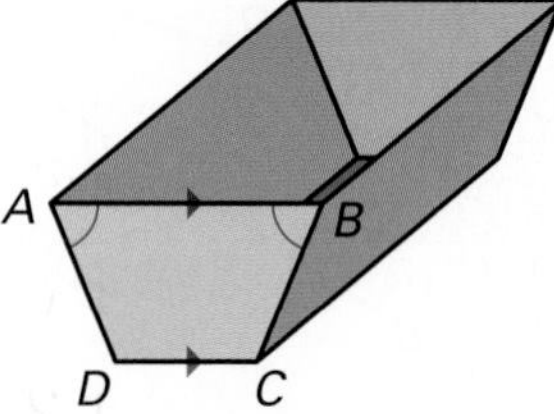

Performance Task

Land

A plot of land is being divided into three sections. The original plot is represented by *PQRST* where $\angle Q \cong \angle S$ and $\angle P$, $\angle R$, and $\angle T$ are right angles. The coordinates of the vertices are as follows: $P(0, 0)$, $Q(0, 50)$, $R(30, 80)$, $S(45, 65)$, and $T(45, 0)$.

a. Draw *PQRST* in a coordinate plane.

b. Classify the polygon. *Justify* your answer.

c. *Explain* how to find the measures of $\angle Q \cong \angle S$.

d. Find the coordinates of point *V* so that the section of land represented by *PQVT* is a rectangle.

e. Find the coordinates of point *W* so that the section of land represented by *QWSV* is a trapezoid.

UNIT 6

Data Analysis and Probability

LESSON 6.1

Use Counting Principles

Georgia Performance Standards: MM1D1a

Goal Use addition and multiplication counting principles.

Vocabulary

The Multiplication Counting Principle

If one event can occur in m ways and another event can occur in n ways, then the number of ways that *both* events can occur together is $m \cdot n$. This principle can be extended to three or more events.

The Addition Counting Principle

If the possibilities being counted can be divided into groups with no possibilities in common, then the total number of possibilities is the sum of the numbers of possibilities in each group.

UNIT 6

Example 1 Use the multiplication counting principle

Skateboards At a sporting goods store, skateboards are available in 8 different deck designs. Each deck design is available with 4 different wheel assemblies. How many skateboard choices does the store offer?

Solution

You can use the multiplication counting principle to find the number of skateboard choices. Multiply the number of deck designs (8) and the number of wheel assemblies (4).

The store offers $8 \cdot 4 = 32$ skateboard choices.

Example 2 Use the addition counting principle

Codes Every purchase made on a company's website is given a randomly generated confirmation code. The code consists of 3 symbols (letters and digits). How many codes can be generated if at least one letter is used in each?

Solution

To find the number of codes, find the sum of the numbers of possibilities for 1-letter codes, 2-letter codes, and 3-letter codes.

1-letter: There are 26 choices for each letter and 10 choices for each digit. So, there are $26 \cdot 10 \cdot 10 = 2600$ letter-digit-digit possibilities. The letter can be in any of the three positions, so there are $3 \cdot 2600 = 7800$ possibilities.

2-letters: There are $26 \cdot 26 \cdot 10 = 6760$ letter-letter-digit possibilities. The digit can be in any of the three positions, so there are $3 \cdot 6760 = 20{,}280$ possibilities.

3-letters: There are $26 \cdot 26 \cdot 26 = 17{,}576$ letter-letter-letter possibilities.

So, there are $7800 + 20{,}280 + 17{,}576 = 45{,}656$ possible codes.

Georgia Performance Standards

MM1D1a Apply the addition and multiplication principles of counting.

Example 3 Find a probability

Lunch Orders You are having lunch at a restaurant. You order the special from the menu shown. If you randomly choose the soup and sandwich, what is the probability that your order includes vegetable soup?

Lunch Special $5.95	
Choose 1 soup and 1 sandwich.	
Soups	**Sandwiches**
French Onion	Chicken
Vegetable	Club
	Grilled Cheese

Solution

Because there are 2 soup choices and 3 sandwich choices, the total number of possible lunch orders is $2 \cdot 3 = 6$. If you limit yourself to only 1 soup, vegetable soup, then the number of orders that include vegetable soup is $1 \cdot 3 = 3$.

$$P(\text{vegetable soup}) = \frac{\text{Orders that include vegetable soup}}{\text{Total possible lunch orders}} = \frac{3}{6} = \frac{1}{2}$$

Example 4 Solve a multi-step problem

Game Playing a game, you and four friends each roll a six-sided number cube. What is the probability that you each roll the same number?

STEP 1 **List** the favorable outcomes. There are 6:

1-1-1-1-1 2-2-2-2-2 3-3-3-3-3 4-4-4-4-4 5-5-5-5-5 6-6-6-6-6

STEP 2 **Find** the total number of outcomes using the multiplication counting principle.

Total number of outcomes $= 6 \cdot 6 \cdot 6 \cdot 6 \cdot 6 = 7776$

STEP 3 **Find** the probability.

$$P(\text{all the same}) = \frac{\text{Favorable outcomes}}{\text{Total outcomes}} = \frac{6}{7776} = \frac{1}{1296}$$

The probability that you each roll the same number is $\frac{1}{1296}$.

Guided Practice for Examples 1, 2, 3, and 4

1. **What If?** In Example 2, suppose that the only letters that can be in the codes are consonants. How many different codes are possible?

2. **What If?** In Example 3, suppose that in addition to soup and a sandwich, you can choose one of 4 different side dishes. If you randomly choose the soup, sandwich, and side dish, what is the probability that your order includes vegetable soup and a club sandwich?

3. **Number Cube** You roll a six-sided yellow number cube, a six-sided green number cube, and a six-sided white number cube. What is the probability that the yellow number cube is a 1, the green number cube is a 5, and the white number cube is a 4?

LESSON 6.1 **Exercise Set A**

MM1D1a Apply the addition and multiplication principles of counting.

In Exercises 1–4, use the multiplication counting principle to find the number of choices that are available.

1. Choose apple, blueberry, or cherry pie with juice or milk.

2. Choose a small, medium, large, or extra large shirt in black or white.

3. Choose a hat, scarf, or gloves in gray, brown, or black.

4. Choose one of 4 essay questions and one of 5 extra credit questions.

5. **Error Analysis** *Describe* and correct the error in solving the following problem: A snack stand sells small, medium, and large drinks in 4 flavors. How many drink choices are available?

> $m = 3$ and $n = 4$
>
> There are $3 + 4 = 7$ drink choices. X

6. **Weekend Plans** You would like to go to a movie, a play, or the zoo. You can go with your cousin, your brother, or your friend. You can go on Friday, Saturday, or Sunday. How many different options do you have?

7. **Lunch Cart** You want a sandwich, a side order, and a drink from a lunch cart that offers 4 types of sandwiches, 5 different side orders, and 4 drink choices. How many lunches are possible?

8. **Class Election** The ballot shows the candidates in a class election. Find the number of different ways a president, treasurer, and secretary can be chosen.

PRESIDENT	TREASURER	SECRETARY
❒ Amy	❒ Jessica	❒ Scott
❒ Hector	❒ Michael	❒ Nicole
❒ Lisa	❒ Carson	❒ Thomas
❒ Jeremy	❒ Isabel	❒ Angela

9. **Restaurant Choices** A restaurant has 84 possible meals that you can choose. A meal includes a main course, a salad, and a dessert. The menu lists 7 main courses and 3 types of salads. How many desserts are available? *Explain.*

10. **Lockers** The combination for your school locker consists of 3 symbols (letters and digits). How many combinations are possible if at least one digit is used?

11. **License Plate** You want your license plate to consist of 3 letters grouped together and 3 digits grouped together. You have no preference as to whether the letters or numbers are first. How many different license plates are possible?

12. **Movies** You and two friends each randomly pick a movie from 5 choices. What is the probability that you all pick the same movie?

13. **Passwords** A website randomly generates a password after a new user registers. The password consists of 3 letters. Find the probability that the password fits the given description. Count only a, e, i, o, and u as vowels.

a. starts with a consonant
b. contains only vowels
c. code is xyz
d. uses the same letter in each position

UNIT 6

LESSON 6.1

Exercise Set B

MM1D1a Apply the addition and multiplication principles of counting.

In Exercises 1–6, use the number of outcomes of the events to find the number of ways that the events can occur together.

1. **Event A:** 5 outcomes
   Event B: 16 outcomes
2. **Event A:** 14 outcomes
   Event B: 15 outcomes
3. **Event A:** 13 outcomes
   Event B: 16 outcomes
4. **Event A:** 27 outcomes
   Event B: 9 outcomes
   Event C: 3 outcomes
5. **Event A:** 15 outcomes
   Event B: 20 outcomes
   Event C: 25 outcomes
6. **Event A:** 26 outcomes
   Event B: 26 outcomes
   Event C: 10 outcomes
7. **Class Election** Your class is having an election. There are 4 candidates for president, 6 for vice president, 3 for secretary, and 7 for treasurer. How many ways can a president, vice president, secretary, and treasurer be chosen?
8. **Sandwiches** A sandwich shop has 6 types of bread, 5 types of cheese, and 3 types of ham to use on a ham-and-cheese sandwich.
   a. You are limited to 1 type of bread, 1 type of cheese, and 1 type of ham. How many different ham-and-cheese sandwiches are possible?
   b. The shop has a pre-made ham-and-cheese sandwich. What is the probability that a randomly made sandwich has the types of bread, cheese, and ham that you want?
9. **Digital Clocks** On a digital clock, the numbers 1 through 12 are used for the hour display and the numbers 00 through 59 are used for the minute display. How many time displays are possible? If a light for A.M. and P.M. is added, how does this affect the possible number of displays?
10. **Vision** A doctor creates a vision test using lower case letters, upper case letters, and digits. The third line contains five characters, where at most one is a digit. How many different third lines are possible?
11. **Working Backward** The number of ways that events A, B, and C can occur together is 155. Event B can occur in 5 ways. The number of ways Event A can occur is less than the number of ways Event B can occur. In how many ways can Event A occur? In how many ways can Event C occur?
12. **States** You and your friend randomly choose the name of a state. What is the probability that you both choose a state whose name begins with the letter K?
13. **Code Generation** A website randomly generates a confirmation code after purchases. The code consists of 5 letters. Find the probability that the code fits the given description. Count only a, e, i, o, and u as vowels.
    a. starts with a vowel
    b. contains no vowels
    c. code is abcde
    d. uses the same letter in each position
14. **Ice Cream** You work at an ice cream stand that offers 6 different flavors. On a busy day, you take orders for one-scoop cones from 5 people, but forget the flavors. How many flavors do you have to remember for the probability that you randomly get all the other flavors correct on the first try to be greater than 0.01? *Explain.*

UNIT 6

LESSON 6.2

Find Probabilities Using Permutations

Georgia Performance Standards: MM1D1b

Goal Use the formula for the number of permutations.

Vocabulary

For any positive integer n, the product of the integers from 1 to n is called ***n* factorial** and is written as $n!$. The value of $0!$ is defined to be 1.

A **permutation** is an arrangement of objects in which order is important. The number of permutations of n objects is given by ${}_nP_n = n!$. The number of permutations of n objects taken r at a time, where $r \le n$, is given by ${}_nP_r = \frac{n!}{(n-r)!}$.

Example 1 Count permutations

Consider the number of permutations of the letters in the word APRIL.

a. In how many ways can you arrange all of the letters?

b. In how many ways can you arrange 3 of the letters?

Solution

a. Use the multiplication counting principle to find the number of permutations of the letters in the word APRIL.

Number of permutations	=	Choices for 1st letter	•	Choices for 2nd letter	•	Choices for 3rd letter	•	Choices for 4th letter	•	Choices for 5th letter
	=	5	•	4	•	3	•	2	•	1
	= 120									

There are 120 ways you can arrange all of the letters in the word APRIL.

b. When arranging 3 letters of the word APRIL, you have 5 choices for the first letter, 4 for the second letter, and 3 for the third letter.

Number of permutations	=	Choices for 1st letter	•	Choices for 2nd letter	•	Choices for 3rd letter
	=	5	•	4	•	3
	= 60					

There are 60 ways you can arrange 3 of the letters in the word APRIL.

Guided Practice for Example 1

Count the permutations.

1. In how many ways can you arrange the letters in the word FLOWER?

2. In how many ways can you arrange 4 of the letters in the word PANTHER?

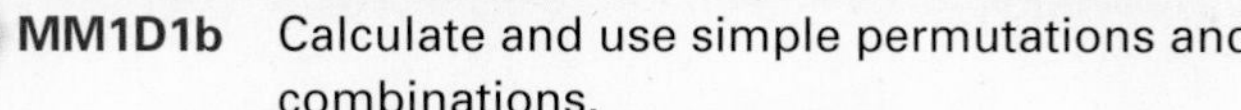

Georgia Performance Standards

MM1D1b Calculate and use simple permutations and combinations.

Example 2 Use the permutation formula

CD Recording Your band has written 11 songs and plans to record 5 of them for a CD. In how many ways can you arrange the songs on the CD?

Solution

To find the number of permutations of 5 songs chosen from 11, find ${}_{11}P_5$.

$${}_{11}P_5 = \frac{11!}{(11-5)!}$$ Permutation formula

$$= \frac{11!}{6!}$$ Subtract.

$$= \frac{11 \cdot 10 \cdot 9 \cdot 8 \cdot 7 \cdot \cancel{6!}}{\cancel{6!}}$$ Expand 11!. Divide out common factorial, 6!.

$$= 55{,}440$$ Multiply.

There are 55,440 ways to arrange 5 songs out of 11.

Example 3 Find a probability using permutations

Softball There are 10 players on a softball team. Each game the batting order is chosen randomly. Find the probability that you are chosen to bat first, and your best friend is chosen to bat second.

Solution

STEP 1 **Write** the number of possible outcomes as the number of permutations of the 10 players on the team. This is ${}_{10}P_{10} = 10!$.

STEP 2 **Write** the number of favorable outcomes as the number of permutations of the players given that you are the first batter, and your best friend is the second batter. This is ${}_8P_8 = 8!$.

STEP 3 **Calculate** the probability.

$$P\begin{pmatrix}\text{you are first,}\\ \text{best friend is second}\end{pmatrix} = \frac{8!}{10!}$$ Form a ratio of favorable to possible outcomes.

$$= \frac{\cancel{8!}}{10 \cdot 9 \cdot \cancel{8!}}$$ Expand 10!. Divide out common factor, 8!.

$$= \frac{1}{90}$$ Simplify.

Guided Practice for Examples 2 and 3

3. What If? In Example 2, suppose your band has written 16 songs and you plan to record 9 of them for a CD. In how many ways can you arrange the songs on the CD?

4. What If? In Example 3, suppose there are 15 players on the team and that everyone gets to bat. Find the probability that you are the first batter and that your best friend is the second batter.

UNIT 6

LESSON 6.2

Exercise Set A

MM1D1b Calculate and use simple permutations and combinations.

Find the number of ways you can arrange (a) all of the letters in the given word and (b) 2 of the letters in the word.

1. TACK
2. MAR
3. GAMER

Write the meaning of the notation in words.

4. ${}_{14}P_3$
5. ${}_{24}P_{10}$
6. ${}_{30}P_{20}$

Evaluate the expression.

7. $6!$
8. $9!$
9. $11!$
10. $\frac{8!}{3!}$
11. $\frac{12!}{9!}$
12. $\frac{15!}{14!}$
13. ${}_6P_3$
14. ${}_4P_4$
15. ${}_{15}P_3$
16. ${}_8P_7$
17. ${}_{10}P_6$
18. ${}_5P_0$

Complete the statement using >, <, or =.

19. ${}_6P_4 \underline{\ ?\ } {}_4P_1$
20. ${}_8P_6 \underline{\ ?\ } {}_{10}P_8$
21. ${}_3P_0 \underline{\ ?\ } {}_6P_5$
22. ${}_6P_3 \underline{\ ?\ } {}_4P_1$
23. ${}_{24}P_1 \underline{\ ?\ } {}_4P_4$
24. ${}_7P_5 \underline{\ ?\ } {}_{12}P_3$

25. **Summer Reading List** At the beginning of the summer, you have 6 books to read. In how many orders can you read the books?

26. **Air Conditioning Repair** An air conditioner repair person has repairs to make at 7 different homes. In how many orders can the repairs be made?

27. **Multiple Representations** You and 3 friends are bike messengers working for a delivery company. The supervisor assigns new deliveries to the messengers in a particular order. This order remains the same, so that all messengers are likely to have the same number of deliveries by the end of the day.

    a. **Making a List** List all the possible orders in which the supervisor can assign deliveries to the messengers.

    b. **Using a Formula** Use the formula for permutations to find the number of ways in which the supervisor can assign deliveries to the messengers.

    c. **Describing in Words** What is the likelihood that you are assigned the first delivery? *Explain* your answer using probability.

28. **Math Exam** On an exam, you are asked to list the 6 steps to solving a particular kind of problem in order. You guess the order of the steps at random. What is the probability that you choose the correct order?

LESSON 6.2 **Exercise Set B**

MM1D1b Calculate and use simple permutations and combinations.

Find the number of ways you can arrange (a) all of the letters in the given word and (b) 3 of the letters in the word.

1. VIDEO
2. TARP
3. MASTER

4. *Describe* a real-world situation where the number of possibilities is given by ${}_6P_2$.

Evaluate the expression.

5. ${}_7P_4$
6. ${}_{10}P_{10}$
7. ${}_8P_2$
8. ${}_{13}P_0$
9. ${}_5P_1$
10. ${}_{20}P_3$
11. ${}_{14}P_6$
12. ${}_{12}P_5$
13. ${}_{25}P_5$
14. $2({}_8P_5)$
15. $\frac{1}{4}({}_{10}P_4)$
16. $\frac{3}{5}({}_7P_3)$
17. ${}_4P_2 + {}_2P_1$
18. ${}_{15}P_4 - {}_7P_5$
19. $\frac{{}_6P_5}{{}_3P_3}$

Complete the statement using >, <, or =.

20. ${}_6P_4 \underline{\ ?\ } {}_8P_6$
21. ${}_{110}P_1 \underline{\ ?\ } {}_{11}P_2$
22. ${}_4P_4 \underline{\ ?\ } {}_5P_2$

23. **Roofing** A roofing company has 8 roofing jobs to complete so far in the upcoming season. In how many orders can the jobs be completed?

24. **Soapbox Racing** You are in a soapbox racing competition. In each heat, 7 cars race and the positions of the cars are randomly assigned.
    - **a.** In how many ways can the positions be assigned?
    - **b.** What is the probability that you are chosen to be in the last position? *Explain* how you found your answer.
    - **c.** What is the probability that you are chosen to be in the first or second position of the heat in which you are racing? *Explain* how you found your answer.
    - **d.** What is the probability that you are chosen to be in the second or third position of the heat in which you are racing? *Compare* your answer with your answer to part (c).

25. **Battle of the Bands** Your band is one of 12 bands competing in a battle of the bands. The order of the performances is determined at random. The first 6 performances are on a Friday night and the next 6 performances are on the following night.
    - **a.** What is the probability that your band gives the last performance on Friday night and your rival band performs immediately before you?
    - **b.** What is the probability that your band does not give the last performance?

UNIT 6

Georgia Performance Standards

MM1D1b Calculate and use simple permutations and combinations.

Investigating Math Activity
Combinations

Use before Lesson 6.3

Question

Eight people pair up to give a presentation. How many different pairs are possible?

Explore

Find the number of different pairs.

STEP 1 **Make a list**

Call the 8 people A, B, C, D, E, F, G, and H. List all the possible pairs of 2 letters. Be sure to use an organized method.

AB	AC	AD	AE	AF	AG	AH
BA	BC	BD	BE	BF	BG	BH
CA	CB	CD	CE	CF	CG	CH
DA	DB	DC	DE	DF	DG	DH
EA	EB	EC	ED	EF	EG	EH
FA	FB	FC	FD	FE	FG	FH
GA	GB	GC	GD	GE	GF	GH
HA	HB	HC	HD	HE	HF	HG

STEP 2 **Eliminate duplicates**

Because order is not important when 2 people pair up, cross out any duplicate pairs.

AB	AC	AD	AE	AF	AG	AH
~~BA~~	BC	BD	BE	BF	BG	BH
~~CA~~	~~CB~~	CD	CE	CF	CG	CH
~~DA~~	~~DB~~	~~DC~~	DE	DF	DG	DH
~~EA~~	~~EB~~	~~EC~~	~~ED~~	EF	EG	EH
~~FA~~	~~FB~~	~~FC~~	~~FD~~	~~FE~~	FG	FH
~~GA~~	~~GB~~	~~GC~~	~~GD~~	~~GE~~	~~GF~~	GH
~~HA~~	~~HB~~	~~HC~~	~~HD~~	~~HE~~	~~HF~~	~~HG~~

STEP 3 **Count the remaining pairs**

There are 28 pairs remaining.

So, when 8 people pair up, 28 different pairs are possible.

Draw Conclusions

1. How many different pairs are possible when 10 people pair up? 12 people?
2. Writing *Describe* the relationship between the number of different pairs possible when n people pair up and ${}_nP_2$. *Explain* your reasoning.

LESSON 6.3

Find Probabilities Using Combinations

Georgia Performance Standards: MM1D1b

Goal Use combinations to count possibilities.

Vocabulary

A **combination** is a selection of objects in which order is *not* important. The number of combinations of n objects taken r at a time, where $r \le n$, is given by ${}_nC_r = \frac{n!}{(n-r)! \cdot r!}$.

Example 1 Count combinations

Count the combinations of 3 letters from the list A, B, C, D.

Solution

List all of the permutations of 3 letters from the list A, B, C, D. Because order is not important in a combination, cross out any duplicate groupings.

ABC, ~~ACB~~, ABD, ~~ADB~~, ACD, ~~ADC~~

~~BAC~~, ~~BCA~~, BCD, ~~BDC~~, ~~BDA~~, ~~BAD~~

~~CAB~~, ~~CBA~~, ~~CBD~~, ~~CDB~~, ~~CAD~~, ~~CDA~~

~~DAB~~, ~~DBA~~, ~~DAC~~, ~~DCA~~, ~~DBC~~, ~~DCB~~

There are 4 possible combinations of 3 letters from the list A, B, C, D.

Guided Practice for Example 1

1. Count the combinations of 2 letters from the list A, B, C, D, E, F.

Example 2 Use the combinations formula

Photo Background For your school pictures, you can choose 4 backgrounds from a list of 10. How many combinations of backdrops are possible?

Solution

The order in which you choose the backgrounds is not important. So, to find the number of combinations of 10 backgrounds taken 4 at a time, find ${}_{10}C_4$.

${}_{10}C_4 = \frac{10!}{(10-4)! \cdot 4!}$	Combination formula
$= \frac{10!}{6! \cdot 4!}$	Subtract.
$= \frac{10 \cdot 9 \cdot 8 \cdot 7 \cdot \cancel{6!}}{\cancel{6!} \cdot (4 \cdot 3 \cdot 2 \cdot 1)}$	Expand factorials. Divide out common factorial, 6!.
$= 210$	Multiply.

There are 210 different combinations of backgrounds you can choose.

UNIT 6

Georgia Performance Standards

MM1D1b Calculate and use simple permutations and combinations.

Example 3 Find a probability using combinations

Student Council A school's student council has 16 members, including 4 seniors. There are 4 members randomly chosen to represent the student council at a school open house. What is the probability that all 4 council members chosen are seniors?

STEP 1 **Write** the number of possible outcomes as the number of combinations of 16 people chosen 4 at a time, or ${}_{16}C_4$, because the order in which the people are chosen is not important.

$$ {}_{16}C_4 = \frac{16!}{(16-4)! \cdot 4!} = \frac{16!}{12! \cdot 4!} = \frac{16 \cdot 15 \cdot 14 \cdot 13 \cdot \cancel{12!}}{\cancel{12!} \cdot 4 \cdot 3 \cdot 2 \cdot 1} = 1820 $$

STEP 2 **Find** the number of favorable outcomes. Only one of the possible outcomes includes all 4 seniors.

STEP 3 **Calculate** the probability: $P(\text{all seniors are chosen}) = \frac{1}{1820}$

Example 4 Find a probability using combinations

Group Project There are 28 students in your math class. Your teacher chooses 5 students at random to complete a group project. Find the probability that you and your best friend are chosen to work in the group.

STEP 1 **Write** the number of possible outcomes as the number of combinations of 28 students chosen 5 at a time, or ${}_{28}C_5$, because the order in which the students are chosen is not important.

$$ {}_{28}C_5 = \frac{28!}{(28-5)! \cdot 5!} = \frac{28!}{23! \cdot 5!} = \frac{28 \cdot 27 \cdot 26 \cdot 25 \cdot 24 \cdot \cancel{23!}}{\cancel{23!} \cdot 5 \cdot 4 \cdot 3 \cdot 2 \cdot 1} = 98{,}280 $$

STEP 2 **Find** the number of favorable outcomes. If you and your best friend are chosen, 3 more students must be chosen from the remaining 26 students. So, the number of favorable outcomes is ${}_{26}C_3$, or 2600.

STEP 3 **Calculate** the probability.

$$ P(\text{you and your best friend are chosen}) = \frac{2600}{98{,}280} = \frac{5}{189} $$

Guided Practice for Examples 2, 3, and 4

2. What If? In Example 2, suppose you can choose 3 backgrounds out of the list of 10. How many combinations are possible?

3. What If? In Example 3, suppose there are 12 members on the Student Council, 4 of whom are seniors. Find the probability that the seniors are the 4 members chosen for the open house.

4. What If? In Example 4, suppose there are 32 students in your math class. Find the probability that you and your best friend are chosen to work in the group.

LESSON 6.3 **Exercise Set A**

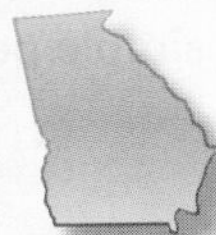

MM1D1b Calculate and use simple permutations and combinations.

Evaluate the expression.

1. ${}_8C_4$
2. ${}_5C_5$
3. ${}_{12}C_0$
4. ${}_7C_1$
5. ${}_{15}C_{11}$
6. ${}_{10}C_3$
7. ${}_6C_5$
8. ${}_4C_2$
9. ${}_{16}C_8$

10. **Error Analysis** *Describe* and correct the error in evaluating ${}_5C_2$.

$${}_5C_2 = \frac{5!}{(5-2)!} = \frac{5!}{3!} = 20$$

Complete the statement using >, <, or =.

11. ${}_{10}C_6 \ \underline{\ ?\ }\ {}_8C_5$
12. ${}_{22}C_3 \ \underline{\ ?\ }\ {}_{18}C_4$
13. ${}_9C_6 \ \underline{\ ?\ }\ {}_9C_3$
14. ${}_8C_2 \ \underline{\ ?\ }\ {}_{15}C_{14}$
15. ${}_7C_7 \ \underline{\ ?\ }\ {}_{14}C_{14}$
16. ${}_5C_3 \ \underline{\ ?\ }\ {}_8C_3$

In Exercises 17 and 18, tell whether the question can be answered using *combinations* or *permutations*. *Explain* your choice, then answer the question.

17. Five students from the 90 students in your class not running for class president will be selected to count the ballots for the vote for class president. In how many ways can the 5 students be selected?

18. Twenty students are running for 3 different positions on student council. In how many ways can the 3 positions be filled?

19. **Sweaters** The buyer for a retail store must decide which sweaters to stock for the upcoming fall season. A sweater from one manufacturer comes in 5 different colors and 3 different textures. The buyer decides that the store will stock the sweater in 3 different colors and 2 different textures. How many different sweaters are possible?

20. **Greeting Cards** A greeting card company packages 4 different cards together that are randomly selected from 10 different cards with a different animal on each card. What is the probability that one of the cards in a package is the card that has a dog on it?

21. **Open-Mike Night** A coffee shop offers an open-mike night for poetry. Tonight, 15 people would like to read, but there is only enough time to have 7 people read.
    a. Seven of the 15 people who would like to read are randomly chosen. How many combinations of 7 readers from the group of people that would like to read are possible?
    b. You and your friend are part of the group that would like to read. What is the probability that you and your friend are chosen? What is the probability that you are chosen first and your friend is chosen second? Which event is more likely to occur?

UNIT 6

LESSON 6.3 **Exercise Set B**

MM1D1b Calculate and use simple permutations and combinations.

Evaluate the expression.

1. ${}_9C_3$
2. ${}_6C_6$
3. ${}_{15}C_0$
4. ${}_{18}C_3$
5. ${}_{13}C_5$
6. ${}_8C_2$
7. ${}_{22}C_5$
8. ${}_{30}C_{20}$
9. ${}_{17}C_{10}$

Complete the statement using >, <, or =.

10. ${}_{14}C_2 \underline{\ ?\ } {}_9C_5$
11. ${}_{25}C_5 \underline{\ ?\ } {}_{20}C_7$
12. ${}_{12}C_4 \underline{\ ?\ } {}_{12}C_8$
13. ${}_{15}C_3 \underline{\ ?\ } {}_{24}C_{22}$
14. ${}_8C_0 \underline{\ ?\ } {}_8C_2$
15. ${}_{11}C_4 \underline{\ ?\ } {}_{15}C_4$

In Exercises 16–18, tell whether the question can be answered using *combinations* or *permutations*. *Explain* your choice, then answer the question.

16. Five students from the 90 students in your class will be selected to answer a questionnaire about participating in school sports. How many groups of 5 students are possible?

17. Eleven students are trying out for 5 different positions in the school band. In how many ways can the 5 positions be filled?

18. To complete a quiz, you must answer 4 questions from a list of 12 questions. In how many ways can you complete the quiz?

19. **Athletic Shoes** The buyer for a sporting goods store must decide which athletic shoes to stock for the upcoming selling season. A shoe from one manufacturer comes in 6 different styles and 4 different colors. The buyer decides that the store will stock the shoes in 4 different styles and 2 different colors. How many different shoe combinations are possible?

20. **Committee** You have been working on the prom planning committee with 5 other people. Your committee has decided to choose 2 committee members randomly to present the prom plan to the student body.
    a. How many combinations of 2 committee members are possible?
    b. What is the probability that you are one of the 2 people?

21. **Volunteers** Your class is participating in the school fair and will run the refreshments table. Your teacher has asked for 4 volunteers to run the table. Fifteen of the students in the class volunteer, so your teacher will randomly choose 4 people from the group. You and your friend are part of the group that would like to volunteer. What is the probability that you and your friend are chosen? What is the probability that you are chosen first and your friend is chosen second? Which event is more likely to occur? *Explain* how you found your answer.

LESSON 6.4

Find Probabilities of Compound Events

Georgia Performance Standards: MM1D2a, MM1D2b, MM1D2c

Goal Find the probability of compound events.

Vocabulary

A **compound event** combines two or more events, using the word *and* or the word *or*.

Mutually exclusive events have no common outcomes. **Overlapping events** have at least one common outcome.

Two events are **independent events** if the occurrence of one event has no effect on the occurrence of the other. Two events are **dependent events** if the occurrence of one event affects the occurrence of the other.

The formulas for the probabilities of mutually exclusive events, overlapping events, independent events, and dependent events appear on page 379.

If A and B are dependent events, then the probability that event B will occur given that event A has occurred is called the **conditional probability** of B given A.

Example 1 Find the probability of *A* or *B*

You randomly choose a card from a standard deck of 52 playing cards.

a. Find the probability that you choose a Queen or an Ace.

b. Find the probability that you choose a King or a club.

Solution

a. Choosing a Queen or an Ace are mutually exclusive events.

$$P(\text{Queen or Ace}) = P(\text{Queen}) + P(\text{Ace})$$

$$= \frac{4}{52} + \frac{4}{52}$$

$$= \frac{8}{52} = \frac{2}{13}$$

b. Because there is a King of clubs, choosing a King and a club are overlapping events. There are 4 Kings, 13 clubs, and 1 card that is both.

$$P(\text{King or club}) = P(\text{King}) + P(\text{club}) - P(\text{King and club})$$

$$= \frac{4}{52} + \frac{13}{52} - \frac{1}{52}$$

$$= \frac{16}{52} = \frac{4}{13}$$

Guided Practice for Example 1

1. You choose a card from a standard deck of 52 playing cards. Find the probability that you choose (a) a heart or a spade, and (b) a card with an even number or a heart.

UNIT 6

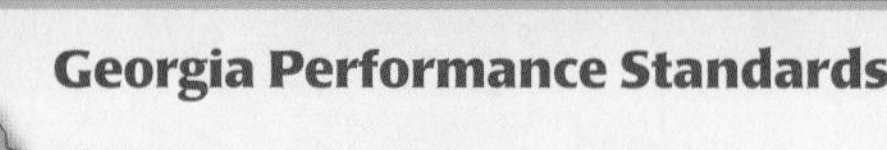

Georgia Performance Standards

MM1D2a Find the probabilities of mutually exclusive events. ☑

MM1D2b Find the probabilities of dependent events. ☑

MM1D2c Calculate conditional probabilities. ☑

Example 2 Find the probability of *A* and *B*

Inspection A quality inspector at a bolt manufacturer randomly selects one bolt from each batch of 50 bolts to inspect for problems or non-conformance. The first batch of 50 bolts has 4 non-conforming bolts. The second batch of 50 bolts has 5 non-conforming bolts. Find the probability that the inspector selects a non-conforming bolt both times.

Solution

The events are independent. The selection from the first batch of bolts does not affect the selection from the second batch of bolts.

$P(\text{non-conforming in batch 1}) = \frac{4}{50}$ $\qquad$ $P(\text{non-conforming in batch 2}) = \frac{5}{50}$

Multiply the probabilities of the two events:

$$P(\text{both bolts non-conforming}) = \frac{4}{50} \cdot \frac{5}{50} = \frac{1}{125}$$

The probability of randomly choosing non-conforming bolts both times is $\frac{1}{125}$.

UNIT 6

Example 3 Find the probability of *A* and *B*

Goldfish An aquarium contains 6 male goldfish and 4 female goldfish. You randomly select a fish from the tank, do not replace it, and then randomly select a second fish. What is the probability that both fish are male?

Solution

Because you do not replace the first fish, the events are dependent. Before selecting the first fish there are 10 fish, 6 of them male. So, the probability that the first fish is male is $\frac{6}{10}$. After the first male fish is selected, there are 9 fish, 5 of them are male. So, the conditional probability that the second fish is male, given that the first fish is male, is $\frac{5}{9}$.

$$P(\text{male and then male}) = P(\text{male}) \cdot P(\text{male given male}) = \frac{6}{10} \cdot \frac{5}{9} = \frac{1}{3}$$

Guided Practice for Examples 2 and 3

2. **Apples** A basket of apples contains 6 red apples, 2 green apples, and 3 yellow apples. You randomly select 2 apples, one at a time. Find the probability that both are yellow if (a) you replace the first apple, then select the second or (b) you eat the first apple, then select the second.

LESSON 6.4 **Exercise Set A**

MM1D2a Find the probabilities of mutually exclusive events.

MM1D2b Find the probabilities of dependent events.

MM1D2c Calculate conditional probabilities.

In Exercises 1–4, you draw a card from a bag that contains 4 yellow cards numbered 1–4 and 5 blue cards numbered 1–5. Tell whether the events *A* and *B* are *mutually exclusive* or *overlapping*. Then find *P*(*A* or *B*).

1. **Event *A*:** You choose a card with an even number.
   Event *B*: You choose a number 4 card.

2. **Event *A*:** You choose a yellow card.
   Event *B*: You choose a number 5 card.

3. **Event *A*:** You choose a blue number 3 card.
   Event *B*: You choose a blue card.

4. **Event *A*:** You choose a card with an odd number.
   Event *B*: You choose a blue card.

In Exercises 5 and 6, tell whether the events *A* and *B* are *dependent* or *independent*. Then find *P*(*A* and *B*).

5. A bag contains 6 red balls and 5 green balls. You randomly draw one ball, replace it, and randomly draw a second ball.
   Event *A*: The first ball is green.
   Event *B*: The second ball is green.

6. You write each of the letters of the word BRILLIANT on pieces of paper and place them in a bag. You randomly draw one letter, do not replace it, then randomly draw a second letter.
   Event *A*: The first letter is an L.
   Event *B*: The second letter is a T.

7. **Eating Habits** A survey of 500 students in a school found that about 100 households consist of only vegetarians, 240 consist of vegetarians and non-vegetarians, and 160 consist of only non-vegetarians.
   a. What is the probability that one of the households surveyed, chosen at random, consists of only vegetarians or only non-vegetarians?
   b. What is the probability that one of the households surveyed, chosen at random, consists of vegetarians and non-vegetarians?
   c. *Explain* how your answers to parts (a) and (b) are related.

8. **Coordinating Time** You study with a group for an upcoming math competition on Mondays, Tuesdays, and Thursdays. You volunteer at a hospital on Mondays, Wednesdays, and Thursdays.
   a. Make a Venn diagram that shows the days of the week that you participate in each activity.
   b. Your class is taking a field trip that could be scheduled for any day of the week (Monday through Friday). Find the probability that it is scheduled for a day when you are studying with your group or are volunteering.

LESSON 6.4

Exercise Set B

MM1D2a Find the probabilities of mutually exclusive events.

MM1D2b Find the probabilities of dependent events.

MM1D2c Calculate conditional probabilities.

In Exercises 1–4, you draw a card from a bag that contains 6 yellow cards numbered 1–6 and 5 blue cards numbered 1–5. Tell whether the events *A* and *B* are *mutually exclusive* or *overlapping*. Then find *P*(*A* or *B*).

1. **Event A:** You choose a blue card.
   Event B: You choose a number 6 card.

2. **Event A:** You choose a blue card.
   Event B: You choose a card with a prime number.

3. **Event A:** You choose a yellow card.
   Event B: You choose a card with an odd number.

4. **Event A:** You choose a card with an odd number.
   Event B: You choose a blue card.

In Exercises 5 and 6, tell whether the events *A* and *B* are *dependent* or *independent*. Then find *P*(*A* and *B*).

5. A bag contains 4 red balls, 3 yellow balls, and 6 green balls. You randomly draw one ball, replace it, and randomly draw a second ball.

   Event A: The first ball is green.

   Event B: The second ball is yellow.

6. You write each of the letters of the word MASTERMIND on pieces of paper and place them in a bag. You randomly draw one letter, do not replace it, then randomly draw a second letter.

   Event A: The first letter is an N.

   Event B: The second letter is an M.

7. **Multiple Representations** You practice with your debate team on Tuesdays, Wednesdays, and Thursdays. You volunteer at a food kitchen on Mondays, Wednesdays, and Fridays.
   a. **Making a Table** Make a table that shows your schedule for the week.
   b. **Drawing a Diagram** Make a Venn diagram that shows the days of the week that you participate in each activity.
   c. **Using a Formula** Your class is taking a field trip that could be scheduled for any day of the week (Monday through Friday). Find the probability that it is scheduled for a day when you are practicing with the debate team or are volunteering.

8. **Driving** You and five friends have rented a minivan for a road trip. To decide who will drive the first leg of the trip, you place 6 slips of paper in a bag, each of which is labeled with the position in the minivan. Everyone chooses a slip of paper from the bag at random.
   a. What is the probability that you will have to drive?
   b. What is the probability that you will have to drive and your best friend will be in the passenger seat next to you?
   c. *Explain* how you could solve the problem in part (b) by using permutations.

LESSON 6.5

Find Expected Value

Georgia Performance Standards: MM1D2d

Goal Use expected value.

Vocabulary

A collection of outcomes is partitioned into n events, no two of which have any outcomes in common. The probabilities of the n events occurring are $p_1, p_2, p_3, \ldots, p_n$ where $p_1 + p_2 + p_3 + \cdots + p_n = 1$. The values of the n events are $x_1, x_2, x_3, \ldots, x_n$. The **expected value** E of the collection of outcomes is the sum of the products of the events' probabilities and their values.

$$E = p_1x_1 + p_2x_2 + p_3x_3 + \cdots + p_nx_n$$

Example 1 Find an expected value

Consider a game in which two players each choose an integer from 1 to 3. If the sum of the two integers is even, then player A scores 4 points and player B loses 2 points. If the sum is odd, then player B scores 4 points and player A loses 2 points. Find the expected value for player A.

Solution

The possible outcomes are $1 + 1, 1 + 2, 1 + 3, 2 + 1, 2 + 2, 2 + 3, 3 + 1, 3 + 2$, and $3 + 3$. The probability of an even sum is $\frac{5}{9}$. The probability of an odd sum is $\frac{4}{9}$.

Player A: $E = 4\left(\frac{5}{9}\right) + (-2)\left(\frac{4}{9}\right) = \frac{12}{9} = \frac{4}{3}$

Example 2 Use expected value

Test Strategy You take an exam that has 4 possible answers for each question. You gain 3 points for each correct answer, lose 1 point for each incorrect answer, and do not gain or lose points for answers left blank. If you do not know the correct answer to a particular question, is it to your advantage to guess the answer?

STEP 1 **Find** the probability of each outcome. Because each question has 4 possible answers and only 1 correct answer, the probability of guessing correctly is $\frac{1}{4}$ and the probability of guessing incorrectly is $\frac{3}{4}$.

STEP 2 **Find** the expected value of guessing an answer. Multiply the points gained or lost by the corresponding probability. Then find the sum of these products.

$$E = 3\left(\frac{1}{4}\right) + (-1)\left(\frac{3}{4}\right) = 0$$

Because the expected value is zero when guessing, it is neither to your advantage nor to your disadvantage to guess.

Georgia Performance Standards

MM1D2d Use expected value to predict outcomes. 

Example 3 Find expected value

Raffle At a raffle, 2500 tickets are sold at \$5 each for three prizes of \$1000, \$500, and \$100. You buy one ticket. What is the expected value of your gain?

Solution

STEP 1 **Find** the gain for each prize by subtracting the price of the ticket from the prize. For instance, your gain for the \$1000 prize is $\$1000 - \$5 = \$995$.

STEP 2 **Find** the probability of each outcome.

There are 2500 tickets sold, so for each prize, the probability that you will win is $\frac{1}{2500}$. Because there are 3 prizes, there are 3 winning tickets and $2500 - 3 = 2497$ losing tickets. So, the probability that you will *not* win a prize is $\frac{2497}{2500}$.

STEP 3 **Summarize** the information in a table.

Gain, *x*	\$995	\$495	\$95	−\$5
Probability, *p*	$\frac{1}{2500}$	$\frac{1}{2500}$	$\frac{1}{2500}$	$\frac{2497}{2500}$

STEP 4 **Find** the expected value by finding the sum of the value of each outcome multiplied by its corresponding probability.

$$E = \$995\left(\frac{1}{2500}\right) + \$495\left(\frac{1}{2500}\right) + \$95\left(\frac{1}{2500}\right) + (-\$5)\left(\frac{2497}{2500}\right)$$

$$= -\$4.36$$

The expected value of your gain is −\$4.36. This means that you can expect to lose an average of \$4.36 for each ticket you buy.

Guided Practice for Examples 1, 2, and 3

1. **What If?** In Example 1, suppose that if the sum of the two integers is odd, then player A loses that sum of points, and player B scores that sum of points. If the sum is even, then Player B loses 4 points and Player A scores 4 points. Find the expected value for each player.

2. **What If?** In Example 2, suppose there are 5 possible answers for each question. Is it to your advantage to guess the answer to a question? *Explain.*

3. **Fundraiser** At a fundraiser, 8000 tickets are sold at \$10 each for four prizes: a new car worth \$30,000, a European vacation worth \$9000, a home theater system worth \$4000, and a cash prize of \$1000. You buy one ticket. What is the expected value of your gain?

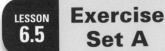

LESSON 6.5

Exercise Set A

MM1D2d Use expected value to predict outcomes.

In Exercises 1 and 2, use the information in the table to find the expected value.

1.

Outcome value, x	-2	2
Probability, p	0.32	0.68

2.

Outcome value, x	15	45	30
Probability, p	$\frac{1}{2}$	$\frac{1}{3}$	$\frac{1}{6}$

3. **Coin Game** Consider a game in which two players each flip a coin. If both coins land heads up, then player A scores 3 points and player B loses 3 points. If one or both of the coins land tails up, then player B scores 1 point and player A loses 1 point. Find the expected value of the game for each player.

4. **Basketball** Amanda has injured her leg and may not be able to play in the next basketball game. If she can play, the coach estimates the team will score 68 points. If she is not able to play, the coach estimates the team will score 54 points. Her doctor states there is a 50% chance she will be able to play and a 50% chance she will not be able to play. Determine the expected number of points the team scores.

5. **Lawn Mowing** A landscaper mows 25 lawns per day on sunny days and 15 lawns per day on cloudy days. If the weather is sunny 65% of the time and cloudy 35% of the time, find the expected number of lawns the landscaper mows per day.

6. **Seminar Attendance** A hospital is holding a public seminar. Officials estimate that 24 people will attend if it does not rain and 16 people will attend if it rains. The weather forecast indicates there is a 30% chance it will rain on the day of the seminar. Find the expected number of people who will attend the seminar.

7. **Multiple Representations** In a proposed business venture, a company estimates that there is a 60% probability it will make $95,000, a 20% probability it will break even, and a 20% probability it will lose $65,000.

a. **Making a Table** Make a table that shows each amount and its corresponding probability.

b. **Using a Formula** Use the information in the table to find the expected value.

c. **Applying Expected Value** How much can the company expect to gain or lose?

8. **Test Taking Strategy** You are taking an exam in which there are 5 possible choices for each question. The instructions indicate that you will gain 4 points for each correct answer, lose 3 points for each incorrect answer, and that no points will be lost or gained for answers left blank.

a. If you do not know the correct answer to a particular question, is it to your advantage or disadvantage to guess the answer? *Explain.*

b. Suppose you do not know the correct answer but you can eliminate one of the choices. Is it to your advantage or disadvantage to guess the answer? *Explain.*

9. **Raffle** Two thousand raffle tickets are sold for $1 each. One prize worth $400 is to be awarded. What is your expected value if you purchase one ticket?

LESSON 6.5

Exercise Set B

MM1D2d Use expected value to predict outcomes.

In Exercises 1 and 2, use the information in the table to find the expected value.

1.

Outcome value, *x*	8000	−8000	4000
Probability, *p*	0.39	0.43	0.18

2.

Outcome value, *x*	12	19	36	−3
Probability, *p*	$\frac{1}{2}$	$\frac{1}{4}$	$\frac{1}{6}$	$\frac{1}{12}$

3. **Integer Game** Consider a game in which two players each choose an integer from 1 to 5. If the product of the two integers is even, then player A scores 5 points and player B loses 2 points. If the product of the two integers is odd, then player B scores 5 points and player A loses 2 points. Find the expected value of the game for each player.

4. **Airline Profit** An airline is considering adding a route to the city of Shreveport, Louisiana. Market research predicts that if the airline serves Shreveport, there is a 42% probability of making a \$700,000 profit, a 22% probability of breaking even, and a 36% probability of losing \$1,000,000. What is the expected value of adding a route to Shreveport?

5. **Number Cube Game** You are playing a number cube game in which you need to score 80 points to win. On each turn, you roll two six-sided number cubes. Your score for the turn is 0 if the number cubes do not show the same number. Your score for the turn is the product of the numbers if they do show the same number. What is the expected value for each turn? How many turns will it take on average to score 80 points?

6. **Sales** During a one-year selling period (225 days), a sales representative made between 0 and 8 sales per day, as shown in the table.

Number of sales per day, *x*	0	1	2	3	4	5	6	7	8
Frequency, *f* (in days)	35	43	54	44	23	12	9	4	1

   a. Identify the possible outcomes and find the probability of each number of sales per day.

   b. If this pattern continues, what is the expected value for the number of sales per day for the sales representative?

7. **Contest** A national restaurant chain is having a contest with five prizes. No purchase is necessary to enter. What is the expected value of one contest entry?

Prize	**Value**	**Probability of winning**
Gift certificate	\$10	0.0002
Wide-screen TV	\$3000	0.0000004
Vacation getaway	\$12,000	0.00000008
Car	\$60,000	0.000000003
Cash	\$1,000,000	0.000000002

UNIT 6

LESSON 6.6

Analyze Surveys and Samples

Georgia Performance Standards: MM1D3c

Goal Identify populations and sampling methods.

Vocabulary

A **survey** is a study of one or more characteristics of a group.

The entire group you want information about is called a **population.**

A **sample** is a part of the population.

In a **random sample,** every member of the population has an equal chance of being selected.

In a **stratified random sample,** the population is divided into distinct groups. Members are selected at random from each group.

In a **systematic sample,** a rule is used to select members of the population.

In a **convenience sample,** only members of the population who are easily accessible are selected.

In a **self-selected sample,** members of the population select themselves by volunteering.

A **representative sample** is a sample that accurately reflects the characteristics of a population.

A **biased sample** is a sample that is not representative of the population.

A question that encourages a particular response is a **biased question.**

UNIT 6

Example 1 Classify a sampling method

Library survey A university is conducting a survey to determine whether a public library has hours of business that satisfy most of its patrons. At the library, students question every tenth library patron who exits the library. Identify the population and classify the sampling method.

Solution

The population is all library patrons. Because a rule is used to select members of the population (every tenth patron), the sample is a systematic sample.

Guided Practice for Example 1

1. **What If?** In Example 1, suppose the university students conduct the survey by asking all patrons checking out books to fill out a form and mail it back to the university. Classify the sampling method.

Representative Samples A sample chosen for a survey should be representative of the population. Random samples and stratified random samples are the most likely types of samples to be representative. A systematic sample (as in Example 1) may be representative if the rule used to choose individuals is not biased. In a biased sample, parts of the population may be over-represented or under-represented.

Georgia Performance Standards

MM1D3c Understand that a random sample is used to improve the chance of selecting a representative sample. 

Example 2 Identify a potentially biased sample

In Example 1, suppose the university students question 20 library patrons chosen at random on a Monday morning between 9:00 A.M. and 11:00 A.M. Is this method likely to result in a *representative sample* or a *biased sample*? Explain.

Solution

Because school-age children may be in school and many working adults may be at work, this method may not select an adequate sample of the population. Therefore the method may result in a biased sample.

Biased Questions A question that encourages a particular response is a biased question. Survey questions should be worded to avoid bias.

Example 3 Identify potentially biased questions

Tell whether the question is potentially biased. Explain your answer. If the question is potentially biased, rewrite it so that it is not.

a. Because there is a lack of affordable entertainment for teenagers in the city, do you think the city should sponsor more youth activities?

b. Do you think the city should risk an increase in taxes by allowing a new elementary school to be built?

Solution

a. This question is biased because it suggests that there is a lack of affordable activities for teenagers. An unbiased question is "Do you think the city should sponsor more youth activities?"

b. This question is biased because it encourages a negative response by suggesting that building a new elementary school may increase taxes. An unbiased question is "Do you think a new elementary school is necessary?"

Guided Practice for Examples 2 and 3

2. Driving Tests In a survey about the need to improve driver safety, 50 randomly selected adults at a senior-citizen resident facility were asked, "Do you think driver safety would improve if drivers were required to pass a driving test every ten years when renewing a driver's license?"

a. Is the sampling method likely to result in a *representative sample* or a *biased sample*? *Explain.*

b. Is the question potentially biased? *Explain* your answer. If the question is potentially biased, rewrite it so that it is not.

LESSON 6.6

Exercise Set A

MM1D3c Understand that a random sample is used to improve the chance of selecting a representative sample.

Identify the population and classify the sampling method.

1. The manager of a music store wants to evaluate how customers rate the selection of music the store has in stock. Customers are given comment cards with their receipts.

2. Your school's administrators want to know if students are satisfied with the choices of activities for activity period. In each grade, every seventh student in alphabetical order is surveyed.

In Exercises 3 and 4, tell whether the survey method used is likely to result in a *representative sample* or a *biased sample*. *Explain*.

3. A bicycling club wants to gather information about biking conditions throughout a city. A survey for bicycle riders is posted on the club's website.

4. A management company that owns several apartment buildings wants to gather information about tenant satisfaction with the condition of the apartments. They survey 30 random tenants in each of the buildings.

5. **Error Analysis** The Student Council wants to produce an unbiased sample to find out if students prefer to attend sporting events or performances such as school plays and concerts. *Describe* and correct the error in the sampling method.

Student Council members survey the students at a drama club meeting after school.

UNIT 6

Tell whether the question is potentially biased. *Explain* your answer.

6. Don't you think that the lunch menu should include grilled chicken rather than pizza because grilled chicken is healthier for you?

7. Do you think that the city's excess revenue should be spent on road repairs or building a new sports stadium?

In Exercises 8 and 9, explain why the question is biased. Then rewrite it so that it is not.

8. Don't you agree that it is better to offer an accounting class as an elective rather than a computer programming class?

9. Would you pay even higher taxes to fund a new highway?

10. **Bus Stop Conditions** A newspaper does a report on the condition of the bus stops in a large city. Part of the report includes a survey of people living in the area. The survey is done by asking people at a local mall what they think of the condition of the bus stops. Is the sample likely to be representative or biased? *Explain.*

11. **Afterschool Activities** You plan a report on the participation of students at your school in afterschool activities for your school's website. *Describe* how you could choose a representative sample. *Justify* your sampling method.

LESSON 6.6 **Exercise Set B**

MM1D3c Understand that a random sample is used to improve the chance of selecting a representative sample.

In Exercises 1 and 2, identify the population and classify the sampling method.

1. Your school's administrators want to know where students want to go on the class trip at the end of the year. The administrators randomly survey 30 freshmen, 30 sophomores, 30 juniors, and 30 seniors.

2. The manager at a local bookstore is selecting authors for readings at the bookstore. The bookstore surveys every other person who buys books at the store to determine which authors will bring in the biggest audience.

In Exercises 3 and 4, tell whether the survey method used is likely to result in a *representative sample* or a *biased sample*. *Explain*.

3. The owners of an ice cream shop want to determine whether or not they should keep their stores open an hour later. They survey the customers in one of their stores at random.

4. A group of students at your school wants to gather information about the need for additional funding for the school library. They survey every third person in the library.

In Exercises 5 and 6, tell whether the question is potentially biased. *Explain* your answer.

5. Do you think that the city bus schedule should run later in the day?

6. Don't you agree that a new baseball stadium should be built because baseball is America's favorite sport?

In Exercises 7 and 8, explain why the question is biased. Then rewrite it so that it is not.

7. Don't you agree that it is better to offer two hot lunches on the menu rather than a cold lunch and a hot lunch?

8. Don't you agree that a moped is more fun to ride than a bicycle?

9. **School Sports** You plan to report for your school newspaper on which sport students would like added to the athletic program. *Describe* how you could choose a representative sample. *Justify* your sampling method. Then write at least one unbiased question you could use to collect information. *Explain* why your question is unbiased.

10. **Stratified Random Sample** A stratified random sample of a population is used for a survey that contains unbiased questions. *Explain* how it is possible for the survey to be biased. *Describe* a situation in which this might occur.

LESSON 6.7

Use Measures of Central Tendency and Dispersion

Georgia Performance Standards: MM1D4

Goal Compare meaures of central tendency and dispersion.

Vocabulary

The **mean,** or average, of a numerical data set is denoted by $\bar{x}$, which is read "x-bar."

For the data set $x_1, x_2, \ldots, x_n$, the mean is $\bar{x} = \frac{x_1 + x_2 + \cdots + x_n}{n}$.

The **median** of a numerical data set is the middle number when the values are written in numerical order. If the data set has an even number of values, the median is the mean of the two middle values.

The **mode** of a data set is the value that occurs most frequently. There may be one mode, no mode, or more than one mode.

A **measure of dispersion** describes the dispersion, or spread of data.

The **range** of a numerical data set gives the length of the interval containing the data. It is the difference of the greatest value and the least value of a numerical data set.

The **deviation from the mean** is the difference of a data value and the mean of a data set.

The **mean absolute deviation** of a numerical data set is the average deviation of the data from the mean. The mean absolute deviation of the data $x_1, x_2, \ldots, x_n$ is given by:

$$\text{Mean absolute deviation} = \frac{|x_1 - \bar{x}| + |x_2 - \bar{x}| + \cdots + |x_n - \bar{x}|}{n}$$

UNIT 6

Example 1 Compare measures of central tendency

Test Scores The test scores received by students on a history exam are listed below. Which measure of central tendency best represents the data?

65, 68, 71, 77, 81, 82, 86, 88, 93, 93, 95, 97

Solution

$$\bar{x} = \frac{65 + 68 + 71 + 77 + 81 + 82 + 86 + 88 + 93 + 93 + 95 + 97}{12}$$

$$= \frac{996}{12}$$

$$= 83$$

The median is the mean of the two middle values, 84.

The mode is 93.

The mean and median best represent the data. The mode is significantly greater than most of the data.

Georgia Performance Standards

MM1D4 Students will explore variability of data by determining the mean absolute deviation (the average of the absolute values of the deviations).

Example 2 Compare measures of dispersion

Golf Tournament In a golf tournament, the 18-hole totals for the top 6 golfers in the men's competition and the top 6 golfers in the women's competition are given. Compare the spread of the data for the two sets using (a) the range and (b) the mean absolute deviation.

Tournament Leader Board	
Men	**Women**
67	68
69	70
69	72
71	73
74	74
76	75

Solution

a. Men: $76 - 67 = 9$ Women: $75 - 68 = 7$

The range of the men's set is greater than the range of the women's set. So, the data in the men's set cover a wider interval than the data in the women's set.

b. The mean of the men's set is 71, so the mean absolute deviation is:

$$\frac{|67 - 71| + |69 - 71| + \cdots + |76 - 71|}{6} = \frac{16}{6} = 2.\overline{6}$$

The mean of the women's set is 72, so the mean absolute deviation is:

$$\frac{|68 - 72| + |70 - 72| + \cdots + |75 - 72|}{6} = \frac{12}{6} = 2$$

The mean absolute deviation of the men's set is greater, so the average variation from the mean is greater for the data in the men's set than for the data in the women's set.

Guided Practice for Examples 1 and 2

In Exercises 1 and 2, use the data: 5, 9, 11, 12, 13, 15, 15, 22, 60.

1. Find the mean, median, and mode of the data.
2. Which measure of central tendency best represents the data?
3. **Golf Tournament** In a golf tournament, the top 6 men's scores and women's scores are given. *Compare* the spread of the data for the two sets of scores using (a) the range and (b) the mean absolute deviation.

   Men's: 65, 68, 70, 72, 73, 75

   Women's: 69, 71, 73, 74, 77, 80
4. **Swimming** The top 8 finishing times (in seconds) for swimmers in the 50-yard freestyle and the 100-yard freestyle are given. *Compare* the spread of the data for the two sets using (a) the range and (b) the mean absolute deviation.

   50-yard: 24.22, 24.26, 24.33, 24.44, 24.55, 24.75, 24.91, 25.02

   100-yard: 52.84, 52.91, 52.96, 52.98, 53.02, 53.09, 53.15, 53.24

LESSON 6.7 **Exercise Set A**

MM1D4 Students will explore variability of data by determining the mean absolute deviation (the average of the absolute values of the deviations).

Find the mean, median, and mode(s) of the data.

1. 6, 1, 3, 8, 5, 11, 1, 5
2. 15, 27, 10, 25, 9, 22, 25
3. 23, 6, 8, 14, 28, 8, 13, 28
4. 4.2, 2.2, 3.7, 2.8, 1.1

For the set of data, determine which measure of central tendency best represents the data.

5. 89, 86, 96, 87, 100, 86
6. 38, 35, 40, 36, 36, 33, 42, 37, 39, 34
7. 87, 77, 151, 105, 65, 141, 104, 166
8. 100, 106, 180, 41, 161, 292, 116, 213

Find the range and mean absolute deviation of the data. Round to the nearest hundredth, if necessary.

9. 10, 7, 13, 10, 8
10. 110, 114, 104, 108, 106
11. 87, 75, 85, 77, 74, 82
12. 15, 17, 15, 17, 21, 17, 15, 23
13. 40, 46, 41, 46, 49, 49, 46, 44, 44
14. 50.8, 51.6, 51.9, 52, 52.5, 52.8, 53.1

15. **Bean Plants** The heights (in inches) of eight bean plants are 28, 36, 41, 50, 35, 42, 46, and 52.
    a. What is the range of the bean plant heights?
    b. Find the mean, median, and mode(s) of the bean plant heights.
    c. Which measure of central tendency best represents the data? *Explain.*

16. **Hotel Stay** You are planning a trip to Washington, D.C. and are looking up hotel room rates. On the Internet, you find the following rates for a one-night stay in a hotel in Washington, D.C.

    $109, $126.50, $175.95, $139, $77.50, $145, $162.35, $173, $181.50, $105

    a. Find the mean, median, and mode(s) of the rates.
    b. Which measure of central tendency best represents the data? *Explain.*

17. **Temperature** The high and low temperatures for the last seven days are given.

    High temperatures: 81°F, 78°F, 83°F, 89°F, 90°F, 87°F, 89°F

    Low temperatures: 64°F, 53°F, 62°F, 66°F, 68°F, 69°F, 67°F

    a. Find the mean, median, and mode of each data set. Round your answers to the nearest tenth.
    b. For each data set, determine which measure of central tendency best represents the data. *Explain.*
    c. *Compare* the spreads of data by using the range.
    d. *Compare* the spreads of data by using the mean absolute deviation. Round your answers to the nearest hundredth.

UNIT 6

LESSON 6.7

Exercise Set B

MM1D4 Students will explore variability of data by determining the mean absolute deviation (the average of the absolute values of the deviations).

Find the mean, median, and mode(s) of the data.

1. 48, 23, 97, 36, 27, 72, 48, 41, 58

2. 420, 360, 398, 196, 398, 400

3. 330, 410, 212, 335, 245, 410, 390, 300

4. 5.04, 5.13, 4.68, 4.52, 5.08

5. 7.8, 7.2, 8.0, 7.5, 8.2, 7.5

6. 15.8, 15.2, 14.9, 15.9, 15.4, 15.2

For the set of data, determine which measure of central tendency best represents the data.

7. 6.2, 4.8, 5.8, 5.4, 5.2

8. 161, 200, 239, 252, 278, 317, 382, 395

9. 25, 27, 27, 25, 25, 29, 33, 27

10. 9.04, 8.88, 5.2, 9.52, 5.6, 12.44

Find the range and mean absolute deviation of the data. Round to the nearest hundredth, if necessary.

11. 13, 15, 9, 35, 25

12. 43, 57, 58, 47, 40, 50, 38, 52

13. 1.10, 1.70, 1.35, 1.45, 1.60, 1.85, 1.50

14. 410, 408, 505, 530, 490, 485, 492, 510

15. 64.2, 68.1, 55.7, 59.2, 48.3, 54.7, 77.3

16. 80, 125, 146, 134, 290, 125, 116, 125

17. Create a data set that has a mean of 15, a median of 15, and modes of 7 and 10.

18. **Population Densities** The population densities (in people per square mile) of the 10 fastest-growing big cities in the United States in 2003 were 2696, 3649, 4563, 3380, 1183, 4180, 3459, 2396, 2764, and 2924. The population densities of the 10 fastest-shrinking big cities in the United States in 2003 were 5367, 7781, 7020, 5851, 4069, 6566, 1579, 4501, 5945, and 3833.

a. Find the mean, median, and mode of each data set.

b. For each data set, determine which measure of central tendency best represents the data. *Explain.*

c. *Compare* the spreads of data by using the range.

d. *Compare* the spreads of data by using the mean absolute deviation.

19. **Golf** So far this season, your golfing scores have been 90, 108, 88, 75, 95, and 101. You will golf one more time this season, and want to finish the season with an average of 90 or less.

a. Let x represent your last golf score. Write an expression for the mean of your golf scores. Then write and solve an inequality to find the possible scores you can achieve in order to meet your goal.

b. After you finish the last round, your friend adds up your score and tells you that the median of your seven scores is 95. Can you tell whether you met your goal? *Explain.*

UNIT 6

Georgia Performance Standards

MM1D4 Students will explore variability of data by determining the mean absolute deviation (the average of the absolute values of the deviations).

Technology Activity

Finding the Mean Absolute Deviation

Use after Lesson 6.7

Question

How can you use a graphing calculator to find the mean, median, and mean absolute deviation of a data set?

Example

Find the mean, median, and mean absolute deviation of a data set.

Use a graphing calculator to find the mean, median, and mean absolute deviation of the data listed below.

10, 5, 2, 8, 13, 3, 14, 1, 12, 6, 1, 19, 17, 6, 15

STEP 1 Enter the data in list L_1.

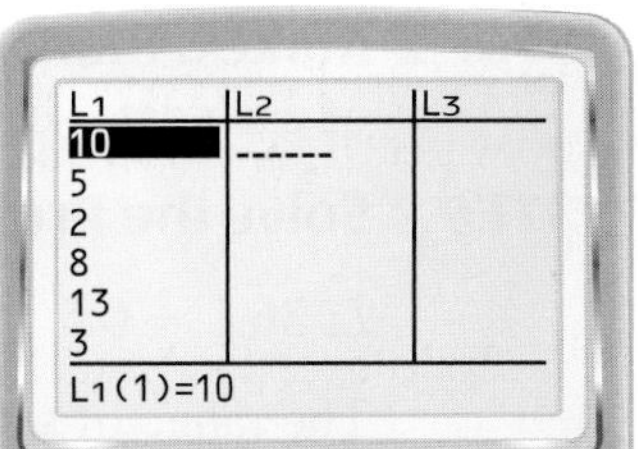

STEP 2 Press **2nd** [LIST]. From the MATH submenu, choose *mean* and then *median*.

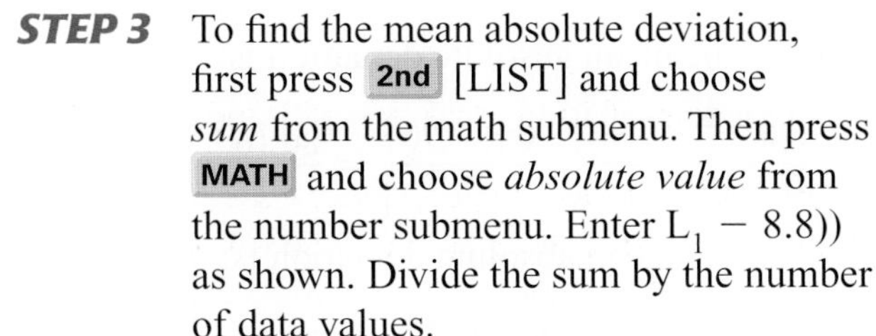

STEP 3 To find the mean absolute deviation, first press **2nd** [LIST] and choose *sum* from the math submenu. Then press **MATH** and choose *absolute value* from the number submenu. Enter $L_1 - 8.8$)) as shown. Divide the sum by the number of data values.

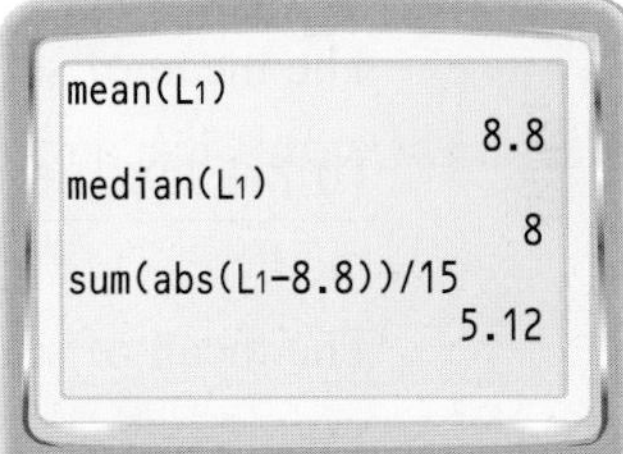

Practice

In Exercises 1–3, use a graphing calculator to find the mean, median, and mean absolute deviation of the data. Round to the nearest tenth, if necessary.

1. 5, 3, 15, 5, 12, 17, 19, 10, 2, 9, 13, 8, 17
2. 7.6, 1.9, 4.5, 4.3, 3.1, 2.7, 3.1, 8.1, 5.2, 4.7
3. 1559, 2795, 1380, 2044, 1653, 2400, 2926, 2850, 2297, 2396, 1030
4. The data set below gives the ages of the first 43 presidents of the United States when they first took office. Use a graphing calculator to find the mean, median, and mean absolute deviation of the data set.

   57, 61, 57, 57, 58, 57, 61, 54, 68, 51, 49, 64, 50, 48, 65, 52, 56, 46, 54, 49, 51, 47, 55, 55, 54, 42, 51, 56, 55, 51, 54, 51, 60, 62, 43, 55, 56, 61, 52, 69, 64, 46, 54

UNIT 6

Georgia Performance Standards

MM1D4 Students will explore variability of data by determining the mean absolute deviation (the average of the absolute values of the deviations).

LESSON 6.7

Problem Solving Workshop

Problem The populations (in millions) of the 10 largest states by land area and the 10 smallest states by land area in 2005 are given. *Compare* the spread of the data for the two sets using the range and the mean absolute deviation.

Largest (L): 0.7, 22.9, 36.1, 0.9, 1.9, 5.9, 2.4, 4.7, 0.5, 3.6
Smallest (S): 1.1, 0.8, 3.5, 1.3, 8.7, 6.4, 1.3, 0.6, 5.6, 1.8

STEP 1 **Read and Understand**

What do you know?

The populations of the 10 largest and 10 smallest states by land area

What do you want to find out?

The comparisons between the ranges and mean absolute deviations

STEP 2 **Make a Plan** Use what you know to find the range and mean absolute deviation of each data set.

STEP 3 **Solve the Problem** Find the range of each data set.

L: $36.1 - 0.5 = 35.6$ S: $8.7 - 0.6 = 8.1$

The range of set L is greater than the range of set S. So, the data in set L cover a wider interval than the data in set S.

The mean of set L is 7.96, so the mean absolute deviation is:

$$\frac{|0.7 - 7.96| + |22.9 - 7.96| + \cdots + |3.6 - 7.96|}{10} = \frac{86.16}{10} = 8.616$$

The mean of set S is 3.11, so the mean absolute deviation is:

$$\frac{|1.1 - 3.11| + |0.8 - 3.11| + \cdots + |1.8 - 3.11|}{10} = \frac{23.52}{10} = 2.352$$

The mean absolute deviation of set L is greater, so the average variation from the mean is greater for the data in set L than for the data in set S.

STEP 4 **Look Back** Double-check to make sure that you did not forget any numbers when calculating the mean absolute deviations.

Practice

1. **What If?** Suppose the first 5 numbers in each data set above give the populations (in millions) of the 5 largest states by land area and the 5 smallest states by land area in 2005. *Compare* the spread of the data for the two sets using the range and the mean absolute deviation.

2. **Salary** The salaries (in thousands of dollars) for all 6 employees at business A and business B are given. *Compare* the spread of the data for the two sets using the range and the mean absolute deviation.

   A: 24, 22, 18, 28, 26, 75
   B: 64, 26, 54, 20, 25, 48

UNIT 6

LESSON 6.8

Compare Statistics from Samples

Georgia Performance Standards: MM1D3a, MM1D3b

Goal Compare statistics from different samples.

Vocabulary

A **quartile** is the median of an ordered data set, the median of the upper half of an ordered data set, called the **upper quartile,** or the median of the lower half of an ordered data set, called the **lower quartile.**

The **interquartile range** of a data set is the difference between the upper quartile and the lower quartile.

Example 1 Compare statistics from different samples

Baseball The data sets below give the number of home runs by each player on the Bears and Wildcats during a season of the Oakmont Baseball League. Compare the data using the mean, median, range, and interquartile range.

Bears: 28, 25, 21, 19, 18, 14, 10, 8, 7, 5, 3, 2

Wildcats: 20, 19, 18, 16, 15, 15, 12, 11, 9, 8, 6, 5, 4

Solution

Bears' Statistics	Wildcats' Statistics
$\bar{x} = \frac{28 + 25 + \cdots + 2}{12} = \frac{160}{12} \approx 13.3$	$\bar{x} = \frac{20 + 19 + \cdots + 4}{13} = \frac{158}{13} \approx 12.2$
Median: $\frac{14 + 10}{2} = \frac{24}{2} = 12$	Median: 12
Range: $28 - 2 = 26$	Range: $20 - 4 = 16$
Lower Quartile: $\frac{7 + 5}{2} = \frac{12}{2} = 6$	Lower Quartile: $\frac{8 + 6}{2} = \frac{14}{2} = 7$
Upper Quartile: $\frac{21 + 19}{2} = \frac{40}{2} = 20$	Upper Quartile: $\frac{18 + 16}{2} = \frac{34}{2} = 17$
Interquartile Range: $20 - 6 = 14$	Interquartile Range: $17 - 7 = 10$

The Bears' mean is greater than the Wildcats' mean, so the Bears averaged more home runs per player than the Wildcats.

The Wildcats' range is less than the Bears' range, so their data is less spread out than the Bears' data.

The Wildcats' interquartile range is less than the Bears' interquartile range, so the Wildcats' middle 50% of the data showed less variation than the middle 50% of the Bears' data.

Georgia Performance Standards

MM1D3a Compare summary statistics (mean, median, quartiles, and interquartile range) from one sample data distribution to another sample data distribution in describing center and variability of the data distributions. 

MM1D3b Compare the averages of the summary statistics from a large number of samples to the corresponding population parameters. ☑

Guided Practice for Example 1

1. **What If?** In Example 1, suppose the numbers of home runs by each player on the Ravens baseball team are 28, 24, 18, 18, 17, 16, 15, 15, 13, 10, and 8. *Compare* the Ravens' data and the Wildcats' data using the mean, range, and interquartile range.

Example 2 Compare sample and population statistics

Baseball At the end of the season, summary home run statistics for the Oakmont Baseball League were posted. The table below shows the summary data for the Bisons, the Tigers, and for the entire league. Find the averages of the summary statistics from four samples: the Bears and the Wildcats from Example 1, the Bisons, and the Tigers. Then compare each average statistic to the population measure.

	Mean	Median	Range	Interquartile Range
Bisons	10.5	11.5	22	14.5
Tigers	13.4	13	26	16.5
League	11.6	12	28	15

Solution

Average Mean: $\bar{x} \approx \frac{13.3 + 12.2 + 10.5 + 13.4}{4} = \frac{49.4}{4} = 12.35$

Average Median: $\frac{12 + 12 + 11.5 + 13}{4} = \frac{48.5}{4} = 12.125$

Average Range: $\frac{26 + 16 + 22 + 26}{4} = \frac{90}{4} = 22.5$

Average Interquartile Range: $\frac{14 + 10 + 14.5 + 16.5}{4} = \frac{55}{4} = 13.75$

The average mean and median are more than the corresponding population measures. The average range and interquartile range are less than the corresponding population measures.

Guided Practice for Example 2

2. **What If?** The table shows the summary home run statistics for the Cougars. How does inclusion of the Cougars' statistics change the averages in Example 2?

	Mean	Median	Range	Interquartile Range
Cougars	14	15	26	21

LESSON 6.8

Exercise Set A

MM1D3a Compare summary statistics (mean, median, quartiles, and interquartile range) from one sample data distribution to another sample data distribution in describing center and variability of the data distributions.

MM1D3b Compare the averages of the summary statistics from a large number of samples to the corresponding population parameters.

In Exercises 1–4, find the mean, median, range, lower quartile, upper quartile, and interquartile range of the data set.

1. 5, 9, 3, 6, 12, 10, 8, 7, 12
2. 54, 32, 87, 49, 67, 45, 71, 58, 64, 76
3. 5.9, 7.1, 2.4, 1.9, 5.5, 4.3, 6.7, 3.8
4. 110, 65, 141, 126, 99, 81, 156, 184, 73

5. **Error Analysis** *Describe* and correct the error in finding the quartiles of the given data set.

   23, 16, 12, 20, 19, 24, 15

Median = 20
Lower Quartile = 16
Upper Quartile = 24

In Exercises 6 and 7, compare the two samples using mean, median, range, and interquartile range.

6. Sample A: 41, 37, 58, 62, 46, 33, 74, 51, 69, 81
   Sample B: 56, 68, 39, 47, 75, 68, 64, 52, 42, 59

7. Sample A: 182, 117, 149, 172, 161, 105, 179, 142, 187, 170, 155, 129
   Sample B: 114, 167, 159, 192, 100, 125, 174, 103, 181, 203, 151, 134

In Exercises 8 and 9, use the following information.

Final Exam Scores Mrs. Hitchcock is analyzing final exam scores for the AP history course that she has taught for the last ten years. The table shows the summary statistics for the years 1999, 2001, 2003, 2005, 2006, and for all Mrs. Hitchcock's AP history students over the ten years.

	Mean	Median	Range	Lower Quartile	Upper Quartile	Interquartile Range
1999	88	91	29	82	95.5	13.5
2001	85.2	88	31	78.5	92	13.5
2003	83.8	82	50	73	89	16
2005	87	88.5	35	82.5	91	8.5
2006	89	87.5	28	85	94.5	9.5
All Students	86.3	87.5	52	80	93	13

8. Find the averages of the summary statistics from the five samples. Then compare each average statistic to the corresponding population measure.
9. What happens to the averages in Exercise 8 if you exclude the data from 2003?

LESSON 6.8

Exercise Set B

MM1D3a Compare summary statistics (mean, median, quartiles, and interquartile range) from one sample data distribution to another sample data distribution in describing center and variability of the data distributions.

MM1D3b Compare the averages of the summary statistics from a large number of samples to the corresponding population parameters.

In Exercises 1–4, find the mean, median, range, lower quartile, upper quartile, and interquartile range of the data set.

1. 11, 16, 18, 17, 20, 10, 14, 10, 17, 12
2. 124, 179, 250, 196, 297, 221, 170, 276, 141
3. 25, 37, 59, 50, 33, 64, 42, 46
4. 5.8, 3.1, 4.7, 1.2, 2.4, 5.3, 4.2, 1.8, 3.9

In Exercises 5 and 6, compare the two samples using the mean, median, range, and interquartile range.

5. Sample A: 10, 63, 52, 40, 8, 12, 73, 49, 26, 57, 32, 19
   Sample B: 56, 28, 21, 39, 69, 21, 11, 45, 56, 27, 35, 42
6. Sample A: 3.0, 5.3, 2.1, 4.2, 8.9, 6.7, 4.9, 1.6, 2.5, 3.4
   Sample B: 7.8, 2.4, 6.2, 3.5, 1.2, 7.1, 5.3, 2.9, 4.1, 4.7

UNIT 6

In Exercises 7–9, use the following information.

Bowling Scores The owner of a bowling alley keeps track of all league scores and has calculated statistics for the entire population. The table below shows the summary statistics for five different leagues, and all of the league bowlers.

	Mean	Median	Range	Lower Quartile	Upper Quartile	Interquartile Range
Monday Men	195	199.5	154	167	236	69
Tuesday Mixed	145	141	185	117.5	201.5	84
Wed. Women	162	158.5	154	138	197	59
Thurs. Couples	136	140.5	201	111	208	97
Juniors	119	121	178	94	168.5	74.5
All League Bowlers	157	172.5	258	128	210	82

7. Find the averages of the statistics from the five samples.
8. *Compare* each average statistic to the corresponding population value.
9. **Writing** *Explain* why the averages of statistics from samples are sometimes very close to the population values and sometimes very far from the population values. In your explanation, refer to the bowling leagues that were chosen as samples.

TEST | for Unit 6

Use the number of outcomes of the events to find the number of ways that the events can occur together.

1. **Event A:** 12 outcomes
   Event B: 6 outcomes

2. **Event A:** 2 outcomes
   Event B: 3 outcomes
   Event C: 4 outcomes

3. **Event A:** 9 outcomes
   Event B: 9 outcomes
   Event C: 9 outcomes

Find the number of ways you can arrange (a) all of the letters in the given word and (b) 2 of the letters in the word.

4. MATH
5. PEACH
6. PENCIL

Evaluate the expression.

7. $\frac{71!}{70!}$
8. ${}_{16}P_6$
9. ${}_{12}C_3$
10. ${}_{40}C_{38}$
11. ${}_{12}P_3$
12. ${}_{27}C_{23}$
13. ${}_9P_9$
14. $\frac{{}_2P_2}{{}_4P_4}$
15. $\frac{{}_8C_1}{{}_4C_2}$

In Exercises 16–18, complete the statement using >, < , or =.

16. $\frac{6!}{3!}$ __?__ 120
17. ${}_{10}C_5$ __?__ ${}_{10}P_5$
18. ${}_{11}P_7$ __?__ $\frac{11!}{(11-7)! \cdot 7!}$

19. **Playing Cards** You choose a card from a standard deck of 52 playing cards. Find the probability that you choose (a) a king or a queen, and (b) a red card or a 10.

20. **Marbles** A bag contains 5 blue marbles and 9 red marbles. You choose one marble at random, then choose another marble at random. Find the probability that both marbles are blue when (a) you replace the first marble, and (b) you do not replace the first marble.

Use the information in the table to find the expected value.

21.

Outcome value, x	100	−250
Probability, p	0.85	0.15

22.

Outcome value, x	5	17	33
Probability, p	$\frac{1}{8}$	$\frac{3}{8}$	$\frac{1}{2}$

In Exercises 23 and 24, identify the population and classify the sampling method.

23. **Customer Satisfaction** A restaurant wants to gather information on customer satisfaction. The manager randomly asks 30 customers to complete a survey before they leave.

24. **Intramural Sports** Your school wants to know whether there is interest in starting an intramural sports program. Administrators randomly survey 25 freshmen, 25 sophomores, 25 juniors, and 25 seniors.

UNIT 6

Find the mean, median, mode(s), range, and mean absolute deviation of the data.

25. 50, 47, 48, 49, 47, 52, 50

26. 115, 112, 125, 116, 121, 113

27. **Boat Racing** You are in a boat racing competition. In each heat, 4 boats race and the positions of the boats are randomly assigned.

a. In how many ways can a position be assigned?

b. What is the probability that you are chosen to be the first or second position of the heat in which you are racing? *Explain.*

c. What is the probability that you are chosen to be the second or third position of the heat in which you are racing? *Compare* your answer with your answer to part (c).

28. **Game Show Contestants** On a television game show, 8 members of the studio audience are randomly selected to be eligible contestants.

a. Five of the 8 eligible contestants are randomly chosen to play a game on the stage. How many combinations of 5 players from the group of eligible contestants are possible?

b. You and your friend are part of the group of 8 eligible contestants. What is the probability that both of you are chosen to play the game on stage?

29. **Automobile Mileage** A consumer testing service obtained the following miles per gallon in several test runs performed with two types of compact cars. *Compare* the statistics for the two cars using the mean, median, range, and interquartile range.

Car A: 28, 32, 28, 30, 34, 29, 31, 33, 30

Car B: 31, 29, 30, 29, 31, 30, 32, 31, 29

Performance Task

Power Outage

Over the past year, your neighborhood has been affected by 8 power outages that are summarized in the table below. One morning, the power fails while you are getting ready to go to work. The sun has not risen yet and you still need to get dressed.

Outage duration (minutes)	1	10	13	44	80
Number of outages	3	2	1	1	1

a. How long can you expect the outage to last? *Explain.*

b. Determine which measure of central tendency best represents the average number of minutes an outage lasts. Then state that average. How does this value compare to your answer to part (a)?

c. In the dark, you pick one work shirt and one pair of work pants from your closet. You have 4 blue shirts, 3 black shirts, and 3 gray shirts. You have 6 pairs of blue pants, 2 pairs of black pants, and 2 pairs of gray pants. What is the probability that you select a shirt and pants that are the same color? Different colors?

d. You select a pair of socks from your sock drawer, which contains 8 pairs of white socks and 6 pairs of gray socks. What is the probability that both socks are white? That both socks are gray? That both socks match?

Student Resources

Tables

Table of Symbols

Symbol	Meaning	Page
$\stackrel{?}{=}$	is equal to?	3
$\neq$	is not equal to	3
$-a$	the opposite of a	8
(x, y)	ordered pair	11
b	y-intercept	17
m	slope	23
$f(x)$	the value of the function f at x	38
$\approx$	is approximately equal to	46
$\|a\|$	the absolute value of a	51
$<$	is less than	51
$>$	is greater than	51
a^4	the fourth power of a, or $a \cdot a \cdot a \cdot a$	59
$\leq$	is less than or equal to	99
$\sqrt{a}$	the nonnegative square root of a, $a \geq 0$	119
$\pm$	plus or minus	119
$x \rightarrow +\infty$	x approaches positive infinity	126
$x \rightarrow -\infty$	x approaches negative infinity	126
$\geq$	is greater than or equal to	136
. . .	and so on	197
$^\circ$	degree(s)	204
$\overleftrightarrow{AB}$	line AB	206

Symbol	Meaning	Page
$\perp$	is perpendicular to	206
$\angle$	angle	206
$m\angle A$	measure of angle A	207
$\overrightarrow{AB}$	ray AB	209
$\cong$	is congruent to	211
¬	right angle symbol	217
AB	the length of $\overline{AB}$	217
$\overline{AB}$	segment AB	218
$\parallel$	is parallel to	232
$\triangle ABC$	triangle ABC	236
$\angle$s	angles	250
n-gon	polygon with n sides	301
$\square ABCD$	parallelogram $ABCD$	304
$\ncong$	is not congruent to	324
$P(A)$	the probability of an event A	339
$n!$	n factorial, or $n \cdot (n-1) \cdot \cdots \cdot 2 \cdot 1$ where n is a positive integer; $0!$ is defined to be 1	342
${}_nP_r$	the number of permutations of n objects taken r at a time, $r \leq n$	342
${}_nC_r$	the number of combinations of n objects taken r at a time, $r \leq n$	347
$\bar{x}$	x bar, the mean of numerical data	363

Time

60 seconds (sec) = 1 minute (min)
60 minutes = 1 hour (h)
24 hours = 1 day
7 days = 1 week
4 weeks (approx.) = 1 month

365 days, 52 weeks (approx.), 12 months = 1 year
10 years = 1 decade
100 years = 1 century

Measures

Metric	*United States Customary*
Length 10 millimeters (mm) = 1 centimeter (cm) 100 cm, 1000 mm = 1 meter (m) 1000 m = 1 kilometer (km)	**Length** 12 inches (in.) = 1 foot (ft) 36 in., 3 ft = 1 yard (yd) 5280 ft, 1760 yd = 1 mile (mi)
Area 100 square millimeters (mm^2) = 1 square centimeter (cm^2) 10,000 cm^2 = 1 square meter (m^2) 10,000 m^2 = 1 hectare (ha)	**Area** 144 square inches ($in.^2$) = 1 square foot (ft^2) 9 ft^2 = 1 square yard (yd^2) 43,560 ft^2, 4840 yd^2 = 1 acre (A)
Volume 1000 cubic millimeters (mm^3) = 1 cubic centimeter (cm^3) 1,000,000 cm^3 = 1 cubic meter (m^3)	**Volume** 1728 cubic inches ($in.^3$) = 1 cubic foot (ft^3) 27 ft^3 = 1 cubic yard (yd^3)
Liquid Capacity 1000 milliliters (mL), 1000 cubic centimeters (cm^3) = 1 liter (L) 1000 L = 1 kiloliter (kL)	**Liquid Capacity** 8 fluid ounces (fl oz) = 1 cup (c) 2 c = 1 pint (pt) 2 pt = 1 quart (qt) 4 qt = 1 gallon (gal)
Mass 1000 milligrams (mg) = 1 gram (g) 1000 g = 1 kilogram (kg) 1000 kg = 1 metric ton (t)	**Weight** 16 ounces (oz) = 1 pound (lb) 2000 lb = 1 ton
Temperature **Degrees Celsius (°C)** 0°C = freezing point of water 37°C = normal body temperature 100°C = boiling point of water	**Temperature** **Degrees Fahrenheit (°F)** 32°F = freezing point of water 98.6°F = normal body temperature 212°F = boiling point of water

TABLES

Area and Volume Formulas

Rectangle

Area
$A = \ell w$

Perimeter
$P = 2\ell + 2w$

Circle

Area
$A = \pi r^2$

Circumference
$C = \pi d$ or $C = 2\pi r$

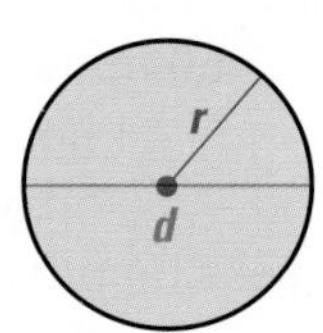

Square

Area
$A = s^2$

Perimeter
$P = 4s$

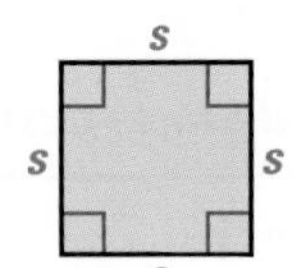

Prism

Surface Area
$S = 2B + Ph$

Volume
$V = Bh$

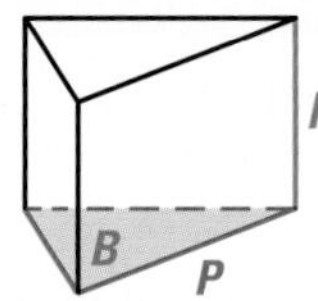

Triangle

Area
$A = \frac{1}{2}bh$

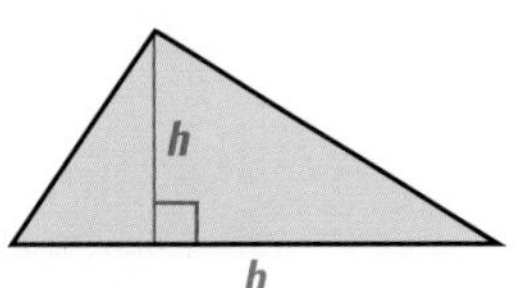

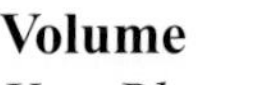

Cylinder

Surface Area
$S = 2B + Ch = 2\pi r^2 + 2\pi rh$

Volume
$V = Bh = \pi r^2 h$

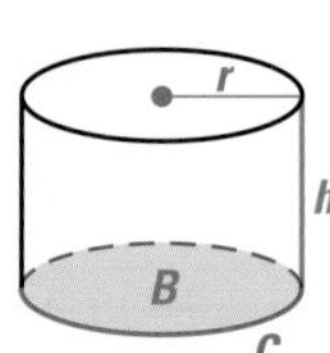

Parallelogram

Area
$A = bh$

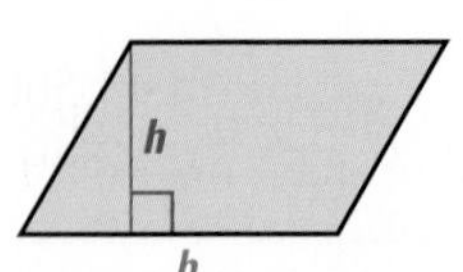

Pyramid

Surface Area
$S = B + \frac{1}{2}P\ell$

Volume
$V = \frac{1}{3}Bh$

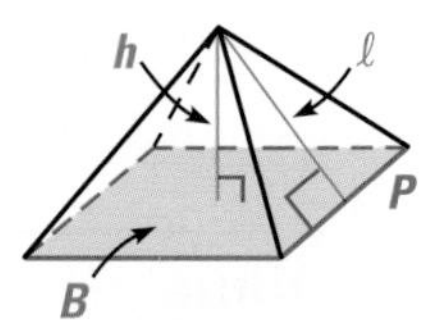

Trapezoid

Area
$A = \frac{1}{2}(b_1 + b_2)h$

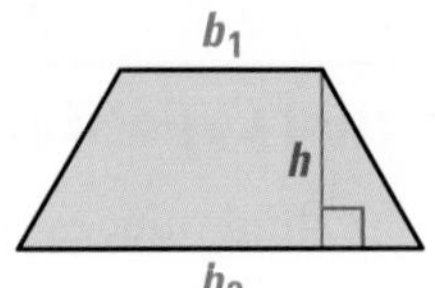

Cone

Surface Area
$S = B + \pi r\ell = \pi r^2 + \pi r\ell$

Volume
$V = \frac{1}{3}Bh = \frac{1}{3}\pi r^2 h$

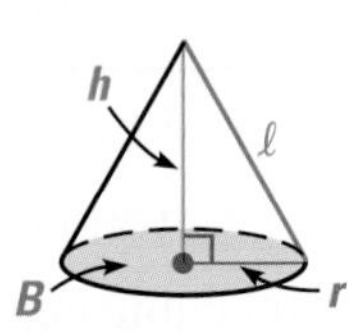

Other Formulas

Name of Formula	*Statement of Formula*	*Page*
Slope formula	The slope m of a nonvertical line passing through the two points (x_1, y_1) and (x_2, y_2) is $m = \frac{y_2 - y_1}{x_2 - x_1}$.	23
Special product patterns	**Sum and difference** $(a + b)(a - b) = a^2 - b^2$ **Square of a binomial** $(a + b)^2 = a^2 + 2ab + b^2$ $(a - b)^2 = a^2 - 2ab + b^2$ **Cube of a binomial** $(a + b)^3 = a^3 + 3a^2b + 3ab^2 + b^3$ $(a - b)^3 = a^3 - 3a^2b + 3ab^2 - b^3$	68, 72, 130

Other Formulas *(continued)*

Name of Formula	*Statement of Formula*	*Page*
Average rate of change formula	Average rate of change of f from x_1 to $x_2 = \dfrac{f(x_2) - f(x_1)}{x_2 - x_1}$	180
Pythagorean Theorem	In a right triangle, $a^2 + b^2 = c^2$ where a and b are the lengths of the legs and c is the length of the hypotenuse.	192
Distance formula	The distance d between any two points (x_1, y_1) and (x_2, y_2) is $d = \sqrt{(x_2 - x_1)^2 + (y_2 - y_1)^2}$.	193
Midpoint formula	The midpoint M of the line segment with endpoints $A(x_1, y_1)$ and $B(x_2, y_2)$ is $M\left(\dfrac{x_1 + x_2}{2}, \dfrac{y_1 + y_2}{2}\right)$.	193
Sum of the measures of the interior angles of a convex *n*-gon	$(n - 2) \cdot 180°$	298
Sum of the measures of the exterior angles of a convex polygon	$360°$	298
Multiplication counting principle	If one event can occur in m ways and another event can occur in n ways, then the number of ways that both events can occur is $m \cdot n$.	338
Addition counting principle	If the possibilities being counted can be divided into groups with no possibilities in common, then the total number of possibilities is the sum of the numbers of the possibilities in each group.	338
Permutations formula	The number of permutations of n objects taken r at a time, where $r \le n$, is given by ${}_nP_r = \dfrac{n!}{(n - r)!}$.	342
Combinations formula	The number of combinations of n objects taken r at a time, where $r \le n$, is given by ${}_nC_r = \dfrac{n!}{(n - r)! \cdot r!}$.	347
Probability of mutually exclusive or overlapping events	If A and B are mutually exclusive events, then $P(A \text{ or } B) = P(A) + P(B)$. If A and B are overlapping events, then $P(A \text{ or } B) = P(A) + P(B) - P(A \text{ and } B)$.	351
Probability of independent or dependent events	If A and B are independent events, then $P(A \text{ and } B) = P(A) \cdot P(B)$. If A and B are dependent events, then $P(A \text{ and } B) = P(A) \cdot P(B \text{ given } A)$.	351
Formula of mean of a data set	$\overline{x} = \dfrac{x_1 + x_2 + \cdots + x_n}{n}$ where $\overline{x}$ (read "x-bar") is the mean of the data $x_1, x_2, \ldots, x_n$.	363
Mean absolute deviation formula	$\dfrac{\lvert x_1 - \overline{x}\rvert + \lvert x_2 - \overline{x}\rvert + \cdots + \lvert x_n - \overline{x}\rvert}{n}$ where $\overline{x}$ (read "x-bar") is the mean of the data $x_1, x_2, \ldots, x_n$.	363

Postulates

Postulate	Statement of Postulate	Page
Linear Pair Postulate	If two angles form a linear pair, then they are supplementary.	223
Side-Side-Side (SSS) Congruence Postulate	If three sides of one triangle are congruent to three sides of a second triangle, then the two triangles are congruent.	236
Side-Angle-Side (SAS) Congruence Postulate	If two sides and the included angle of one triangle are congruent to two sides and the included angle of a second triangle, then the two triangles are congruent.	242
Angle-Side-Angle (ASA) Congruence Postulate	If two angles and the included side of one triangle are congruent to two angles and the included side of a second triangle, then the two triangles are congruent.	249

Theorems

Theorem or Corollary	Statement of Theorem or Corollary	Page
4.1 Properties of Segment Congruence	Segment congruence is reflexive, symmetric, and transitive. **Reflexive** For any segment AB, $\overline{AB} \cong \overline{AB}$. **Symmetric** If $\overline{AB} \cong \overline{CD}$, then $\overline{CD} \cong \overline{AB}$. **Transitive** If $\overline{AB} \cong \overline{CD}$ and $\overline{CD} \cong \overline{EF}$, then $\overline{AB} \cong \overline{EF}$.	218
4.2 Properties of Angle Congruence	Angle congruence is reflexive, symmetric, and transitive. **Reflexive** For any angle A, $\angle A \cong \angle A$. **Symmetric** If $\angle A \cong \angle B$, then $\angle B \cong \angle A$. **Transitive** If $\angle A \cong \angle B$ and $\angle B \cong \angle C$, then $\angle A \cong \angle C$.	218
4.3 Right Angles Congruence Theorem	All right angles are congruent.	223
4.4 Congruent Supplements Theorem	If two angles are supplementary to the same angle (or to congruent angles), then the two angles are congruent.	223
4.5 Congruent Complements Theorem	If two angles are complementary to the same angle (or to congruent angles), then the two angles are congruent.	223
4.6 Vertical Angles Congruence Theorem	Vertical angles are congruent.	223
4.7	If two lines intersect to form a linear pair of congruent angles, then the lines are perpendicular.	229
4.8	If two lines are perpendicular, then they intersect to form four right angles.	229
4.9	If two sides of two adjacent acute angles are perpendicular, then the angles are complementary.	229

TABLES

Theorems *(continued)*

Theorem or Corollary		*Statement of Theorem or Corollary*	*Page*
4.10	**Perpendicular Transversal Theorem**	If a transversal is perpendicular to one of two parallel lines, then it is perpendicular to the other line.	229
4.11	**Lines Perpendicular to a Transversal Theorem**	In a plane, if two lines are perpendicular to the same line, then they are parallel to each other.	229
4.12	**Hypotenuse-Leg (HL) Congruence Theorem**	If the hypotenuse and a leg of a right triangle are congruent to the hypotenuse and a leg of a second right triangle, then the two triangles are congruent.	242
4.13	**Angle-Angle-Side (AAS) Congruence Theorem**	If two angles and a non-included side of one triangle are congruent to two angles and the corresponding non-included side of a second triangle, then the two triangles are congruent.	249
5.1	**Midsegment Theorem**	The segment connecting the midpoints of two sides of a triangle is parallel to the third side and is half as long as that side.	258
5.2	**Perpendicular Bisector Theorem**	If a point is on a perpendicular bisector of a segment, then it is equidistant from the endpoints of the segment.	264
5.3	**Converse of the Perpendicular Bisector Theorem**	If a point is equidistant from the endpoints of a segment, then it is on the perpendicular bisector of the segment.	264
5.4	**Concurrency of Perpendicular Bisectors Theorem**	The perpendicular bisectors of a triangle intersect at a point that is equidistant from the vertices of the triangle.	264
5.5	**Angle Bisector Theorem**	If a point is on the bisector of an angle, then it is equidistant from the two sides of the angle.	272
5.6	**Converse of the Angle Bisector Theorem**	If a point is in the interior of an angle and is equidistant from the sides of the angle, then it lies on the bisector of the angle.	272
5.7	**Concurrency of Angle Bisectors of a Triangle**	The angle bisectors of a triangle intersect at a point that is equidistant from the sides of the triangle.	272
5.8	**Concurrency of Medians of a Triangle**	The medians of a triangle intersect at a point that is two thirds of the distance from each vertex to the midpoint of the opposite side.	278
5.9	**Concurrency of Altitudes of a Triangle**	The lines containing the altitudes of a triangle are concurrent.	278
5.10		If one side of a triangle is longer than another side, then the angle opposite the longer side is larger than the angle opposite the shorter side.	284
5.11		If one angle of a triangle is larger than another angle, then the side opposite the larger angle is longer than the side opposite the smaller angle.	284

TABLES

Theorems *(continued)*

Theorem or Corollary	*Statement of Theorem or Corollary*	*Page*
5.12 Triangle Inequality Theorem	The sum of the lengths of any two sides of a triangle is greater than the length of the third side.	284
5.13 Exterior Angle Inequality Theorem	The measure of an exterior angle of a triangle is greater than the measure of either of the nonadjacent interior angles.	284
5.14 Hinge Theorem	If two sides of one triangle are congruent to two sides of another triangle, and the included angle of the first is larger than the included angle of the second, then the third side of the first is longer than the third side of the second.	292
5.15 Converse of the Hinge Theorem	If two sides of one triangle are congruent to two sides of another triangle, and the third side of the first is longer than the third side of the second, then the included angle of the first is larger than the included angle of the second.	292
5.16 Polygon Interior Angles Theorem **Corollary**	The sum of the measures of the interior angles of a convex n-gon is $(n - 2) \cdot 180°$. The sum of the measures of the interior angles of a quadrilateral is 360°.	298
5.17 Polygon Exterior Angles Theorem	The sum of the measures of the exterior angles of a convex polygon, one angle at each vertex, is 360°.	298
5.18	If a quadrilateral is a parallelogram, then its opposite sides are congruent.	304
5.19	If a quadrilateral is a parallelogram, then its opposite angles are congruent.	304
5.20	If a quadrilateral is a parallelogram, then its consecutive angles are supplementary.	304
5.21	If a quadrilateral is a parallelogram, then its diagonals bisect each other.	304
5.22	If both pairs of opposite sides of a quadrilateral are congruent, then the quadrilateral is a parallelogram.	311
5.23	If both pairs of opposite angles of a quadrilateral are congruent, then the quadrilateral is a parallelogram.	311
5.24	If one pair of opposite sides of a quadrilateral are congruent and parallel, then the quadrilateral is a parallelogram.	311
5.25	If the diagonals of a quadrilateral bisect each other, then the quadrilateral is a parallelogram.	311

TABLES

Theorems *(continued)*

Theorem or Corollary	*Statement of Theorem or Corollary*	*Page*
Rhombus Corollary	A quadrilateral is a rhombus if and only if it has four congruent sides.	317
Rectangle Corollary	A quadrilateral is a rectangle if and only if it has four right angles.	317
Square Corollary	A quadrilateral is a square if and only if it is a rhombus and a rectangle.	317
5.26	A parallelogram is a rhombus if and only if its diagonals are perpendicular.	317
5.27	A parallelogram is a rhombus if and only if each diagonal bisects a pair of opposite angles.	317
5.28	A parallelogram is a rectangle if and only if its diagonals are congruent.	317
5.29	If a trapezoid is isosceles, then both pairs of base angles are congruent.	323
5.30	If a trapezoid has a pair of congruent base angles, then it is an isosceles trapezoid.	323
5.31	A trapezoid is isosceles if and only if its diagonals are congruent.	323
5.32 Midsegment Theorem for Trapezoids	The midsegment of a trapezoid is parallel to each base and its length is one half the sum of the lengths of the bases.	323
5.33	If a quadrilateral is a kite, then its diagonals are perpendicular.	323
5.34	If a quadrilateral is a kite, then exactly one pair of opposite angles are congruent.	323

Properties of Equality

Property	Statement of Property
Addition Property of Equality	Adding the same number to each side of an equation produces an equivalent equation. If $x - a = b$, then $x - a + a = b + a$, or $x = b + a$.
Subtraction Property of Equality	Subtracting the same number from each side of an equation produces an equivalent equation. If $x + a = b$, then $x + a - a = b - a$, or $x = b - a$.
Multiplication Property of Equality	Multiplying each side of an equation by the same nonzero number produces an equivalent equation. If $\frac{x}{a} = b$ and $a \neq 0$, then $a \cdot \frac{x}{a} = a \cdot b$, or $x = ab$.
Division Property of Equality	Dividing each side of an equation by the same nonzero number produces an equivalent equation. If $ax = b$ and $a \neq 0$, then $\frac{ax}{a} = \frac{b}{a}$, or $x = \frac{b}{a}$.

Properties of Radicals

Property	Statement of Property	Page
Product Property of Radicals	The square root of a product equals the product of the square roots of the factors. $\sqrt{ab} = \sqrt{a} \cdot \sqrt{b}$, $a \geq 0$ and $b \geq 0$	142
Quotient Property of Radicals	The square root of a quotient equals the quotient of the square roots of the numerator and denominator. $\sqrt{\frac{a}{b}} = \frac{\sqrt{a}}{\sqrt{b}}$, $a \geq 0$ and $b > 0$	142

TABLES

Table of Squares and Square Roots

No.	Square	Sq. Root	No.	Square	Sq. Root	No.	Square	Sq. Root
1	1	1.000	51	2601	7.141	101	10,201	10.050
2	4	1.414	52	2704	7.211	102	10,404	10.100
3	9	1.732	53	2809	7.280	103	10,609	10.149
4	16	2.000	54	2916	7.348	104	10,816	10.198
5	25	2.236	55	3025	7.416	105	11,025	10.247
6	36	2.449	56	3136	7.483	106	11,236	10.296
7	49	2.646	57	3249	7.550	107	11,449	10.344
8	64	2.828	58	3364	7.616	108	11,664	10.392
9	81	3.000	59	3481	7.681	109	11,881	10.440
10	100	3.162	60	3600	7.746	110	12,100	10.488
11	121	3.317	61	3721	7.810	111	12,321	10.536
12	144	3.464	62	3844	7.874	112	12,544	10.583
13	169	3.606	63	3969	7.937	113	12,769	10.630
14	196	3.742	64	4096	8.000	114	12,996	10.677
15	225	3.873	65	4225	8.062	115	13,225	10.724
16	256	4.000	66	4356	8.124	116	13,456	10.770
17	289	4.123	67	4489	8.185	117	13,689	10.817
18	324	4.243	68	4624	8.246	118	13,924	10.863
19	361	4.359	69	4761	8.307	119	14,161	10.909
20	400	4.472	70	4900	8.367	120	14,400	10.954
21	441	4.583	71	5041	8.426	121	14,641	11.000
22	484	4.690	72	5184	8.485	122	14,884	11.045
23	529	4.796	73	5329	8.544	123	15,129	11.091
24	576	4.899	74	5476	8.602	124	15,376	11.136
25	625	5.000	75	5625	8.660	125	15,625	11.180
26	676	5.099	76	5776	8.718	126	15,876	11.225
27	729	5.196	77	5929	8.775	127	16,129	11.269
28	784	5.292	78	6084	8.832	128	16,384	11.314
29	841	5.385	79	6241	8.888	129	16,641	11.358
30	900	5.477	80	6400	8.944	130	16,900	11.402
31	961	5.568	81	6561	9.000	131	17,161	11.446
32	1024	5.657	82	6724	9.055	132	17,424	11.489
33	1089	5.745	83	6889	9.110	133	17,689	11.533
34	1156	5.831	84	7056	9.165	134	17,956	11.576
35	1225	5.916	85	7225	9.220	135	18,225	11.619
36	1296	6.000	86	7396	9.274	136	18,496	11.662
37	1369	6.083	87	7569	9.327	137	18,769	11.705
38	1444	6.164	88	7744	9.381	138	19,044	11.747
39	1521	6.245	89	7921	9.434	139	19,321	11.790
40	1600	6.325	90	8100	9.487	140	19,600	11.832
41	1681	6.403	91	8281	9.539	141	19,881	11.874
42	1764	6.481	92	8464	9.592	142	20,164	11.916
43	1849	6.557	93	8649	9.644	143	20,449	11.958
44	1936	6.633	94	8836	9.695	144	20,736	12.000
45	2025	6.708	95	9025	9.747	145	21,025	12.042
46	2116	6.782	96	9216	9.798	146	21,316	12.083
47	2209	6.856	97	9409	9.849	147	21,609	12.124
48	2304	6.928	98	9604	9.899	148	21,904	12.166
49	2401	7.000	99	9801	9.950	149	22,201	12.207
50	2500	7.071	100	10,000	10.000	150	22,500	12.247

English-Spanish Glossary

A

absolute value (p. 51) The absolute value of a number a is the distance between a and 0 on a number line. The symbol $|a|$ represents the absolute value of a.

$|2| = 2$, $|-5| = 5$, and $|0| = 0$

valor absoluto (pág. 51) El valor absoluto de un número a es la distancia entre a y 0 en una recta numérica. El símbolo $|a|$ representa el valor absoluto de a.

$|2| = 2$, $|-5| = 5$, y $|0| = 0$

---

absolute value function (p. 51) A function that contains an absolute value expression.

$y = |x|$, $y = |x - 3|$, and $y = 4|x + 8| - 9$ are absolute value functions.

función de valor absoluto (pág. 51) Función que contiene una expresión de valor absoluto.

$y = |x|$, $y = |x - 3|$ e $y = 4|x + 8| - 9$ son funciones de valor absoluto.

---

adjacent angles (p. 223) Two angles that share a common vertex and side, but have no common interior points.

ángulos adyacentes (pág. 223) Dos ángulos que comparten un vértice y un lado comunes, pero que no tienen puntos interiores comunes.

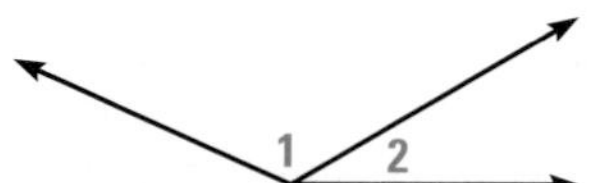

$\angle 1$ and $\angle 2$ are adjacent angles.
$\angle 1$ y $\angle 2$ son ángulos adyacentes.

---

altitude of a triangle (p. 278) The perpendicular segment from one vertex of the triangle to the opposite side or to the line that contains the opposite side.

altura de un triángulo (pág. 278) El segmento perpendicular que va desde uno de los vértices del triángulo hasta el lado opuesto o hasta la recta que contiene el lado opuesto.

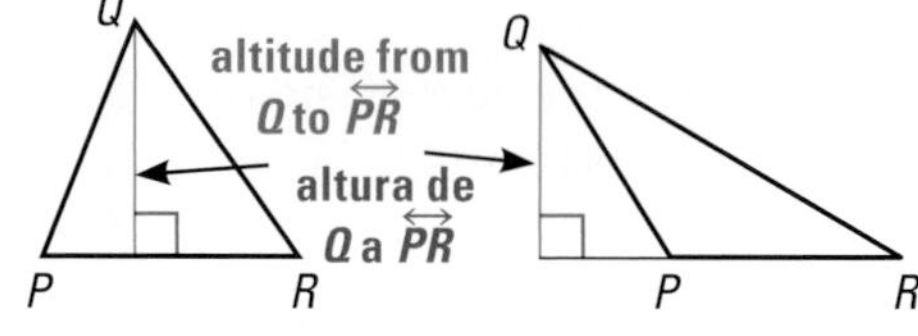

---

angle bisector (p. 272) A ray that divides an angle into two angles that are congruent.

bisectriz de un ángulo (pág. 272) Rayo que divide a un ángulo en dos ángulos congruentes.

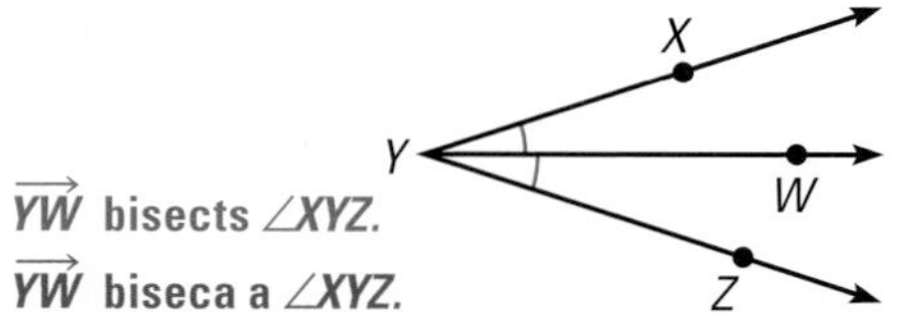

$\overrightarrow{YW}$ bisects $\angle XYZ$.
$\overrightarrow{YW}$ biseca a $\angle XYZ$.

---

area model for polynomial arithmetic (p. 64) A way to visually represent multiplying two polynomials using geometry.

modelo del área para aritmética de polinomios (pág. 64) Una manera de representar visualmente la multiplicación de dos polinomios usando geometría.

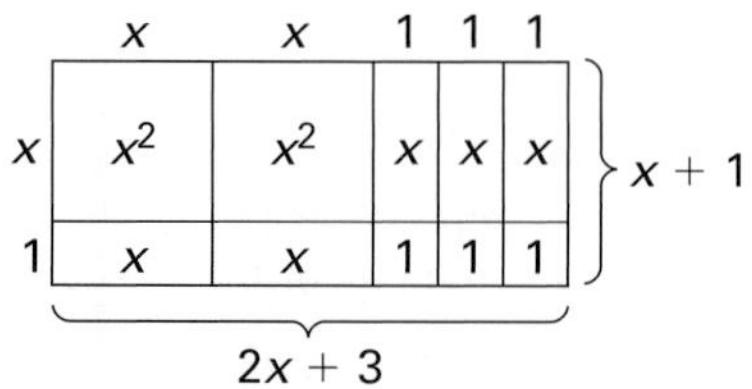

The area model represents $(2x + 3)(x + 1)$, or $2x^2 + 5x + 3$.

El modelo del área representa $(2x + 3)(x + 1)$, y $2x^2 + 5x + 3$.

ENGLISH-SPANISH GLOSSARY

asymptote (p. 150) A line that a graph approaches more and more closely.

asíntotas de una hipérbola (pág. 150) Recta a la que se aproxima una gráfica cada vez más.

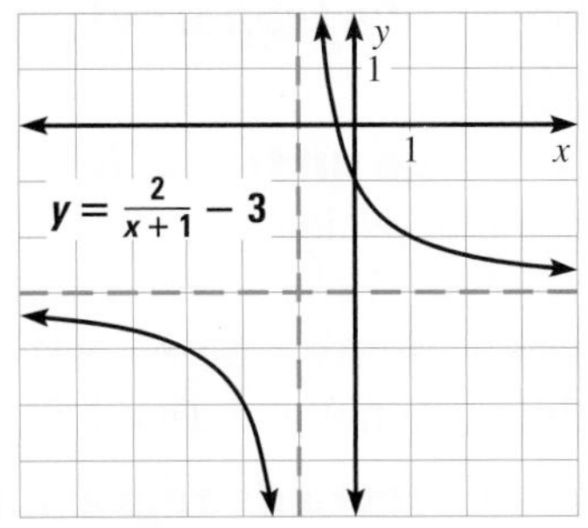

The asymptotes of the graph are the lines $x = -1$ and $y = -3$.

hipérbola. Las asíntotas de la gráphica son las rectas $x = -1$ e $y = -3$.

average rate of change for a function (p. 180) For a function f the average rate of change between any two points $(x_1, f(x_1))$ and $(x_2, f(x_2))$ is the slope of the line through the two points.

Average rate of change $= \frac{f(x_2) - f(x_1)}{x_2 - x_1}$.

The average rate of change of $f(x) = x^3 + 3x^2$ from $(-1, 2)$ to $(1, 4)$ is $\frac{4 - 2}{1 - (-1)}$, or 1.

tasa de cambio promedio de una función (pág. 180) Para un función f la tasa de cambio promedio entre dos puntos cualesquiera $(x_1, f(x_1))$ y $(x_2, f(x_2))$ es la pendiente de la recta que atraviesa los dos puntos.

Tasa de cambio promedio $= \frac{f(x_2) - f(x_1)}{x_2 - x_1}$.

La tasa de cambio promedio de $f(x) = x^3 + 3x^2$ de $(-1, 2)$ a $(1, 4)$ es $\frac{4 - 2}{1 - (-1)}$ ó 1.

axis of symmetry (p. 98) The line that passes through the vertex and divides the parabola into two symmetric parts.

eje de simetría (pág. 98) La recta que pasa por el vértice y divide a la parábola en dos partes simétricas.

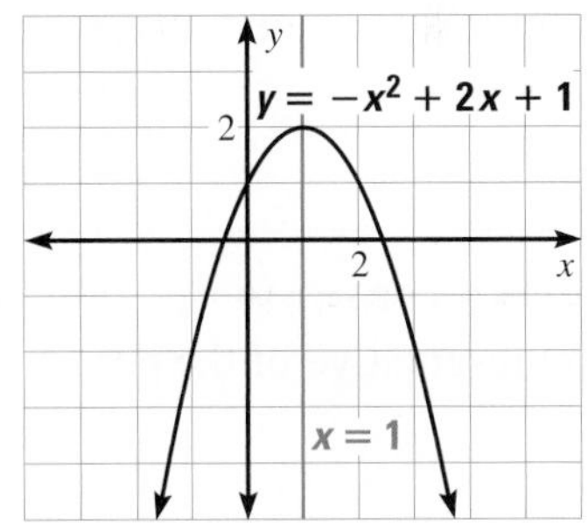

The axis of symmetry of the graph of $y = -x^2 + 2x + 1$ is the line $x = 1$.

El eje de simetría de la gráfica de $y = -x^2 + 2x + 1$ es la recta $x = 1$.

B

base angles of a trapezoid (p. 323) Either pair of angles whose common side is a base of a trapezoid.

ángulos básicos de un trapecio (pág. 323) Cualquier par de ángulos cuyo lado común es una base del trapecio.

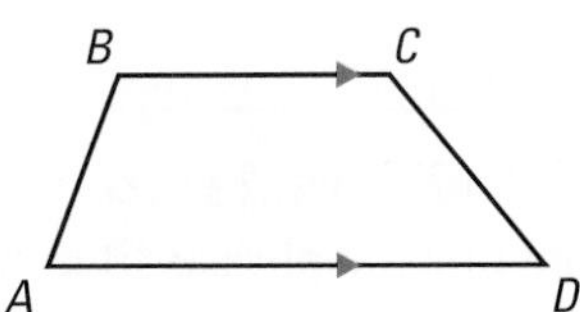

$\angle A$ and $\angle D$ are a pair of base angles. $\angle B$ and $\angle C$ are another pair.

$\angle A$ y $\angle D$ son un par de ángulos básicos. $\angle B$ y $\angle C$ son otro par.

bases of a trapezoid (p. 323) The parallel sides of a trapezoid.

See trapezoid.

bases de un trapecio (pág. 323) Los lados paralelos de un trapecio.

Ver trapecio.

best-fitting line (p. 45) The line that most closely follows a trend in data, found using technology.

mejor recta de regresión (pág. 45) La recta que se ajusta más a la tendencia de los datos y que se encuentra mediante tecnología.

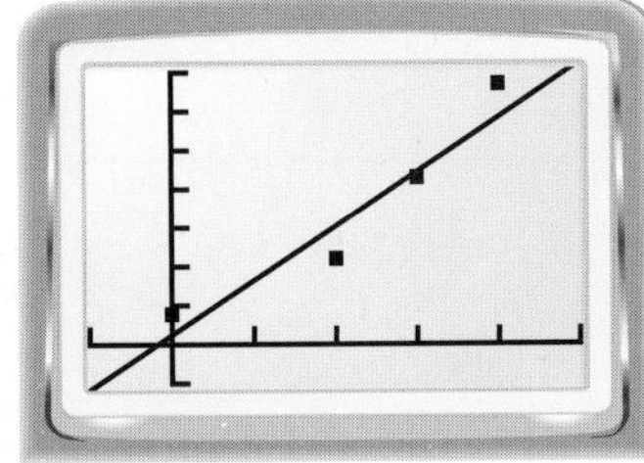

The graph shows the best-fitting line for the data in the scatter plot.

La gráfica muestra la mejor recta de regresión para los datos del diagrama de dispersión.

biased question (p. 359) A question that encourages a particular response.

"Don't you agree that the voting age should be lowered to 16 because many 16-year-olds are responsible and informed?" is a biased question.

pregunta capciosa (pág. 359) Pregunta que impulsa a dar una respuesta determinada.

"¿No estás de acuerdo en que se debe bajar la edad para votar a los 16 años ya que muchos jóvenes de 16 años son responsables y están bien informados?" es una pregunta capciosa.

biased sample (p. 359) A sample that is not representative of the population.

The members of a school's basketball team would form a biased sample for a survey about whether to build a new gym.

muestra sesgada (pág. 359) Muestra que no es representativa de la población.

Los miembros del equipo de baloncesto de una escuela formarían una muestra sesgada si participaran en una encuesta sobre si quieren que se construya un nuevo gimnasio.

biconditional statement (p. 204) A statement that contains the phrase "if and only if."

Two lines are perpendicular if and only if they intersect to form a right angle.

enunciado bicondicional (pág. 204) Enunciado que contiene la frase "si y sólo si".

Dos rectas son perpendiculares si y sólo si se cortan para formar un ángulo recto.

binomial (p. 59) A polynomial with two terms.

binomio (pág. 59) Polinomio con dos términos.

$t^3 - 4t$ and $2x + 5$ are binomials.

$t^3 - 4t$ y $2x + 5$ son binomios.

---

binomial theorem (p. 72) The binomial expansion of $(a + b)^n$ for any positive integer n: $(a + b)^n = {}_nC_0a^nb^0 + {}_nC_1a^{n-1}b^1 + {}_nC_2a^{n-2}b^2 + \cdots + {}_nC_na^0b^n$.

teorema binomial (pág. 72) La expansión binomial de $(a + b)^n$ para cualquier número entero positivo n: $(a + b)^n = {}_nC_0a^nb^0 + {}_nC_1a^{n-1}b^1 + {}_nC_2a^{n-2}b^2 + \cdots + {}_nC_na^0b^n$.

$$(x^2 + y)^3$$
$$= {}_3C_0(x^2)^3y^0 + {}_3C_1(x^2)^2y^1 + {}_3C_2(x^2)^1y^2 + {}_3C_3(x^2)^0y^3$$
$$= (1)(x^6)(1) + (3)(x^4)(y) + (3)(x^2)(y^2) + (1)(1)(y^3)$$
$$= x^6 + 3x^4y + 3x^2y^2 + y^3$$

C

centroid of a triangle (p. 278) The point of concurrency of the three medians of the triangle.

baricentro de un triángulo (pág. 278) El punto de concurrencia de las tres medianas del triángulo.

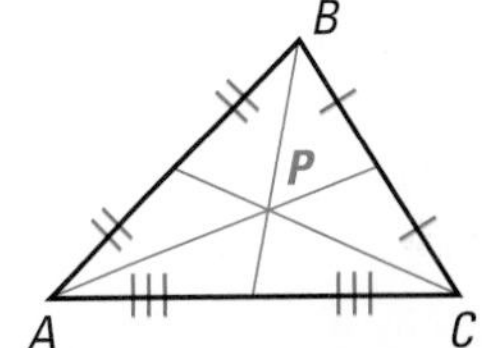

P is the centroid of $\triangle ABC$.

P es el baricentro de $\triangle ABC$.

---

circumcenter of a triangle (p. 264) The point of concurrency of the three perpendicular bisectors of the triangle.

circuncentro de un triángulo (pág. 264) El punto de concurrencia de las tres mediatrices del triángulo.

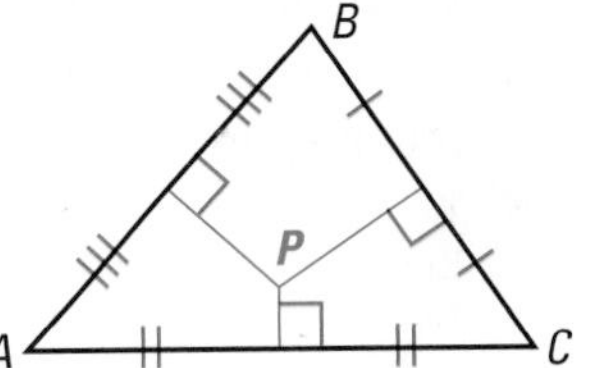

P is the circumcenter of $\triangle ABC$.

P es el circuncentro de $\triangle ABC$.

---

combination (p. 347) A selection of objects in which order is *not* important.

combinación (pág. 347) Selección de objetos en la que el orden *no* es importante.

There are 6 combinations of two of the letters from the list A, B, C, D: AB, AC, AD, BC, BD, and CD.

Hay 6 combinaciones de dos de las letras de la lista A, B, C, D: AB, AC, AD, BC, BD y CD.

---

compound event (p. 351) An event that combines two or more events, using the word *and* or the word *or*.

suceso compuesto (pág. 351) Suceso que combina dos o más sucesos usando la palabra *y* o la palabra *o*.

When you roll a number cube, the event "roll a 2 or an odd number" is a compound event.

Cuando lanzas un cubo numerado, el suceso "salir el 2 ó número impar" es un suceso compuesto.

ENGLISH-SPANISH GLOSSARY

conclusion (p. 204) The "then" part of a conditional statement.

See conditional statement.

conclusión (pág. 204) La parte de "entonces" de un enunciado condicional.

Ver enunciado condicional.

concurrent (p. 264) Three or more lines, rays, or segments that intersect in the same point.

See point of concurrency.

concurrentes (pág. 264) Tres o más rectas, rayos o segmentos que se cortan en el mismo punto.

Ver punto de concurrencia.

conditional probability (p. 351) The conditional probability of B given A, written $P(B \mid A)$, is the probability that event B will occur given that event A has occurred.

Two cards are randomly selected from a standard deck of 52 cards. Let event A be "the first card is a club" and let event B be "the second card is a club." Then $P(B \mid A) = \frac{12}{51} = \frac{4}{17}$ because there are 12 (out of 13) clubs left among the remaining 51 cards.

probabilidad condicional (pág. 351) La probabilidad condicional de B dado A, escrito $P(B \mid A)$, es la probabilidad de que ocurra el suceso B dado que ha ocurrido el suceso A.

Dos cartas se seleccionan al azar de una baraja normal de 52 cartas. Sea el suceso A "la primera carta es de tréboles" y sea el suceso B "la segunda carta es de tréboles". Entonces $P(B \mid A) = \frac{12}{51} = \frac{4}{17}$ ya que quedan 12 (del total de 13) cartas de tréboles entre las 51 cartas restantes.

conditional statement (p. 204) A type of logical statement that has two parts, a hypothesis and a conclusion.

$\underbrace{\text{If } m\angle A = 88°}_{\text{Hypothesis}}$, $\underbrace{\text{then } \angle A \text{ is acute.}}_{\text{Conclusion}}$

enunciado condicional (pág. 204) Tipo de enunciado lógico que tiene dos partes, una hipótesis y una conclusión.

$\underbrace{\text{Si } m\angle A = 88°}_{\text{Hipótesis}}$, $\underbrace{\text{entonces } \angle A \text{ es agudo.}}_{\text{Conclusión}}$

congruent figures (p. 236) Two geometric figures that have exactly the same size and shape. When two figures are congruent, all pairs of corresponding sides and corresponding angles are congruent.

figuras congruentes (pág. 236) Dos figuras geométricas de igual tamaño y forma. Cuando dos figuras son congruentes, todos los pares de lados correspondientes y de ángulos correspondientes son congruentes.

$\triangle ABC \cong \triangle FED$
$\angle A \cong \angle F$, $\angle B \cong \angle E$, $\angle C \cong \angle D$
$\overline{AB} \cong \overline{FE}$, $\overline{BC} \cong \overline{ED}$, $\overline{AC} \cong \overline{FD}$

B
A
C
E
F
D

conjecture (p. 197) An unproven statement that is based on observations. **conjetura** (pág. 197) Enunciado sin demostrar que se basa en observaciones.	**Conjecture: All prime numbers are odd.** **Conjetura: Todos los números primos son impares.**
contrapositive (p. 204) The equivalent statement formed by negating the hypothesis and conclusion of the converse of a conditional statement. **contrapositivo** (pág. 204) El enunciado equivalente formado al negar la hipótesis y la conclusión del recíproco de un enunciado condicional.	**Statement: If $m\angle A = 90°$, then $\angle A$ is right.** **Contrapositive: If $\angle A$ is not right, then $m\angle A \neq 90°$.** **Enunciado: Si $m\angle A = 90°$, entonces $\angle A$ es recto.** **Contrapositivo: Si $\angle A$ no es recto, entonces $m\angle A \neq 90°$.**
convenience sample (p. 359) A sample in which only members of a population who are easily accessible are selected. **muestra de conveniencia** (pág. 359) Muestra en la que se selecciona sólo a los miembros de una población fácilmente accesibles.	**You can select a convenience sample of a school's student population by choosing only students who are in your classes.** **Para seleccionar una muestra de conveniencia de la población de estudiantes de una escuela, puedes escoger sólo a los estudiantes que están en tus clases.**
converse (p. 204) The statement formed by exchanging the hypothesis and conclusion of a conditional statement. **recíproco** (pág. 204) El enunciado formado al intercambiar la hipótesis y la conclusión de un enunciado condicional.	**Statement: If $m\angle A = 90°$, then $\angle A$ is right.** **Converse: If $\angle A$ is right, then $m\angle A = 90°$.** **Enunciado: Si $m\angle A = 90°$, entonces $\angle A$ es recto.** **Recíproco: Si $\angle A$ es recto, entonces $m\angle A = 90°$.**
coordinate proof (p. 236) A type of proof that involves placing geometric figures in a coordinate plane. **prueba de coordenadas** (pág. 236) Tipo de prueba en la que se colocan figuras geométricas en un plano de coordenadas.	**See Example 2 on page 237.** **Ver el ejemplo 2 de la página 237.**

corresponding parts (p. 236) A pair of sides or angles that have the same relative position in two congruent or similar figures.

partes correspondientes (pág. 236) Un par de lados o ángulos que tienen la misma posición relativa en dos figuras congruentes o semejantes.

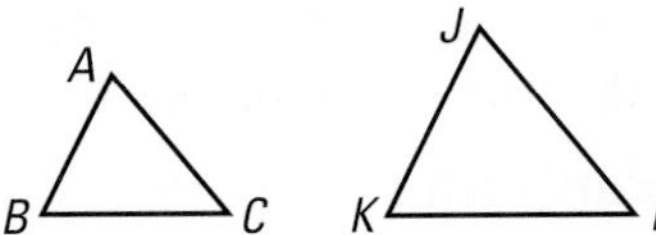

$\angle A$ and $\angle J$ are corresponding angles. $\overline{AB}$ and $\overline{JK}$ are corresponding sides.

$\angle A$ y $\angle J$ son ángulos correspondientes. $\overline{AB}$ y $\overline{JK}$ son lados correspondientes.

---

counterexample (p. 197) A specific case that shows a conjecture is false.

Conjecture: All prime numbers are odd. Counterexample: 2, a prime number that is not odd

contraejemplo (pág. 197) Caso específico que muestra la falsedad de una conjetura.

Conjetura: Todos los números primos son impares. Contraejemplo: 2, un número primo que no es impar

---

cubic function (p. 126) A nonlinear function that can be written in the standard form $y = ax^3 + bx^2 + cx + d$ where $a \neq 0$.

función cúbica (pág. 126) Una función no lineal que puede escribirse como forma estándar $y = ax^3 + bx^2 + cx + d$ donde $a \neq 0$.

$y = 2x^3 + 3x^2 - 5x - 8$ is a cubic function.

$y = 2x^3 + 3x^2 - 5x - 8$ es una función cúbica.

D

deductive reasoning (p. 211) A process that uses facts, definitions, accepted properties, and the laws of logic to form a logical argument.

You use deductive reasoning in writing geometric proofs.

razonamiento deductivo (pág. 211) Proceso que usa datos, definiciones, propiedades aceptadas y las leyes de la lógica para formar un argumento lógico.

Puedes usar el razonamiento deductivo para escribir pruebas geométricas.

---

degree of a monomial (p. 59) The sum of the exponents of the variables in the monomial. The degree of a nonzero constant term is 0.

The degree of $\frac{1}{2}ab^2$ is 1 + 2, or 3.

grado de un monomio (pág. 59) La suma de los exponentes de las variables del monomio. El grado de un término constante distinto de cero es 0.

El grado de $\frac{1}{2}ab^2$ es 1 + 2, ó 3.

---

degree of a polynomial (p. 59) The greatest degree of the terms of the polynomial.

The polynomial $2x^2 + x - 5$ has a degree of 2.

grado de un polinomio (pág. 59) El mayor grado de los términos del polinomio.

El polinomio $2x^2 + x - 5$ tiene un grado de 2.

dependent events (p. 351) Two events such that the occurrence of one event affects the occurrence of the other event.

A bag contains 3 red marbles and 5 white marbles. You randomly draw one marble, do not replace it, then randomly draw another marble. The events "draw a red marble first" and "draw a white marble second" are dependent events.

sucesos dependientes (pág. 351) Dos sucesos tales que la ocurrencia de uno de ellos afecta a la ocurrencia del otro.

Una bolsa contiene 3 canicas rojas y 5 blancas. Sacas al azar una canica sin reemplazarla y luego sacas al azar otra canica. Los sucesos "sacar primero una canica roja" y "sacar después una canica blanca" son sucesos dependientes.

dependent variable (p. 7) The output variable of a function.

In the function equation $y = x + 3$, y is the dependent variable.

variable dependiente (pág. 7) La variable de salida de una función.

En la ecuación de función $y = x + 3$, y es la variable dependiente.

deviation from the mean (p. 363) The difference of a data value and the mean of a data set.

14, 17, 18, 19, 20, 24, 24, 30, 32

Because the mean of the data set is 22, the deviation of 30 is 8.

desviación de la media (pág. 363) La diferencia entre el valor de un dato y la media de un conjunto de datos.

Como la media del conjunto de datos es 22, la desviación de 30 es 8.

diagonal of a polygon (p. 298) A segment that joins two nonconsecutive vertices of a polygon.

diagonal de un polígono (pág. 298) Segmento que une dos vértices no consecutivos de un polígono.

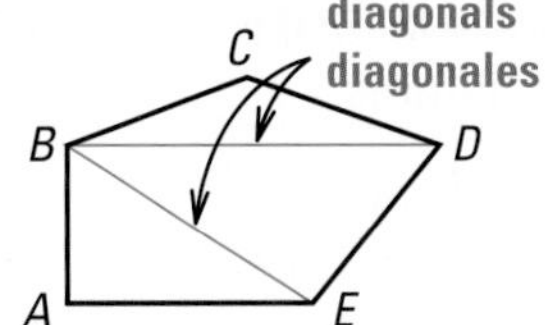

distance formula (p. 193) The distance d between any two points (x_1, y_1) and (x_2, y_2) is $d = \sqrt{(x_2 - x_1)^2 + (y_2 - y_1)^2}$.

The distance d between $(-1, 3)$ and $(5, 2)$ is:

$$d = \sqrt{(5 - (-1))^2 + (2 - 3)^2} = \sqrt{37}$$

fórmula de la distancia (pág. 193) La distancia d entre dos puntos cualesquiera (x_1, y_1) y (x_2, y_2) es $d = \sqrt{(x_2 - x_1)^2 + (y_2 - y_1)^2}$.

La distancia d entre $(-1, 3)$ y $(5, 2)$ es:

$$d = \sqrt{(5 - (-1))^2 + (2 - 3)^2} = \sqrt{37}$$

ENGLISH-SPANISH GLOSSARY

distance from a point to a line (p. 229) The length of the perpendicular segment from the point to the line.

distancia de un punto a una recta (pág. 229) La longitud del segmento perpendicular del punto a la recta.

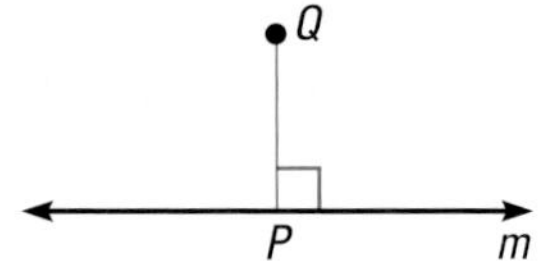

The distance from Q to m is QP.
La distancia de Q a m es QP.

domain of a function (p. 7) The set of all inputs of a function.

See **function.**

dominio de una función (pág. 7) El conjunto de todas las entradas de una función.

Ver **función.**

E

end behavior (p. 126) The behavior of the graph of a function as x approaches positive infinity $(+\infty)$ or negative infinity $(-\infty)$.

comportamiento (pág. 126) El comportamiento de la gráfica de una función al aproximarse x a infinito positivo $(+\infty)$ o a infinito negativo $(-\infty)$.

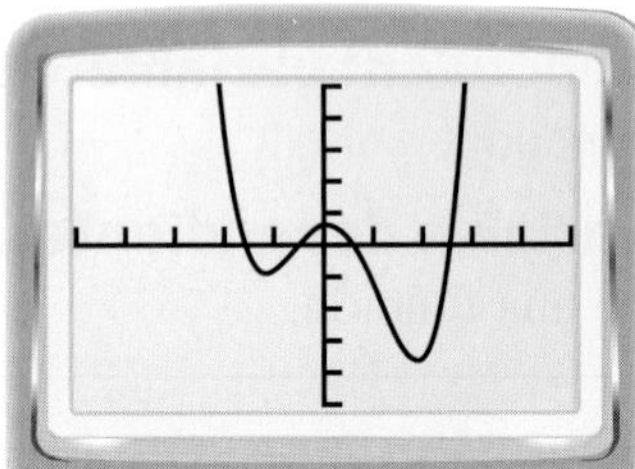

$f(x) \to +\infty$ as $x \to -\infty$ or as $x \to +\infty$.

$f(x) \to +\infty$ según $x \to -\infty$ o según $x \to +\infty$.

equidistant (p. 264) The same distance from one figure as from another figure.

equidistante (pág. 264) Situado a igual distancia de dos figuras.

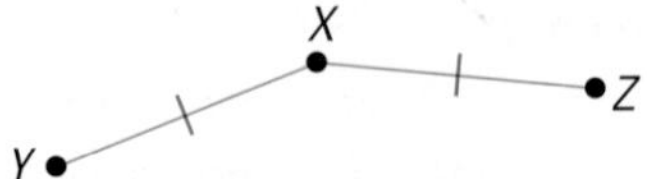

X is equidistant from Y and Z.
X es equidistante de Y y Z.

equivalent statements (p. 204) Two statements that are both true or both false.

A conditional statement and its contrapositive are equivalent statements.

enunciados equivalentes (pág. 204) Dos enunciados que son ambos verdaderos o ambos falsos.

Un enunciado condicional y su contrapositivo son enunciados equivalentes.

even function (p. 126) A function $f(x)$ such that $f(-x) = f(x)$.

función par (pág. 126) Una función $f(x)$ de modo que $f(-x) = f(x)$.

$f(x) = |x|$ **and** $f(x) = x^2$ **are examples of even functions.**

$f(x) = |x|$ **y** $f(x) = x^2$ **son ejemplos de funciones pares.**

excluded value (p. 161) A number that makes a rational expression undefined.

3 is an excluded value of the expression $\frac{2}{x-3}$ because 3 makes the value of the denominator 0.

valor excluido (pág. 161) Número que hace que una expresión racional sea indefinida.

3 es un valor excluido de la expresión $\frac{2}{x-3}$ ya que 3 hace que el valor del denominador sea 0.

---

expected value (p. 355) The expected value E of the collection of outcomes of mutually exclusive events is the sum of the products of the probability p and the value x of each event.

$E = p_1x_1 + p_2x_2 + \ldots + p_nx_n$

In a game at a fair, a person has a 50% chance of winning no money, a 25% chance of winning \$2, a 15% chance of winning \$3, and a 10% chance of winning \$5. The expected value of the game is 0.5(0) + 0.25(2) + 0.15(3) + 0.1(5)= \$1.45.

valor esperado (pág. 355) El valor esperado E de la colección de resultados de sucesos mutuamente excluyentes es la suma de los productos de la probabilidad p y el valor x de cada suceso.

$E = p_1x_1 + p_2x_2 + \ldots + p_nx_n$

En un juego de una feria, una persona tiene un 50% de probabilidad de no ganar dinero, un 25% de probabilidad de ganar \$2, un 15% de ganar \$3, y un 10% de ganar \$5. El valor esperado del juego es 0.5(0)+0.25(2)+0.15(3)+ 0.1(5) = \$1.45.

---

exterior angles of a polygon (p. 298) When the sides of a polygon are extended, the angles that are adjacent to the interior angles.

ángulos exteriores de un polígono (pág. 298) Los ángulos adyacentes a los ángulos interiores al prolongar los lados del polígono.

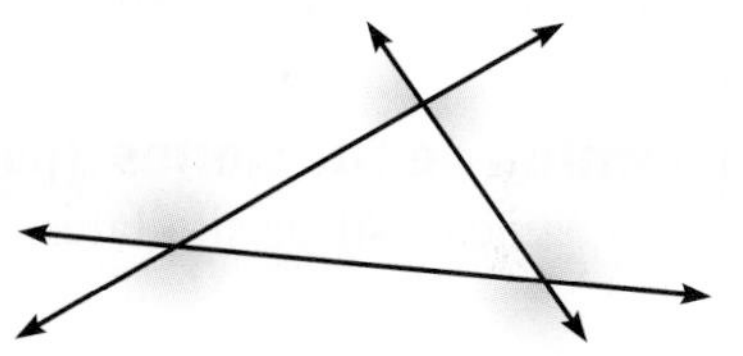

---

extraneous solution (p. 146) A solution of a transformed equation that is not a solution of the original equation.

When you square both sides of the radical equation $\sqrt{6-x} = x$, the resulting equation has two solutions, 2 and −3, but −3 is an extraneous solution because it does not satisfy the original equation $\sqrt{6-x} = x$.

solución extraña (pág. 146) Solución de una ecuación transformada que no es solución de la ecuación original.

Al elevar al cuadrado ambos miembros de la ecuación radical $\sqrt{6-x} = x$, la ecuación resultante tiene dos soluciones, 2 y −3, pero −3 es una solución extraña ya que no satisface la ecuación original $\sqrt{6-x} = x$.

ENGLISH-SPANISH GLOSSARY

factor by grouping (p. 93) To factor a polynomial with four terms by grouping, factor a common monomial from pairs of terms, and then look for a common binomial factor.

factorizar por grupos (pág. 93) Para factorizar por grupos un polinomio con cuatro términos, factoriza un monomio común a partir de los pares de términos y luego busca un factor binómico común.

$$\begin{aligned} &x^3 + 3x^2 + 5x + 15 \\ &= (x^3 + 3x^2) + (5x + 15) \\ &= x^2(x + 3) + 5(x + 3) \\ &= (x + 3)(x^2 + 5) \end{aligned}$$

---

factor completely (p. 93) A factorable polynomial with integer coefficients is factored completely if it is written as a product of unfactorable polynomials with integer coefficients.

The polynomial $x^3 - x$ is *not* factored completely when written as $x(x^2 - 1)$ but is factored completely when written as $x(x + 1)(x - 1)$.

factorizar completamente (pág. 93) Un polinomio que puede descomponerse en factores y que tiene coeficientes enteros está completamente factorizado si está escrito como producto de polinomios que no pueden descomponerse en factores y que tienen coeficientes enteros.

El polinomio $x^3 - x$ *no* está completamente factorizado cuando se escribe $x(x^2 - 1)$, pero sí está completamente factorizado cuando se escribe $x(x + 1)(x - 1)$.

---

family of functions (p. 38) A group of functions with similar characteristics.

Functions that have the form $f(x) = mx + b$ constitute the family of linear functions.

familia de funciones (pág. 38) Grupo de funciones con características similares.

Las funciones que tienen la forma $f(x) = mx + b$ constituyen la familia de las funciones lineales.

---

flow proof (p. 249) A type of proof that uses arrows to show the flow of a logical argument.

See Example 2 on page 250.

prueba de flujo (pág. 249) Tipo de prueba que usa flechas para indicar el flujo de un argumento lógico.

Ver el ejemplo 2 de la página 250.

---

formula (p. 2) An equation that relates two or more quantities.

The formula $d = rt$ relates the distance traveled to the rate of speed and travel time.

fórmula (pág. 2) Ecuación que relaciona dos o más cantidades.

La fórmula $d = rt$ relaciona la distancia recorrida con la velocidad y el tiempo transcurrido.

ENGLISH-SPANISH GLOSSARY

function (p. 7) A function consists of:

- A set called the domain containing numbers called inputs, and a set called the range containing numbers called outputs.
- A pairing of inputs with outputs such that each input is paired with exactly one output.

función (pág. 7) Una función consta de:

- Un conjunto llamado dominio que contiene los números conocidos como entradas, y otro conjunto llamado rango que contiene los números conocidos como salidas.
- Una correspondencia entre las entradas y las salidas tal que a cada entrada le corresponde una sola salida.

The pairing in the table below is a function, because each input is paired with exactly one output.

La correspondencia que aparece en la tabla de abajo es una función ya que a cada entrada le corresponde una sola salida.

Input, x Entrada, x	0	1	2	3	4
Output, y Salida, y	3	4	5	6	7

The domain is the set of inputs: 0, 1, 2, 3, and 4. The range is the set of outputs: 3, 4, 5, 6, and 7.
El dominio es el conjunto de entradas: 0, 1, 2, 3 y 4. El rango es el conjunto de salidas: 3, 4, 5, 6 y 7.

function notation (p. 38) A way to name a function using the symbol $f(x)$ instead of y. The symbol $f(x)$ is read as "the value of f at x" or as "f of x."

notación de función (pág. 38) Forma de nombrar una función usando el símbolo $f(x)$ en lugar de y. El símbolo $f(x)$ se lee "el valor de f en x" o "f de x".

The function $y = 2x - 9$ can be written in function notation as $f(x) = 2x - 9$.

La función $y = 2x - 9$ escrita en notación de función es $f(x) = 2x - 9$.

H

hypotenuse (p. 242) In a right triangle, the side opposite the right angle.

hipotenusa (pág. 242) En un triángulo rectángulo, el lado opuesto al ángulo recto.

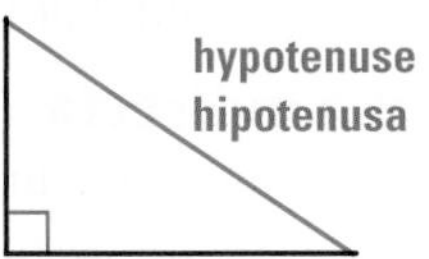

hypothesis (p. 204) The "if" part of a conditional statement.

hipótesis (pág. 204) La parte de "si" de un enunciado condicional.

See **conditional statement.**

Ver **enunciado condicional.**

I

if-then form (p. 204) The form of a conditional statement that uses the words "if" and "then." The "if" part contains the hypothesis and the "then" part contains the conclusion.

forma de "si..., entonces..." (pág. 204) La forma de un enunciado condicional que usa las palabras "si" y "entonces". La parte de "si" contiene la hipótesis, y la parte de "entonces" contiene la conclusión.

See **conditional statement.**

Ver **enunciado condicional.**

incenter of a triangle (p. 272) The point of concurrency of the three angle bisectors of the triangle.

incentro de un triángulo (pág. 272) El punto de concurrencia de las tres bisectrices de los ángulos del triángulo.

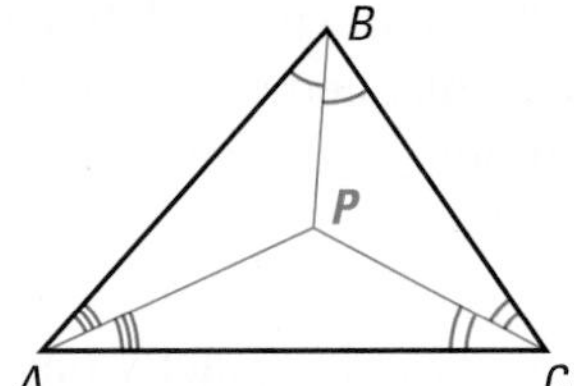

P is the incenter of $\triangle ABC$.

P es el incentro de $\triangle ABC$.

---

independent events (p. 351) Two events such that the occurrence of one event has no effect on the occurrence of the other event.

You roll a number cube twice. The events "roll a 3 first" and "roll a 6 second" are independent events.

sucesos independientes (pág. 351) Dos sucesos tales que la ocurrencia de uno de ellos no afecta a la ocurrencia del otro.

Lanzas un cubo numerado dos veces. Los sucesos "salir primero el 3" y "salir después el 6" son sucesos independientes.

---

independent variable (p. 7) The input variable of a function.

In the function equation $y = x + 3$, x is the independent variable.

variable independiente (pág. 7) La variable de entrada de una función.

En la ecuación de función $y = x + 3$, x es la variable independiente.

---

indirect proof (p. 292) A proof in which you prove that a statement is true by first assuming that its opposite is true. If this assumption leads to an impossibility, then you have proved that the original statement is true.

See Example 3 on page 293.

prueba indirecta (pág. 292) Prueba en la que, para demostrar que un enunciado es verdadero, primero se supone que su opuesto es verdadero. Si esta suposición lleva a una imposibilidad, entonces se habrá demostrado que el enunciado original es verdadero.

Ver el ejemplo 3 de la página 293.

---

inductive reasoning (p. 197) A process that includes looking for patterns and making conjectures.

Given the number pattern 1, 5, 9, 13, ..., you can use inductive reasoning to determine that the next number in the pattern is 17.

razonamiento inductivo (pág. 197) Proceso en el que se buscan patrones y se hacen conjeturas.

Dado el patrón numérico 1, 5, 9, 13, ..., puedes utilizar el razonamiento inductivo para determinar que el número siguiente del patrón es 17.

---

input (p. 7) A number in the domain of a function.

See function.

entrada (pág. 7) Número del dominio de una función.

Ver función.

interior angles of a polygon (p. 298) When the sides of a polygon are extended, the original angles of the polygon.

ángulos interiores de un polígono (pág. 298) Los ángulos originales de un polígono al prolongar los lados del polígono.

interquartile range (p. 369) The difference of the upper and the lower quartiles of a data set.

The interquartile range of the data set below is $23 - 10 = 13$.

lower quartile ↓ upper quartile ↓

8 **10** 14 17 20 **23** 50

rango intercuartílico (pág. 369) La diferencia entre el cuartil superior y el cuartil inferior de un conjunto de datos.

El rango intercuartílico del siguiente conjunto de datos es $23 - 10 = 13$.

cuartil inferior ↓ cuartil superior ↓

8 **10** 14 17 20 **23** 50

inverse (p. 204) The statement formed by negating the hypothesis and conclusion of a conditional statement.

Statement: If $m\angle A = 90°$, then $\angle A$ is right.
Inverse: If $m\angle A \neq 90°$, then $\angle A$ is not right.

inverso (pág. 204) El enunciado formado al negar la hipótesis y la conclusión de un enunciado condicional.

Enunciado: Si $m\angle A = 90°$, entonces $\angle A$ es recto.
Inverso: Si $m\angle A \neq 90°$, entonces $\angle A$ no es recto.

isosceles trapezoid (p. 323) A trapezoid with congruent legs.

trapecio isósceles (pág. 323) Trapecio que tiene los catetos congruentes.

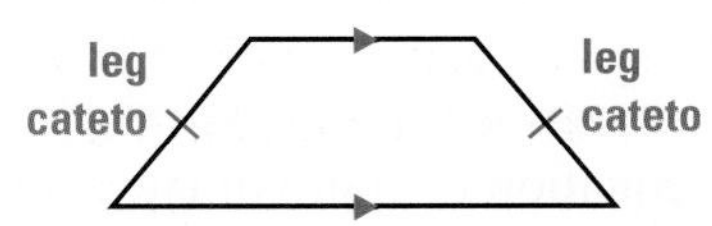

K

kite (p. 323) A quadrilateral that has two pairs of consecutive congruent sides, but in which opposite sides are not congruent.

cometa (pág. 323) Cuadrilátero que tiene dos pares de lados congruentes consecutivos pero cuyos lados opuestos no son congruentes.

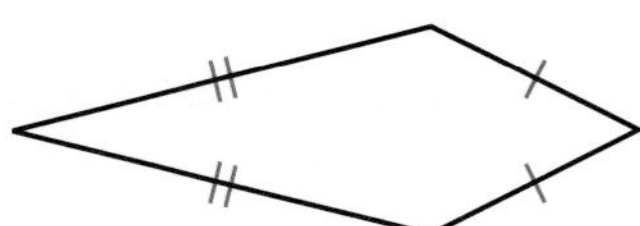

L

leading coefficient (p. 59) When a polynomial is written so that the exponents of a variable decrease from left to right, the coefficient of the first term is the leading coefficient.

The leading coefficient of the polynomial $2x^3 + x^2 - 5x + 12$ is 2.

coeficiente inicial (pág. 59) Cuando un polinomio se escribe de tal manera que los exponentes de una variable disminuyen de izquierda a derecha, el coeficiente del primer término es el coeficiente inicial.

El coeficiente inicial del polinomio $2x^3 + x^2 - 5x + 12$ es 2.

least common denominator (LCD) of rational expressions (p. 171) The product of the factors of the denominators of the rational expressions with each common factor used only once.

The LCD of $\frac{5}{(x-3)^2}$ and $\frac{3x+4}{(x-3)(x+2)}$ is $(x-3)^2(x+2)$.

mínimo común denominador (m.c.d.) de las expresiones racionales (pág. 171) El producto de los factores de los denominadores de las expresiones racionales usando cada factor común una sola vez.

El m.c.d. de $\frac{5}{(x-3)^2}$ y $\frac{3x+4}{(x-3)(x+2)}$ es $(x-3)^2(x+2)$.

legs of a right triangle (p. 242) In a right triangle, the sides adjacent to the right angle.

catetos de un triángulo rectángulo (pág. 242) En un triángulo rectángulo, los lados adyacentes al ángulo recto.

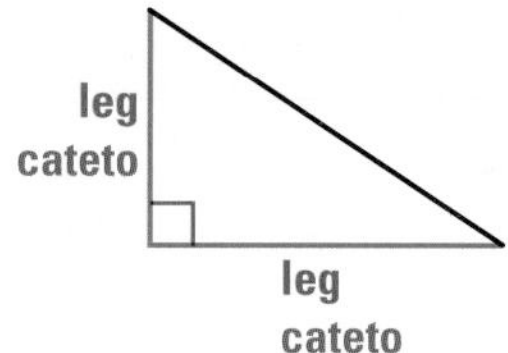

legs of a trapezoid (p. 323) The nonparallel sides of a trapezoid.

***See* trapezoid.**

catetos de un trapecio (pág. 323) Los lados no paralelos de un trapecio.

***Ver* trapecio.**

linear extrapolation (p. 45) Using a line or its equation to approximate a value outside the range of known values.

extrapolación lineal (pág. 45) El uso de una recta o su ecuación para hallar por aproximación un valor situado fuera del rango de los valores conocidos.

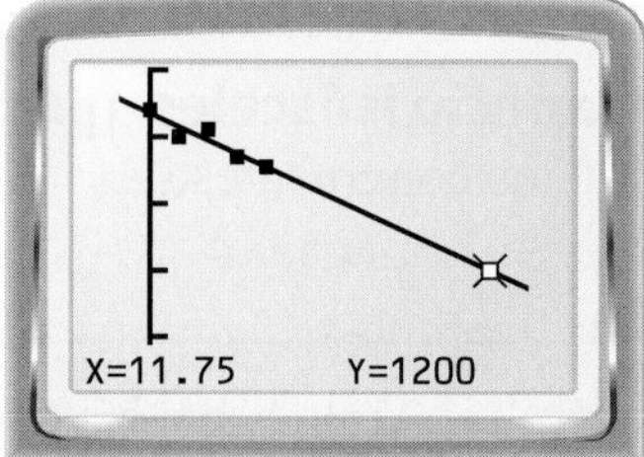

The best-fitting line can be used to estimate that when $y = 1200$, $x \approx 11.75$.

La mejor recta de regresión puede utilizarse para estimar que cuando $y = 1200$, $x \approx 11.75$.

linear interpolation (p. 45) Using a line or its equation to approximate a value between two known values.

interpolación lineal (pág. 45) El uso de una recta o su ecuación para hallar por aproximación un valor situado entre dos valores conocidos.

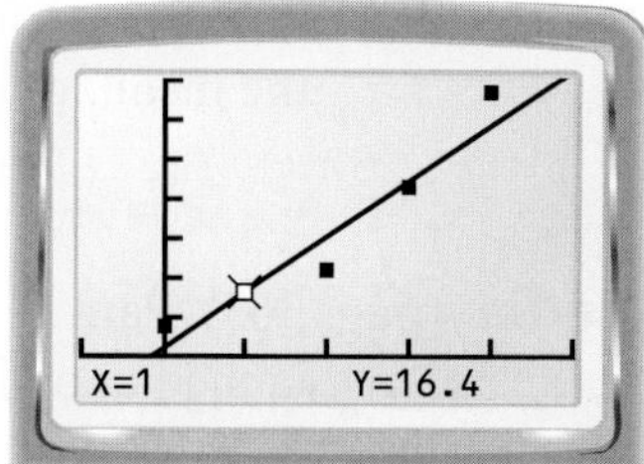

The best-fitting line can be used to estimate that when $x = 1$, $y \approx 16.4$.

La mejor recta de regresión puede utilizarse para estimar que cuando $x = 1$, $y \approx 16.4$.

linear pair (p. 223) Two adjacent angles whose noncommon sides are opposite rays.

par lineal (pág. 223) Dos ángulos adyacentes cuyos lados no comunes son rayos opuestos.

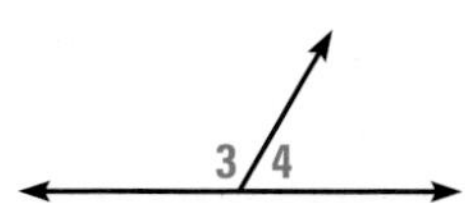

$\angle 3$ and $\angle 4$ are a linear pair.

$\angle 3$ y $\angle 4$ son un par lineal.

lower quartile (p. 369) The median of the lower half of an ordered data set.

cuartil inferior (pág. 369) La mediana de la mitad inferior de un conjunto de datos ordenados.

The lower quartile of the data set below is 10.

lower quartile ↓   median ↓

8 **10** 14 17 20 23 50

El cuartil inferior del siguiente conjunto de datos es 10.

cuartil inferior ↓   mediana ↓

8 10 14 17 20 23 50

M

maximum value (p. 104) For $y = ax^2 + bx + c$ where $a < 0$, the y-coordinate of the vertex is the maximum value of the function.

valor máximo (pág. 104) Para $y = ax^2 + bx + c$ donde $a < 0$, la coordenada y del vértice es el valor máximo de la función.

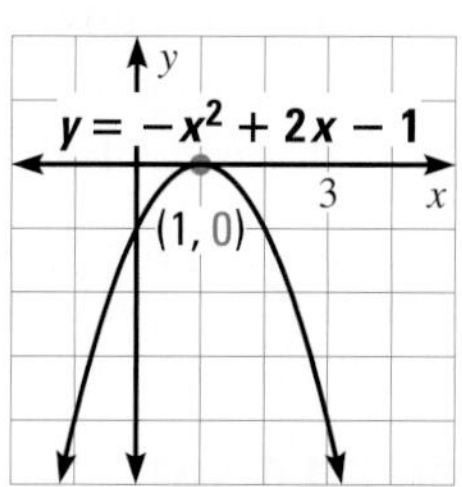

The maximum value of the function $y = -x^2 + 2x - 1$ is 0.

El valor máximo de la función $y = -x^2 + 2x - 1$ es 0.

mean (p. 363) For the numerical data set $x_1, x_2, \ldots, x_n$, the mean, or average, is: $$\bar{x} = \frac{x_1 + x_2 + \ldots + x_n}{n}$$ **media** (pág. 363) Para el conjunto de datos numéricos $x_1, x_2, \ldots, x_n$, la media, o el promedio, es: $$\bar{x} = \frac{x_1 + x_2 + \ldots + x_n}{n}$$	**The mean of 5, 9, 14, 23 is $\frac{5 + 9 + 14 + 23}{4} = \frac{51}{4} = 12.75$.** **La media de 5, 9, 14, 23 es $\frac{5 + 9 + 14 + 23}{4} = \frac{51}{4} = 12.75$.**
mean absolute deviation (p. 363) The mean absolute deviation of the data set $x_1, x_2, \ldots, x_n$ is a measure of dispersion given by: $$\frac{\lvert x_1 - \bar{x}\rvert + \lvert x_2 - \bar{x}\rvert + \ldots + \lvert x_n - \bar{x}\rvert}{n}$$ **desviación absoluta media** (pág. 363) La desviación absoluta media del conjunto de datos $x_1, x_2, \ldots, x_n$ es una medida de dispersión dada por: $$\frac{\lvert x_1 - \bar{x}\rvert + \lvert x_2 - \bar{x}\rvert + \ldots + \lvert x_n - \bar{x}\rvert}{n}$$	**The mean absolute deviation of the data set 3, 9, 13, 23 (with mean = 12) is:** $\frac{\lvert 3-12\rvert + \lvert 9-12\rvert + \lvert 13-12\rvert + \lvert 23-12\rvert}{4} = 6$ **La desviación absoluta media del conjunto de datos 3, 9, 13, 23 (con media = 12) es:** $\frac{\lvert 3-12\rvert + \lvert 9-12\rvert + \lvert 13-12\rvert + \lvert 23-12\rvert}{4} = 6$
measure of dispersion (p. 363) A measure that describes the dispersion, or spread, of data. **medida de dispersión** (pág. 363) Medida que describe la dispersión, o extensión, de los datos.	***See* range *and* mean absolute deviation.** ***Ver* rango *y* desviación absoluta media.**
median (p. 363) The median of a numerical data set is the middle number when the values are written in numerical order. If the data set has an even number of values, the median is the mean of the two middle values. **mediana** (pág. 363) La mediana de un conjunto de datos numéricos es el número central cuando los valores se escriben en orden numérico. Si el conjunto de datos tiene un número par de valores, la mediana es la media de los dos valores centrales.	**The median of 5, 9, 14, 23 is the mean of 9 and 14, or $\frac{9 + 14}{2} = 11.5$.** **La mediana de 5, 9, 14, 23 es la media de 9 y 14, ó $\frac{9 + 14}{2} = 11.5$.**
median of a triangle (p. 278) A segment from one vertex of the triangle to the midpoint of the opposite side. **mediana de un triángulo** (pág. 278) Segmento que va desde uno de los vértices del triángulo hasta el punto medio del lado opuesto.	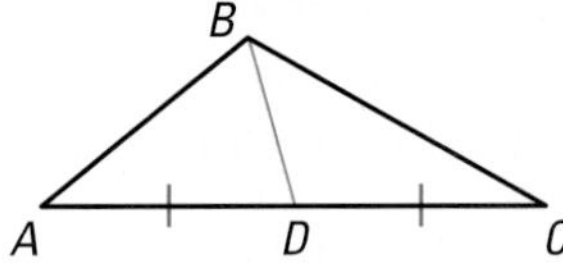 $\overline{BD}$ is a median of $\triangle ABC$. $\overline{BD}$ es una mediana de $\triangle ABC$.

ENGLISH-SPANISH GLOSSARY

midpoint (p. 193) The midpoint of a line segment is the point on the segment that is equidistant from the endpoints. The midpoint of a segment divides the segment into two congruent segments.

punto medio (pág. 193) El punto medio de un segmento de recta es el punto del segmento que es equidistante de los extremos. El punto medio de un segmento divide el segmento en dos segmentos congruentes.

M is the midpoint of $\overline{AB}$.

M en el punto medio de $\overline{AB}$.

midpoint formula (p. 193) The midpoint M of the line segment with endpoints $A(x_1, y_1)$ and $B(x_2, y_2)$ is $M\left(\frac{x_1 + x_2}{2}, \frac{y_1 + y_2}{2}\right)$.

fórmula del punto medio (pág. 193) El punto medio M del segmento de recta cuyos extremos son $A(x_1, y_1)$ y $B(x_2, y_2)$ es $M\left(\frac{x_1 + x_2}{2}, \frac{y_1 + y_2}{2}\right)$.

The midpoint M of the line segment with endpoints $(-1, -2)$ and $(3, -4)$ is:
$$\left(\frac{-1 + 3}{2}, \frac{-2 + (-4)}{2}\right) = (1, -3)$$

El punto medio M del segmento de recta cuyos extremos son $(-1, -2)$ y $(3, -4)$ es:
$$\left(\frac{-1 + 3}{2}, \frac{-2 + (-4)}{2}\right) = (1, -3)$$

midsegment of a trapezoid (p. 323) A segment that connects the midpoints of the legs of a trapezoid.

paralela media de un trapecio (pág. 323) Segmento que une los puntos medios de los catetos del trapecio.

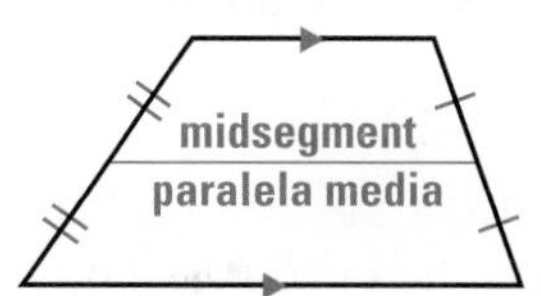

midsegment of a triangle (p. 258) A segment that connects the midpoints of two sides of the triangle.

paralela media de un triángulo (pág. 258) Segmento que une los puntos medios de dos lados del triángulo.

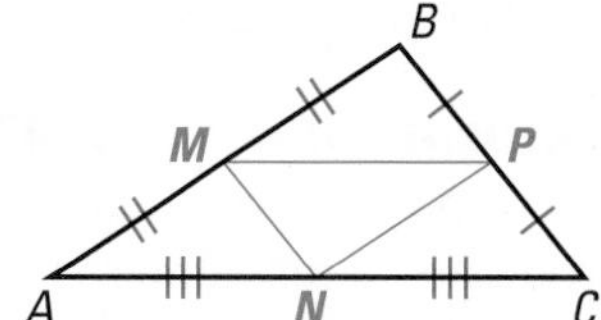

The midsegments of $\triangle ABC$ are $\overline{MP}$, $\overline{MN}$, and $\overline{NP}$.

Las paralelas medias de $\triangle ABC$ son $\overline{MP}$, $\overline{MN}$ y $\overline{NP}$.

minimum value (p. 104) For $y = ax^2 + bx + c$ where $a > 0$, the y-coordinate of the vertex is the minimum value of the function.

valor mínimo (pág. 104) Para $y = ax^2 + bx + c$ donde $a > 0$, la coordenada y del vértice es el valor mínimo de la función.

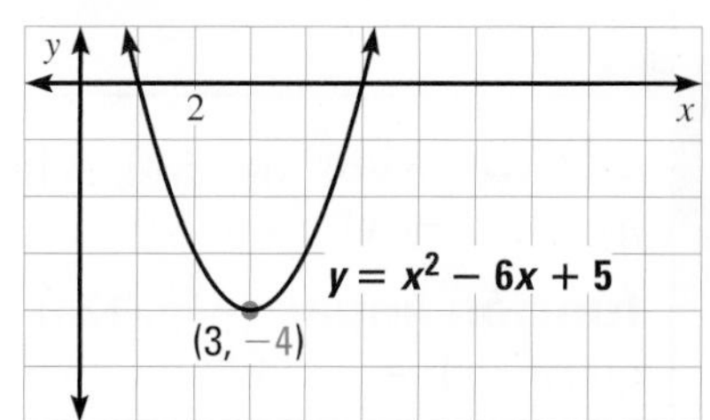

The minimum value of the function $y = x^2 - 6x + 5$ is -4.

El valor mínimo de la función $y = x^2 - 6x + 5$ es -4.

ENGLISH-SPANISH GLOSSARY

mode (p. 363) The mode of a data set is the value that occurs most frequently. There may be one mode, no mode, or more than one mode.	**The mode of the data set 4, 7, 9, 11, 11, 12, 18 is 11.**
moda (pág. 363) La moda de un conjunto de datos es el valor que ocurre más veces. Puede haber una moda, más de una moda o ninguna moda.	**La moda del conjunto de datos 4, 7, 9, 11, 11, 12, 18 es 11.**
monomial (p. 59) A number, variable, or the product of a number and one or more variables with whole number exponents.	**10, $3x$, $\frac{1}{2}ab^2$, and $-1.8m^5$ are monomials.**
monomio (pág. 59) Un número, una variable o el producto de un número y una o más variables que tienen exponentes expresados por números naturales.	**10, $3x$, $\frac{1}{2}ab^2$ y $-1.8m^5$ son monomios.**
mutually exclusive events (p. 351) Events that have no common outcome.	**When you roll a number cube, "roll a 3" and "roll an even number" are mutually exclusive events.**
sucesos mutuamente excluyentes (pág. 351) Sucesos que no tienen ningún caso en común.	**Cuando lanzas un cubo numerado, "salir el 3" y "salir número par" son sucesos mutuamente excluyentes.**

ENGLISH-SPANISH GLOSSARY

N

***n* factorial** (p. 342) For any positive integer n, n factorial, written $n!$, is the product of the integers from 1 to n; $0! = 1$.	**$5! = 5 \cdot 4 \cdot 3 \cdot 2 \cdot 1 = 120$**
factorial de *n* (pág. 342) Para cualquier número entero positivo n, el factorial de n, escrito $n!$, es el producto de los números enteros de 1 a n; $0! = 1$.	
negation (p. 204) The opposite of a statement. The symbol for negation is ~.	**Statement: The ball is red. Negation: The ball is not red.**
negación (pág. 204) El opuesto de un enunciado. El símbolo de la negación es ~.	**Enunciado: La pelota es roja. Negación: La pelota no es roja.**

O

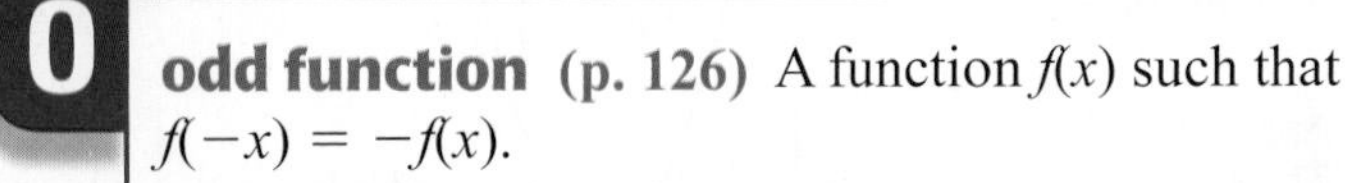

odd function (p. 126) A function $f(x)$ such that $f(-x) = -f(x)$.	**$f(x) = x$ and $f(x) = x^3$ are examples of odd functions.**
función impar (pág. 126) Una función $f(x)$ de modo que $f(-x) = -f(x)$.	**$f(x) = x$ y $f(x) = x^3$ son ejemplos de funciones impares.**

orthocenter of a triangle (p. 278) The point at which the lines containing the three altitudes of the triangle intersect.

ortocentro de un triángulo (pág. 278) El punto donde se cortan las rectas que contienen las tres alturas del triángulo.

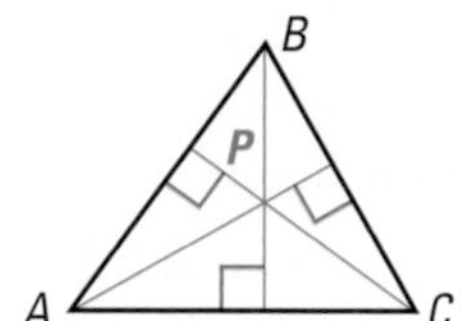

P is the orthocenter of $\triangle ABC$.

P es el ortocentro de $\triangle ABC$.

output (p. 7) A number in the range of a function.

salida (pág. 7) Número que pertenece al rango de una función.

See function.

Ver función.

overlapping events (p. 351) Events that have at least one common outcome.

sucesos de intersección (pág. 351) Sucesos que tienen al menos un caso en común.

When you roll a number cube, "roll a 3" and "roll an odd number" are overlapping events.

Cuando lanzas un cubo numerado, "salir el 3" y "salir número impar" son sucesos de intersección.

P

parabola (p. 98) The U-shaped graph of a quadratic function.

parábola (pág. 98) La gráfica en forma de U de una función cuadrática.

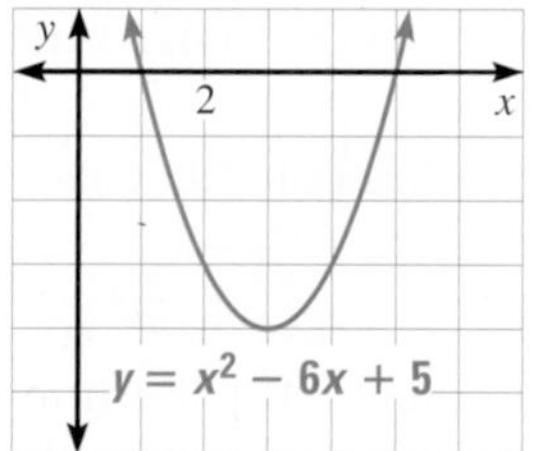

The graph of $y = x^2 - 6x + 5$ is a parabola.

La gráfica de $y = x^2 - 6x + 5$ es una parábola.

parallel lines (p. 30) Two lines in the same plane that do not intersect.

rectas paralelas (pág. 30) Dos rectas del mismo plano que no se cortan.

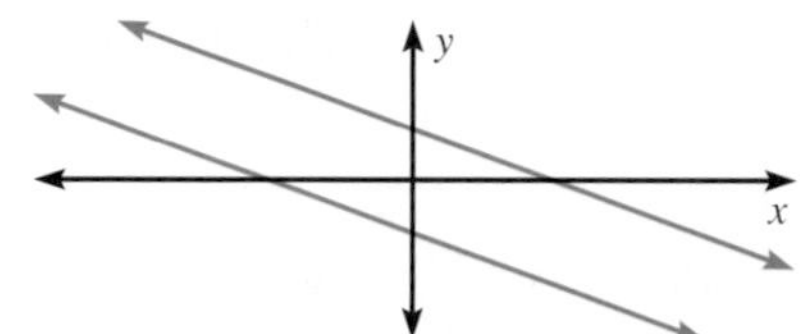

parallelogram (p. 304) A quadrilateral with both pairs of opposite sides parallel.

paralelogramo (pág. 304) Cuadrilátero que tiene ambos pares de lados opuestos paralelos.

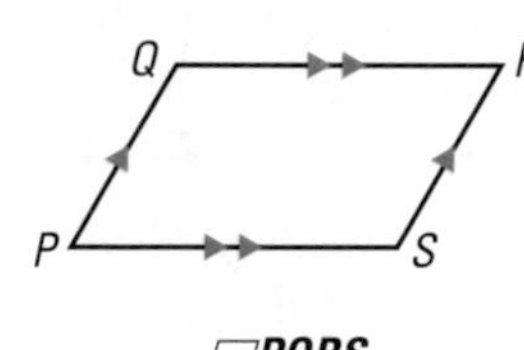

$\square PQRS$

parent linear function (p. 38) The function $f(x) = x$, which is the most basic function in the family of linear functions.

función lineal básica (pág. 38) La función $f(x) = x$, que es la más básica de la familia de las funciones lineales.

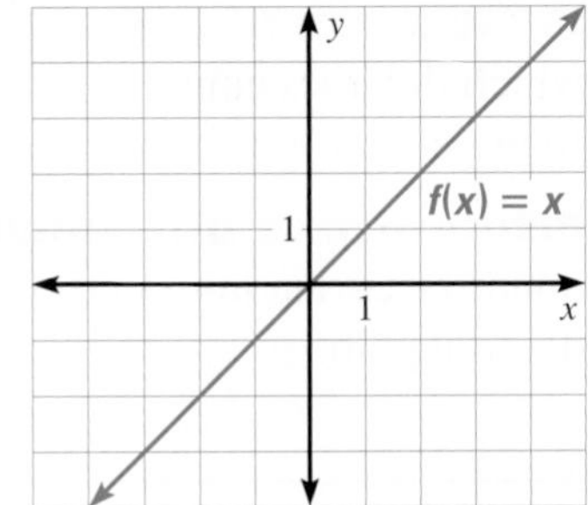

parent quadratic function (p. 98) The function $y = x^2$, which is the most basic function in the family of quadratic functions.

función cuadrática básica (pág. 98) La función $y = x^2$, que es la más básica de la familia de las funciones cuadráticas.

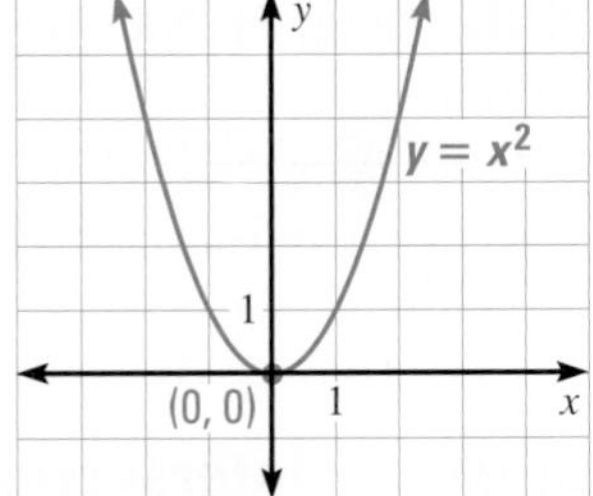

parent square root function (p. 135) The function $y = \sqrt{x}$, which is the most basic function in the family of square root functions.

función con raíz cuadrada básica (pág. 135) La función $y = \sqrt{x}$, que es la más básica de la familia de las funciones con raíz cuadrada.

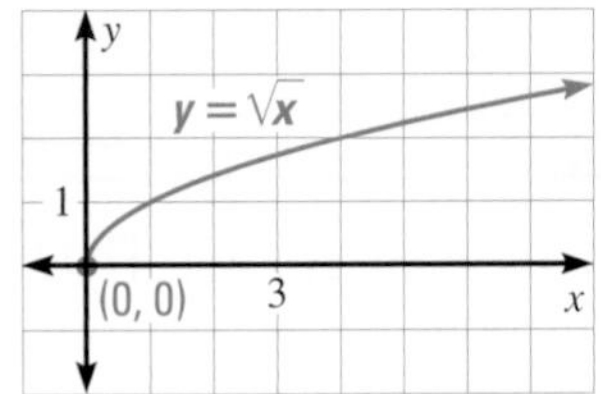

Pascal's triangle (p. 72) An arrangement of numbers in a triangular pattern in which each entry in a row is the sum of the entry directly above to the right and directly above to the left.

triángulo de Pascal (pág. 72) Disposición de los números en un patrón triangular en el que cada entrada de una fila es la suma de la entrada que se encuentra directamente arriba a la derecha y directamente arriba a la izquierda.

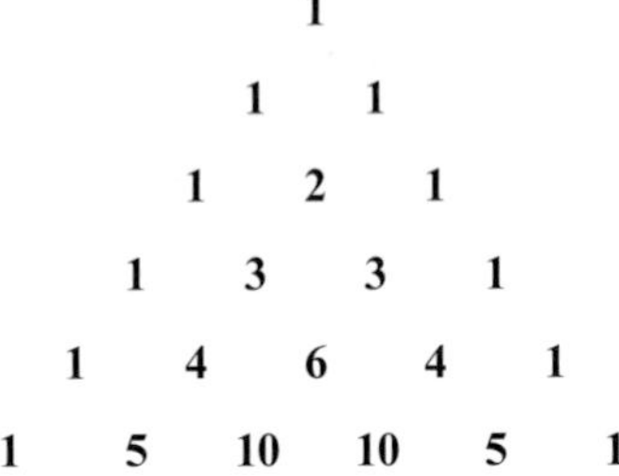

perfect square (p. 119) A number that is the square of an integer.

cuadrado perfecto (pág. 119) Número que es el cuadrado de un número entero.

49 is a perfect square, because $49 = 7^2$.

49 es un cuadrado perfecto ya que $49 = 7^2$.

perfect square trinomials (p. 89) Trinomials of the form $a^2 + 2ab + b^2$ and $a^2 - 2ab + b^2$.

trinomios cuadrados perfectos (pág. 89) Trinomios de la forma $a^2 + 2ab + b^2$ y $a^2 - 2ab + b^2$.

$x^2 + 6x + 9$ and $x^2 - 10x + 25$ are perfect square trinomials.

$x^2 + 6x + 9$ y $x^2 - 10x + 25$ son trinomios cuadrados perfectos.

permutation (p. 342) An arrangement of objects in which order is important.

There are 6 permutations of the numbers 1, 2, and 3: 123, 132, 213, 231, 312, and 321.

permutación (pág. 342) Disposición de objetos en la que el orden es importante.

Existen 6 permutaciones de los números 1, 2 y 3: 123, 132, 213, 231, 312 y 321.

perpendicular bisector (p. 264) A segment, ray, line, or plane that is perpendicular to a segment at its midpoint.

mediatriz (pág. 264) Segmento, rayo, recta o plano que es perpendicular a un segmento en su punto medio.

perpendicular lines (p. 204) Two lines that intersect to form a right angle.

rectas perpendiculares (pág. 204) Dos rectas que se cortan para formar un ángulo recto.

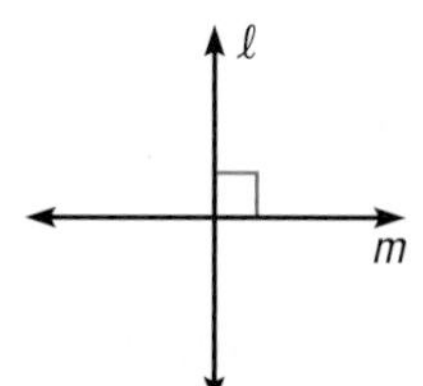

point of concurrency (p. 264) The point of intersection of concurrent lines, rays, or segments.

punto de concurrencia (pág. 264) El punto de intersección de rectas, rayos o segmentos concurrentes.

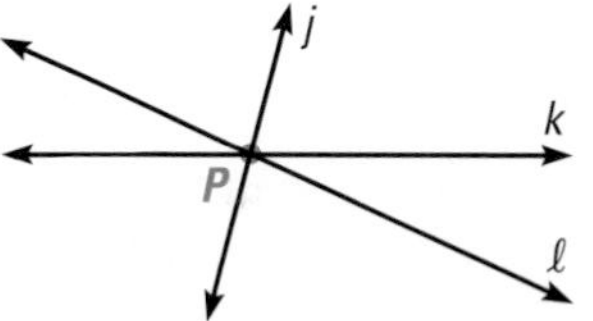

P is the point of concurrency for lines *j*, *k*, and *ℓ*.

***P* es el punto de concurrencia de las rectas *j*, *k* y *ℓ*.**

polynomial (p. 59) A monomial or a sum of monomials, each called a term of the polynomial.

9, $2x^2 + x - 5$, and $7bc^3 + 4b^4c$ are polynomials.

polinomio (pág. 59) Monomio o suma de monomios; cada uno se llama término del polinomio.

9, $2x^2 + x - 5$ y $7bc^3 + 4b^4c$ son polinomios.

population (p. 359) The entire group that you want information about.

A magazine invites its readers to mail in answers to a questionnaire rating the magazine. The population consists of all the magazine's readers.

población (pág. 359) El grupo entero sobre el que se desea información.

Una revista invita a sus lectores a enviar por correo las respuestas a un cuestionario sobre la calidad de la revista. La población está formada por todos los lectores de la revista.

postulate (p. 217) A rule that is accepted without proof. Also called *axiom*.

The Segment Addition Postulate states that if B is between A and C, then $AB + BC = AC$.

postulado (pág. 217) Regla aceptada sin necesidad de pruebas. También se llama *axioma*.

El postulado de la suma de segmentos establece que si B está entre A y C, entonces $AB + BC = AC$.

proof (p. 217) A logical argument that shows a statement is true.

***See* two-column proof, paragraph proof, *and* flow proof.**

prueba (pág. 217) Argumento lógico que muestra que un enunciado es verdadero.

***Ver* prueba de dos columnas, prueba en forma de párrafo *y* prueba de flujo.**

Q

quadratic equation (p. 112) An equation that can be written in the standard form $ax^2 + bx + c = 0$ where $a \neq 0$.

The equations $x^2 - 2x = 3$ and $0.1x^2 = 40$ are quadratic equations.

ecuación cuadrática (pág. 112) Ecuación que puede escribirse en la forma general $ax^2 + bx + c = 0$, donde $a \neq 0$.

$x^2 - 2x = 3$ y $0.1x^2 = 40$ son ecuaciones cuadráticas.

quadratic function (p. 98) A nonlinear function that can be written in the standard form $y = ax^2 + bx + c$ where $a \neq 0$.

$y = 2x^2 + 5x - 3$ is a quadratic function.

función cuadrática (pág. 98) Función no lineal que puede escribirse en la forma general $y = ax^2 + bx + c$, donde $a \neq 0$.

$y = 2x^2 + 5x - 3$ es una función cuadrática.

quartile (p. 369) The median of an ordered data set, the median of the upper half of an ordered data set, or the median of the lower half of an ordered data set.

14, 17, 18, 19, 20, 24, 24, 30, 32

The quartiles of the data set are 17.5, 20, and 27.

cuartil (pág. 369) La mediana de un conjunto ordenado de datos, la mediana de la mitad superior de un conjunto ordenado de datos o la mediana de la mitad inferior de un conjunto ordenado de datos.

Los cuartiles del conjunto de datos son 17.5, 20, y 27.

R

radical conjugates (p. 142) The expressions $a + \sqrt{b}$ and $a - \sqrt{b}$ where a and b are rational numbers.

The radical conjugate of $7 + \sqrt{2}$ is $7 - \sqrt{2}$.

conjugados radicales (pág. 142) Las expresiones $a + \sqrt{b}$ y $a - \sqrt{b}$ cuando a y b son números racionales.

El conjugado radical de $7 + \sqrt{2}$ es $7 - \sqrt{2}$.

radical equation (p. 146) An equation that contains a radical expression with a variable in the radicand.

ecuación radical (pág. 146) Ecuación que contiene una expresión radical en cuyo radicando aparece una variable.

$2\sqrt{x} - 8 = 0$ and $\sqrt{3x - 17} = \sqrt{x + 21}$ are radical equations.

$2\sqrt{x} - 8 = 0$ y $\sqrt{3x - 17} = \sqrt{x + 21}$ son ecuaciones radicales.

radical expression (p. 135) An expression that contains a radical, such as a square root, cube root, or other root.

expresión radical (pág. 135) Expresión que contiene un radical, como una raíz cuadrada, una raíz cúbica u otra raíz.

$3\sqrt{2x}$ and $\sqrt[3]{x - 1}$ are radical expressions.

$3\sqrt{2x}$ y $\sqrt[3]{x - 1}$ son expresiones radicales.

radical function (p. 135) A function that contains a radical expression with the independent variable in the radicand.

función radical (pág. 135) Función que contiene una expresión radical y en cuyo radicando aparece la variable independiente.

$y = \sqrt[3]{2x}$ and $y = \sqrt{x + 2}$ are radical functions.

$y = \sqrt[3]{2x}$ e $y = \sqrt{x + 2}$ son funciones radicales.

radicand (p. 119) The number or expression inside a radical symbol.

radicando (pág. 119) El número o la expresión que aparece bajo el signo radical.

The radicand of $\sqrt{9}$ and $-\sqrt{9}$ is 9.

El radicando de $\sqrt{9}$ y $-\sqrt{9}$ es 9.

random sample (p. 359) A sample in which every member of the population has an equal chance of being selected.

You can select a random sample of a school's student population by having a computer randomly choose 100 student identification numbers.

muestra aleatoria (pág. 359) Muestra en la que cada miembro de la población tiene igual probabilidad de ser seleccionado.

Para seleccionar una muestra aleatoria de la población de estudiantes de una escuela, puedes usar la computadora para elegir al azar 100 números de identificación estudiantil.

range of a data set (p. 363) The range of a numerical data set is a measure of dispersion. It is the difference of the greatest value and the least value.

rango de un conjunto de datos (pág. 363) El rango de un conjunto de datos numéricos es una medida de dispersión. Es la diferencia entre los valores mayor y menor.

The range of the data set 4, 7, 9, 11, 11, 12, 18 is $18 - 4 = 14$.

El rango del conjunto de datos 4, 7, 9, 11, 11, 12, 18 es $18 - 4 = 14$.

range of a function (p. 7) The set of all outputs of a function.

See function.

rango de una función (pág. 7) El conjunto de todas las salidas de una función.

Ver función.

---

rate of change (p. 23) A comparison of a change in one quantity with a change in another quantity. In real-world situations, you can interpret the slope of a line as a rate of change.

You pay \$7 for 2 hours of computer use and \$14 for 4 hours of computer use. The rate of change is $\frac{\text{change in cost}}{\text{change in time}} = \frac{14 - 7}{4 - 2} = 3.5$, or \$3.50 per hour.

relación de cambio (pág. 23) Comparación entre el cambio producido en una cantidad y el cambio producido en otra cantidad. En situaciones de la vida real, se puede interpretar la pendiente de una recta como una relación de cambio.

Pagas \$7 por usar la computadora 2 horas y \$14 por usarla 4 horas. La relación de cambio es $\frac{\text{cambio en el costo}}{\text{cambio en el tiempo}} = \frac{14 - 7}{4 - 2} = 3.5$, o \$3.50 por hora.

---

rational equation (p. 150) An equation that contains one or more rational expressions.

The equations $\frac{6}{x + 4} = \frac{x}{2}$ and $\frac{x}{x - 2} + \frac{1}{5} = \frac{2}{x - 2}$ are rational equations.

ecuación racional (pág. 150) Ecuación que contiene una o más expresiones racionales.

$\frac{6}{x + 4} = \frac{x}{2}$ y $\frac{x}{x - 2} + \frac{1}{5} = \frac{2}{x - 2}$ son ecuaciones racionales.

---

rational expression (p. 161) An expression that can be written as a ratio of two polynomials where the denominator is not 0.

$\frac{x + 8}{10x}$ and $\frac{5}{x^2 - 1}$ are rational expressions.

expresión racional (pág. 161) Expresión que puede escribirse como razón de dos polinomios, donde el denominador no es 0.

$\frac{x + 8}{10x}$ y $\frac{5}{x^2 - 1}$ son expresiones racionales.

---

rational function (p. 150) A function whose rule is given by a fraction whose numerator and denominator are polynomials and whose denominator is not 0.

The equations $y = \frac{-1}{x}$ and $y = \frac{2x - 1}{x - 2}$ are rational functions.

función racional (pág. 150) Función cuya regla viene dada por una fracción cuyo numerador y denominador son polinomios y cuyo denominador no es 0.

Las ecuaciones $y = \frac{-1}{x}$ e $y = \frac{2x - 1}{x - 2}$ son funciones racionales.

rationalizing the denominator (p. 142) The process of eliminating a radical from an expression's denominator by multiplying the expression by an appropriate form of 1.

To rationalize the denominator of $\frac{5}{\sqrt{7}}$, multiply the expression by $\frac{\sqrt{7}}{\sqrt{7}}$:

$$\frac{5}{\sqrt{7}} = \frac{5}{\sqrt{7}} \cdot \frac{\sqrt{7}}{\sqrt{7}} = \frac{5\sqrt{7}}{\sqrt{49}} = \frac{5\sqrt{7}}{7}$$

racionalizar el denominador (pág. 142) El proceso de eliminar el radical del denominador de una expresión multiplicando la expresión por la forma apropiada de 1.

Para racionalizar el denominador de $\frac{5}{\sqrt{7}}$, multiplica la expresión por $\frac{\sqrt{7}}{\sqrt{7}}$:

$$\frac{5}{\sqrt{7}} = \frac{5}{\sqrt{7}} \cdot \frac{\sqrt{7}}{\sqrt{7}} = \frac{5\sqrt{7}}{\sqrt{49}} = \frac{5\sqrt{7}}{7}$$

---

rectangle (p. 317) A parallelogram with four right angles.

rectángulo (pág. 317) Paralelogramo que tiene los cuatro ángulos rectos.

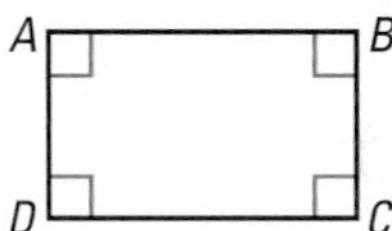

---

representative sample (p. 359) A sample that accurately reflects the characteristics of a population.

A random sample of 100 students will likely result in a representative sample of a school's population.

muestra representativa (p. 359) Una muestra que refleja con exactitud las características de una población.

Una muestra aleatoria de 100 estudiantes probablemente dé como resultado una muestra representativa de la población de una escuela.

---

rhombus (p. 317) A parallelogram with four congruent sides.

rombo (pág. 317) Paralelogramo que tiene los cuatro lados congruentes.

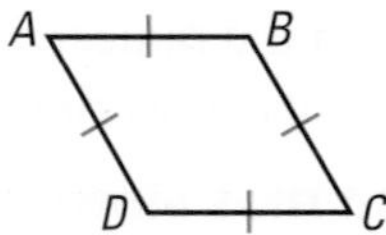

---

roots (p. 77) The solutions of an equation in which one side is zero and other side is a product of polynomial factors.

The roots of the equation $(x - 4)(x + 2) = 0$ are 4 and -2.

raíces (pág. 77) Las soluciones de una ecuación en la que un lado es cero y el otro lado es el producto de factores polinómicos.

Las raíces de la ecuación $(x - 4)(x + 2) = 0$ son 4 y -2.

S

sample (p. 359) A part of a population.

To predict the results of an election, a survey is given to a sample of voters.

muestra (pág. 359) Parte de una población.

Para predecir los resultados de una elección, se realiza una encuesta entre una muestra de votantes.

self-selected sample (p. 359) A sample in which members of the population select themselves by volunteering.

You can obtain a self-selected sample of a school's student population by asking students to return surveys to a collection box.

muestra autoseleccionada (pág. 359) Muestra en la que los miembros de la población se seleccionan a sí mismos ofreciéndose a participar.

Para obtener una muestra autoseleccionada de la población de estudiantes de una escuela, puedes pedir a los estudiantes que hagan la encuesta que la depositen en un recipiente de recogida.

sequence (p. 185) A function whose domain is a set of consecutive whole numbers. The domain gives the relative position of each term of the sequence. The range gives the terms of the sequence.

For the domain $n = 1, 2, 3$, and 4, the sequence defined by $a_n = 2n$ has the terms 2, 4, 6, and 8.

progresión (pág. 185) Función cuyo dominio es un conjunto de números naturales consecutivos. El dominio da la posición relativa de cada término de la progresión. El rango da los términos de la progresión.

Para el dominio $n = 1, 2, 3$ y 4, la secuencia definida por $a_n = 2n$ tiene los términos 2, 4, 6 y 8.

simplest form of a radical expression (p. 142) A radical expression that has no perfect square factors other than 1 in the radicand, no fractions in the radicand, and no radicals appearing in the denominator of a fraction.

In simplest form, $\sqrt{32}$ is written as $4\sqrt{2}$, and $\frac{5}{\sqrt{7}}$ is written as $\frac{5\sqrt{7}}{7}$.

forma más simple de una expresión radical (pág. 142) Expresión radical que no tiene en el radicando fracciones ni factores cuadrados perfectos distintos de 1 y que no tiene radicales en el denominador de las fracciones.

En la forma más simple, $\sqrt{32}$ se escribe $4\sqrt{2}$, y $\frac{5}{\sqrt{7}}$ se escribe $\frac{5\sqrt{7}}{7}$.

simplest form of a rational expression (p. 161) A rational expression whose numerator and denominator have no factors in common other than 1.

The simplest form of $\frac{2x}{x(x-3)}$ is $\frac{2}{x-3}$.

forma más simple de una expresión racional (pág. 161) Expresión racional cuyo numerador y denominador no tienen más factores en común que el 1.

La forma más simple de $\frac{2x}{x(x-3)}$ es $\frac{2}{x-3}$.

slope (p. 23) The slope m of a nonvertical line is the ratio of the vertical change (the *rise*) to the horizontal change (the *run*) between any two points (x_1, y_1) and (x_2, y_2) on the line:

$$m = \frac{y_2 - y_1}{x_2 - x_1}.$$

pendiente (pág. 23) La pendiente m de una recta no vertical es la razón del cambio vertical (*distancia vertical*) al cambio horizontal (*distancia horizontal*) entre dos puntos cualesquiera (x_1, y_1) y (x_2, y_2) de la recta:

$$m = \frac{y_2 - y_1}{x_2 - x_1}.$$

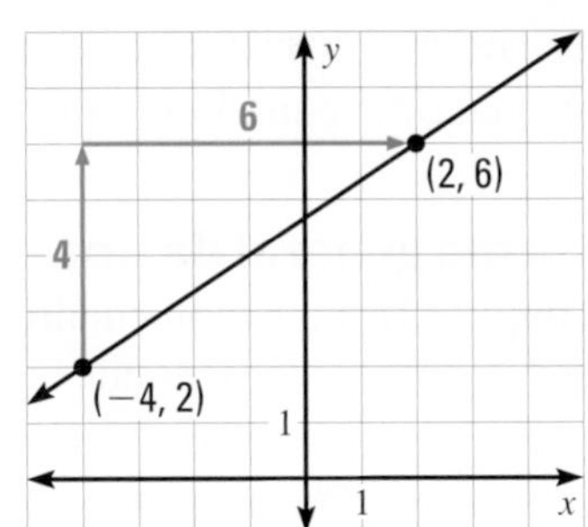

The slope of the line shown is $\frac{4}{6}$, or $\frac{2}{3}$.

La pendiente de la recta indicada es $\frac{4}{6}$, ó $\frac{2}{3}$.

slope-intercept form (p. 30) A linear equation written in the form $y = mx + b$ where m is the slope and b is the y-intercept of the equation's graph.

forma pendiente-intercepto (pág. 30) Ecuación lineal escrita en la forma $y = mx + b$, donde m es la pendiente y b es el intercepto en y de la gráfica de la ecuación.

$y = 3x + 4$ is in slope-intercept form. The slope of the line is 3, and the y-intercept is 4.

$y = 3x + 4$ está en la forma pendiente-intercepto. La pendiente de la recta es 3, y el intercepto en y es 4.

square (p. 317) A parallelogram with four congruent sides and four right angles.

cuadrado (pág. 317) Paralelogramo que tiene los cuatro lados congruentes y los cuatro ángulos rectos.

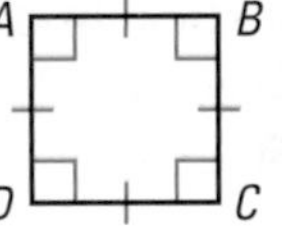

square root (p. 119) If $b^2 = a$, then b is a square root of a. The radical symbol $\sqrt{}$ represents a nonnegative square root.

raíz cuadrada (pág. 119) Si $b^2 = a$, entonces b es una raíz cuadrada de a. El signo radical $\sqrt{}$ representa una raíz cuadrada no negativa.

The square roots of 9 are 3 and -3, because $3^2 = 9$ and $(-3)^2 = 9$. So, $\sqrt{9} = 3$ and $-\sqrt{9} = -3$.

Las raíces cuadradas de 9 son 3 y -3 ya que $3^2 = 9$ y $(-3)^2 = 9$. Así pues, $\sqrt{9} = 3$ y $-\sqrt{9} = -3$.

square root function (p. 135) A radical function whose equation contains a square root with the independent variable in the radicand.

función con raíz cuadrada (pág. 135) Función radical representada por una ecuación con una raíz cuadrada en cuyo radicando aparece la variable independiente.

$y = 2\sqrt{x + 2}$ and $y = \sqrt{x} + 3$ are square root functions.

$y = 2\sqrt{x + 2}$ e $y = \sqrt{x} + 3$ son funciones con raíz cuadrada.

ENGLISH-SPANISH GLOSSARY

standard form of a quadratic equation (p. 112) A quadratic equation in the form $ax^2 + bx + c = 0$ where $a \neq 0$.

The quadratic equation $x^2 - 2x - 3 = 0$ is in standard form.

forma general de una ecuación cuadrática (pág. 112) Ecuación cuadrática de la forma $ax^2 + bx + c = 0$, donde $a \neq 0$.

La ecuación cuadrática $x^2 - 2x - 3 = 0$ está en la forma general.

---

standard form of a quadratic function (p. 98) A quadratic function in the form $y = ax^2 + bx + c$ where $a \neq 0$.

The quadratic function $y = 2x^2 + 5x - 3$ is in standard form.

forma general de una función cuadrática (pág. 98) Función cuadrática de la forma $y = ax^2 + bx + c$, donde $a \neq 0$.

La función cuadrática $y = 2x^2 + 5x - 3$ está en la forma general.

---

stratified random sample (p. 359) A sample in which a population is divided into distinct groups, and members are selected at random from each group.

You can select a stratified random sample of a school's student population by having a computer randomly choose 25 students from each grade level.

muestra aleatoria estratificada (pág. 359) Muestra en la que la población está dividida en grupos diferenciados, y los miembros de cada grupo se seleccionan al azar.

Para seleccionar una muestra aleatoria estratificada de la población de estudiantes de una escuela, puedes usar la computadora para elegir al azar a 25 estudiantes de cada grado.

---

survey (p. 359) A study of one or more characteristics of a group.

A magazine invites its readers to mail in answers to a questionnaire rating the magazine.

encuesta (pág. 359) Estudio de una o más características de un grupo.

Una revista invita a sus lectores a enviar por correo las respuestas a un cuestionario sobre la calidad de la revista.

---

systematic sample (p. 359) A sample in which a rule is used to select members of the population.

You can select a systematic sample of a school's student population by choosing every tenth student on an alphabetical list of all students at the school.

muestra sistemática (pág. 359) Muestra en la que se usa una regla para seleccionar a los miembros de la población.

Para seleccionar una muestra sistemática de la población de estudiantes de una escuela, puedes elegir a cada décimo estudiante de una lista ordenada alfabéticamente de todos los estudiantes de la escuela.

terms of a sequence (p. 185) The values in the range of a sequence.

The first 4 terms of the sequence 1, −3, 9, −27, 81, −243, . . . are 1, −3, 9, and −27.

términos de una progresión (pág. 185) Los valores del rango de una progresión.

Los 4 primeros términos de la progresión 1, −3, 9, −27, 81, −243, . . . son 1, −3, 9 y −27.

---

theorem (p. 217) A true statement that follows as a result of other true statements.

Vertical angles are congruent.

teorema (pág. 217) Enunciado verdadero que surge como resultado de otros enunciados verdaderos.

Los ángulos opuestos por el vértice son congruentes.

---

transversal (p. 229) A line that intersects two or more coplanar lines at different points.

transversal (pág. 229) Recta que corta a dos o más rectas coplanarias en distintos puntos.

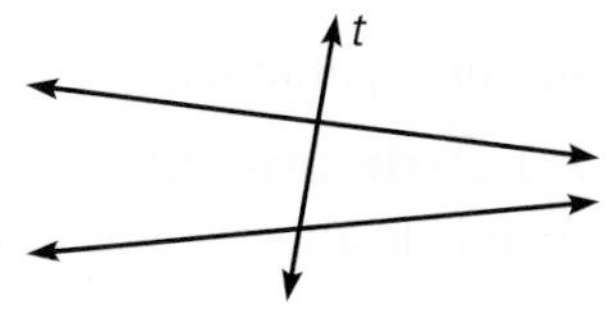

transversal t

---

trapezoid (p. 323) A quadrilateral with exactly one pair of parallel sides, called bases. The nonparallel sides are legs.

trapecio (pág. 323) Cuadrilátero que tiene sólo un par de lados paralelos, llamados bases. Los lados no paralelos son catetos.

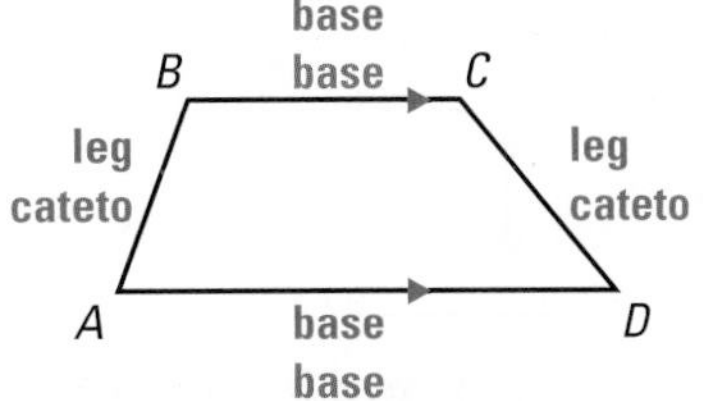

---

trinomial (p. 59) A polynomial with three terms.

$2x^2 + x - 5$ is a trinomial.

trinomio (pág. 59) Polinomio con tres términos.

$2x^2 + x - 5$ es un trinomio.

---

two-column proof (p. 217) A type of proof written as numbered statements and corresponding reasons that show an argument in a logical order.

See Example 1 on page 217.

prueba de dos columnas (pág. 217) Tipo de prueba en la que se escriben enunciados numerados y razones correspondientes que muestran un argumento siguiendo un orden lógico.

Ver el ejemplo 1 de la página 217.

ENGLISH-SPANISH GLOSSARY

upper quartile (p. 369) The median of the upper half of an ordered data set.

cuartil superior (pág. 369) La mediana de la mitad superior de un conjunto de datos ordenados.

The upper quartile of the data set below is 23.

			median		upper quartile	
			↓		↓	
8	10	14	17	20	23	50

El cuartil superior del siguiente conjunto de datos es 23.

			mediana		cuartil superior	
			↓		↓	
8	10	14	17	20	23	50

vertex of a parabola (p. 98) The lowest or highest point on a parabola.

vértice de una parábola (pág. 98) El punto más bajo o más alto de la parábola.

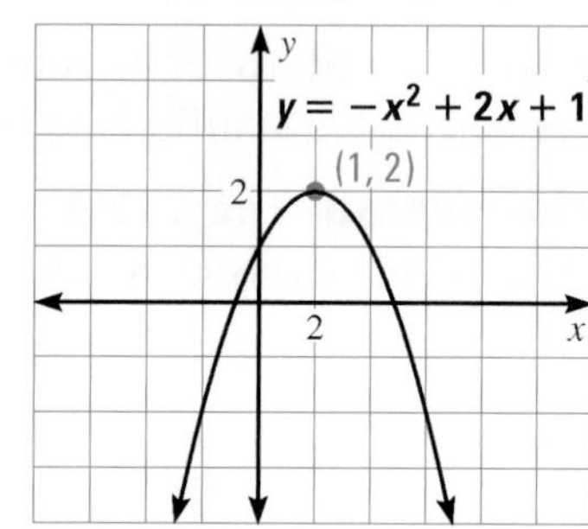

The vertex of the graph of $y = -x^2 + 2x + 1$ is the point (1, 2).

El vértice de la gráfica de $y = -x^2 + 2x + 1$ es el punto (1, 2).

vertical motion model (p. 77) A model for the height of an object that is propelled into the air but has no power to keep itself in the air.

The vertical motion model for an object thrown upward with an initial vertical velocity of 20 feet per second from an initial height of 8 feet is $h = -16t^2 + 20t + 8$ where h is the height (in feet) of the object t seconds after it is thrown.

modelo de movimiento vertical (pág. 77) Modelo para representar la altura de un objeto que es lanzado hacia arriba pero que no tiene potencia para mantenerse en el aire.

El modelo de movimiento vertical de un objeto lanzado hacia arriba con una velocidad vertical inicial de 20 pies por segundo desde una altura inicial de 8 pies es $h = -16t^2 + 20t + 8$, donde h es la altura (en pies) del objeto t segundos después del lanzamiento.

volume model for polynomial arithmetic (p. 64) A way to visually represent multiplying three polynomials using geometry.

modelo de volumen para aritmética de polinomios (p. 64) Una manera de representar visualmente la multiplicación de tres polinomios usando geometría.

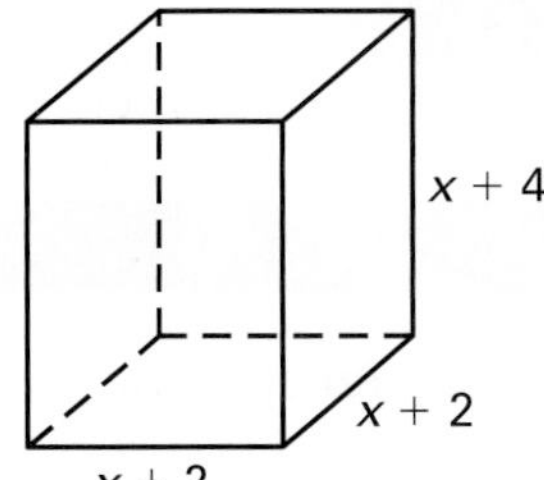

The volume model represents $(x + 2)(x + 2)(x + 4)$, or $x^3 + 8x^2 + 20x + 16$.

El modelo de volumen representa $(x + 2)(x + 2)(x + 4)$, o $x^3 + 8x^2 + 20x + 16$.

X

***x*-intercept** (p. 17) The x-coordinate of a point where a graph crosses the x-axis.

intercepto en *x* (pág. 17) La coordenada x de un punto donde la gráfica corta al eje de x.

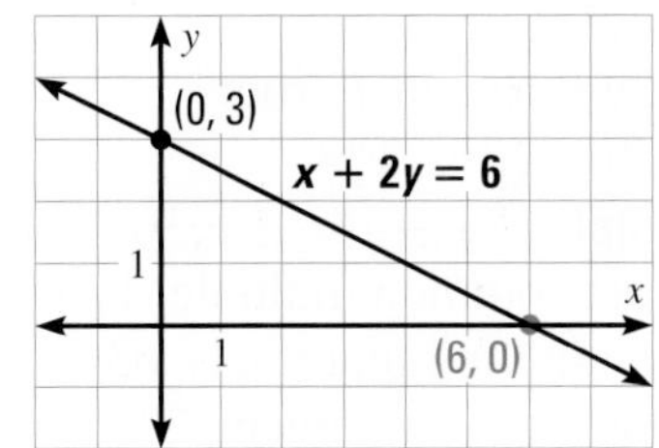

The x-intercept is 6.

El intercepto en x es 6.

Y

***y*-intercept** (p. 17) The y-coordinate of a point where a graph crosses the y-axis.

intercepto en *y* (pág. 17) La coordenada y de un punto donde la gráfica corta al eje de y.

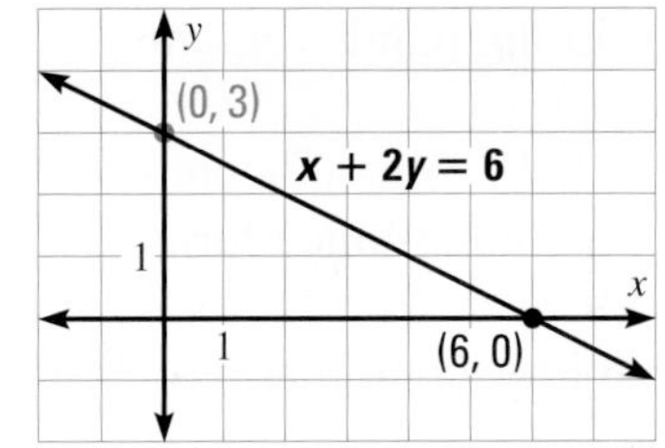

The y-intercept is 3.

El intercepto en y es 3.

Z

zero of a function (p. 45) An x-value for which $f(x) = 0$ (or $y = 0$).

cero de una función (pág. 45) Un valor x para el que $f(x) = 0$ (o $y = 0$).

The zero of $f(x) = 2x - 4$ is 2 because $f(2) = 0$.

El cero de $f(x) = 2x - 4$ es 2 ya que $f(2) = 0$.

Index

C

INDEX

D

E

INDEX

INDEX

INDEX

M

N

O

P

Q

R

S

U

V

W

X

Y

Z

Selected Answers

UNIT 1

1.1 Exercise Set A (p. 4)

1. Know: Number of boxes and number of blueberry muffins in one box; Need to find out: How many dozen blueberry muffins need to be made **3.** Know: How long you have been driving and your average speed; Need to find out: The distance that you travel

5. $d = rt$ **7.** \$80 **9.** 12; \$59.40

1.1 Exercise Set B (p. 5)

3. $x + 3x = 500$ **5.** $d = rt$; $d = 250$; $t = 5$

7. 30 ft by 15 ft **9.** 0°C; 35.6°C

1.2 Exercise Set A (p. 9)

1. independent **3.** function **5.** not a function

7.

Domain	10	20	30	40
Range	4	5	6	7

9. $y = 5x$ **11.** $y = x - 2$

13. $y = 10 + 3x$; independent: number of hours left in shift; dependent: number of loaves baked; 22 loaves

1.2 Exercise Set B (p. 10)

1. function **3.** not a function

5.

Domain	12	15	18	21
Range	0	1	2	3

7.

Domain	10	20	30	40
Range	1	$\frac{4}{3}$	$\frac{5}{3}$	2

9. $y = \frac{1}{2}x - 1$

11. $y = 8 + 4x$; 32 sandwich rings

1.3 Exercise Set A (pp. 13–14)

1. (0, 3), (1, 5), (2, 7), (3, 9), (4, 11)

3. (3, 2), (6, 2), (9, 4), (12, 4), (15, 6)

5. (0, 6), (1, 8), (2, 10), (3, 12); domain: 0, 1, 2, 3; range: 6, 8, 10, 12

7.

x	0	1	2	3
y	2	5	8	11

9.

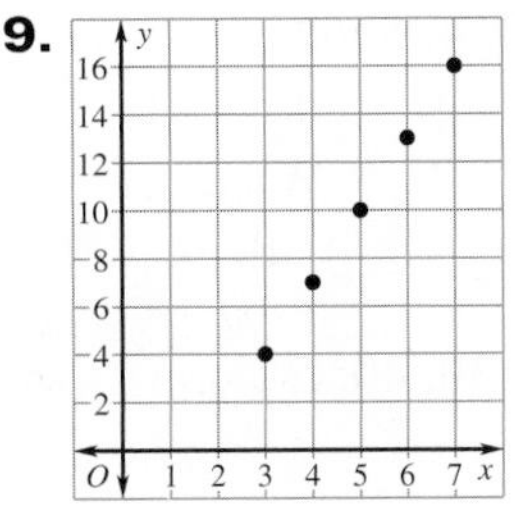

11.

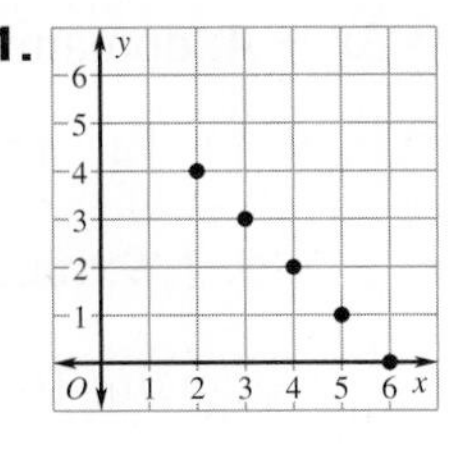

13.

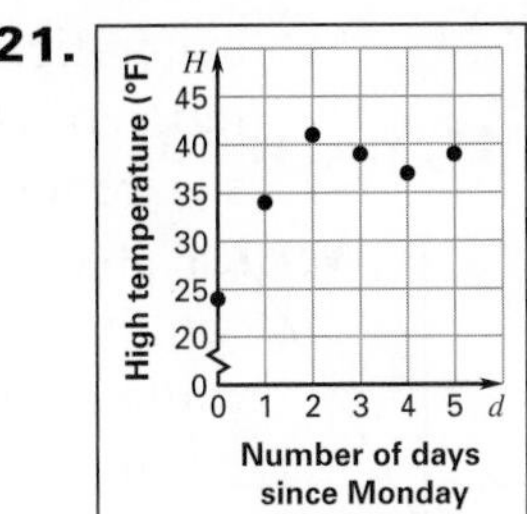

15. $y = x + 6$; domain: 0, 1, 2, 3; range: 6, 7, 8, 9

17. $y = 2x + 5$; domain: 0, 1, 2, 3; range: 5, 7, 9, 11

19. $y = 6x - 4$; domain: 1, 2, 3, 4; range: 2, 8, 14, 20

21.

Sample answer: The high temperatures increase from Monday to Wednesday, decrease from Wednesday to Friday, and then increase from Friday to Saturday.

1.3 Exercise Set B (pp. 15–16)

1. (4, 8), (6, 12), (8, 16), (10, 20), (12, 24)

3. (−3, −15), (3, −9), (9, −3), (15, 3), (21, 9)

5. (−1, −4), (0, −2), (1, 0), (2, 2); domain: −1, 0, 1, 2; range −4, −2, 0, 2

7.

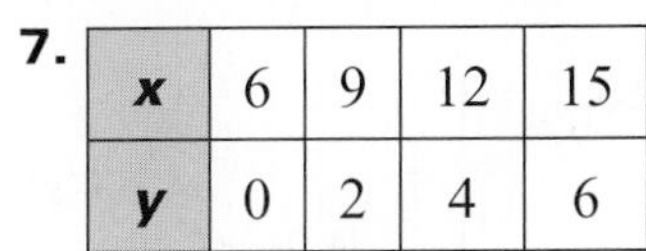

x	6	9	12	15
y	0	2	4	6

9.

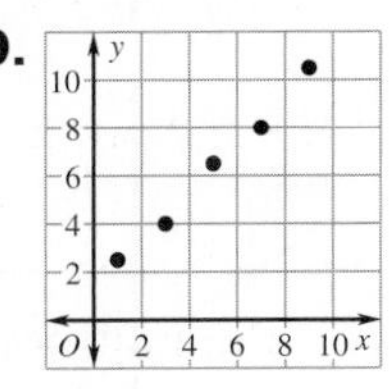

11.

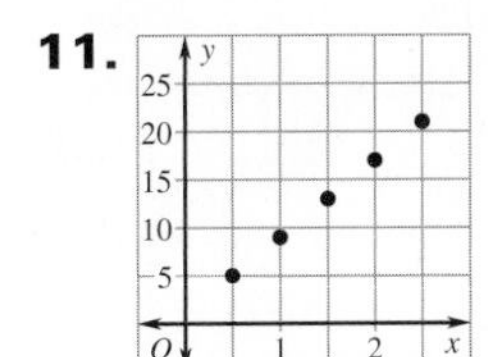

13.

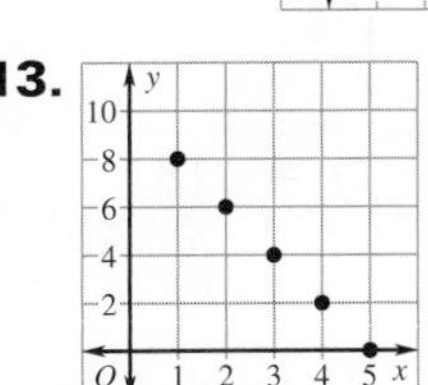

SELECTED ANSWERS

15. $y = 3x - 4$; domain: 2, 3, 4, 5, 6; range: 2, 5, 8, 11, 14 **17.** $y = \frac{1}{2}x - \frac{1}{2}$; domain: 1, 3, 5, 7, 9; range: 0, 1, 2, 3, 4

19. $y = \frac{1}{10}x$; domain: 10, 20, 30, 40; range: 1, 2, 3, 4

21. a.

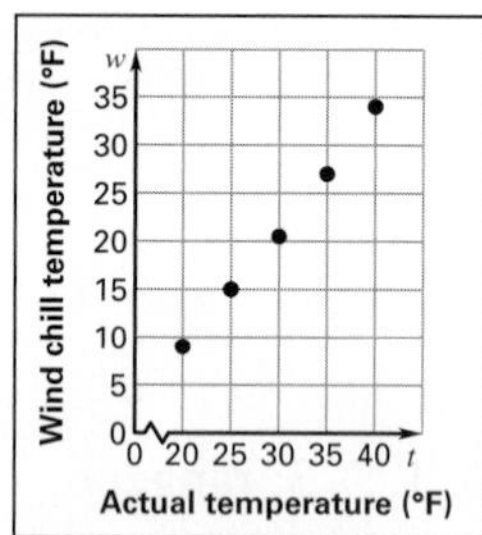

b. As the temperature decreases, the wind chill temperature decreases.

1.4 Exercise Set A (pp. 19–20)

1. x: 4; y: 3 **3.** x: 3; y: 2 **5.** x: -5; y: 5

7. x: 6; y: 3 **9.** x: 2; y: -8 **11.** x: $\frac{1}{2}$; y: -3

13.

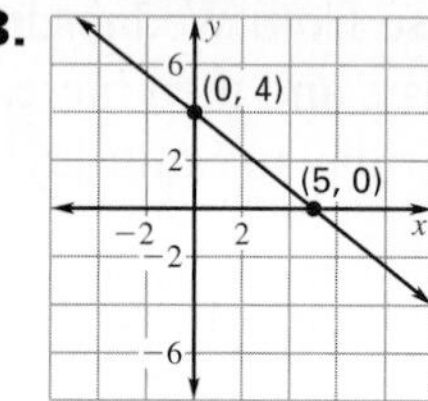

15.

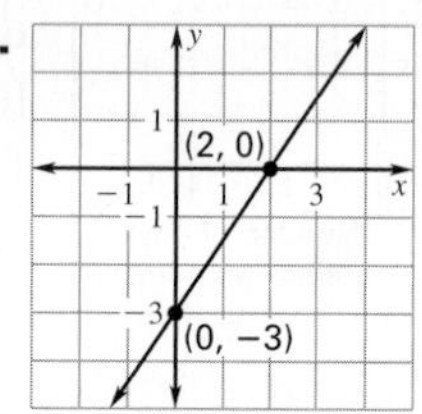

17.

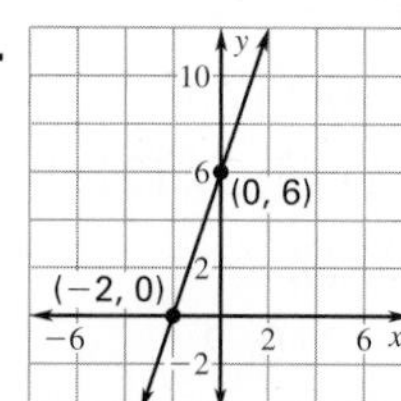

19.

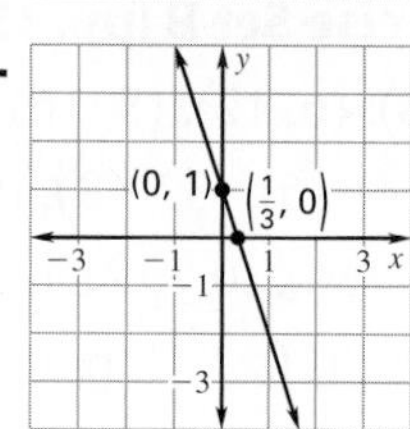

21.

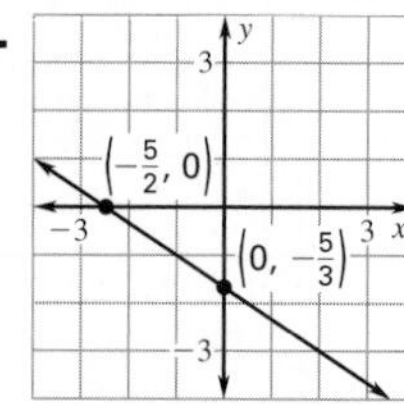

23.

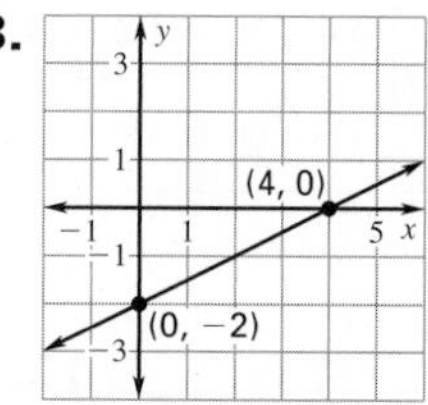

29. a. $2x + 2y = 118$

b. x: 59; y: 59

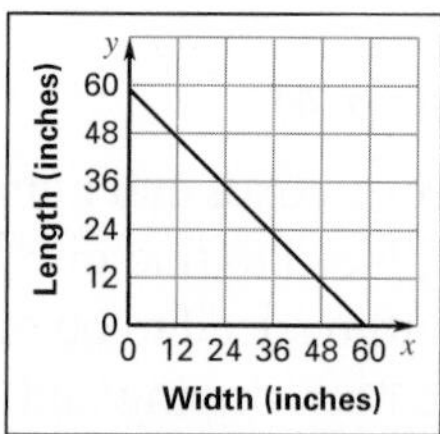

31. a. x: 42; y: 56

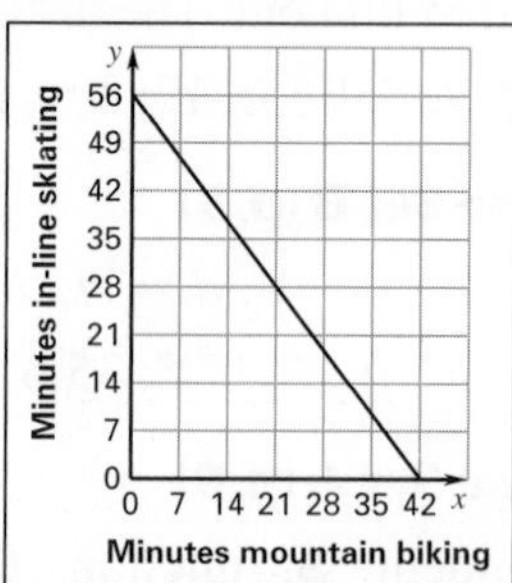

b. The x-intercept is the number of calories burned when the man only mountain bikes and the y-intercept is the number of calories burned when the man only in-line skates. **c.** *Sample answer:* 42 minutes mountain biking and 0 minutes in-line skating; 0 minutes mountain biking and 56 minutes in-line skating; 21 minutes mountain biking and 28 minutes in-line skating

1.4 Exercise Set B (pp. 21–22)

1. x: -2; y: -1 **3.** x: -3; y: -4 **5.** x: -5; y: 7

7. x: -2; y: $-\frac{1}{4}$ **9.** x: $\frac{15}{7}$; y: -15

11. x: -3.75; y: -9

13.

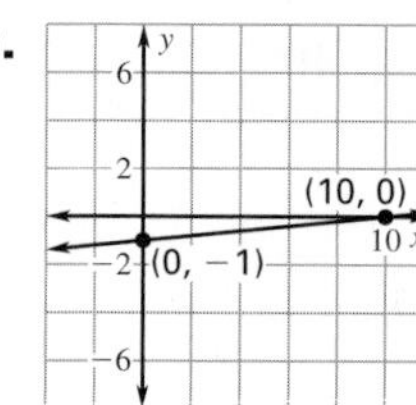

15.

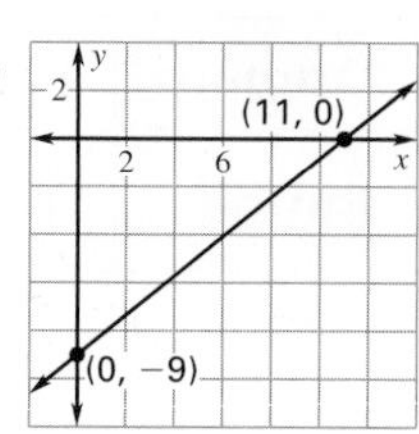

17.

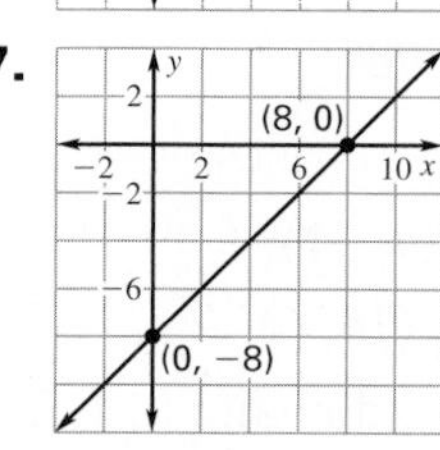

19.

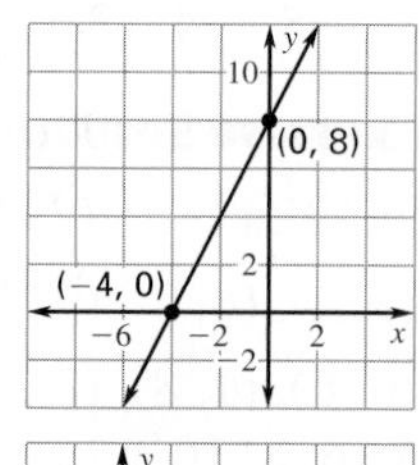

21.

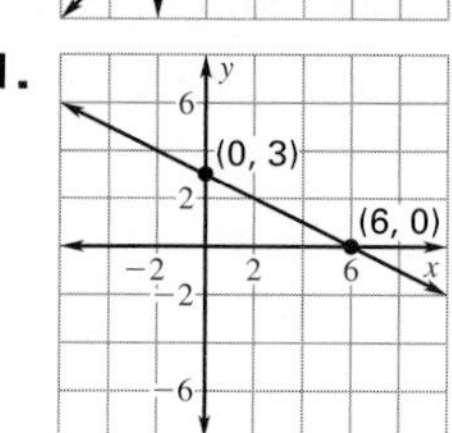

23.

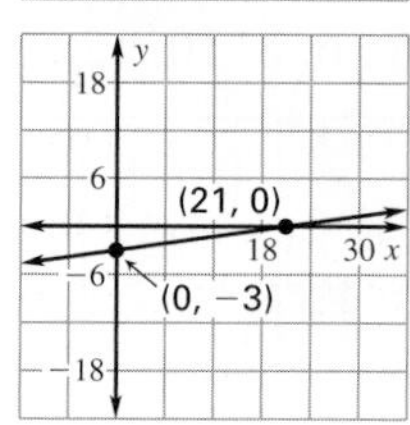

25.

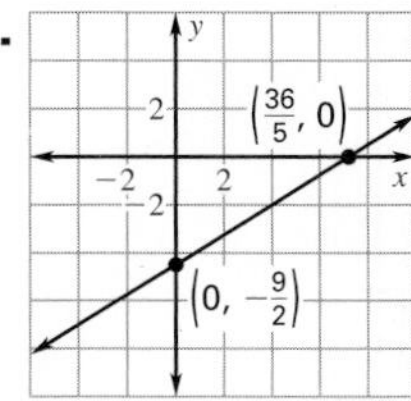

27.

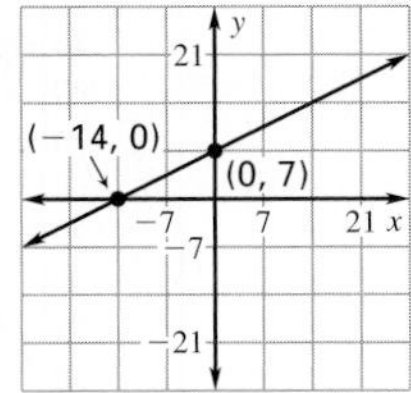

33. a.

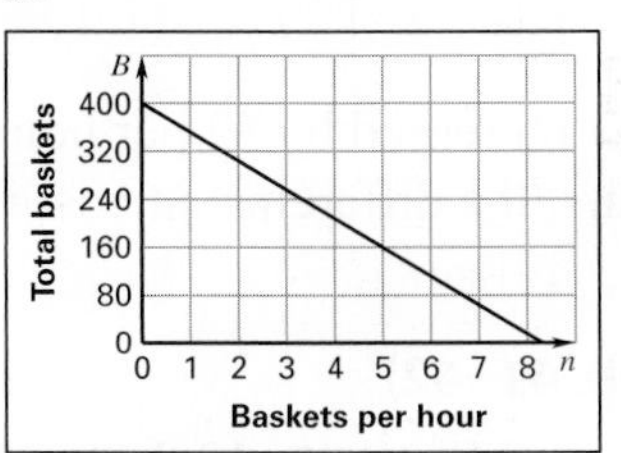

domain: $0 \le n \le 8\frac{1}{3}$

range: $0 \le B \le 400$

$8\frac{1}{3}$ baskets per hour

b. The intercepts change and the slant of the graph changes; 7.5 baskets per hour

1.5 Exercise Set A (pp. 25–26)

1. positive **3.** undefined

5. undefined

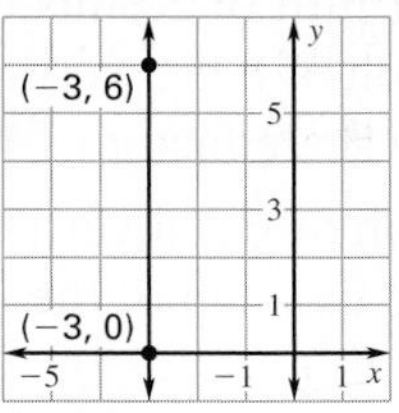

7. negative

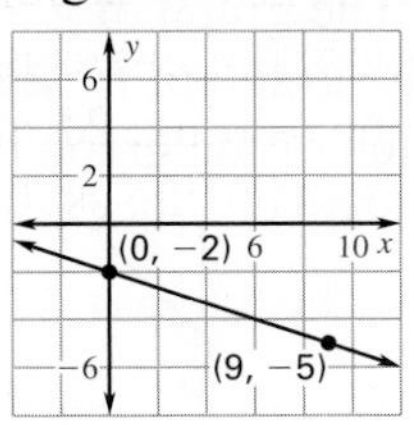

9. negative

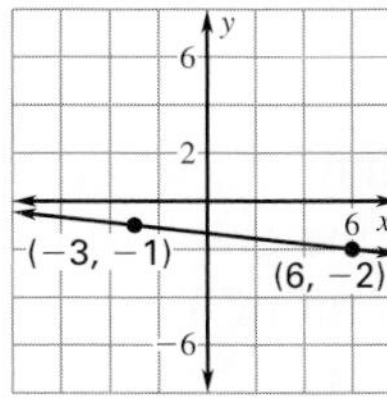

11. undefined

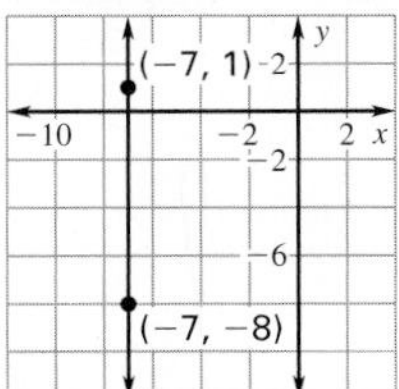

13. $\frac{2}{3}$ **15.** 0 **17.** $\frac{3}{5}$ **19.** $\frac{5}{6}$ **21.** undefined

23. $\frac{1}{2}$ **25.** 0 **27.** $\frac{1}{3}$ **29.** 4 **31.** 8 **33.** 6

35. a. From 1980 to 1985: −29.4 buses per year; From 1985 to 1990: 31.2 buses per year; From 1990 to 1995: 10.6 buses per year; From 1995 to 2000: 13.2 buses per year; From 1980 to 1985, the number of buses decreased, but then the number of buses increased after that. **b.** Greatest: From 1985 to 1990; Least: From 1990 to 1995

37. The person's heartrate increased for 0 to 12 minutes, then it slowly decreased until the end of the workout.

1.5 Exercise Set B (pp. 27–28)

1. positive **3.** zero

5. undefined

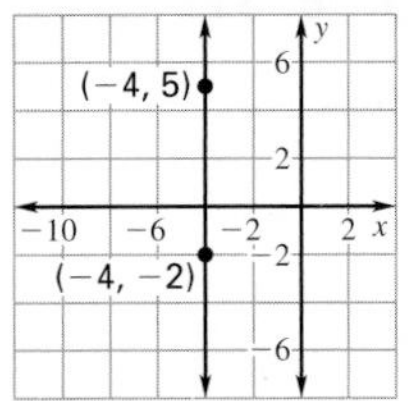

7. zero

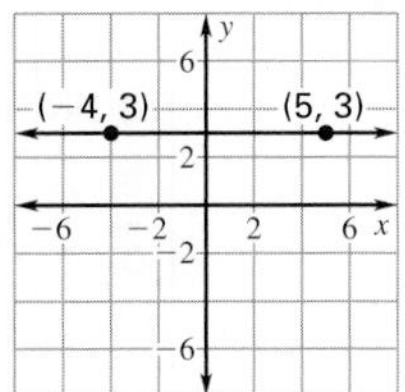

9. positive

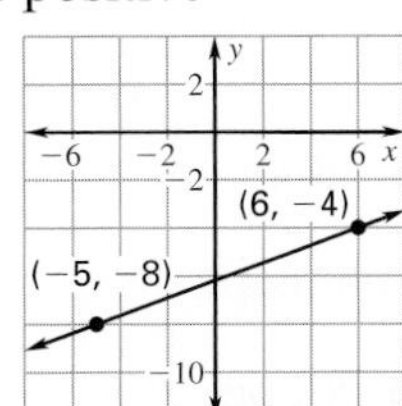

11. $-\frac{11}{6}$ **13.** $\frac{4}{3}$ **15.** 0 **17.** $-\frac{2}{3}$ **19.** $\frac{3}{5}$

21. undefined **23.** $\frac{4}{7}$ **25.** 0 **27.** $\frac{1}{6}$ **29.** 4 **31.** 9

33. −3 **35. a.** From 10 to 15 min **b.** From 0 to 5 min **c.** Your speed increased from 0 to 15 minutes, then you slowed down for the rest of the ride.

1.6 Exercise Set A (pp. 32–33)

1. Slope: −2; y-intercept: 1 **3.** Slope: $\frac{1}{2}$; y-intercept: 0 **5.** Slope: −4; y-intercept: 10

7. Slope: −4; y-intercept: 3 **9.** Slope: $-\frac{2}{5}$; y-intercept: 2 **11.** Slope: $-\frac{3}{2}$; y-intercept: $\frac{1}{2}$

13. Slope: −1; y-intercept: $\frac{3}{5}$

15. Slope: undefined; y-intercept: none

19.

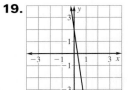

21.

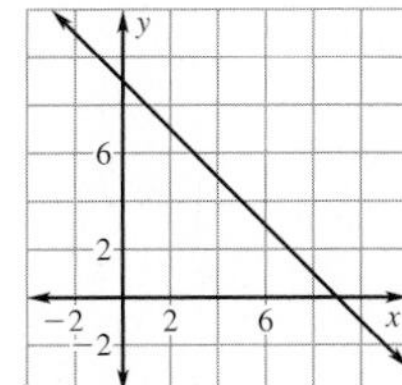

23.

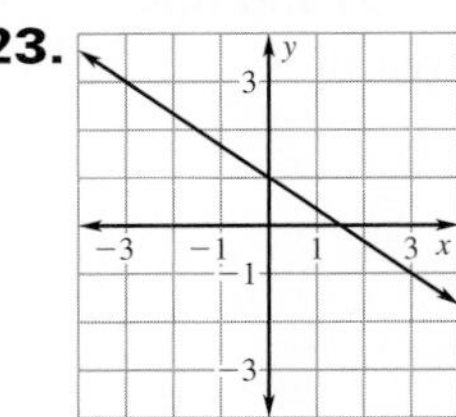

SELECTED ANSWERS

25. line through $(-1, -4)$ and $(0, 2)$ and line through $(1, 3)$ and $(2, 9)$ **27.** neither

29. perpendicular **31.** perpendicular

33. a. and **b.**

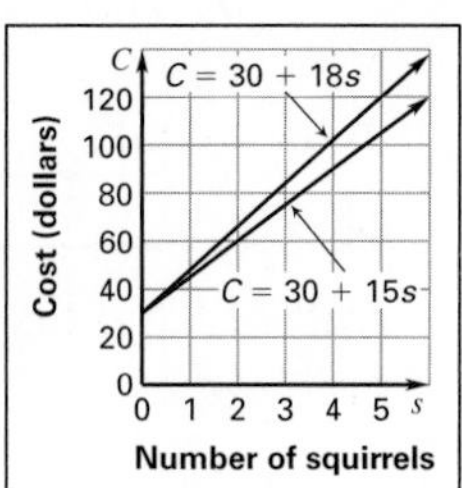

c. \$12

1.6 Exercise Set B (pp. 34–35)

1. Slope: -3; y-intercept: 1 **3.** Slope: $\frac{3}{2}$; y-intercept: 2 **5.** Slope: -6; y-intercept: 19 **7.** Slope: $-\frac{3}{2}$; y-intercept: 4 **9.** Slope: $\frac{4}{3}$; y-intercept: 3 **11.** Slope: $\frac{4}{9}$; y-intercept: -2 **13.** Slope: $\frac{2}{5}$; y-intercept: -2 **15.** Slope: $-\frac{1}{10}$; y-intercept: 2

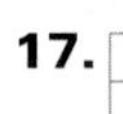

17.

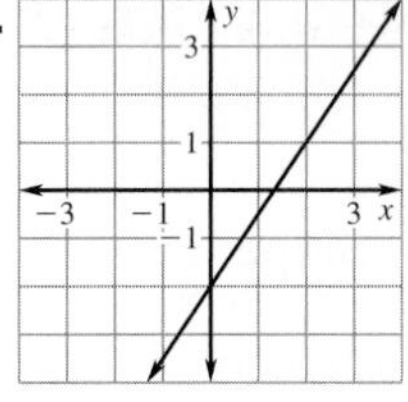

19.

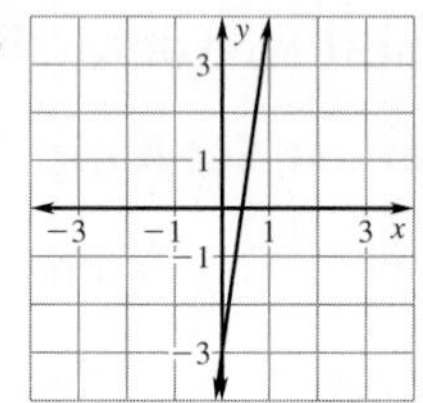

21.

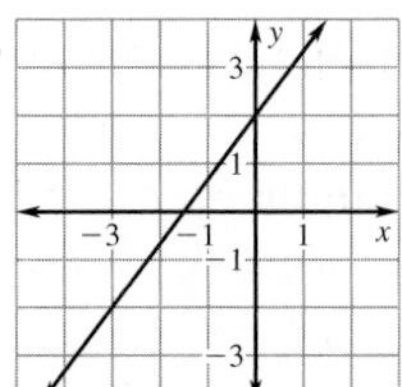

23.

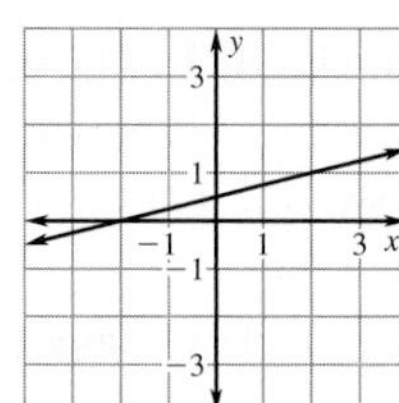

25. The y-intercept is -1, not 1.

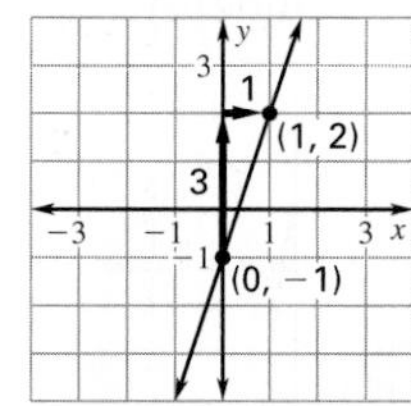

27. line through $(-1, 3)$ and $(0, -3)$ and line through $(0, 2)$ and $(1, -4)$ **29.** parallel

31. neither **33.** -38 **35.** -2

37. a. and **b.**

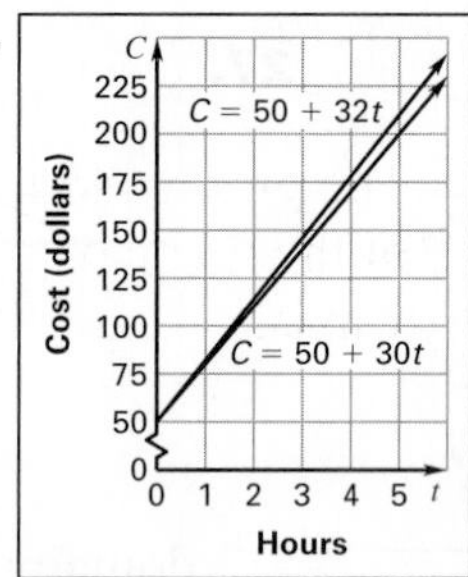

c. \$6; Because the cost increased by \$2 per hour and the job took 3 hours, the difference in cost is $2(3) = 6$.

1.7 Exercise Set A (pp. 41–42)

1. -41; 4; 34 **3.** 16; -5; -19 **5.** 13.2; 0; -8.8

7. $-\frac{22}{5}$; -2; $-\frac{2}{5}$ **9.** $-\frac{57}{8}$; -6; $-\frac{21}{4}$

11. -15.6; -3; 5.4 **13.** 5 **15.** -3 **17.** 4

19. -3 **21.** -5

23. The graph of g is a vertical shift of 2 units up of the graph of f. **25.** The graph of g is a vertical stretch of the graph of f using a scale factor of 1.5.

27.

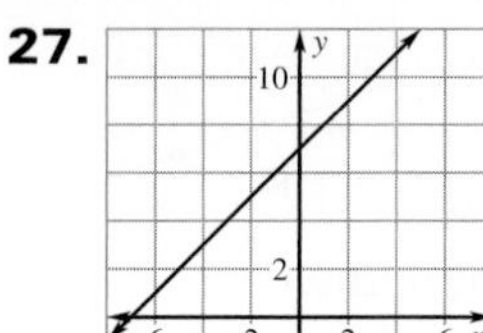

The graph of g is a vertical shift of 7 units up of the graph of f.

29.

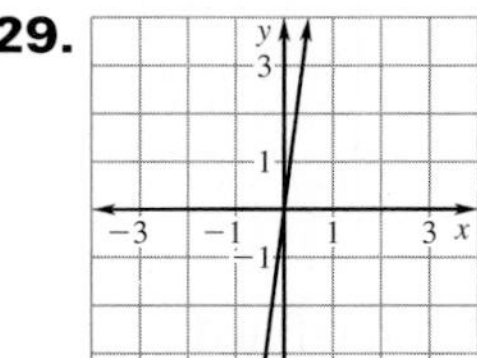

The graph of d is a vertical stretch of the graph of f using a scale factor of 8.

31.

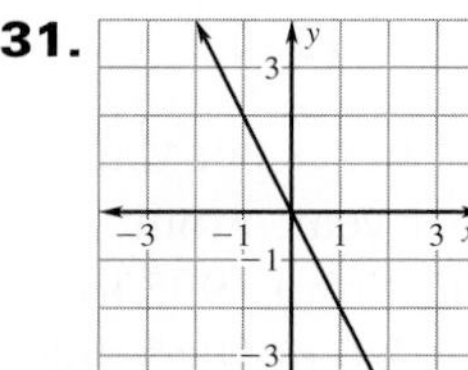

The graph of n is a vertical stretch of the graph of f using a scale factor of 2 and a reflection in the x-axis.

33.

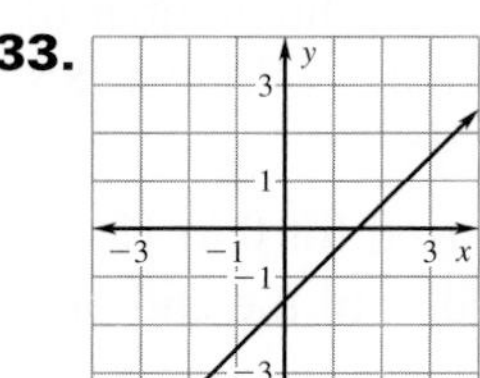

The graph of d is a vertical shift of 1.5 units down of the graph of f.

35. The graph of g is a vertical shift of 5 units up of the graph of f.

39. 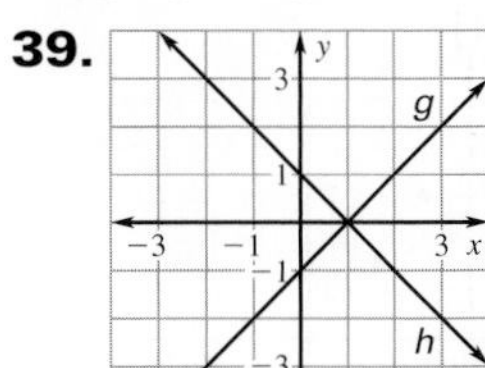

The graph of h is a reflection of the graph of g in the x-axis.

41. a. 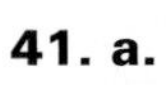 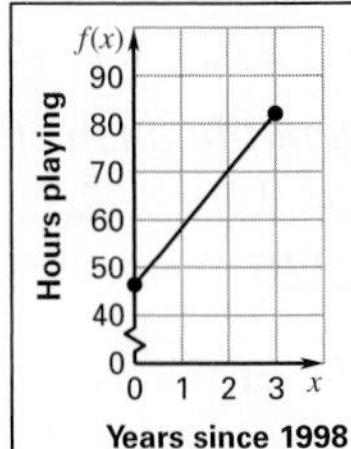

domain: $0 \le x \le 3$
range: $46.4 \le f(x) \le 82.1$

b. $f(2) = 70.2$; In 2000, people spent 70.2 hours each year playing video games. **c.** $f(1.1) \approx 60$; Near the beginning of 1999, people spent 60 hours each year playing video games.

1.7 Exercise Set B (pp. 43–44)

1. -19.6; 6.4; 19.4 **3.** 2.5; -13.5; -21.5

5. -2.3; 22.7; 35.2 **7.** -9; $2\frac{2}{3}$; 8.5

9. 2.75; 0.25; -1 **11.** -9.75; 1.5; 7.125

13. -2 **15.** -3 **17.** 1.5 **19.** 5.4 **21.** -5

23. -3.09

25. The graph of g is a vertical shift of 4 units up of the graph of f. **27.** The graph of g is a vertical shrink of the graph of f using a scale factor of $\frac{1}{2}$.

29.  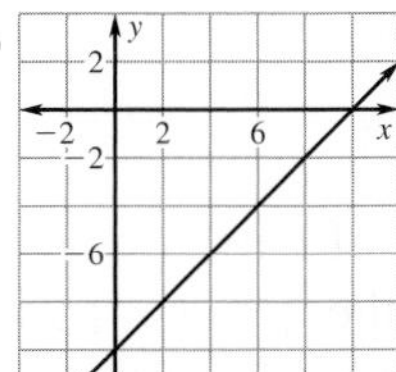
The graph of h is a vertical shift of 10 units down of the graph of f.

31. 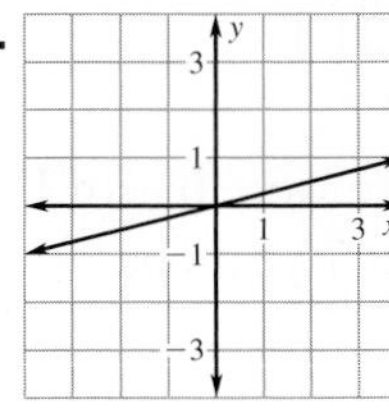
The graph of g is a vertical shrink of the graph of f using a scale factor of $\frac{1}{4}$.

33. 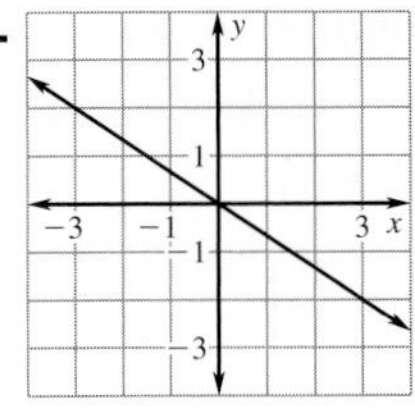
The graph of h is a vertical shrink of the graph of f using a scale factor of $\frac{2}{3}$ and a reflection of the graph of f in the x-axis.

35. 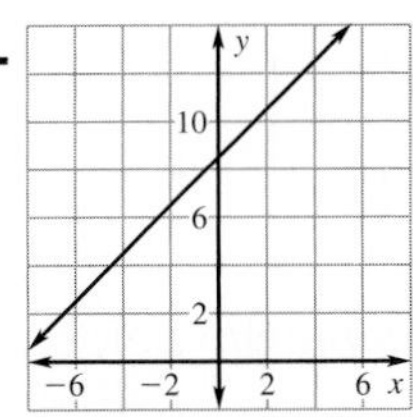
The graph of g is a vertical shift of 8.5 units up of the graph of f.

37. The graph of g is the graph of f shifted 6 units down.

41. 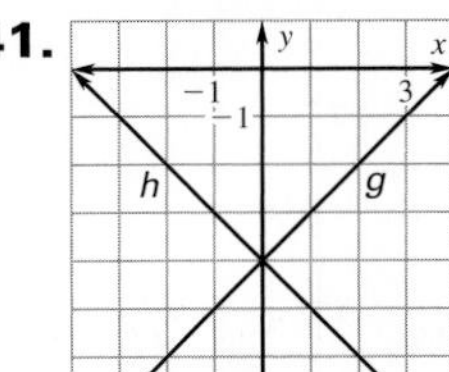

The graph of h is a reflection of the graph of g in the y-axis.

43. a. 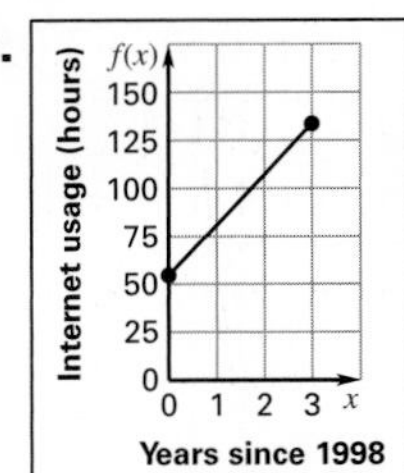

domain: $0 \le x \le 3$
range: $54.4 \le f(x) \le 133.6$

b. $f(2) = 107.2$; In 2000, a person spent 107.2 hours on the Internet. Because 1998 corresponds to 0, 2000 corresponds to 2. So to find the answer find $f(x)$ when $x = 2$. **c.** $f(2.5) \approx 120$; Near the middle of 2000, a person spent 120 hours on the Internet. To find the answer, find x when $f(x) = 120$. Then use the fact that 1998 corresponds to 0 to find the year.

45. 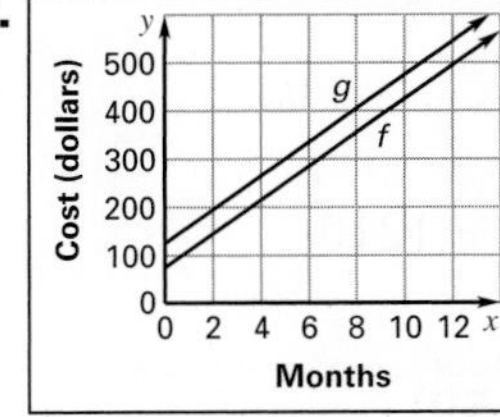

The graphs of f and g are parallel and the graph of g is a vertical shift of 50 units up of the graph of f.

1.8 Exercise Set A (pp. 47–48)

1. *Sample answer:* $y = 1.19x + 0.35$; 1.54

3. *Sample answer:* $y = 0.58x + 0.4$; 0.98

5. *Sample answer:* $y = x + 0.4$; 3.4

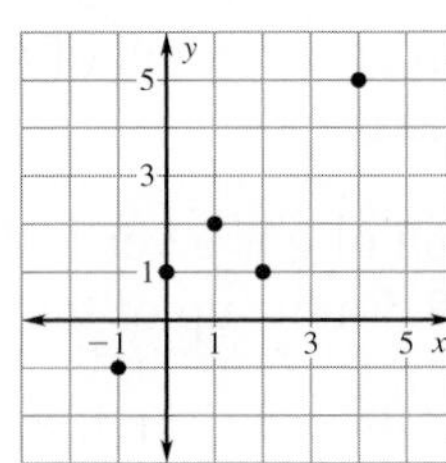

7. *Sample answer:* $y = -1.3x + 2.2$; -1.7

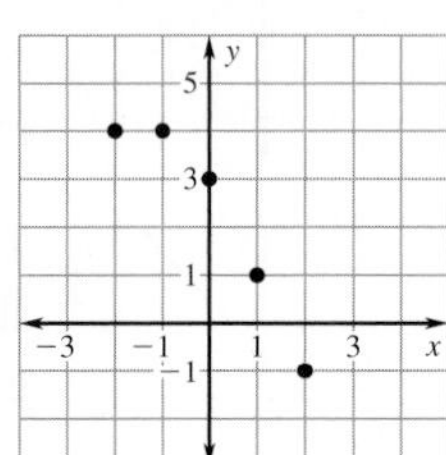

9. *Sample answer:* $y = 0.6x - 0.4$; 2.6

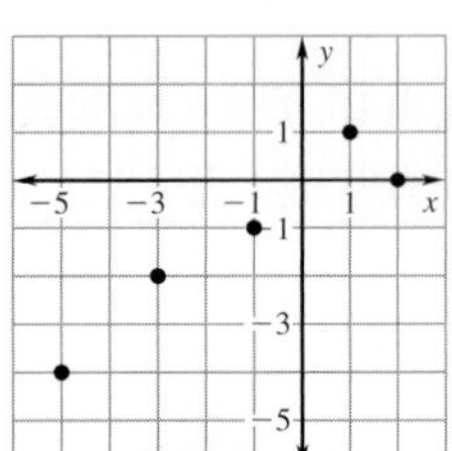

11. *Sample answer:* $y = 1.7x - 0.3$; 8.2

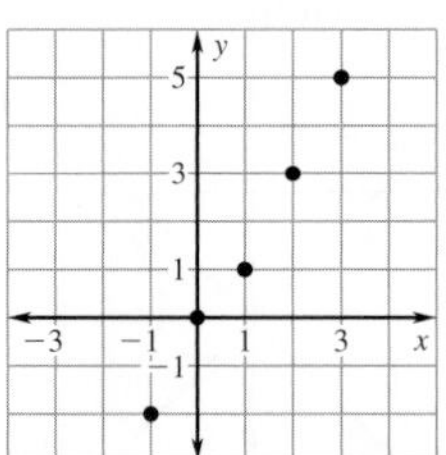

13. *Sample answer:* $y = -0.75x + 0.7$; -3.05

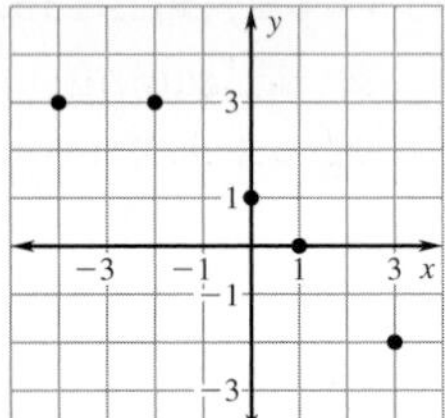

15. 0.5 **17.** -30 **19.** 10 **21.** $\frac{90}{7}$ **23.** 12

25. 18.75 **27.** 30

29. a.

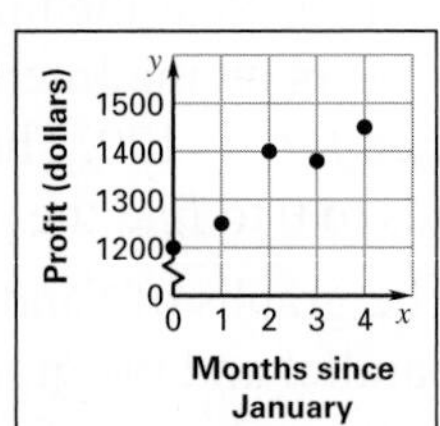

b. *Sample answer:* $y = 63x + 1210$
c. *Sample answer:* $1651

1.8 Exercise Set B (pp. 49–50)

1. *Sample answer:* $y = 0.83x - 0.14$; 0.69

3. *Sample answer:* $y = 2.13x + 9.35$; 11.48

5. *Sample answer:* $y = 0.44x - 2.1$; -2.98

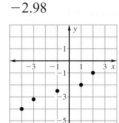

7. *Sample answer:* $y = -0.68x - 0.55$; 0.81

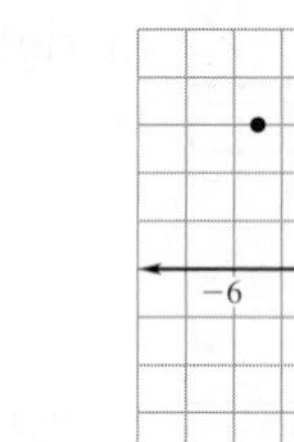

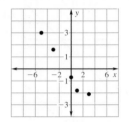

9. *Sample answer:* $y = 0.68x + 1.08$; 1.93

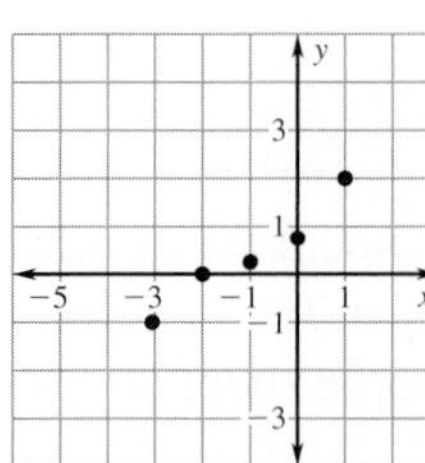

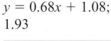

11. *Sample answer:* $y = 1.7x + 2.1$; 4.225

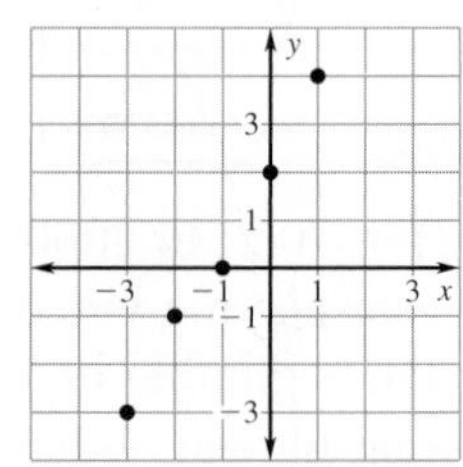

13. *Sample answer:* $y = -0.63x - 1.72$; -2.5

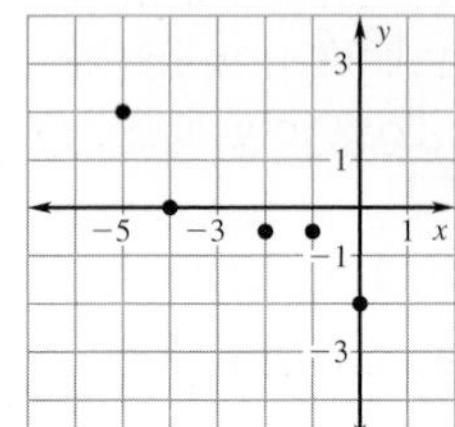

15. 0.2 **17.** -0.9 **19.** 8 **21.** $\frac{1}{2}$ **23.** $\frac{5}{6}$

25. 1 **27.** 10

29. a.

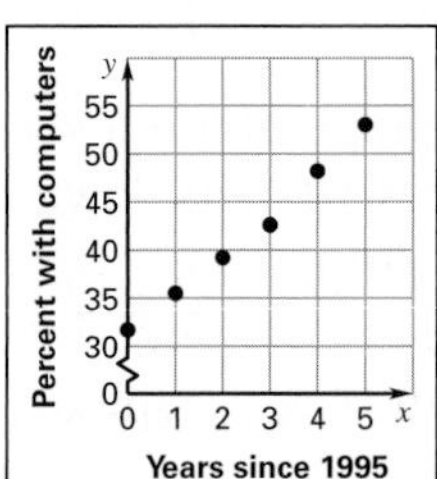

b. *Sample answer:* $y = 4.23x + 31.1$
c. *Sample answer:* 90.32%

d. about -7; this means that there were 0% of U.S. households with computers about 7 years before 1995, or in 1988.

SELECTED ANSWERS

1.9 Exercise Set A (p. 53)

7. 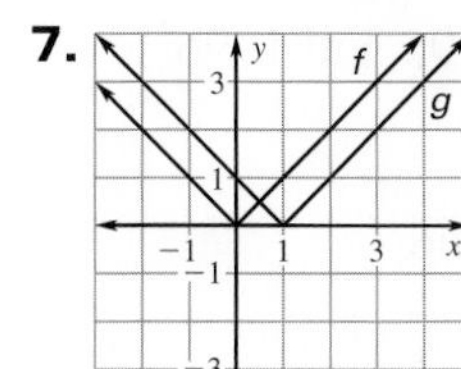 The graph of g is a horizontal shift 1 unit right of the graph of f.

9. 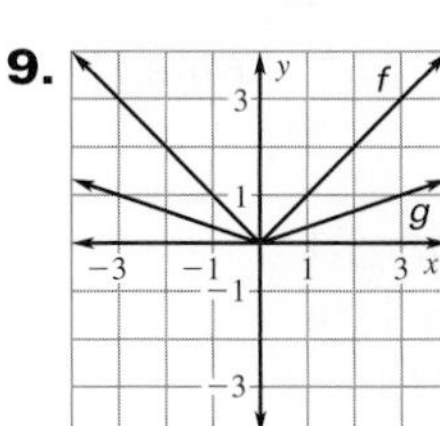 The graph of g is a vertical shrink of the graph of f using a scale factor of $\frac{1}{3}$.

11. 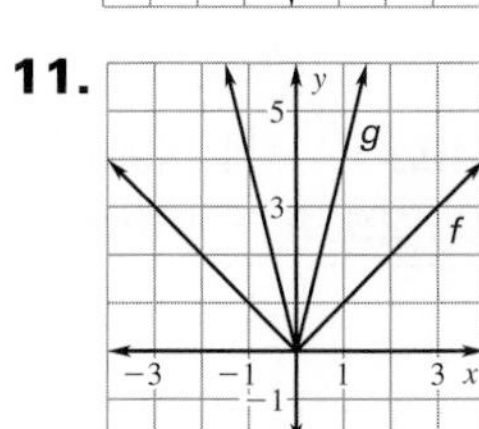 The graph of g is a vertical stretch of the graph of f using a scale factor of 4.

13. 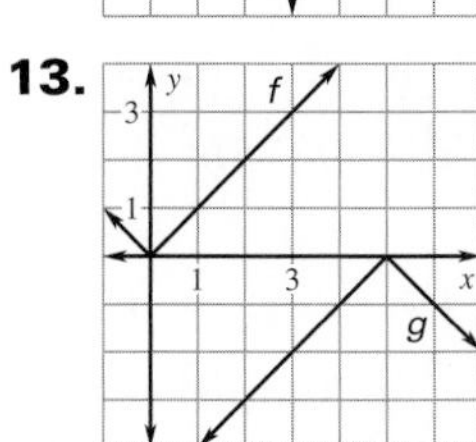 The graph of g is a vertical shift 5 units right and a reflection in the x-axis of the graph of f.

15. 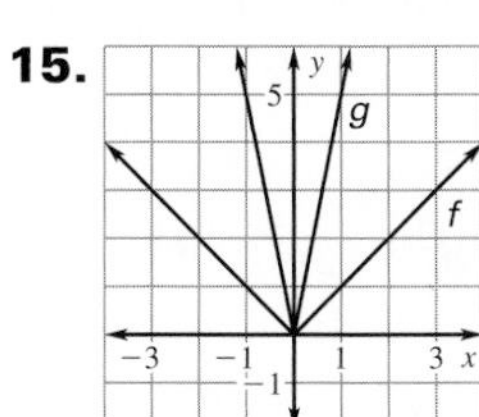 The graph of g is a vertical stretch of the graph of f using a scale factor of 5.

1.9 Exercise Set B (p. 54)

7. 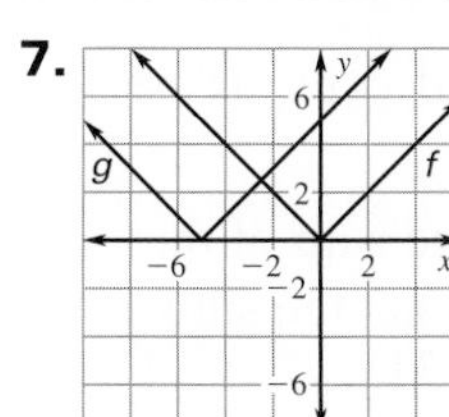 The graph of g is a horizontal shift 5 units left of the graph of f.

9. 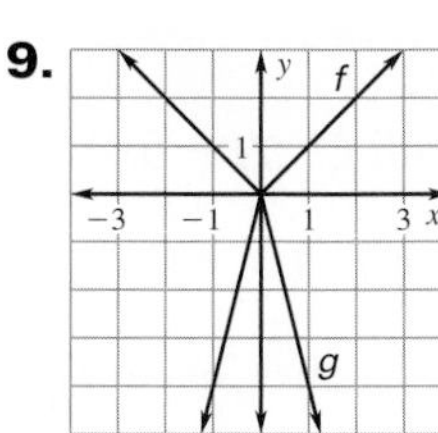 The graph of g is a vertical stretch of the graph of f using a scale factor of 4 and a reflection in the x-axis.

11. 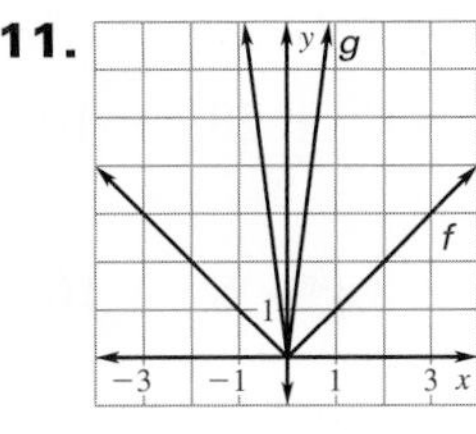 The graph of g is a vertical stretch of the graph of f using a scale factor of 8.

13. 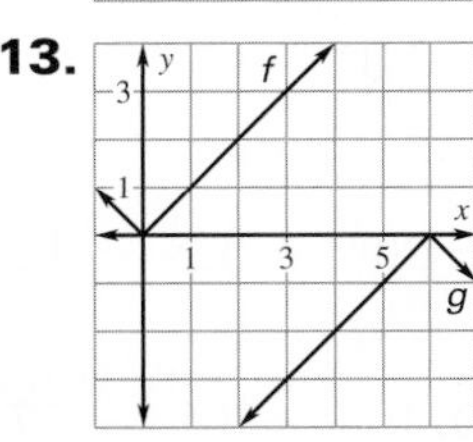 The graph of g is a horizontal shift 6 units right and a reflection of the graph of f in the x-axis.

15. 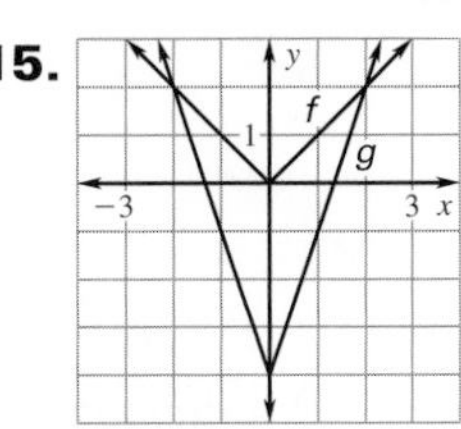 The graph of g is a vertical stretch of the graph of f using a scale factor of 3 and a vertical shift 4 units down.

UNIT 2

2.1 Exercise Set A (p. 61)

1. $4n^5$; degree: 5; leading coefficient: 4 **3.** $4y^4 + 6y^3 - 2y^2 - 5$; degree: 4; leading coefficient: 4 **5.** polynomial; degree: 3; trinomial **7.** $5z^2 + 3z - 7$ **9.** $3x^2 + 6$ **11.** $-4m^2 + 2m - 3$ **13.** $10x + 2$ **15.** Area: $\frac{17}{4}x^2 + 8x - 32$

2.1 Exercise Set B (p. 62)

1. polynomial; degree: 0; monomial **3.** polynomial; degree: 2; trinomial **5.** $-5y^2 - 2y + 9$ **7.** $-4z^2 + 4z + 14$ **9.** $-x^4 - 2x^3 + 6x^2 - 5x$ **11.** $-4a^3b^2 + 15a^2b^2 - 10a^2b + 5$ **13. a.** $T = 4.93t^4 - 56.78t^3 + 177.65t^2 - 126.42t + 1367.51$ **b.** In 1997, 1367.51 thousand metric tons were produced and in 2003, 1129.19 thousand metric tons were produced. So more peat and perlite were produced in 1997.

2.2 Exercise Set A (p. 66)

1. $6x^4 - 3x^3 - x^2$ **3.** $-8d^5 + 20d^4 - 24d^3 + 8d^2$

5. $2y^2 - 7y - 15$ **7.** $5b^2 - 42b + 16$
9. $-3p^3 + 6p^2 - p + 2$ **11.** $-6d^2 + 23d - 10$
13. $w^3 + 5w^2 - 23w - 3$
15. $5x^3y - 20x^2y^2 + 5xy^3$ **17.** $-3x^2 + 8x + 10$
19. $3x^2 + 15x$
21. a. $A = 4x^2 + 22x + 30$ **b.** 72 ft^2

2.2 Exercise Set B (p. 67)

1. $-16y^7 + 40y^5 - 24y^3$ **3.** $-18w^2 + 33w - 12$
5. $2x^3 + 11x^2 + 13x - 6$
7. $6p^6 + 12p^4 - 10p^2 - 20$ **9.** $10z^4 - 39z^2 - 27$
11. $-6x^2y - 15xy$ **13.** $5x^2 + xy - 6y^2$
15. $5x^3y - 20x^2y^2 + 5xy^3$
17. $w^6 + 13w^5 + 3w^4 - 10w^3 + 5w^2$
19. $24x^2 + 22x + 3$
21. a. E: \$14,439.09; P: 12.6%; $E \cdot P$ indicates the amount of money spent on exercise equipment.
b. $E \cdot P = 0.0001112t^8 - 0.0002186t^7 - 0.06424t^6 + 0.983634t^5 - 6.7188068t^4 + 22.667885t^3 - 120.819698t^2 + 568.42959t + 1819.32534$ **c.** \$1819.32534 million dollars

2.3 Exercise Set A (p. 70)

1. $x^2 - 18x + 81$ **3.** $25s^2 + 20s + 4$
5. $16p^2 - 40p + 25$ **7.** $100z^2 - 60z + 9$
9. $9y^2 - 6xy + x^2$ **11.** $z^2 - 400$
13. $36m^2 - 100$ **15.** $81c^2 - 1$ **17.** $-w^2 + 16$
19. Find the product $(20 - 5)(20 + 5)$.
21. Find the product $(20 - 2)^2$.
23. $16x^2 + 4x + 0.25$
25. Using the square of a binomial pattern, $b = 5$, not -5; $s^2 - 10s + 25$

2.3 Exercise Set B (p. 71)

1. $64x^2 - 80x + 25$ **3.** $100m^2 - 220m + 121$
5. $400b^2 - 600b + 225$ **7.** $r^2 - 16rs + 64s^2$
9. $4x^2 - 16xy + 16y^2$ **11.** $121t^2 - 16$
13. $81z^2 - 144$ **15.** $-25p^2 + 36$
17. $100a^2 - 25b^2$
19. Find the product $(40 - 4)(40 + 4)$.
21. Find the product $(50 - 1)^2$. **23.** $324x^2$

27. a. $T = 1.96t^2 - 4.41$
b. 91.63 thousand dollars **c.** 1995 and 1996

2.4 Exercise Set A (p. 75)

1. 1, 8, 28, 56, 70, 56, 28, 8, and 1
3. $x^2 + 2x + 1$
5. $p^4 + 20p^3 + 150p^2 + 500p + 625$
7. $b^6 + 6b^5 + 15b^4 + 20b^3 + 15b^2 + 6b + 1$
9. $x^2 + 8x + 16$
11. $z^5 - 5z^4 + 10z^3 - 10z^2 + 5z - 1$
13. $r^4 - 20r^3 + 150r^2 - 500r + 625$
15. $8x^3 + 12x^2 + 6x + 1$
17. $125y^3 + 150y^2 + 60y + 8$
19. $a^5 + 20a^4b + 160a^3b^2 + 640a^2b^3 + 1280ab^4 + 1024b^5$ **21.** 294 **23.** 19,440 **25.** $n + 1$ terms

2.4 Exercise Set B (p. 76)

1. $x^3 + 12x^2 + 48x + 64$
3. $w^6 + 6w^5 + 15w^4 + 20w^3 + 15w^2 + 6w + 1$
5. $b^6 + 30b^5 + 375b^4 + 2500b^3 + 9375b^2 + 18{,}750b + 15{,}625$
7. $x^6 - 6x^5 + 15x^4 - 20x^3 + 15x^2 - 6x + 1$
9. $b^6 - 24b^5 + 240b^4 - 1280b^3 + 3480b^2 - 6144b + 4096$ **11.** $-27y^3 + 108y^2 - 144y + 64$
13. $64x^3 + 96x^2 + 48x + 8$
15. $27y^3 + 135y^2 + 225y + 125$
17. $729c^6 + 1458c^5d + 1215c^4d^2 + 540c^3d^3 + 135c^2d^4 + 18cd^5 + d^6$
19. $x^8 + 8x^6 + 24x^4 + 32x^2 + 16$
21. $32s^{20} + 400s^{16} + 2000s^{12} + 5000s^8 + 6250s^4 + 3125$ **23.** $-11{,}250$
25. The coefficients for the x and x^2 terms are incorrect; $x^3 + 9x^2 + 27x + 27$.
27. The pattern formed is that the sum of the previous 2 diagonals is added to get the sum of the next diagonal.

2.5 Exercise Set A (p. 79)

1. $-14, 3$ **3.** $-24, -15$ **5.** $-8, \frac{1}{2}$ **7.** $-5, 4$
9. $\frac{2}{3}, 8$ **11.** $-3, \frac{1}{2}$ **13.** $10(x - y)$ **15.** $6(3a^2 - b)$
17. $r(r + 2s)$ **19.** $5q(p^2 + 2)$ **21.** $2w^2(3w - 7)$

23. $-14, 0$ **25.** $-1, 0$ **27.** $-2, 0$ **29.** $-\frac{5}{4}, 0$

31. $0, \frac{1}{2}$ **33.** $-\frac{3}{8}, 0$

35. a. $h = -16t^2 + 14t$ **b.** $\frac{7}{8}$ sec

2.5 Exercise Set B (p. 80)

1. $-3, \frac{2}{5}$ **3.** $-4, 6$ **5.** $-\frac{3}{2}, 9$ **7.** $\frac{2}{9}, \frac{3}{7}$ **9.** $\frac{9}{8}, \frac{5}{2}$

11. $4m(m^2 + 6)$ **13.** $3y(2x^3 + 3y)$

15. $4mn(3m - 2n)$ **17.** $3p(-p^3 + 5p + 2)$

19. $0, \frac{3}{4}$ **21.** $0, \frac{4}{3}$ **23.** $-\frac{1}{2}, 0$ **25.** $-\frac{3}{50}, 0$

27. $-\frac{13}{17}, 0$ **29.** $0, \frac{1}{4}$ **31.** $0, \frac{3}{5}$

2.6 Exercise Set A (p. 83)

1. $(x + 7)(x + 1)$ **3.** $(w - 13)(w + 1)$

5. $(m - 6)(m - 4)$ **7.** $(a + 9)(a + 4)$

9. $(z - 10)(z - 4)$ **11.** $-3, 12$ **13.** $-2, 7$

15. $3, 9$ **17.** $-12, -4$ **19.** $-4, 9$ **21.** $3, 8$

23. $-12, 1$ **25.** $-12, -5$ **27.** $-5, -3$

29. a. $x^2 - 7x + 12$ **b.** 144 in.

2.6 Exercise Set B (p. 84)

1. $(x - 8)(x + 7)$ **3.** $(y - 9)(y - 6)$

5. $(w - 9)(w - 5)$ **7.** $-4, 15$ **9.** 12 **11.** $-12, 11$

13. $-6, 10$ **15.** 8 **17.** $-10, 15$ **19.** $-20, 30$

21. $-8, -5$ **23.** $-2, 12$

25. a. $x^2 + 600x + 80{,}000$ **b.** 25 ft

2.7 Exercise Set A (p. 87)

1. $(-x + 4)(x + 7)$ **3.** $(-m - 8)(m + 5)$

5. $(3a - 1)(a - 4)$ **7.** $(3c + 2)(2c + 1)$

9. $(2w + 3)(6w - 5)$ **11.** $(r + 5)(-3r - 2)$

13. $-4, 5$ **15.** $6, 7$ **17.** $-\frac{5}{2}, 2$ **19.** $-6, -\frac{1}{3}$

21. $-\frac{2}{3}, \frac{4}{5}$ **23.** $-2, \frac{5}{3}$ **27.** $-8, \frac{1}{2}$ **29.** $-1, 2$

31. $-7, \frac{3}{8}$ **33.** $-10, \frac{3}{2}$

35. a. $4x^2 + 24x + 32$ **b.** 8 in. by 16 in.

2.7 Exercise Set B (p. 88)

1. $(-x + 9)(x + 20)$ **3.** $(p - 10)(-3p - 4)$

5. $(b + 3)(14b - 4)$ **7.** $-\frac{5}{4}, \frac{3}{8}$ **9.** $-\frac{2}{5}, \frac{2}{3}$

11. $-\frac{2}{9}, \frac{5}{7}$ **13.** $-\frac{3}{8}, \frac{1}{2}$ **15.** $\frac{1}{3}, 5$ **17.** $\frac{7}{10}, \frac{3}{2}$

19. $-\frac{1}{2}, -\frac{1}{3}$ **21.** $-1, \frac{1}{3}$ **23.** $-1, \frac{2}{5}$ **25.** $\frac{2}{5}, 2$

27. $\frac{5}{6}$ **29.** 2 sec

2.8 Exercise Set A (p. 91)

1. $(x - 6)(x + 6)$ **3.** $(2b - 10)(2b + 10)$

5. $-2(x - 4)(x + 4)$ **7.** $(y + 12)^2$ **9.** $(5w - 2)^2$

11. $-2(3a + 1)^2$ **13.** $(x - 9y)^2$ **15.** $4(2x + 5y)^2$

17. $-\frac{5}{2}, \frac{5}{2}$ **19.** $-3, 3$ **21.** 4 **23.** 10 **25.** $-\frac{5}{3}$

27. $-\frac{3}{8}, \frac{3}{8}$ **29.** 3

2.8 Exercise Set B (p. 92)

1. $(5x - 9)(5x + 9)$ **3.** $(11w - 25)(11w + 25)$

5. $\frac{1}{16}(3r - 1)(3r + 1)$ **7.** $-3(y + 8)^2$

9. $3(2z + 1)^2$ **11.** $-2(3s + 4t)^2$

13. The difference of two squares pattern was used to factor the polynomial instead of perfect square trinomial pattern.

$$\begin{aligned} y^2 - 10y + 25 &= y^2 - 2(y \cdot 5) + 5^2 \\ &= (y - 5)^2 \end{aligned}$$

15. -9 **17.** 10 **19.** $\frac{4}{15}$ **21.** $\frac{4}{7}$ **23.** $\frac{8}{3}$ **25.** $\frac{3}{4}$

27. 140 **29.** 16 **31.** 28

2.9 Exercise Set A (p. 95)

1. $(4x - 3)(x + 5)$ **3.** $(w^2 - 5)(w + 8)$

5. $(y - 1)(x + 15)$ **7.** $(x^2 + 5)(x + 1)$

9. $(m^2 + 2)(m - 6)$ **11.** $(t^2 - 2)(t + 12)$

13. $7x^2(x + 4)$ **15.** $-2p(8p^2 + 1)$

17. $15y(1 - 4y)$ **19.** $5(m^2 + 4m + 8)$

21. $4z(z - 2)(z + 1)$ **23.** $(x^2 + 5)(x + 1)$

25. $-4, -2$ **27.** $\frac{7}{2}$ **29.** $\frac{4}{3}$ **31.** $2(2x + 3)(x + 1)$

33. a. $-16t^2 + 8t + 2$ **b.** 2.64 ft **c.** about 0.7 sec

2.9 Exercise Set B (p. 96)

1. $13a(1 - 2a)$ **3.** $-2(m + 1)(m + 7)$
5. $r(r + 5)^2$ **7.** $4n^3(n + 6)(n - 5)$
9. $-5(2t - 5)(t + 3)$ **11.** $(x^2 - 8)(x + 5)$
13. $3x^3y(x - 9)(x + 9)$ **15.** $25x^2y(x - 4)$
17. $-2, 2$ **19.** $-\frac{15}{4}, \frac{15}{4}$ **21.** $-6, 0$ **23.** $\frac{5}{6}, \frac{9}{2}$
25. $-\frac{9}{4}, 0, \frac{9}{4}$ **27.** 14 **29.** $-3, 9$
33. a. $2\pi r^2 - \frac{1}{2}\pi = 0$ **b.** $\frac{1}{2}$ ft

2.10 Exercise Set A (pp. 100–101)

1.

x	−2	−1	0	1	2
y	36	9	0	9	36

3.

x	−4	−2	0	2	4
y	41	11	1	11	41

5.

x	−2	−1	0	1	2
y	−13	−1	3	−1	−13

11. shift the graph 4 units up and reflect over x-axis
13. stretch vertically by a factor of 5, reflect in x-axis, and shift 1 unit up
15. shrink vertically by a factor of $\frac{3}{4}$, reflect over x-axis, and shift 5 units up

17. 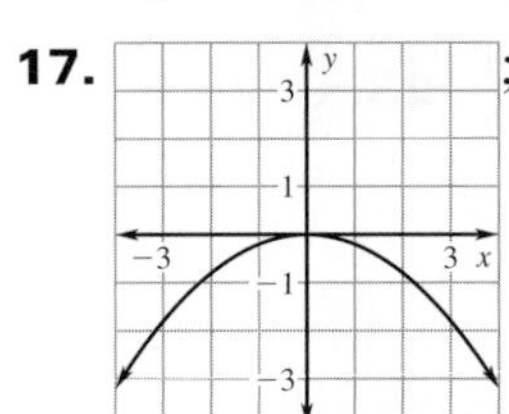
; domain: all reals; range: $y \le 0$; vertical shrink by a factor of $\frac{1}{5}$ and reflection in x-axis

19. 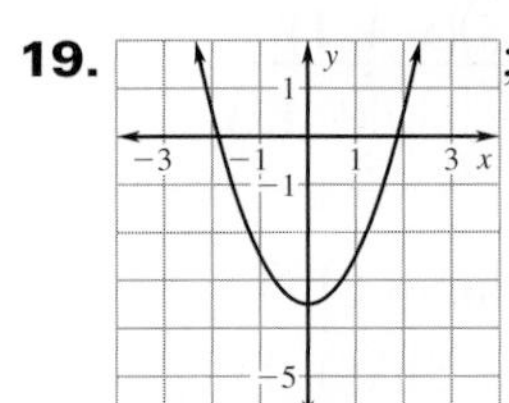
; domain: all reals; range: $y \ge -3.5$; vertical shift 3.5 units down

21. ; domain: all reals; range: $y \le 2$; vertical stretch by a factor of 5, reflection in x-axis, and vertical shift 2 units up

23. 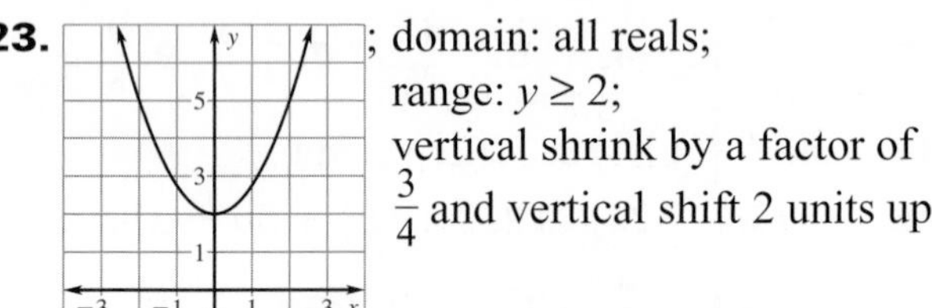
; domain: all reals; range: $y \ge 2$; vertical shrink by a factor of $\frac{3}{4}$ and vertical shift 2 units up.

25. 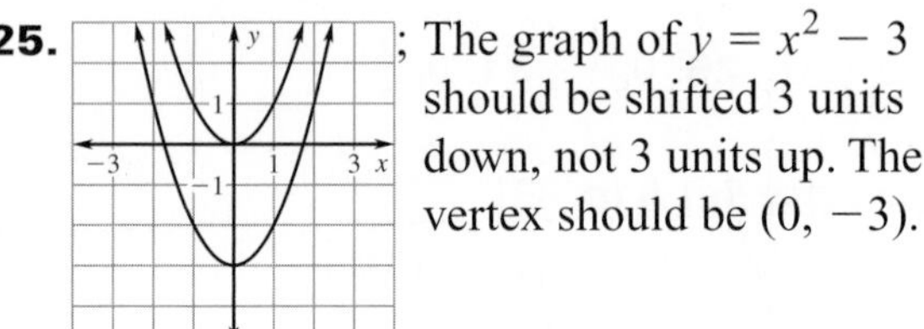
; The graph of $y = x^2 - 3$ should be shifted 3 units down, not 3 units up. The vertex should be $(0, -3)$.

27. a. 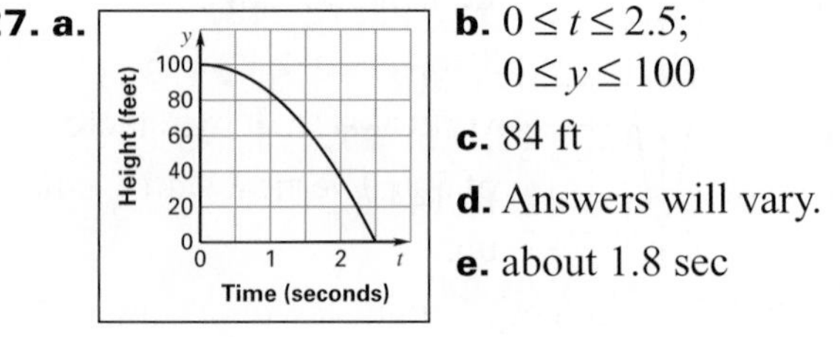

b. $0 \le t \le 2.5$; $0 \le y \le 100$
c. 84 ft
d. Answers will vary.
e. about 1.8 sec

2.10 Exercise Set B (pp. 102–103)

1.

x	−2	−1	0	1	2
y	36	6	−4	6	36

7. 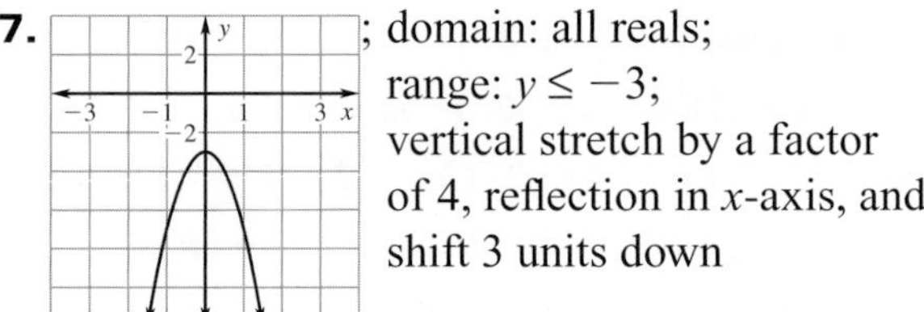
; domain: all reals; range: $y \le -3$; vertical stretch by a factor of 4, reflection in x-axis, and shift 3 units down

9. 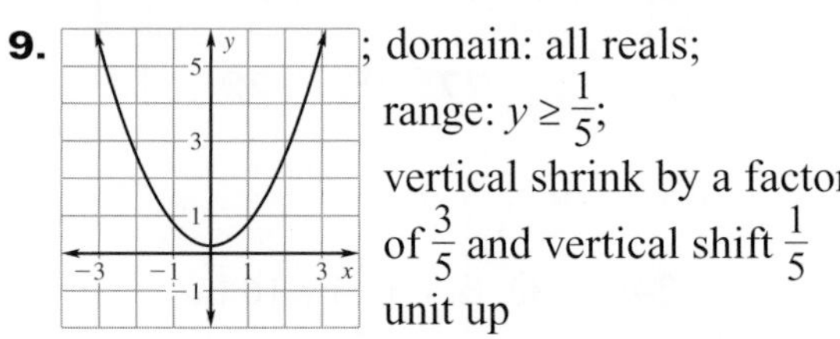
; domain: all reals; range: $y \ge \frac{1}{5}$; vertical shrink by a factor of $\frac{3}{5}$ and vertical shift $\frac{1}{5}$ unit up

11. ; domain: all reals; range: $y \geq \frac{3}{4}$; vertical stretch by a factor of 6 and vertical shift $\frac{3}{4}$ unit up

13. ; domain: all reals; range: $y \leq -\frac{1}{2}$; vertical stretch by a factor of 2, reflection in x-axis, and vertical shift $\frac{1}{2}$ unit down

15. ; domain: all reals; range: $y \geq -9$; vertical stretch by a factor of 4, and vertical shift 9 units down.

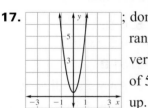

17. ; domain: all reals; range: $y \geq \frac{1}{3}$; vertical stretch by a factor of 5 and vertical shift $\frac{1}{3}$ unit up.

19. shift the graph of f 5 units down **21.** shift the graph of f 16 units up **23.** shrink the graph of f vertically by a factor of $\frac{1}{2}$

25.

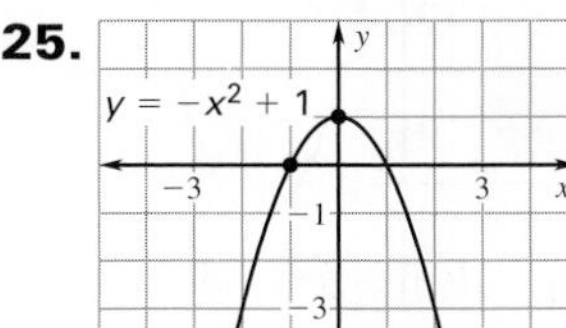

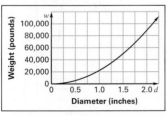

27. a.

b. about 1.5 in.

29. a.

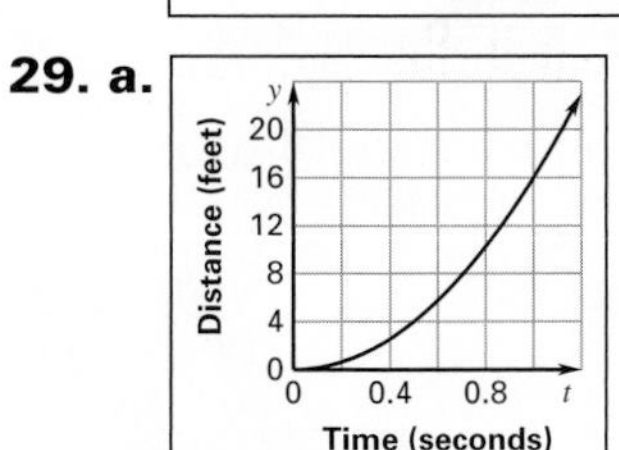

b.

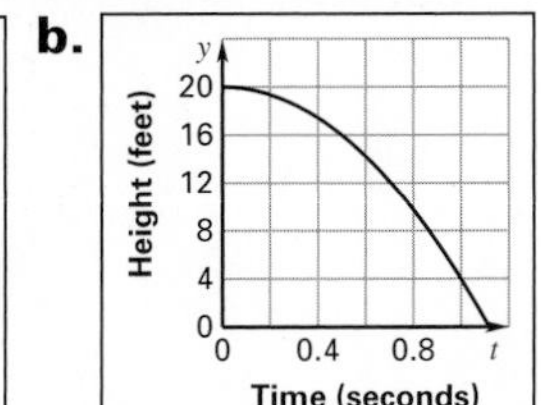

c. The second graph is a transformation of the first graph. The first graph has been reflected in the x-axis and shifted 20 units up to obtain the second graph. For the first graph, find the value of t when $y = 8$. For the second graph, find the value of t when $y = 12$.

2.11 Exercise Set A (pp. 107–108)

1. $a = 6, b = 3, c = 5$

3. $a = 7, b = -3, c = -1$

5. $a = \frac{3}{4}, b = 0, c = -10$

7. upward; $x = 0$; $(0, -5)$ **9.** downward; $x = \frac{3}{2}$; $\left(\frac{3}{2}, \frac{23}{2}\right)$ **11.** upward; $x = -1$; $(-1, -5)$ **13.** upward; $x = -5$; $\left(-5, -\frac{33}{2}\right)$ **15.** downward; $x = \frac{3}{2}$; $\left(\frac{3}{2}, -\frac{5}{4}\right)$ **17.** downward; $x = \frac{7}{4}$; $\left(\frac{7}{4}, \frac{57}{8}\right)$

19.

x	3	4	5	6	7
y	−18	−21	−22	−21	−18

21.

x	−1	0	1	2	3
y	$\frac{17}{2}$	7	$\frac{13}{2}$	7	$\frac{17}{2}$

23. **25.**

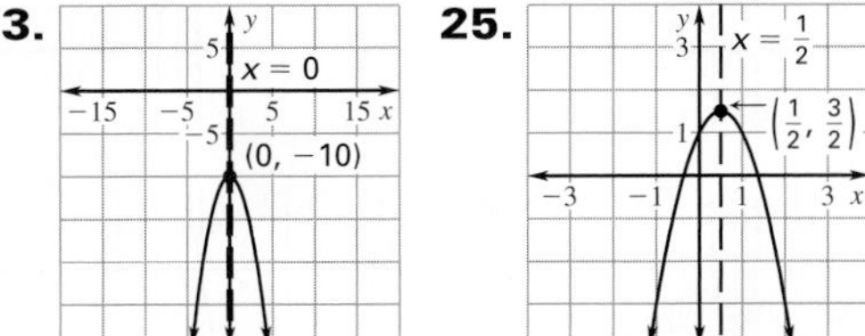

27. **29.**

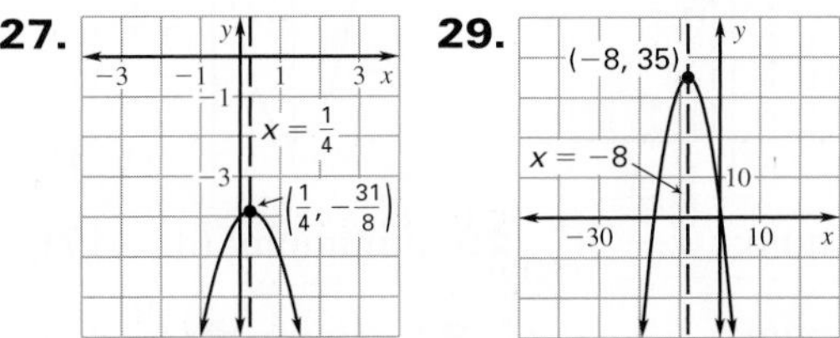

31. **33.** minimum; $(0, -40)$

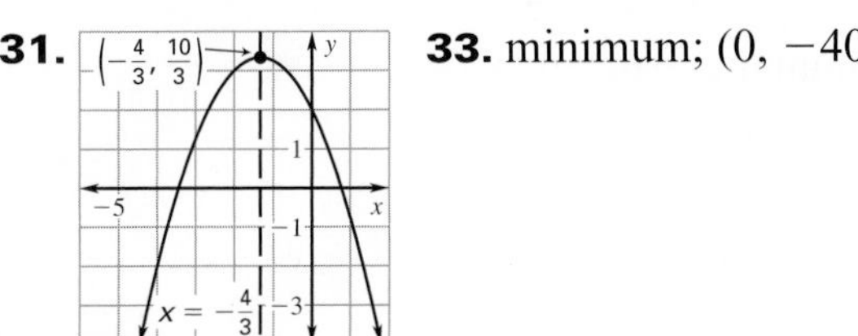

SELECTED ANSWERS

35. minimum; $\left(\frac{1}{4}, \frac{7}{2}\right)$ **37.** The graph of $g(x)$ is a reflection in the y-axis of the graph of $f(x)$.
39. 12 ft

2.11 Exercise Set B (pp. 109–110)

1. downward; $x = \frac{1}{2}$; $\left(\frac{1}{2}, \frac{23}{4}\right)$ **3.** upward; $x = \frac{1}{8}$; $\left(\frac{1}{8}, \frac{23}{8}\right)$ **5.** upward; $x = 0$; $(0, -9)$ **7.** upward; $x = 8$; $(8, -8)$ **9.** downward; $x = 1$; $(1, 11)$ **11.** upward; $x = -1$; $(-1, -8)$

13.

x	2	3	4	5	6
y	2	$\frac{5}{4}$	1	$\frac{5}{4}$	2

15. $x = 0$; $(0, -15)$

17. $\left(\frac{1}{2}, 4\right)$; $x = \frac{1}{2}$

19. $x = 1$; $(1, -1)$

21. $x = 3$; $\left(3, \frac{53}{2}\right)$

23. $(1, 7)$; $x = 1$

25. $x = -10$; $(-10, -179)$

27. minimum; $(0, -36)$ **29.** minimum; $(4, -17)$ **31.** minimum; $\left(-\frac{5}{2}, -\frac{37}{4}\right)$ **33.** minimum; $\left(\frac{9}{2}, \frac{5}{4}\right)$
35. minimum; $(-6, -11)$

37. $f(x) = 4x^2 + 12x + 9$; $g(x) = 4x^2 - 12x + 9$

The graph of $g(x)$ is a reflection in the y-axis of the graph of $f(x)$.

39.

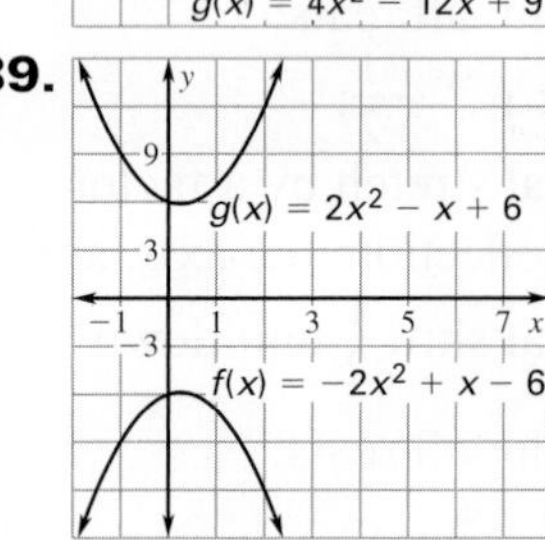

The graph of $g(x)$ is a reflection in the x-axis of the graph of $f(x)$.

41. a. lamp A: 25 cm; lamp B: 20 cm **b.** 5 cm

2.12 Exercise Set A (pp. 114–115)

1. not a solution **3.** not a solution
5. not a solution **7.** −4 **9.** −8, 3 **11.** −5, 5

13. −6, 0

15.

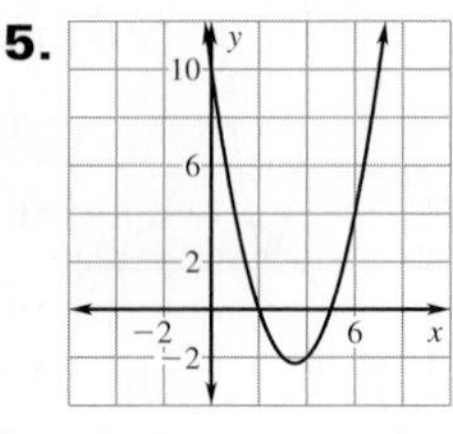

2, 5

17. 3

19.

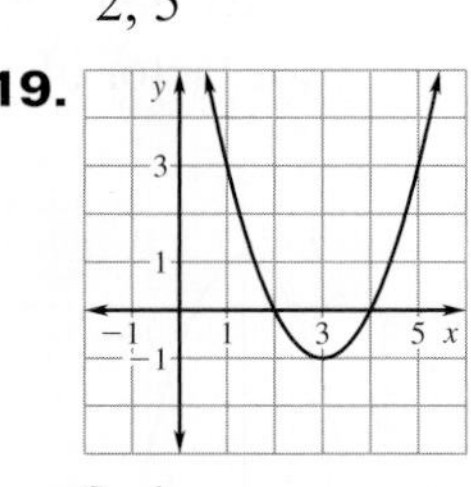

2, 4

21.

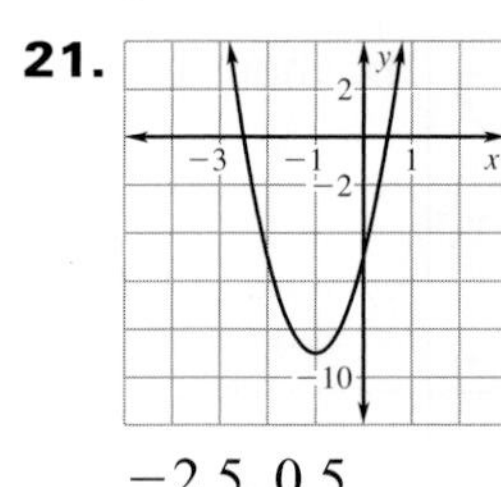

−2.5, 0.5

23.

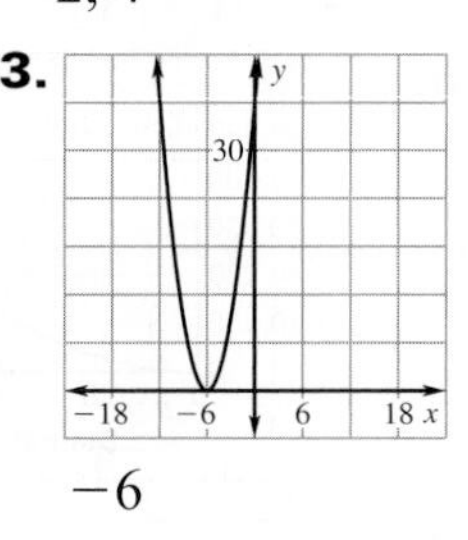

−6

SELECTED ANSWERS

25. 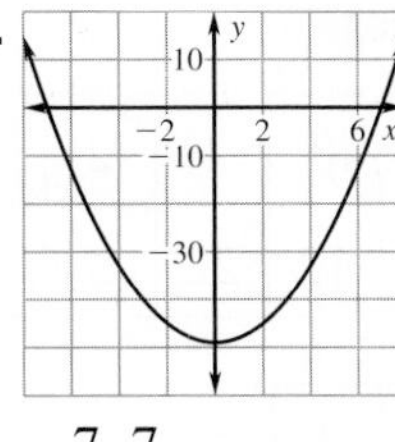

−7, 7

27. 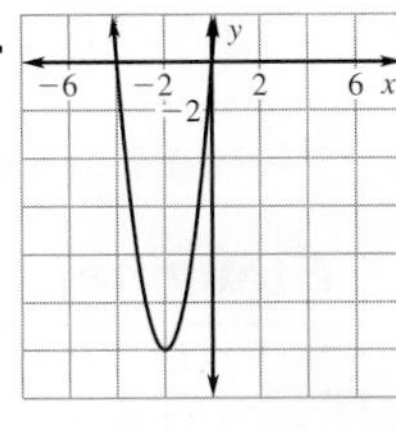

−4, 0

29. a. 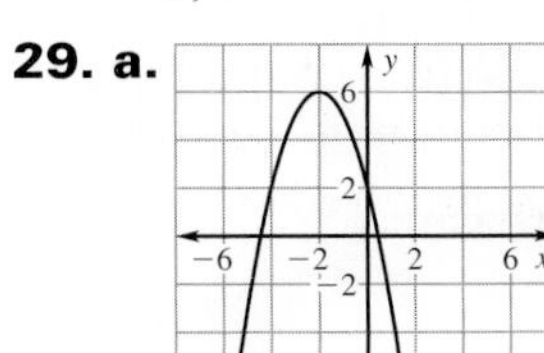

b. −4, 0

31. a. 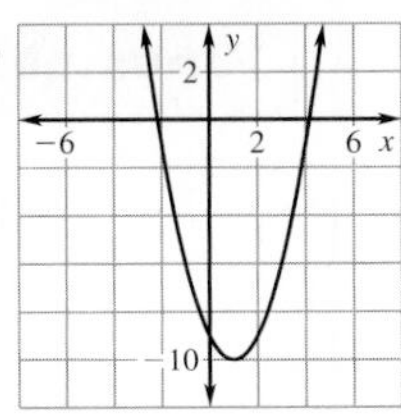

b. −2, 4

33. a. 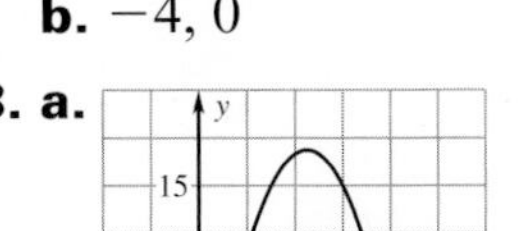

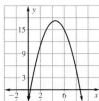

b. 0, 9

35. 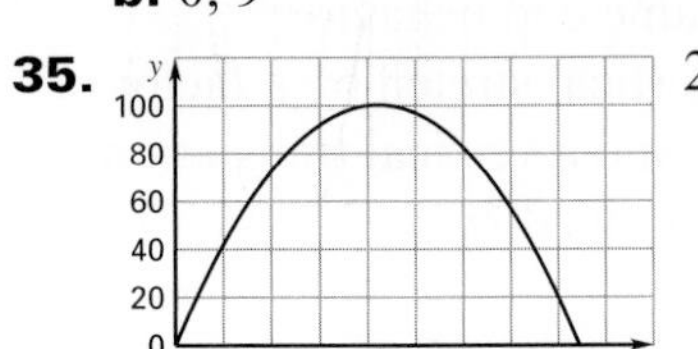

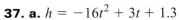

211.1 ft

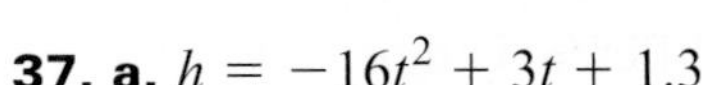

37. a. $h = -16t^2 + 3t + 1.3$

b. 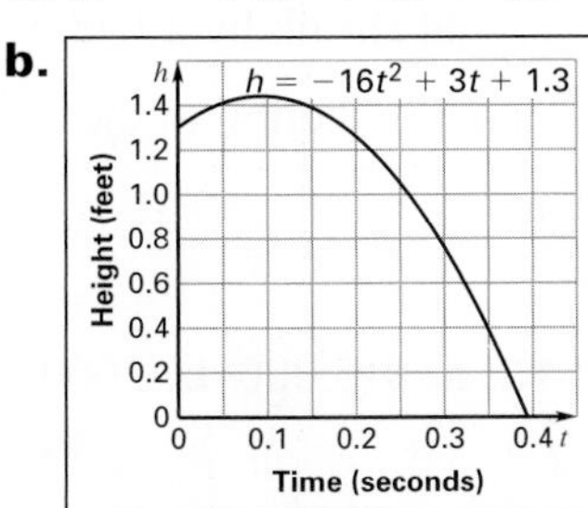

c. about 0.4 sec

d. about 0.34 sec

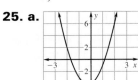

2.12 Exercise Set B (pp. 116–117)

1. 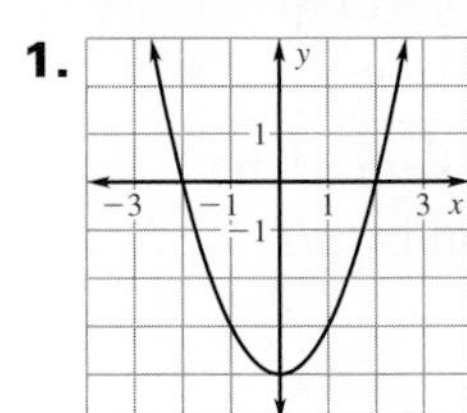

−2, 2

3. 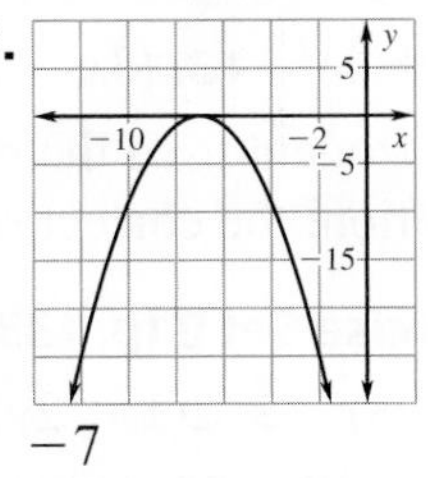

−7

5. 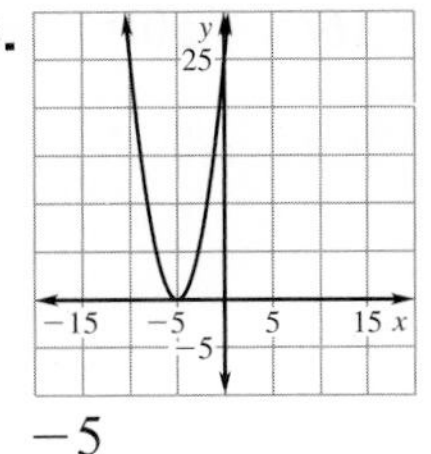

−5

7. 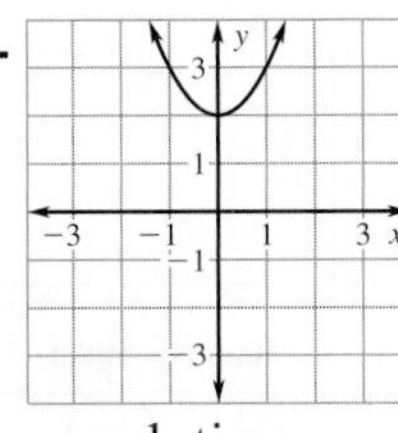

no solution

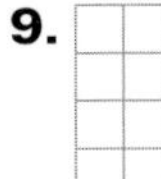

9. 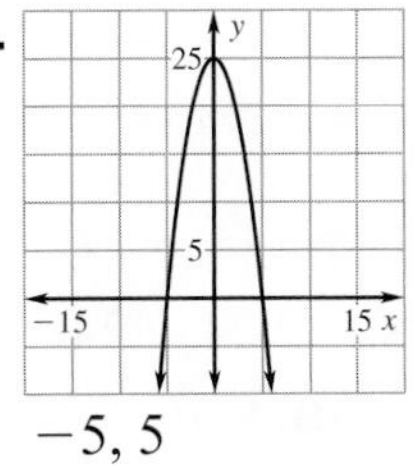

−5, 5

11. 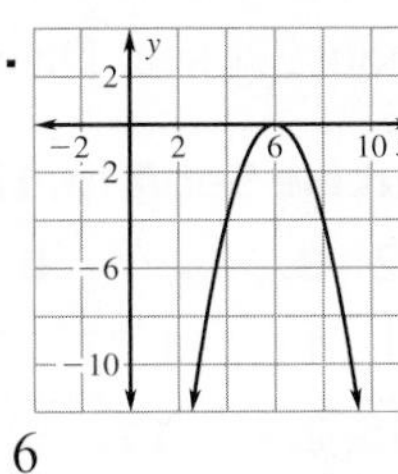

6

13. 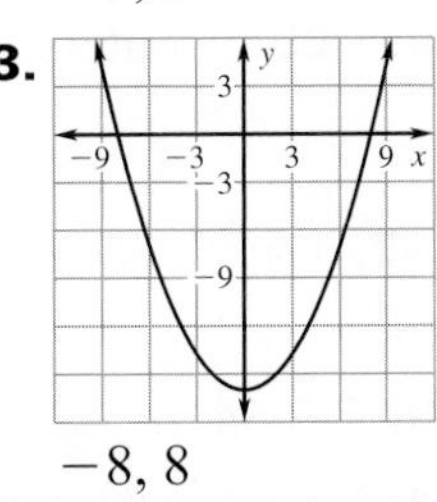

−8, 8

15. 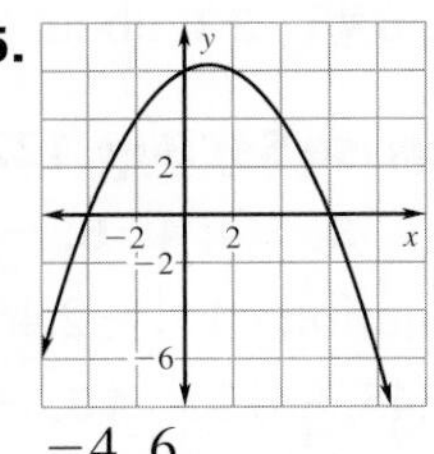

−4, 6

17. 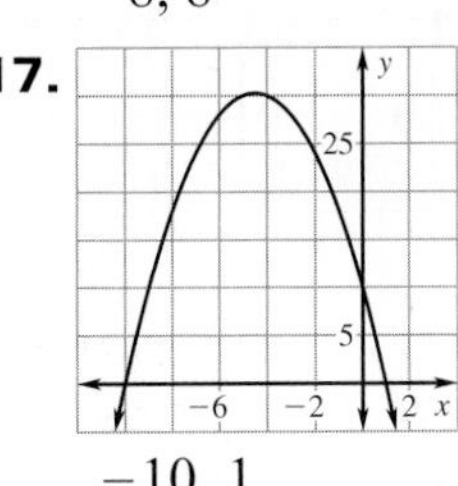

−10, 1

19. 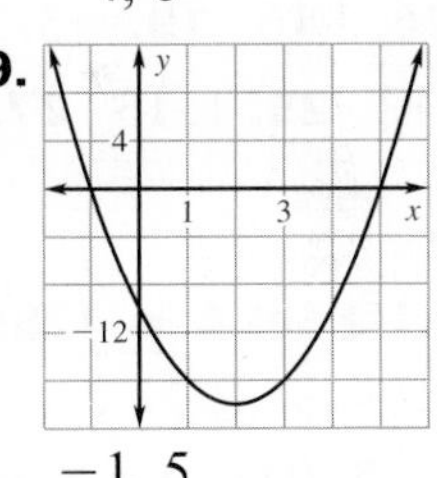

−1, 5

21. 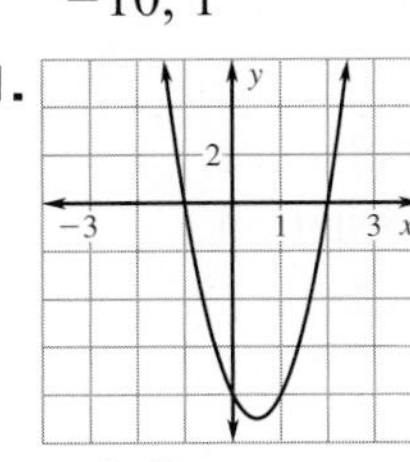

−1, 2

23. a. 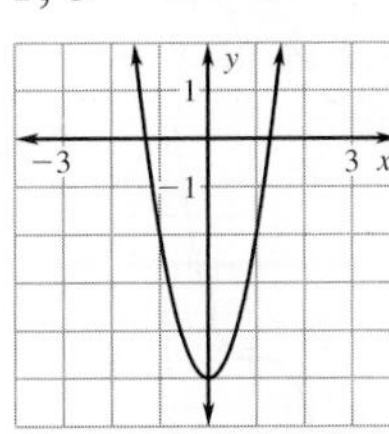

b. −1, 1

25. a. 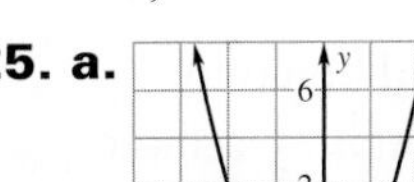

b. −2, 1

27. a. 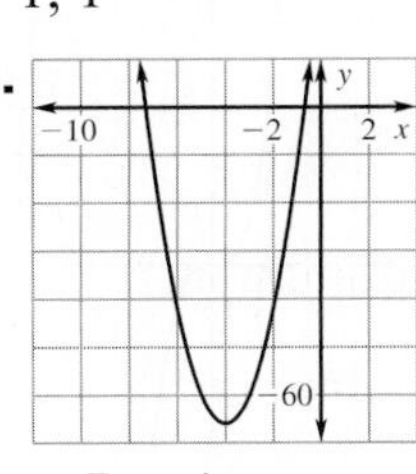

b. −7, −1

29. 4.5 in. **31.** 9.9 cm

33. a. 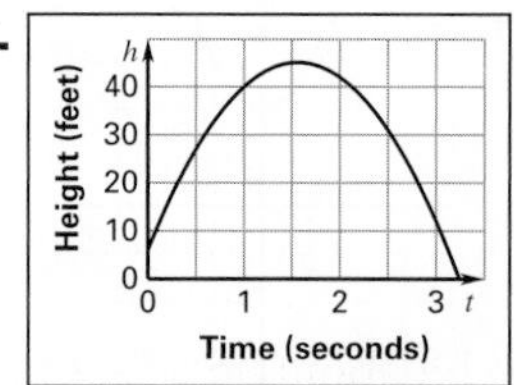

$h = 16t^2 + 50t^2 + 6$

b. about 3.2 sec

c. about 3.1 sec; Determine t when $y = 5$.

2.13 Exercise Set A (p. 121)

1. $-2, 2$ **3.** $-6, 6$ **5.** $-5, 5$ **7.** $-5, 5$ **9.** $-1, 1$ **11.** $-1.73, 1.73$ **13.** $-2.24, 2.24$ **15.** $-2.45, 2.45$ **17.** $-2.5, 2.5$ **19.** $0.76, 5.24$ **21.** $1.55, 6.45$ **23.** about 6.16 in. **25.** about 3 in.

2.13 Exercise Set B (p. 122)

1. $-3, 3$ **3.** $-4, 4$ **5.** $-6, 6$ **7.** $-5.70, 5.70$ **9.** no solution **11.** $-2.45, 2.45$ **13.** $-11.45, -6.55$ **15.** $-10.46, -3.54$ **17.** $-3.16, 3.16$ **19.** $-3, 3$ **21.** $-1.03, 1.03$ **23.** $-8, 12$ **25.** $1, 13$ **27.** $-8, 0$

UNIT 3

3.1 Exercise Set A (p. 128)

1. $f(x) \to -\infty$ as $x \to -\infty$ and $f(x) \to +\infty$ as $x \to +\infty$ **3.** $f(x) \to -\infty$ as $x \to -\infty$ and $f(x) \to +\infty$ as $x \to +\infty$

5. 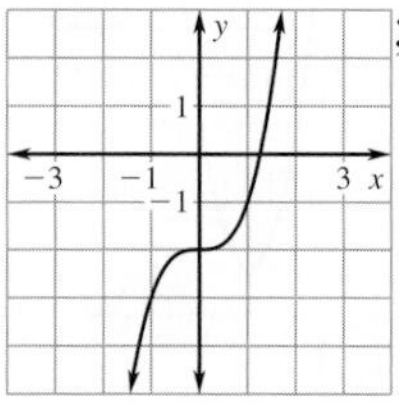 ; same end behavior; vertical translation 2 units down

7. 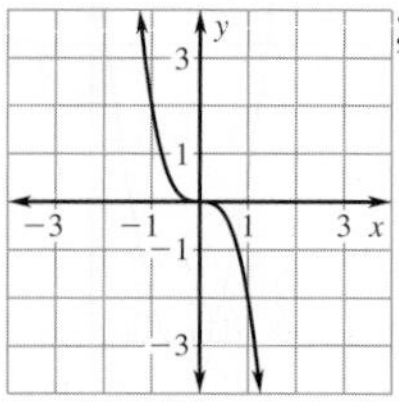 ; different end behavior; vertical stretch by a factor of 2 and a reflection in the x-axis

9. 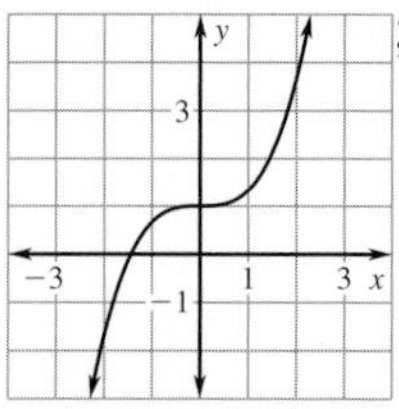 ; same end behavior; vertical shrink by a factor of $\frac{1}{3}$ and a vertical translation 1 unit up

11. odd **13.** neither **15.** neither

17. a.

t (years since 2000)	0	1	2	3
F (number of fish)	12	22	20	12

t (years since 2000)	4	5	6	7
F (number of fish)	4	2	12	40

b.

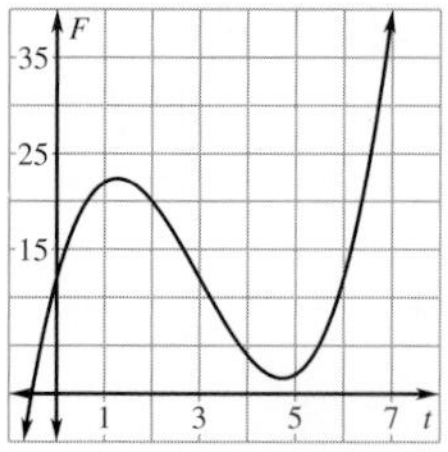

c. decrease

3.1 Exercise Set B (p. 129)

1. $f(x) \to +\infty$ as $x \to -\infty$ and $f(x) \to -\infty$ as $x \to +\infty$ **3.** $f(x) \to -\infty$ as $x \to -\infty$ and $f(x) \to +\infty$ as $x \to +\infty$

5. 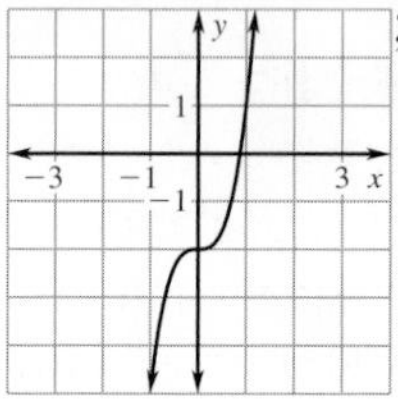 ; same end behavior; vertical stretch by a factor of 3 and a vertical translation 2 units down

7. 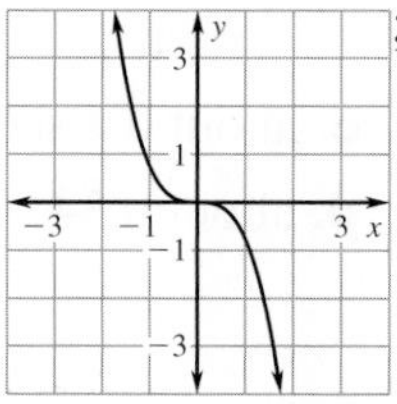 ; different end behavior; vertical shrink by a factor of $\frac{3}{4}$ and a reflection in the x-axis

9. odd **11.** neither **13. a.** \$15,000 **b.** 2000 and 2004 **c.** 2004 and 2007

3.2 Exercise Set A (p. 132)

1. $(x - 2)^3$ **3.** $(2x - 1)^3$ **5.** $(x + 10)^3$ **11.** $(xy + 1)^3$ **13.** $(3x - 2y)^3$

15. The student used the wrong sign in the factorization; the correct solution is $(ab - cd)^3$.

3.2 Exercise Set B (p. 133)

1. $(a + 3)^3$ **3.** $2(1 - 2y)^3$ **5.** They are both correct; Their expressions are equivalent.

7. $(1 - gh)^3$ **9.** $(8x + 5y)^3$ **11.** 144 **13.** 96 **15.** *Sample answer:* =, +, + **17.** 2 times longer

3.3 Exercise Set A (pp. 138–139)

1. ; domain: $x \geq 0$; range: $y \geq 0$; vertical stretch by a factor of 7

3. ; domain: $x \geq 0$; range: $y \leq 0$; vertical stretch by a factor of 4 and reflection in x-axis

5. translate graph of $y = \sqrt{x}$ vertically 3 units up

7. translate graph of $y = \sqrt{x}$ vertically 5 units down

9. translate graph of $y = \sqrt{x}$ horizontally $\frac{1}{2}$ unit right

17. ; domain: $x \geq -4$; range: $y \geq -4$; vertical translation 4 units down and horizontal translation 4 units left

19. ; domain: $x \geq 6$; range: $y \geq 4$; vertical translation 4 units up and horizontal translation 6 units right

21. ; domain: $x \geq 1$; range: $y \geq 2$; vertical translation 2 units up and horizontal translation 1 unit right

23. a.

***h* (feet)**	0	25	100	225
***t* (seconds)**	0	$\frac{5}{4}$	$\frac{5}{2}$	$\frac{15}{4}$

b. ; about 250 feet

c. Yes; the building could be about 250 feet tall.

25. a. ; domain: $w \geq 0$; range: $d \geq 0$

b. 99 lb **c.** 4 lb

3.3 Exercise Set B (pp. 140–141)

1. 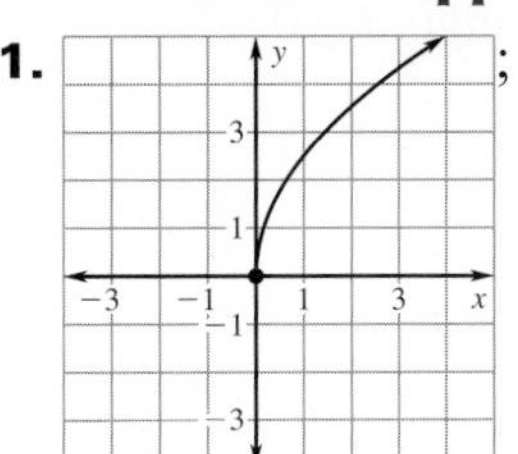 ; domain: $x \geq 0$; range: $y \geq 0$; vertical stretch by a factor of 2.5

3. 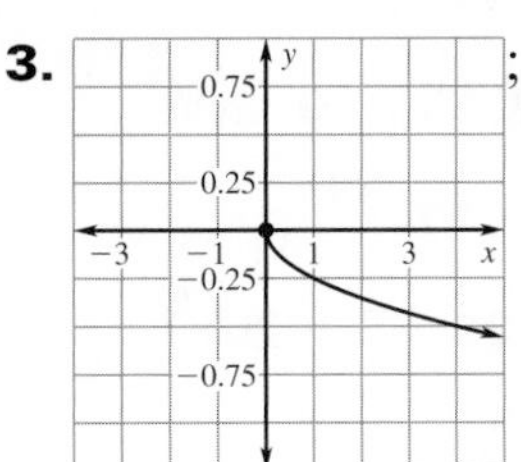 ; domain: $x \geq 0$; range: $y \leq 0$; vertical shrink by a factor of 0.25 and reflection in x-axis

5. translate graph of $y = \sqrt{x}$ vertically $\frac{3}{2}$ units down **7.** translate graph of $y = \sqrt{x}$ horizontally $\frac{1}{4}$ unit right **9.** translate graph of $y = \sqrt{x}$ vertically $\frac{3}{4}$ unit up

17. 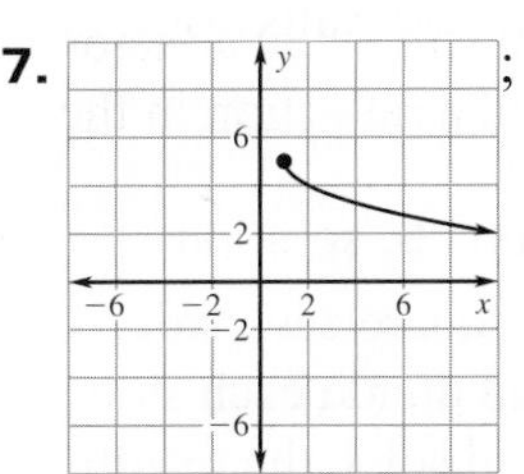 ; domain: $x \geq 1$; range: $y \leq 5$; reflection in x-axis, vertical translation 5 units up, and horizontal translation 1 unit right

SELECTED ANSWERS

19. 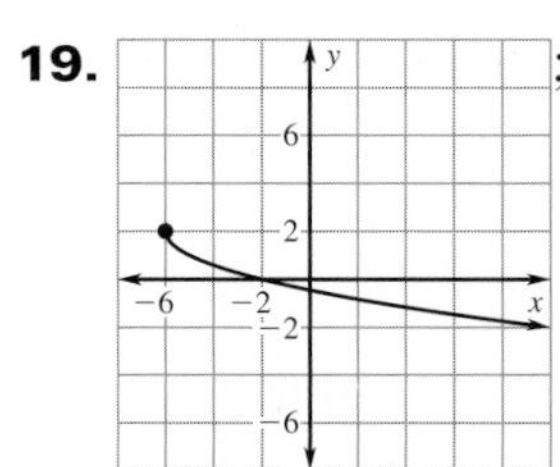
; domain: $x \geq -6$; range: $y \leq 2$; reflection in x-axis, vertical translation 2 units up, and horizontal translation 6 units left

21. 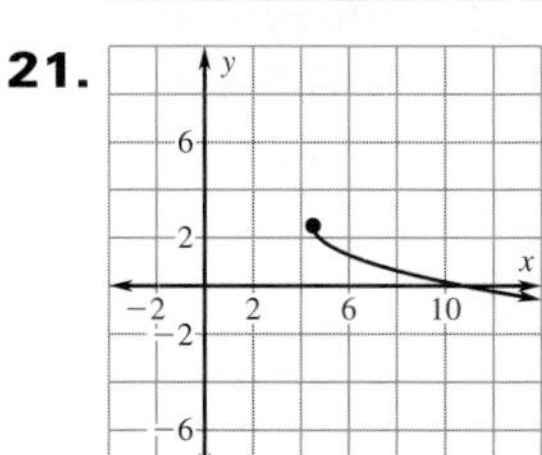
; domain: $x \geq 4.5$; range: $y \leq 2.5$; reflection in x-axis, vertical translation 2.5 units up, and horizontal translation 4.5 units right

25. a. 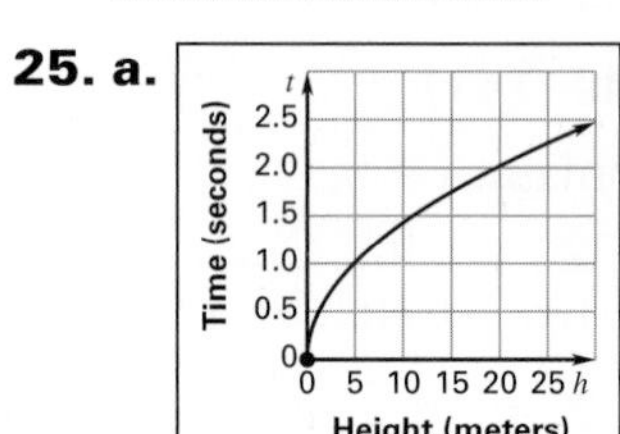

; domain: $h \geq 0$; range: $t \geq 0$

b. 11.025 m

3.4 Exercise Set A (p. 144)

1. $10\sqrt{2}$ **3.** $4\sqrt{7}$ **5.** $3y$ **7.** $3\sqrt{7}$ **9.** $2x\sqrt{5}$ **11.** $\frac{\sqrt{5}}{7}$ **13.** $\frac{4\sqrt{5}}{5}$ **15.** $\frac{9\sqrt{2x}}{2x}$ **17.** $\frac{24 - 6\sqrt{5}}{11}$ **19.** $13\sqrt{7}$ **21.** $-7 + 4\sqrt{7}$ **23.** $37 + 20\sqrt{3}$ **25. a.** 3.87 mi/h **b.** 4.61 mi/h

3.4 Exercise Set B (p. 145)

1. $3s\sqrt{5s}$ **3.** $15c^2\sqrt{2c}$ **5.** $11x^3y^4\sqrt{x}$ **7.** $3y^2\sqrt{15x}$ **9.** $\frac{d}{5}$ **11.** $\frac{m^2\sqrt{77m}}{11}$ **13.** $\frac{5 + \sqrt{3}}{11}$ **15.** $\frac{6\sqrt{5} - 5}{31}$ **17.** $-14 + 3\sqrt{7}$ **19.** $133 + 60\sqrt{3}$ **21.** $\frac{5m\sqrt{5mn}}{n}$ **23.** $\frac{2\sqrt{3}}{3}$ **25. a.** 50 watts **b.** 100 watts

3.5 Exercise Set A (p. 148)

1. not a solution **3.** solution **5.** solution

7. Add 5 to each side, then square each side, subtract 3 from each side, and divide each side by 7. **9.** Square each side and solve the resulting linear equation for x. **11.** Add the second radical expression to each side, square each side, and solve the resulting linear equation for x. **13.** 16 **15.** 46 **17.** 81 **19.** $\frac{32}{5}$ **21.** $\frac{3}{2}$ **23.** 1 **25.** 6 **27.** no solution **29.** 6 **31. a.** 560,000 subscriptions **b.** 312,500 subscriptions

3.5 Exercise Set B (p. 149)

1. Subtract 1 from each side, square each side, and then solve the resulting linear equation for x.

3. Subtract 4 from each side, divide each side by -2, square each side, and then solve the resulting equation for x. **5.** Square each side and solve the resulting linear equation for x. **7.** Divide each side by 3, square each side, and then solve the resulting linear equation for x. **9.** Subtract x from each side, square each side, and solve the resulting quadratic equation for x.

11. $\frac{20}{3}$ **13.** 144 **15.** no solution **17.** no solution **19.** 3 **21.** 2 **23.** 4 **25.** *Sample answer:* $x = \sqrt{7x - 12}$ **27. a.** 4.8°C **b.** 0 m/sec

3.6 Exercise Set A (pp. 153–154)

1. domain: all reals except 3; range: all reals except 1 **3.** domain: all reals except -6; range: all reals except -4 **5.** domain: all reals except -3; range: all reals except 3

9. 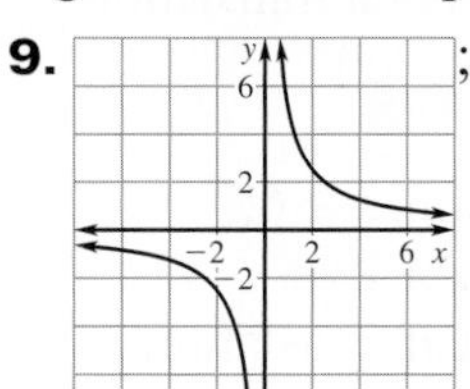
; domain: all reals except 0; range: all reals except 0; vertical stretch

11. 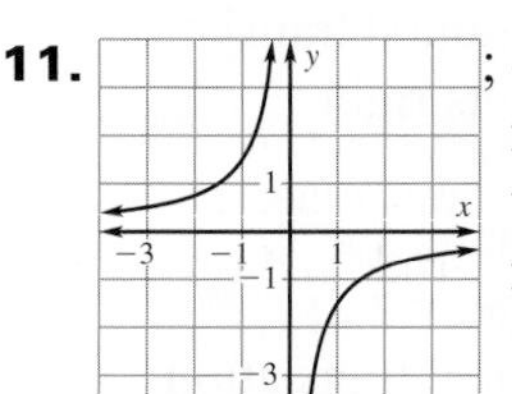
; domain: all reals except 0; range: all reals except 0; vertical stretch and reflection in x-axis

13. 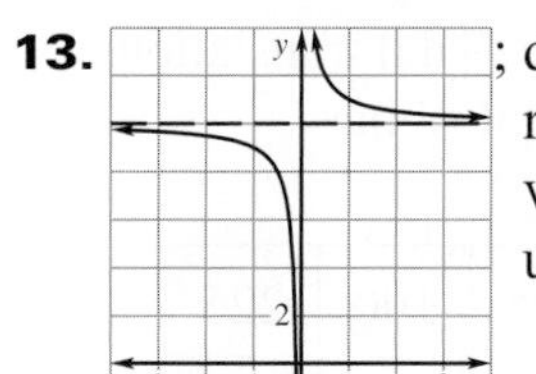
; domain: all reals except 0; range: all reals except 10; vertical translation 10 units up

15. *Sample answer:* $y = \frac{2}{x}$

17. $x = -5, y = -6$ **19.** $x = -7, y = 7$

21. $x = -5, y = 10$ **23.** $x = -12, y = -3$

25. The sign on the vertical asymptote is wrong. It should be $x = -1$.

27. 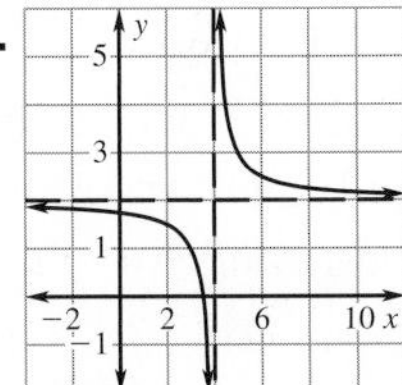

29. a. $C = \frac{28}{r + 2}$

b. 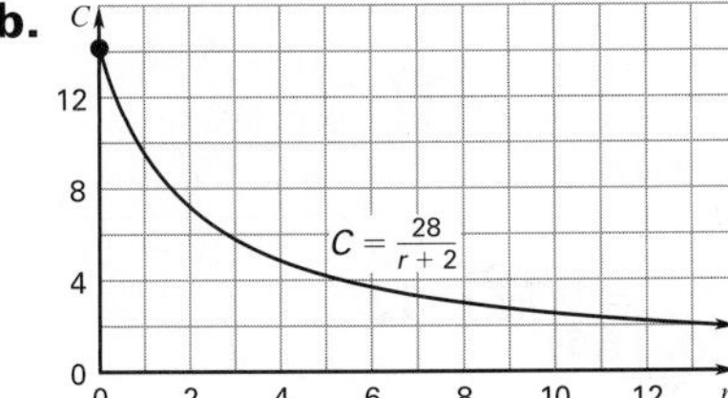

12 additional rentals

31. a. $n = \frac{450}{4 + p}$

b. 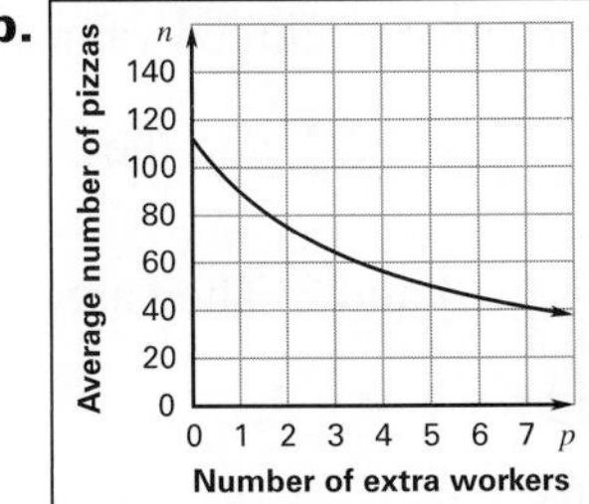

c. 75 pizzas

3.6 Exercise Set B (pp. 155–156)

1. 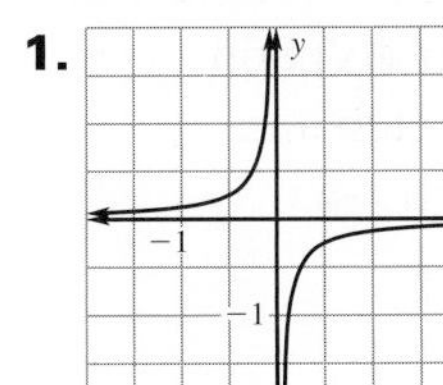 ; domain: all reals except 0; range: all reals except 0; vertical shrink and reflection in x-axis

3. 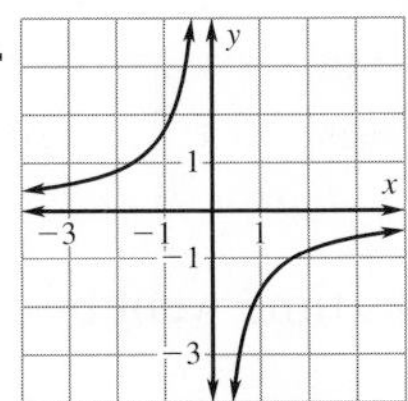 ; domain: all reals except 0; range: all reals except 0; vertical stretch and reflection in x-axis

5. 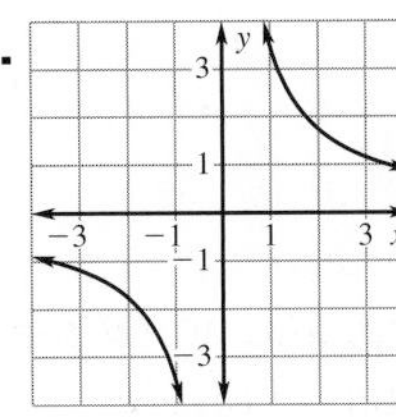 ; domain: all reals except 0; range: all reals except 0; vertical stretch

7. 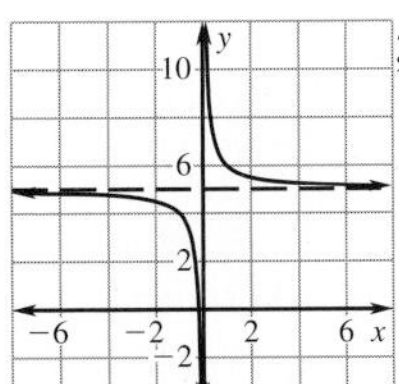 ; domain: all reals except 0; range: all reals except 5; vertical translation 5 units up

9. 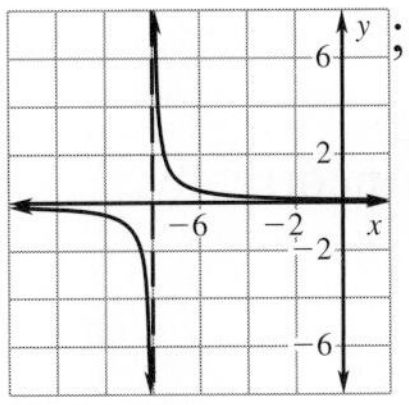 ; domain: all reals except -8; range: all reals except 0; horizontal translation 8 units to the left

11. $x = -13, y = -10$ **13.** $x = -1, y = -3$

15. 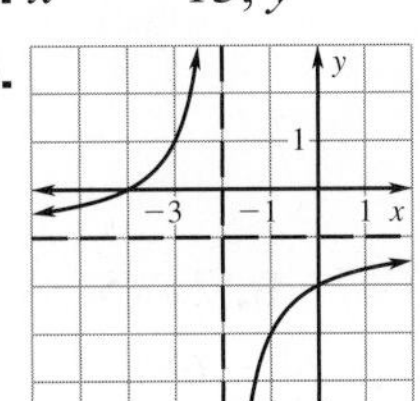

17. 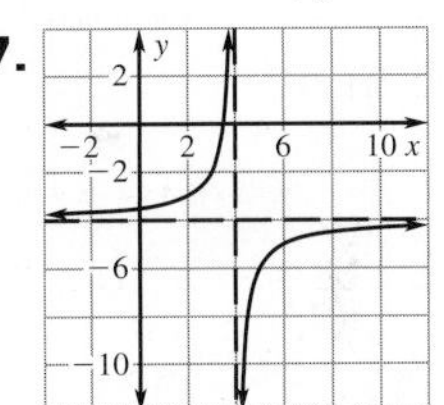

19. 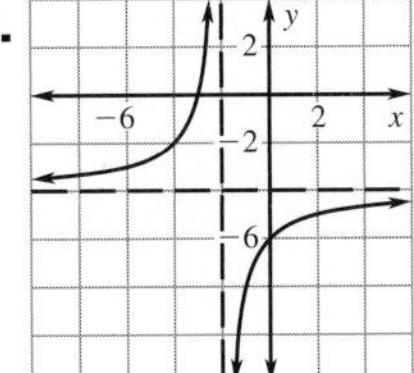

21. $y = \frac{-14}{x + 2} + 5$ **23.** $y = \frac{-7}{x + 4} - 4$

25. a. $h = \frac{80}{5 + b_2}$

Domain: $b_2 > 0$

Range: $0 < h < 16$

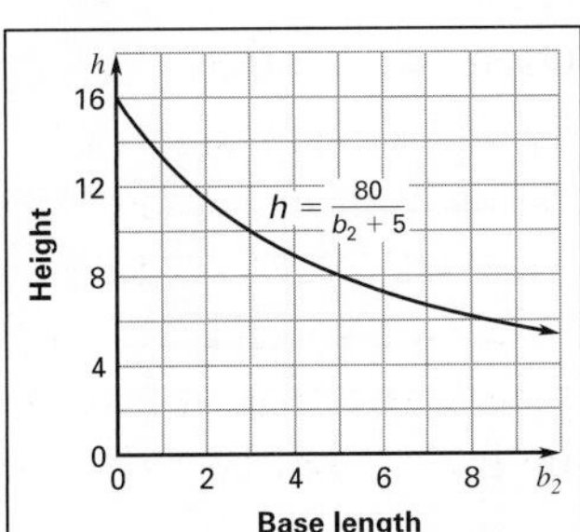

b. about 8.3

27. $n = \dfrac{225}{6 + p}$

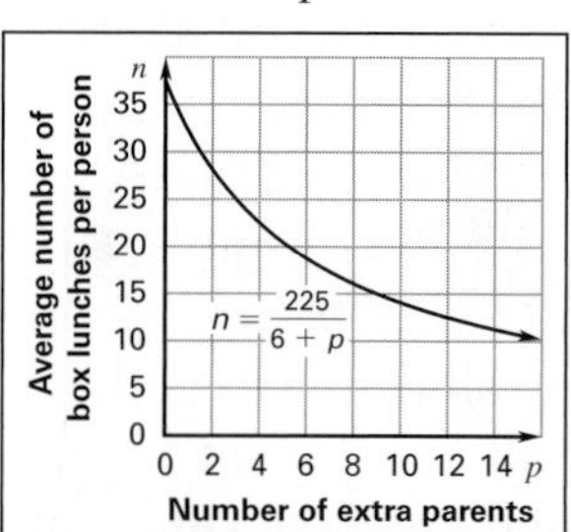

; 9 people

3.7 Exercise Set A (p. 159)

1. $3x^2 - 4x + 2$ **3.** $-11x^3 + 9x - 3$ **5.** $5x - 3$

7. $6x - 2$ **9.** $9x - 4 - \dfrac{2}{x + 1}$

11. The remainder was written incorrectly. The answer is $5 + \dfrac{-6}{x + 2}$.

15. a. $C = \dfrac{40t + 4.5}{t}$

b. $y = \dfrac{4.5}{t} + 40$

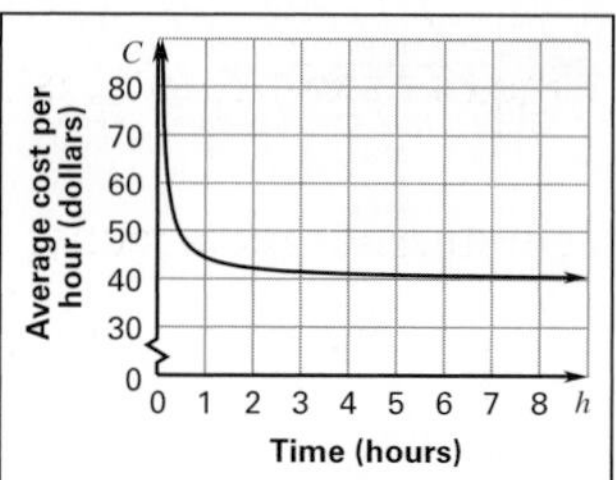

3.7 Exercise Set B (p. 160)

1. $3x^2 - 4x + 2$ **3.** $7x + 16 + \dfrac{27}{x - 2}$

5. $3x + 8 + \dfrac{54}{x - 4}$ **7.** $-x - 10 + \dfrac{17}{-x + 2}$

9. $-x + 4 - \dfrac{9}{x + 4}$

11. $y = \dfrac{12}{x + 7} - 1$

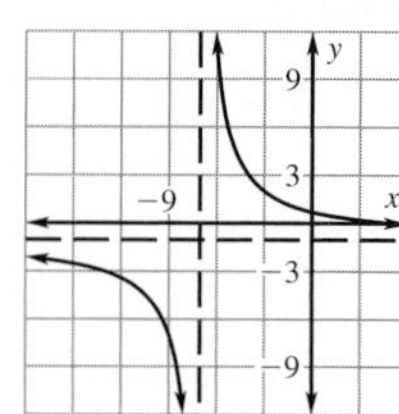

13. $y = \dfrac{28}{x + 4} - 5$

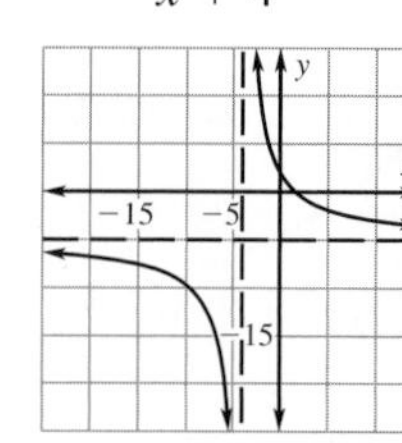

15. 10 **17.** -7

19. a. $R = \dfrac{1}{6} + \dfrac{1049}{546t + 12{,}552}$

b.

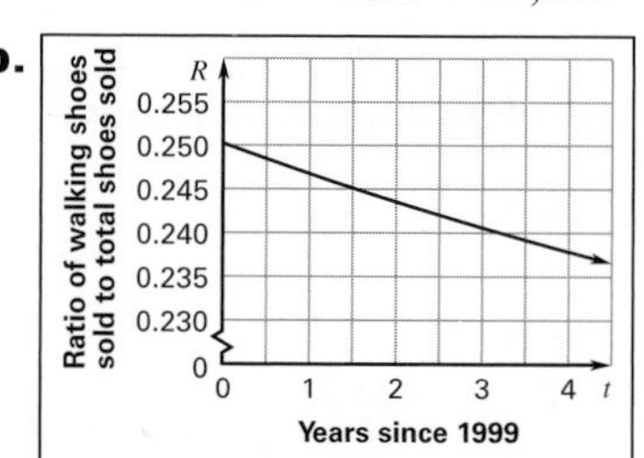

3.8 Exercise Set A (p. 163)

1. 0 **3.** -10 **5.** -3 **7.** 1 **9.** $-5, 5$ **11.** 6; 4

13. $\dfrac{1}{x - 11}$; $-11, 11$

15. in simplest form; $-3, -8$ **17.** $\dfrac{3x + 5}{x(x + 5)}$

19. a. $\dfrac{2(4x + 3) + 2(4x - 2)}{(4x + 3)(4x - 2)}$ **b.** $\dfrac{8x + 1}{(4x + 3)(2x - 1)}$

3.8 Exercise Set B (p. 164)

1. $-4, \dfrac{1}{3}$ **3.** 7 **5.** $\dfrac{-2x^2}{3x - 5}$; $0, \dfrac{5}{3}$ **7.** $\dfrac{3x^3}{3x + 4}$; $-\dfrac{4}{3}, 0$

9. $\dfrac{4x}{2x + 1}$; $-\dfrac{1}{2}, 3$ **11.** $\dfrac{1}{x(x - 4)}$; 0, 4

13. No; they do not have the same excluded values; the excluded values for $\dfrac{x^2 + 2x}{x^2 - 4}$ are ± 2, and the excluded values for $\dfrac{x^2}{x^2 - 2x}$ are 0 and 2. They are not equivalent for $x = 0$ and for $x = -2$.

15. $3x^2 + 8x - 3$, $5x^2 + 16x + 3$; Answers will vary.

17. a. $\dfrac{6(t + 4)}{0.01t^2 - 0.5t + 18}$ **b.** about 400,000

c.

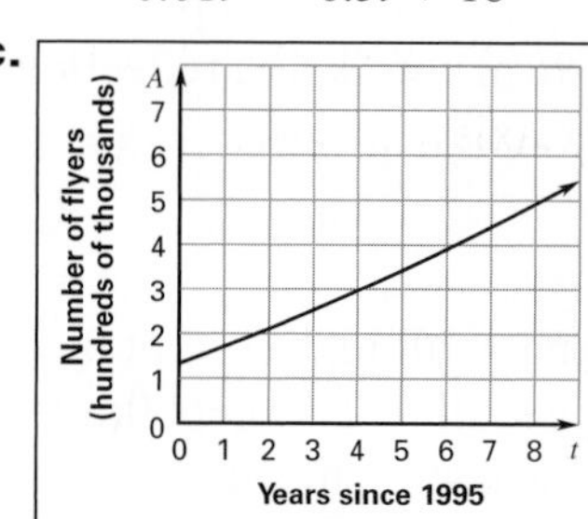

The number of flyers increased as time went by.

SELECTED ANSWERS

3.9 Exercise Set A (p. 167)

1. $\frac{1}{6x^3}$ **3.** $\frac{14}{5}$ **5.** $\frac{1}{2(x+5)}$ **7.** $\frac{x(x+3)}{3(2x-1)}$

9. $3(x+5)$ **11.** $\frac{x^6}{4}$ **13.** $\frac{1}{9}$ **15.** $\frac{1}{4}$ **17.** $\frac{2}{(x+3)^2}$

19. $\frac{125}{150-t}$; about \$8.74 per unit

3.9 Exercise Set B (p. 168)

1. x **3.** $-\frac{1}{2}$ **5.** $\frac{x^5}{9}$ **7.** $\frac{2(x+3)(x+6)}{x^2+6}$ **9.** -1

11. $\frac{x^2(x^2-5)(x-7)}{4(x^2-7)}$ **13.** $\frac{3}{x}$ **15.** $(x+6)(x-6)$

17. $A = \frac{500(t+20)}{1-0.05t}$; about \$13,529

3.10 Exercise Set A (p. 173)

1. $\frac{x+8}{x+5}$ **3.** $\frac{3(2x+1)}{x-9}$ **5.** $\frac{10x-7}{x^2-9}$ **7.** $15x^3$

9. $(x-4)(x+6)$ **11.** $x(x-5)(x+2)$

13. $\frac{85}{14x}$ **15.** $\frac{x(5x+31)}{(x-5)(x+2)}$ **17.** $\frac{25-3x}{x(x-7)}$

19. $\frac{2x^2+5x+1}{(x-1)(x+1)}$ **21.** $\frac{-5}{(x+1)(x+4)(x-4)}$

23. a. $t = \frac{50}{r} + \frac{50}{r+3}$ **b.** 6.1 h **c.** about 1.4 h

3.10 Exercise Set B (p. 174)

1. $\frac{3(x-2)}{x+3}$ **3.** $\frac{-3x+2}{2x-5}$ **5.** $\frac{-2x^2-22x-9}{(x+10)(x-1)}$

7. $\frac{9x^3-16x^2+3x-2}{3x^2(x-2)}$ **9.** $\frac{-15x^2+x-30}{8x(x+6)}$

11. $\frac{5x-7}{(x-3)^2(x+5)}$ **13.** $\frac{-x^2+19x+50}{(x+2)(x+1)}$

15. $\frac{21x^2+79x-2}{(x+1)(x+4)(x+6)}$ **17.** $\frac{11c^2-34c-105}{(3c+4)^2}$

19. a. $y = \frac{1}{t}$ **b.** no; It will take you and your friend over an hour to deliver all of the advertisements.

3.11 Exercise Set A (p. 178)

1. $-9, 9$ **3.** -7 **5.** -5 **7.** -1 **9.** 1

11. $2(x-1)$ **13.** 0 **15.** $\frac{7}{4}$

17. a.

Person	Fraction of room papered each hour	Time (hours)	Fraction of room papered
Assistant	$\frac{1}{x}$	3	$\frac{3}{x}$
Expert	$\frac{3}{2x}$	3	$\frac{9}{2x}$

b. *Sample answer:* The fractions of the job must add up to 1 whole job. **c.** $\frac{3}{x} + \frac{9}{2x} = 1$; 7.5 h

3.11 Exercise Set B (p. 179)

1. $\frac{1}{4}$ **3.** 6 **5.** $\frac{1}{2}$ **7.** $-2, 2$ **9.** $-\frac{19}{3}$

11. $-2, -1$ **13.** no solution **15.** 5 **17.** 4 pt

3.12 Exercise Set A (p. 183)

1. -3 **3.** $-\frac{1}{3}$

5. The average rate of change of f from x_1 to x_2 is greater.

7. The student wrote the denominator incorrectly; the correct answer is $\frac{f(0)-f(-1)}{0-(-1)} = \frac{0-1}{1} = -1$.

9. 0 **11.** 4 **13.** $-2.04, 1.88$

15. a. $f(t) = -16t^2 + 64t + 6$; $g(t) = -16t^2 + 48t + 20$

b.

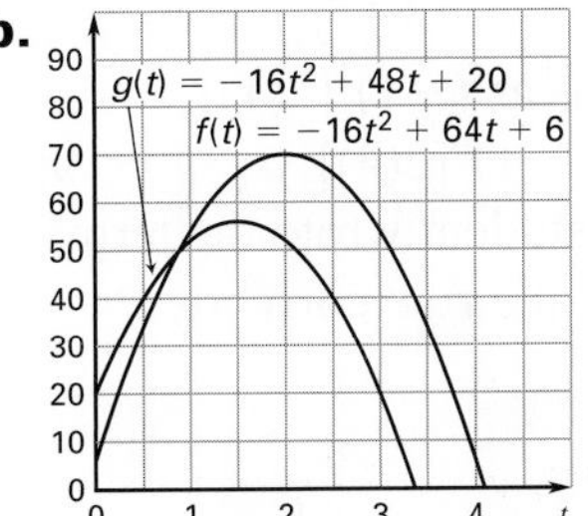

c. $\frac{7}{8}$; After $\frac{7}{8}$ second, the objects are at the same height, 49.75 feet.

3.12 Exercise Set B (p. 184)

1. $-\frac{2}{3}$ **3.** -0.2

5. The average rate of change of g from x_1 to x_2 is greater. **7. a–b.** Answers will vary.

9. $-2, 0, \frac{1}{2}$ **11.** no solution **13.** negative

15. a.

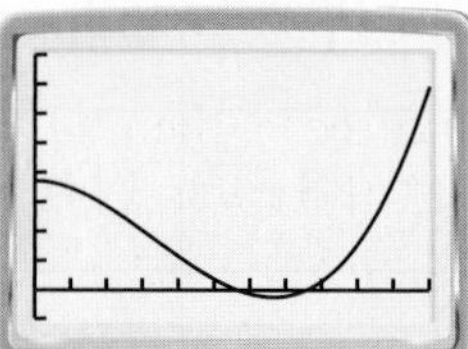

b. 19.6; This shows that the profit increased rapidly from 2004–2007. **c.** 2005–2007; 1999–2001

3.13 Exercise Set A (p. 187)

1. 2, 4, 6, 8, 10, 12 **3.** 2, 1, 0, $-1, -2, -3$

5. 4, 9, 16, 25, 36, 49 **7.** $-2, 4, -8, 16, -32, 64$

9. $\frac{1}{4}, \frac{2}{7}, \frac{3}{10}, \frac{4}{13}, \frac{5}{16}, \frac{6}{19}$

11. You can write the terms as $5 - 2(1)$, $5 - 2(2)$, $5 - 2(3)$, $5 - 2(4)$; $a_5 = -5$; $a_n = 5 - 2n$

13. You can write the terms as $2(1^2) - 1$, $2(2^2) - 1$, $2(3^2) - 1$, $2(4^2) - 1$; $a_5 = 49$; $a_n = 2n^2 - 1$

15. You can write the terms as $-\frac{1^2}{2}, -\frac{2^2}{2}, -\frac{3^2}{2}, -\frac{4^2}{2}$; $a_5 = -\frac{25}{2}$; $a_n = -\frac{n^2}{2}$

3.13 Exercise Set B (p. 188)

1. $-5, -10, -15, -20, -25, -30$

3. 7, 4, $-1, -8, -17, -28$

5. 0, 4, 18, 48, 100, 180 **7.** 1010 **9.** $-\frac{1}{133}$

11. You can write the terms as $(-1)^1[2(1)]$, $(-1)^2[2(2)]$, $(-1)^3[2(3)]$, $(-1)^4[2(4)]$; $a_5 = -10$; $a_n = (-1)^n(2n)$ **13.** The student wrote the terms correctly, but did not write the rule correctly; $a_n = (-1)^{n+1}(n^2)$.

15.

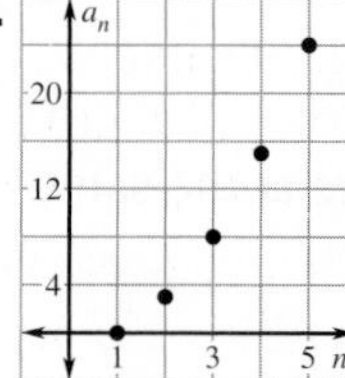

17. True **19.** False; A sequence is a function so an input is paired with exactly one output.

UNIT 4

4.1 Exercise Set A (p. 195)

1. $\sqrt{5}$ **3.** $5\sqrt{2}$ **5.** $\sqrt{37}$ **7.** $4\sqrt{2}$ **9.** $2\sqrt{13}$ **11.** 2

13. $-3, 5$ **15.** $-7, 3$ **17.** $\left(-\frac{17}{2}, 8\right)$ **19.** $\left(\frac{11}{2}, -\frac{3}{2}\right)$

21. $\left(-\frac{3}{2}, 2\right)$ **23.** 15 mi **25.** 8.5 books

4.1 Exercise Set B (p. 196)

1. 13 **3.** $\sqrt{458}$ **5.** $\sqrt{661}$ **7.** $\sqrt{122}$ **9.** $\frac{\sqrt{37}}{3}$

11. 2, 6 **13.** $-4, 22$ **15.** $-4, 24$ **17.** $\left(\frac{5}{2}, 8\right)$

19. (3.75, 9.25) **21.** $(-5.5, 4)$ **23.** $(-2, 8)$

25. a. about 12 mi **b.** (4, 7)

c. about 3 mi; (5.5, 9.5); Find the midpoint between (7, 12) and (4, 7) and then find the distance between that point and (7, 12).

4.2 Exercise Set A (pp. 199–200)

1. **3.** **5.**

7. add 111 to the previous number; 557

9. add 2 to the numerator and 1 to the denominator of the previous number; $\frac{9}{7}$

11. subtract 3 from the previous number; -9

13. double the previous number and then add 1; 47

15. add $\frac{1}{3}$ to the previous number; $-\frac{2}{3}, -\frac{1}{3}, 0$

17. 20 **19.** *Sample answer:* $|5| - |7| = -2$

21. *Sample answer:* $\sqrt{\frac{1}{4}} = \frac{1}{2}, \frac{1}{2} > \frac{1}{4}$

23. $y = 2x - 7$ **25.** $y = \frac{1}{x}$

27. 512 billion bacteria

4.2 Exercise Set B (pp. 201–202)

1. **3.**

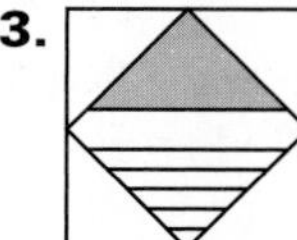

5. add 2 to the absolute value of the previous number and use the opposite sign; 15

7. add 1.1 to the absolute value of the previous number and use the opposite sign; 9.5

9. subtract 1 from both the numerator and the denominator of the previous number; $\frac{6}{7}$

11. add 2^n to the previous (nth) number; 61

13. The rate of decrease is increasing by $5n$; -10

15. Multiply the first number by 10 to get the second number, take half the second number to get the third number, and repeat this pattern; 75

17. *Sample answer:* double the previous number; 8, 16, 32; add n to the previous (nth) number; 7, 11, 16 **19.** *Sample answer:* the nth number is 2^n; 16, 32, 64; add $n + 1$ to the previous number; 13, 19, 26

21. equal to **23.** $1^2 + 3^2 = 10$; 10 is not odd.

25. *Sample answer:* $y = (x + 1)^2$

4.3 Exercise Set A (pp. 207–208)

1. If it is 6 P.M., then it is time for dinner.

3. If an angle is obtuse, then it measures more than 90° and less than 180°.

5. converse: If you go to the hockey game, then you like hockey; **inverse:** If you do not like hockey, then you do not go to the hockey game; **contrapositive:** If you do not go to the hockey game, then you do not like hockey.

7. true **9.** true

11. converse: If an angle is acute, then it measures 30°. **13. converse:** If two circles have the same circumference, then they have the same diameter; **biconditional:** Two circles have the same circumference if and only if they have the same diameter.

15. conditional statement: If two lines are perpendicular, then they intersect to form right angles; **converse:** If two lines intersect to form right angles, then the two lines are perpendicular.

17. yes **19.** yes **21.** A saxophone that has a frequency of 69 cycles per second to 415 cycles per second is called an E-flat baritone saxophone.

23. A saxophone that has a frequency of 138 cycles per second to 830 cycles per second is called an E-flat alto saxophone. **25.** nothing; It could be any of the three saxophones.

4.3 Exercise Set B (pp. 209–210)

1. If a car has leaking antifreeze, then it has a problem. **3.** If a dog is old, then you cannot teach it new tricks. **5.** Learn from your mistakes.

7. Let sleeping dogs lie.

9. if-then: If a circle has a radius of r, then it has a circumference of $2\pi r$. true; **converse:** If a circle has a circumference of $2\pi r$, then it has a radius of r. true; **inverse:** If a circle does not have a radius of r, then it does not have a circumference of $2\pi r$. true; **contrapositive:** If a circle does not have a circumference of $2\pi r$, then it does not have a radius of r. true **11.** false; def. of opp. rays is not satisfied because F does not lie between C and E.

13. true; $\angle CFD$ is a straight angle, so its measure is 180°. **15.** false; $\angle CFE$ and $\angle DFE$ are supplementary, so the sum of their measures is 180° and because they are $\cong$, the measure of each is 90°.

17. A statement is a conditional statement if and only if it is a logical statement that has two parts, a hypothesis and a conclusion.

19. A situation is a counterexample if and only if it represents a specific case for which a given conjecture is false.

21. valid **23.** valid

25. If $-x > -8$, then $x < 8$; True. **27.** no

29. not valid; does not specify that it must form over Atlantic Ocean. **31.** not valid; does not specify that the cyclone must form in the tropics.

4.4 Exercise Set A (pp. 213–214)

1. Law of Detachment **3.** Law of Detachment

5. invalid **7.** deductive reasoning; Deductive reasoning is based on logic and order. If Walt is taller than Peter and Peter is taller than Natalie, then Walt is taller than Natalie. **9.** inductive reasoning; Inductive reasoning depends on previous examples and patterns to form a conjecture. Dana came to her conclusion based on previous examples.

11. not valid; It does not say that Jeff is not allowed to play video games on Saturday afternoon. It says that he does not play video games on Saturday afternoon.

13. not valid; the hypothesis is not necessarily true.

15. false; The mall is open. Therefore Jodi and Dan went shopping, and therefore Dan bought a pretzel. You cannot conclude that Dan also bought a pizza.

17. true; The mall is open. Therefore Jodi and Dan went shopping, and therefore Jodi bought a pizza.

19. D, B, A, E, C; The robot extinguishes the fire.

4.4 Exercise Set B (pp. 215–216)

1. Dr. Klein will operate with precision today; detachment **3.** If a player receives two technical fouls in one game, then the player has to sit out the following game; syllogism **5.** There is significant danger to the firefighters; detachment **7.** If the company contributes $20,000 to the charity, then it will go into a lower tax bracket; syllogism

9. The result is the perfect square; detachment

11. The ball will float in water; detachment

13. inductive; the conclusion is a conjecture based on your specific results from the first three weeks.

15. inductive; you are making a conjecture based on your normal spending habits.

17. *Sample answer:* The area of one circle is one-fourth the area of another circle with a radius that is twice as long.

19. Either a catch platform must be installed or each worker must wear a safety belt attached to an approved lifeline, because the eave is over 16 feet high and the pitch is greater than 4 to 12.

4.5 Exercise Set A (pp. 219–220)

1. 1. Given **2.** Substitution Property of Equality **3.** $\overline{HI} \cong \overline{IJ}$ **4.** Given **5.** Transitive Property of Congruence

3. 1. Given **2.** Reflexive Property of Equality **3.** Addition Property of Equality **4.** Segment Addition Postulate **5.** Segment Addition Postulate **6.** Substitution Property of Equality

5. $x = 6$; Because the angles are congruent, the measures of the angles are congruent by the definition of congruent angles. Set the measures of the angles equal to each other to find x. **7.** $x = 5$; By the transitive property, $\angle ABD \cong \angle EBC$. Because the angles are congruent, the measures of the angles are congruent by the definition of congruent angles. Set the measures of the angles equal to each other to find x.

9. $\overline{UV} \cong \overline{ZY}, \overline{UW} \cong \overline{ZX}$ (Given)
$UV = ZY, UW = ZX$ (Def. of $\cong$)
$VW = UW - UV$ (Segment Addition Postulate)
$YX = ZX - ZY$ (Segment Addition Postulate)
$YX = UW - UV$ (Substitution Property of Equality)
$VW = YX$ (Transitive Property of Equality)
$\overline{VW} \cong \overline{YX}$ (Def. of $\cong$)

4.5 Exercise Set B (pp. 221–222)

1. Given; $m\angle CBD + m\angle DBE$; Substitution Property of Equality; Subtraction Property of Equality; $m\angle DBE$; $\angle CBD \cong \angle DBE$; Transitive Property of Equality **3.** $\angle 5 \cong \angle 7$

5. Reflexive Property of Congruence

7. Transitive Property of Congruence

9. $\overline{RS} \cong \overline{ST}$ and $\overline{ST} \cong \overline{TU}$ by the definition of midpoint. Then $\overline{RS} \cong \overline{TU}$ by the Transitive Property of Congruence, so $RS = TU$. Then $5x + 7 = 7x - 3$ by the Substitution Property of Equality, $10 = 2x$ by the Subtraction Property of Equality, and $5 = x$ by the Division Property of Equality.

11.
1. $\overline{AE} \cong \overline{CE}$, $\overline{AB}$ and $\overline{CD}$ bisect each other. (Given)
2. E is the midpoint of $\overline{AB}$ and of $\overline{CD}$. (Definition of segment bisector)
3. $\overline{EB} \cong \overline{AE}, \overline{CE} \cong \overline{ED}$ (Definition of midpoint)
4. $\overline{AE} \cong \overline{ED}$ (Transitive Property of Congruence)
5. $\overline{EB} \cong \overline{ED}$ (Transitive Property of Congruence)

4.6 Exercise Set A (pp. 225–226)

1. false **3.** false

5. **7.**

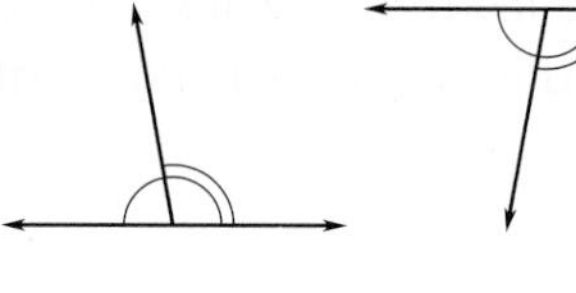

9. 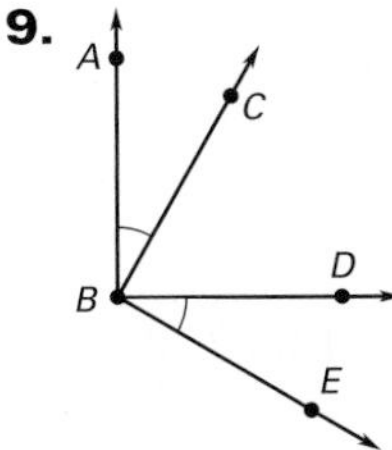

11. $x = 5, y = 26$; 74°, 106°, 74°, 106°

13. $x = 7, y = 9$; 36°, 144°, 36°, 144°

15. It was assumed that $\angle 2$ and $\angle 3$, and $\angle 1$ and $\angle 4$ are linear pairs, but they are not; $\angle 2$ and $\angle 4$, and $\angle 1$ and $\angle 3$ are not vertical angles and are not congruent. **17. 1.** Given **2.** Definition of complementary angles **3.** Given **4.** Definition of congruent angles **5.** Substitution Property of Equality **6.** Substitution Property of Equality **7.** Definition of complementary angles

19. $<$ **21.** $=$

4.6 Exercise Set B (pp. 227–228)

1. The Linear Pair Post. and Vertical Angles Congruence Thm. can be used to deduce that $\angle 5$, $\angle 6$, and $\angle 7$ are right angles. So, $\angle 5$, $\angle 6$, $\angle 7$, and $\angle 8$ are all congruent by the Right Angles Congruence Thm. $\angle 1 \cong \angle 3$ and $\angle 4 \cong \angle 2$ by the Congruent Complements Thm.

3. 37°, 90°, 53°, 37° **5.** 51°, 39°, 90°, 51°

7. $x = 25, y = 14$ **9.** $x = 50, y = 53, z = 127$

11. 118° **13.** 84° **15.** 28° **17.** yes **19.** no

21. yes **23. 1.** Given; **2.** $m\angle STU$; **2.** Angle Addition Post.; **3.** 40° + 50°; **4.** 90°; **5.** Def. of rt. Angle; **6.** $\angle S \cong \angle STU$

4.7 Exercise Set A (pp. 231–232)

1. $r \perp s$; Theorem 4.7 **3.** $\angle 1$ and $\angle 2$ are complementary; Theorem 4.9 **5.** 25 **7.** 105 **9.** 50

11. 30° **13.** 30° **15.** 60° **17.** yes **19.** 2.8

21. 4.5 **23.** 3.6 **25. a.** 90° **b.** 30° **c.** 500 ft **d.** 224 ft

4.7 Exercise Set B (pp. 233–234)

1. 58° **3.** 90° **5.** 52° **7.** 25° **9.** 65° **11.** no

13. 15 **15.** 21 **17.** 12 **19.** 4.9 **21.** 6

23. a. 1.5 miles **b.** 2.8 miles **c.** hiking trail; even though it appears it would be shorter for the hikers to walk to the highway, they can only cross the river at a bridge. So, walking to the trail is the shortest distance.

4.8 Exercise Set A (pp. 238–239)

1. true; SSS **3.** true; SSS **5.** not congruent

7. congruent **9.** not congruent

11. Not stable; there are many possible shapes for a four-sided figure with the given side lengths.

13. Yes; the corresponding sides are congruent. **15. 1.** Given; **2.** Given; **3.** Reflexive Property of Congruence; **4.** SSS Congruence Postulate

17. The second picture frame is stable because the brace and the sides form triangles of fixed side lengths which cannot change shape by the SSS Congruence Postulate.

4.8 Exercise Set B (pp. 240–241)

1. true; SSS **3.** true; SSS **5.** congruent

7. not congruent **9.** Not stable; there are many possible shapes for a four-sided figure with the given side lengths.

11. 1. $\overline{HI} \cong \overline{JK}$; **2.** $\overline{IJ} \cong \overline{KH}$; **3.** $\overline{HJ} \cong \overline{HJ}$; **4.** $\triangle HIJ \cong \triangle JKH$

13. $x = 3$; Setting $2x + 3 = 7x - 12$ and $-x + 14 = 6x - 7$ yields $x = 3$ in both equations.

4.9 Exercise Set A (pp. 244–245)

1. $\angle ABC$ **3.** $\angle ABD$ **5.** $\angle DAB$ **7.** not enough

9. not enough **11.** Yes, HL Congruence Theorem

13. The SAS Congruence Postulate does not apply because the congruent angles are not the included angles of the congruent sides. **15.** $\angle J \cong \angle D$

17. 1. Given; **2.** $\overline{AB} \cong \overline{BE}$; **3.** Given; **4.** $\overline{CB} \cong \overline{BD}$; **5.** Vertical Angles Theorem; **6.** SAS Congruence Postulate

4.9 Exercise Set B (pp. 246–247)

1. not enough **3.** not enough

5. $\angle BCA$; $\angle EDF$ **7.** $\overline{AC}$; $\overline{FD}$ **9. 3.** Definition of perpendicular lines; **4.** $\triangle PRS$ and $\triangle QSR$ are right triangles; **5.** Reflexive Property of Congruence; **6.** HL Congruence Theorem

SELECTED ANSWERS

11. $\triangle AEC \cong \triangle ABD$; From the figure you know that $\overline{AC} \cong \overline{AD}$ and $\overline{CE} \cong \overline{DB}$. $\angle CDE$ is a straight angle so its measure is 180°. To find $m\angle ADB$, add the measures of $\angle ADC$ and $\angle BDE$ then subtract from 180° to get 70°. So, $\angle ADB \cong \angle ACE$. By the SAS Congruence Postulate, $\triangle AEC \cong \triangle ABD$.

4.10 Exercise Set A (pp. 251–252)

1. $\overline{DF} \cong \overline{MO}$ **3.** $\angle D \cong \angle M$ **5.** $\angle B \cong \angle Y$

7. no **9.** Yes, AAS Congruence Theorem

11. Yes, AAS Congruence Theorem

13. No; three pairs of congruent angles is insufficient to prove triangle congruence.

15. Two pairs of corresponding sides $(\overline{BF} \cong \overline{BD}, \overline{EF} \cong \overline{ED})$ and the corresponding included angles $(\angle BFE \cong \angle BDE)$ are congruent.

17. Two pairs of corresponding angles $(\angle ABF \cong \angle CBD, \angle BAF \cong \angle BCD)$ and the corresponding non-included sides $(\overline{AF} \cong \overline{CD})$ are congruent.

4.10 Exercise Set B (pp. 253–254)

1. $\overline{FE} \cong \overline{TR}$ or $\overline{DE} \cong \overline{QR}$ **3.** $\overline{DF} \cong \overline{QT}$

5. Yes; $\angle KNL \cong \angle MLN$ by Alternate Interior Angles Theorem, $\overline{LN} \cong \overline{LN}$ by Reflexive Property of Congruence, $\triangle KLN \cong \triangle MNL$ by ASA Congruence Postulate

7. No, $\angle M$ and $\angle Y$ are not corresponding angles.

9. Yes, AAS Congruence Theorem

11. Two pairs of corresponding sides $(\overline{AF} \cong \overline{BF}, \overline{FD} \cong \overline{FC})$ and the corresponding included angle ($\angle AFD \cong \angle BFC$, by Vertical Angles Theorem) are congruent.

13. $\angle ACD \cong \angle ABD$ is given. $\angle BDC \cong \angle ABD$ by Alternate Interior Angles Theorem. $\overline{DC} \cong \overline{DC}$ by Reflexive Property of Congruence. $\overline{AC} \cong \overline{BD}$ by the Segment Addition Postulate and substitution. $\triangle ACD \cong \triangle BDC$ by the SAS Congruence Theorem.

15. **1.** Given; **2.** Given; **3.** Reflexive Property of Congruence; **4.** AAS Congruence Theorem

17.

Statements	Reasons
1. $\overline{ML} \cong \overline{LK}$, $\angle MLJ \cong \angle KLJ$	1. Given
2. $\angle MLJ$ and $\angle MLN$ form a linear pair. $\angle KLJ$ and $\angle KLN$ form a linear pair.	2. Def. of Linear Pair
3. $\angle MLN \cong \angle KLN$	3. Congruent Complements Thm.
4. $\overline{LN} \cong \overline{LN}$	4. Reflexive Prop. of $\cong$
5. $\triangle MLN \cong \triangle KLN$	5. SAS Congruence Postulate

UNIT 5

5.1 Exercise Set A (pp. 260–261)

1. 14 **3.** 17 **5.** $\overline{JK}$ **7.** $\overline{KS}, \overline{RT}$ **9.** $\overline{LT}, \overline{RS}$

11. *Sample answer:* (0, 0), (7, 0), (7, 4), (0, 4)

13. (0, 0), (12, 0), (0, 12) **15.** 14 **17.** 54 units

19. You do not know that $\overline{PQ}$ and $\overline{NO}$ are parallel.

21. $S\left(\frac{h}{2}, \frac{k}{2}\right)$, $T\left(\frac{3h}{2}, \frac{k}{2}\right)$; $PT = SR = \sqrt{\frac{9h^2 + k^2}{2}}$

23. 72 in.; The crossbar is the midsegment of the legs.

5.1 Exercise Set B (pp. 262–263)

1. $\overline{WY}$ **3.** 4 **5.** 32

7. $A(-h, 4k)$, $C(-2h, 4k)$, $D(-h, 0)$

9. $\overline{BD}$ does not connect the midpoints of two sides of $\triangle ACE$.

11. By the definition of an angle bisector, $\angle ABD \cong \angle CBD$. Use the Distance Formula to show $AB = \sqrt{\frac{c^2}{4} + b^2}$ and $BC = \sqrt{\frac{c^2}{4} + b^2}$. Because $\overline{BD} \cong \overline{BD}$, you can apply the SAS Congruence Postulate to conclude that $\triangle ABD \cong \triangle CBD$.

13. 24; DE is one half the length of $\overline{FG}$. So, $FG = 12$. FG is one half the length of AC. So, $AC = 24$.

5.2 Exercise Set A (pp. 266–267)

1. 4 **3.** 35 **5.** no **7.** 44 **9.** 36 **11.** 31 **13.** 25

15. 24 **17.** 15

19. You do not know that $ML = NL$. So, you cannot conclude that $\overleftrightarrow{JK}$ passes through point L.

21. $AC = BC = 1$ in.

23. Because a point on the ⊥ bisector is equidistant to the endpoints, $\overline{AC} \cong \overline{BC}$. By the Reflexive Property of ≅, $\overline{CD} \cong \overline{CD}$. By the definition of bisector, $\overline{AD} \cong \overline{BD}$. By the SSS Congruence Postulate, $\triangle ACD \cong \triangle BCD$.

25. The post is the ⊥ bisector of the segment between the ends of the wires.

5.2 Exercise Set B (pp. 268–269)

1. 17 **3.** 51 **5.** 40 **7.** 54 **9.** 76 **11.** $2\frac{1}{8}$ in.

13. 10 **15.** always **17.** Because N is on the perpendicular bisector of $\overline{MO}$, you know $\overline{MN} \cong \overline{NO}$ by the Perpendicular Bisector Theorem. $\overline{NR} \cong \overline{NR}$ by the Reflexive Property of Congruence. Because R is on the perpendicular bisector of $\overline{MO}$, you know that $\overline{MR} \cong \overline{RO}$. So, by SSS Congruence Postulate, $\triangle NMR \cong \triangle NOR$.

19. Perpendicular Bisector Theorem; $\overline{AC} \perp \overline{DB}$ and $\overline{AB} \cong \overline{CB}$, so $\overline{DB}$ is the perpendicular bisector of $\overline{AC}$. Because D is on the perpendicular bisector of $\overline{AC}$, it is equidistant from A and C. Therefore, $AD = CD$ and $\overline{AD} \cong \overline{CD}$.

5.3 Exercise Set A (pp. 274–275)

1. 19 **3.** 86° **5.** No; you need to know that the ≅ segments are ⊥ to the sides of the angles.

7. 7 **9.** 8 **11.** No; you need to know that the congruent segments are ⊥ to the rays.

13. HN is not the perpendicular distance from N to $\overline{JG}$. The same is true about KN; the distance from N to each side of the triangle is the same.

15. 7 **17.** 8 **19.** 35 ft

5.3 Exercise Set B (pp. 276–277)

1. 6 **3.** 7.5 **5.** Yes; Converse of the Angle Bisector Theorem **7.** yes **9.** no **11.** 9 **13.** 4

15. Use the Concurrency of Angle Bisectors of a Triangle Theorem to find the incenter of $\triangle ABC$. Then measure the distance from the incenter to B.

5.4 Exercise Set A (pp. 280–281)

1. 8 **3.** 5 **5.** 12 **7. a.** $M(2, 4)$; $P(2, 1)$

b. $N(0, 1)$; $KP = 4$ and $KN = 6$ therefore $KP = \frac{2}{3}KN$.

9. $(5, -2)$ **11.** no; no; no **13.** 12; 78°

15. $\frac{1}{3}$ **17.** $\frac{2}{3}$ **19.** 5 **21.** sometimes **23.** always

25. 36 in.; By Theorem 5.8, the distance from the vertex to the centroid is $\frac{2}{3}$ times the length of the median $(\overline{AB})$.

5.4 Exercise Set B (pp. 282–283)

1. 10 **3.** 12 **5.** 13 **7.** $\frac{1}{3}$ **9.** 2 **11.** 8 **13.** (5, 2)

15. always **17.** 3 in.^{2}; altitude

5.5 Exercise Set A (pp. 287–288)

1–3. Check student's drawings. Longest side and largest angle are opposite each other, shortest side and smallest angle are opposite each other.

5. $\overline{ST}, \overline{RT}, \overline{RS}$; $\angle R, \angle S, \angle T$

7. $\overline{JK}, \overline{JL}, \overline{KL}$; $\angle L, \angle K, \angle J$

9. $\overline{QR}, \overline{PR}, \overline{PQ}$; $\angle P, \angle Q, \angle R$

11.

13. yes

15. yes **17.** yes **19.** 3 in. $< x <$ 15 in.

21. 9 m $< x <$ 27 m **23.** 2 in. $< x <$ 46 in.

25. $m\angle 1 > m\angle 2$; $m\angle 1 > m\angle 3$ **27.** $2 < x < 6$

29. $m\angle ABC < m\angle BAC$ and $m\angle BAD < m\angle ABD$

31. Think of the 60- and 24-ft distances as two sides of a triangle. Then the unknown distance d is 36 ft $< d <$ 84 ft. This doesn't account for the cases when the ball lands straight forward (d = 36 ft) or straight backward (d = 84 ft).

5.5 Exercise Set B (pp. 289–290)

1. smallest, $\angle A$ and $\angle B$; largest, $\angle C$

3. smallest, $\angle H$; largest, $\angle G$

5. shortest, $\overline{KH}$ and $\overline{KJ}$; longest, $\overline{JH}$ **7.** $x > 4$

9. $12 < x < 21$

11. 61; 52°; 31°; 32; 97°; 48 **13.** yes

15. no; $21 + 13 = 34$ **17.** yes

19. $\overline{DE}, \overline{AE}, \overline{AD}, \overline{AB}, \overline{BD}, \overline{BC}, \overline{CD}$

21. 4 in. $< x <$ 14 in. **23.** 60 in. $< x <$ 108 in.

25. 599 feet **27.** $\overline{RT} \perp \overline{TS}$, so $\triangle RTS$ is a right triangle. The largest angle in a right triangle is the right angle, so $m\angle RTS > m\angle RST$, so $RS > RT$. (If one angle of a triangle is larger than another angle, then the side opposite the larger angle is longer than the side opposite the smaller angle.)

5.6 Exercise Set A (pp. 294–295)

1. >; Hinge Thm. with $m\angle R > m\angle U$

3. <; Hinge Thm. with $m\angle JMK < m\angle LKM$

5. >; Converse of Hinge Thm. with the side opposite $\angle 1$ longer than the side opposite $\angle 2$.

7. >; Converse of Hinge Thm. with the side opposite $\angle 1$ longer than the side opposite $\angle 2$.

9. $x < 34$ **11.** Assume temporarily that the two parallel lines contain two sides of a triangle.

13. Assume temporarily that xy is odd.

15. the second angler; The included $\angle$ for the second angler is 96° and for the first angler is 90°.

17. Temporarily assume that $AB > AC$. Because $\overline{AD}$ is a median of $\triangle ABC$, D is the midpoint of $\overline{BC}$. Then $\overline{BD} \cong \overline{CD}$ by the definition of midpoint. Also, $\overline{AD} \cong \overline{AD}$ by the reflexive property. Then $m\angle ADB > m\angle ADC$ by the converse of the Hinge Theorem. But this contradicts the given statement that $m\angle ADB \cong m\angle ADC$. This contradiction shows that the temporary assumption that $AB > AC$ is false.

5.6 Exercise Set B (pp. 296–297)

1. =; Hinge Thm. with $m\angle O = m\angle M$

3. <; Converse of Hinge Thm. with side opposite $\angle 1$ is shorter than the side opposite $\angle 2$.

5. >; Converse of Hinge Thm. with side opposite $\angle ACT$ is longer than the side opposite $\angle BCT$.

7. never **9.** always **11.** never

13. In order to use the Hinge Theorem, the student must know the measure of the included angles $\angle JMK$ and $\angle MKL$. **15.** $x > 1$

17. Assume temporarily that $BC \not> AC$. Then, it follows that either $BC < AC$ or $BC = AC$. Case 1: If $BC < AC$, then $m\angle A < m\angle B$ by Theorem 5.10. This contradicts the given statement that $m\angle A > m\angle B$. Case 2: If $BC = AC$, then $\triangle ABC$ would be an isosceles triangle with $m\angle A = m\angle B$. This contradicts the given statement that $m\angle A > m\angle B$. Both cases lead to contradictions, so the temporary assumption that $BC \not> AC$ cannot be true. This proves that $BC > AC$.

19. Assume temporarily that $RS > RT$ so that $\triangle RST$ is not isosceles. Then, $m\angle T > m\angle S$, but $\triangle RUS \cong \triangle RUT$ by the ASA Congruence Postulate. So, $\angle S \cong \angle T$, or $m\angle T = m\angle S$. This is a contradiction, so $RS \leq RT$. We get a similar contradiction if we assume $RT > RS$; therefore $RS = RT$, and $\triangle RST$ is isosceles by definition.

5.7 Exercise Set A (pp. 300–301)

1. 720° **3.** 1620° **5.** 3240° **7.** triangle

9. heptagon **11.** 16-gon **13.** 30-gon

15. 50-gon **17.** 56 **19.** 64 **21.** 9 **23.** 40°

25. 114° **27.** 135°; 45° **29.** 172°; 8°

31. 176.4°; 3.6° **33.** 75 **35.** 120

37. $x = 70$; $m\angle M = m\angle S = 70°$, $m\angle N = m\angle R = 160°$, $m\angle O = m\angle Q = 150°$, and $m\angle P = 140°$

5.7 Exercise Set B (pp. 302–303)

1. 3420° **3.** 8640° **5.** 19 **7.** 38 **9.** 51

11. 17 **13.** 16 **15.** 3 **17.** 105°

19. about 128.6°; about 51.4°

21. about 158.8°; about 21.2°

23. about 174.9°; about 5.1° **25.** 24 **27.** 72

29. No; The polygon would have 14.4 sides which is not possible.

31. Yes; The polygon would have 72 sides.

33. $x = 13.5$; $m\angle A = 117°$, $m\angle B = 86°$, $m\angle C = 134°$, $m\angle D = 86°$, $m\angle E = 117°$

35. a. $h(n) = \frac{(n-2) \cdot 180°}{n}$ **b.** 144°; 15

c.

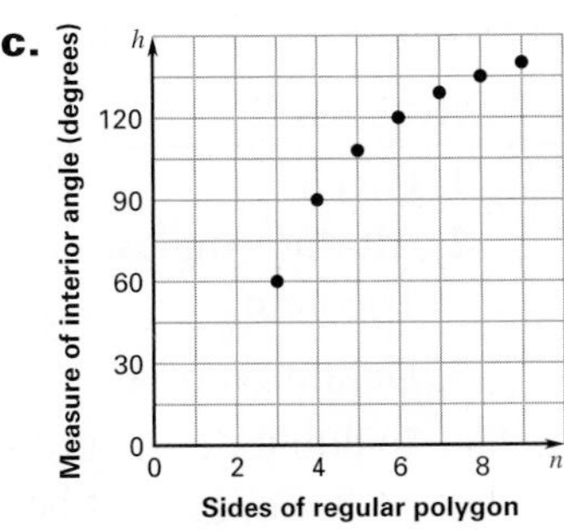

$h(n)$ increases as n increases, but the rate of increase slows down.

5.8 Exercise Set A (pp. 306–307)

1. 116° **3.** 96° **5.** $x = 2$; $y = 17$

7. $f = 78$, $g = 3.5$ **9.** $j = 4.5$, $k = 2$

11. E F 77.5° 102.5° 102.5° 77.5° H G $m\angle E = m\angle G = 77.5°$, $m\angle F = m\angle H = 102.5°$

13. 40° **15.** 80° **17.** 40° **19.** 120° **21.** 5

23. 18° **25.** 30° **27.** 55° **29.** 20

31.

Statements	Reasons
1. $ABCD$ is a ▱.	1. Given
2. Draw $\overline{BD}$.	2. Through any 2 points there exists exactly 1 line.
3. $\overline{AB} \parallel \overline{CD}$, $\overline{BC} \parallel \overline{AD}$	3. Definition of parallelogram
4. $\angle ABD \cong \angle CDB$, $\angle ADB \cong \angle CBD$	4. Alternate Interior Angles Theorem
5. $\overline{BD} \cong \overline{BD}$	5. Reflexive Property of Congruence
6. $\triangle ABD \cong \triangle CDB$	6. ASA Congruence Postulate
7. $\overline{AB} \cong \overline{CD}$, $\overline{BC} \cong \overline{AD}$	7. Corresp. parts of $\cong$ △s are $\cong$.

5.8 Exercise Set B (pp. 308–309)

1. $a = 11$, $b = 12$ **3.** $e = 8$, $t = 3$

5. $j = 14$, $k = 2$ **7.** $p = 4$, $q = 8$ **9.** $t = 9$, $v = 4$

11. 3; Diagonals of ▱ bisect each other.

13. 4; Pythagorean Theorem

15. 5; Pythagorean Theorem or SAS $\cong$ Theorem

17. 37°; Alternate Interior Angles Theorem

19. 53°; Triangle Sum Theorem

21. 20; All 4 △s are $\cong$ with hypotenuse = 5.

23. 61.1° and 118.9°

25. $MN = 4$ and $PO = 4$ so $\overline{MN} \cong \overline{PO}$.

27. Because lines with equal slopes are $\parallel$.

29. **1.** Given **2.** Theorem 5.20 **3.** $m\angle MHN + m\angle ATN = 180°$ **4.** Given **5.** $56° + m\angle ATN = 180°$ **6.** Subtraction property of equality **7.** $\angle MNT \cong \angle ATN$ **8.** Definition of congruent angles **9.** $m\angle MNT = 124°$ **10.** Linear Pair Postulate **11.** $124° + m\angle MNH = 180°$ **12.** Subtraction property of equality

5.9 Exercise Set A (pp. 313-314)

1. Theorem 5.23 **3.** Theorem 5.25

5. 6 **7.** 1 **9.** 20 **11.** 108

13.

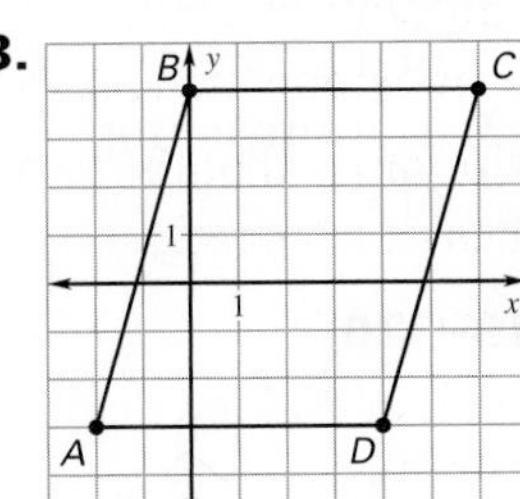

The slope of $\overline{BC}$ and $\overline{AD}$ is 0, so $\overline{BC} \parallel \overline{AD}$. Also, $BC = AD = 6$. By Theorem 5.24, $ABCD$ is a parallelogram.

15. *Sample answer:* Show $\triangle ABD \cong \triangle CDB$ using the AAS Congruence Theorem. This makes $\overline{AB} \cong \overline{CD}$ using corresponding parts of congruent triangles are congruent. Then apply Theorem 5.22.

17. $D(6, -3)$

19. Alternate Interior Angles Congruence Theorem, Reflexive Property of Segment Congruence, Given, SAS, Corresponding Parts of Congruent Triangles are Congruent, Theorem 5.22; **1.** $\overline{QR} \parallel \overline{PS}$ (Given) **2.** $\angle PSQ \cong \angle RQS$ (Alt. Interior ∠s Congruence Thm.) **3.** $\overline{QS} \cong \overline{QS}$ (Reflexive Prop. of Segment Congruence) **4.** $\overline{QR} \cong \overline{PS}$ (Given) **5.** $\triangle RSQ \cong \triangle PQS$ (SAS Congruence Postulate) **6.** $\overline{RS} \cong \overline{PQ}$ (Corr. Parts of $\cong$ △s are $\cong$.) **7.** $PQRS$ is a parallelogram. (Theorem 5.22)

5.9 Exercise Set B (pp. 315–316)

1. 5 **3.** 14 **5.** 12 **7.** yes **9.** no

11. no **13.** yes

15. slope of $\overline{AB}$ = slope of $\overline{CD} = -1$ and slope of $\overline{BC}$ = slope of $\overline{DA} = 5$, so $ABCD$ is a ▱ by definition.

17. (8, 6), (0, −8), and (−8, 10)

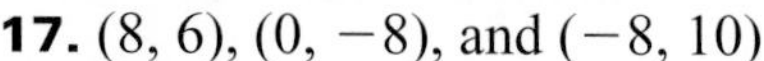

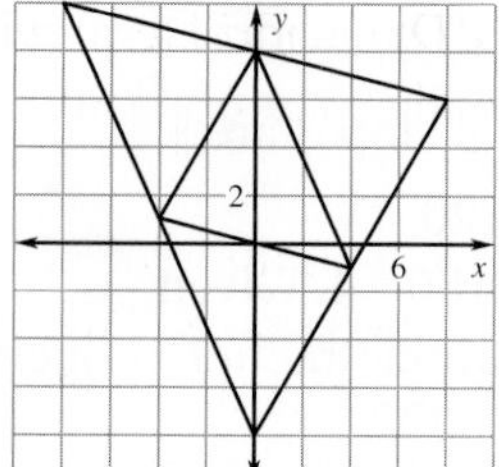

19. The congruent sides must be opposite one another to apply Theorem 5.22.

21.

Statements	Reasons
1. $VWKJ$ and $SJRU$ are ▱.	1. Given
2. $\angle W \cong \angle J$ $\angle J \cong \angle U$	2. Opposite ∠s of a ▱ are ≅.
3. $\angle W \cong \angle U$	3. Transitive Prop. of ≅

5.10 Exercise Set A (pp. 319–320)

1. always; Opposite angles in a rhombus are congruent.

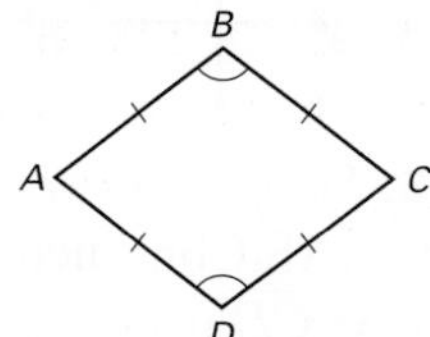

3. always; Every angle in a rectangle is a right angle.

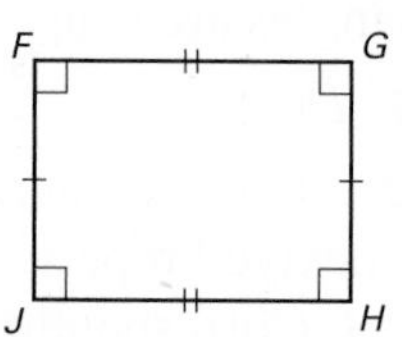

5. rhombus; All sides are congruent.

7. rhombus, square **9.** parallelogram, rhombus

11. rectangle, square

13. parallelogram, rectangle, rhombus, square

15. square; All sides are congruent and all angles are right angles; $x = 2, y = 1$

17. 30° **19.** 12 **21.** 40° **23.** 6 **25.** 90° **27.** 5

29. No; The diagonals of all rectangles are congruent, so the window may not be square.

31.

Statements	Reasons
1. $ABCD$ is a rhombus.	1. Given
2. $\angle ABF \cong \angle CDF$ $\angle BAF \cong \angle DCF$	2. Alt. Int. Angles Theorem
3. $\overline{BA} \cong \overline{DC}$	3. Definition of a rhombus.
4. $\triangle BFA \cong \triangle DFC$	4. ASA Cong. Postulate

5.10 Exercise Set B (pp. 321–322)

1. true; false **3.** true; false **5.** true; true; A rhombus is a square if and only if it is a rectangle.

7. 54° **9.** 54° **11.** 90° **13.** 63° **15.** 60°

17. rhombus; All sides are ≅.; $x = 5, y = 11$

19. 71° **21.** about 28.6 **23.** 34° **25.** 16.5

27. Given; Diagonals of ▱ bisect each other.; $\overline{HD} \cong \overline{DT}$; $DART$ is a rhombus.; Definition of rhombus; Substitution; $WA = WD + DA$, $HT = HD + DT$; $WA = HT$; Theorem 5.28

29. *Sample answer:* Let rectangle $PQRS$ have vertices (0, 0), (p, 0), (p, q), and (0, q), respectively. The diagonal $\overline{PR}$ has a length of $\sqrt{p^2 + q^2}$ and diagonal $\overline{QS}$ has a length of $\sqrt{p^2 + q^2}$. So, $PR = QS = \sqrt{p^2 + q^2}$.

5.11 Exercise Set A (pp. 325–326)

1. trapezoid **3.** 70°, 70°, 110° **5.** 19 **7.** 88°

9. $ST = VS = 5\sqrt{2}$, $TU = UV = 13$

11. 14 **13.** 3.1

15. a. No; None of the side lengths are congruent. **b.** trapezoid **c.** $\frac{3\sqrt{13}}{2}$ units

17. $\overline{MN}$ is the midsegment of isosceles trapezoid $FGHJ$, so $FM = MG = JN = NH$. Also, $\overline{MN} \parallel \overline{FJ}$ by Theorem 5.32. So, $FMNJ$ is an isosceles trapezoid because it has one pair of parallel sides ($\overline{MN} \parallel \overline{FJ}$) and the legs are congruent ($\overline{FM} \cong \overline{JN}$).

5.11 Exercise Set B (pp. 327–328)

1. yes; no **3.** yes; yes **5.** 129° **7.** 20.5 **9.** 7

11. $m\angle T = 113°$, $m\angle W = 97°$

13. $EW = ES = \sqrt{58}$, $ST = WT = \sqrt{109}$

15. $EH = EF = 3\sqrt{34}$, $HG = FG = 9\sqrt{5}$

17. 4.5 **19.** 60°, 60°, 120°, 120°

21. Given; Definition of rectangle; $\angle ILB \cong \angle ROD$; Opposite sides of ▱ are ≅.; $\overline{LB} \cong \overline{DO}$; SAS Congruence Postulate; $\overline{BI} \cong \overline{DR}$; $\overline{BD} \parallel \overline{IR}$; Definition of isosceles trapezoid

5.12 Exercise Set A (pp. 331–332)

	▱	Rect.	Rhom.	Sq.	Kite	Trap.
1.	X	X	X	X		
3.						
5.					X	

7. isosceles trapezoid; A trapezoid with a pair of congruent base angles is isosceles.

9. kite; There are two pairs of consecutive congruent sides, but opposite sides are not congruent.

11. yes; Theorem 5.28 **13.** no

15. rectangle; Opposite sides are congruent and contains 4 right angles.

17. $\overline{FJ}$ and $\overline{HJ}$ **19.** trapezoid

5.12 Exercise Set B (pp. 333–334)

1.

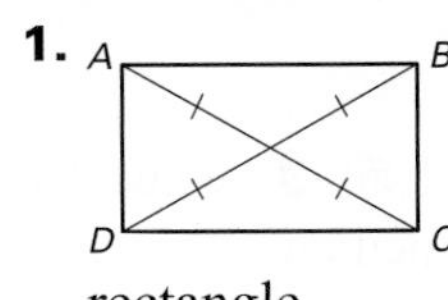

rectangle

3.

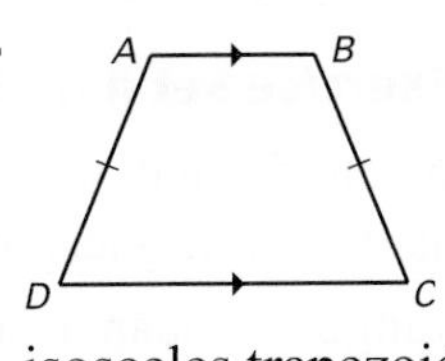

isosceles trapezoid

5.

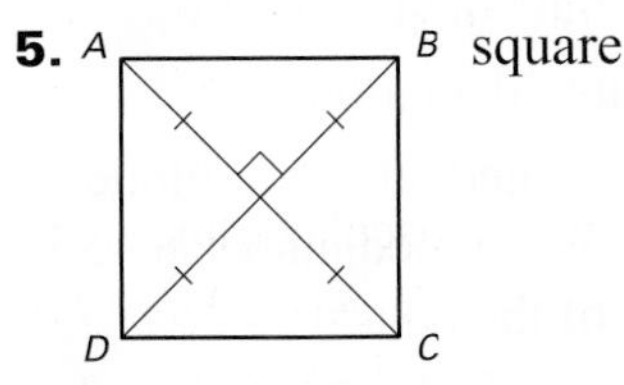

square

7. always **9.** never **11.** never

13. yes; By Theorem 4.11, there is one pair of parallel sides. **15.** no; You must know the other two sides are also parallel.

17. rectangle; slope $\overline{PQ}$ = slope $\overline{RS} = -\frac{1}{4}$; slope $\overline{QR}$ = slope $\overline{PS} = 4$; adjacent sides ⊥ and ≇ $(\sqrt{17} \neq \sqrt{68})$ **19.** $(-5, 5.5)$, $(-8, 2)$, $(-7, -2.5)$, $(-4, 1)$; parallelogram

21. *Sample answer:* $\overline{AB} \cong \overline{AD}$; Quadrilateral with two pairs of consecutive ≅ sides, but opposite sides ≇ is a kite.

23. Yes; **1.** Given **2.** Given **3.** Definition of a midsegment **4.** Midsegment Theorem **5.** $\overline{PR} \cong \overline{QS}$ **6.** $PR = QS$ **7.** Substitution property of equality **8.** Substitution property of equality **9.** Rhombus Corollary

UNIT 6

6.1 Exercise Set A (p. 340)

1. 6 **3.** 9 **5.** The number of choices is the product, not the sum, of 3 and 4: $3 \cdot 4 = 12$. **7.** 80

9. 4; Use the multiplication counting principle and solve the equation $7(3)x = 84$ for x to find the number of desserts. **11.** 35,152,000

13. a. $\frac{21}{26}$ **b.** $\frac{125}{17{,}576}$ **c.** $\frac{1}{17{,}576}$ **d.** $\frac{1}{676}$

6.1 Exercise Set B (p. 341)

1. 80 **3.** 208 **5.** 7500 **7.** 504 **9.** 720; It doubles the number of possible displays to 1440. **11.** 1; 31

13. a. $\frac{5}{26}$ **b.** $\left(\frac{21}{26}\right)^5$ **c.** $\frac{1}{26^5}$ **d.** $\frac{1}{26^4}$

6.2 Exercise Set A (p. 344)

1. a. 24 **b.** 12 **3. a.** 120 **b.** 20 **5.** the number of permutations of 24 objects taken 10 at a time **7.** 720

9. 39,916,800 **11.** 1320 **13.** 120 **15.** 2730

17. 151,200 **19.** > **21.** < **23.** = **25.** 720

6.2 Exercise Set B (p. 345)

1. a. 120 **b.** 60 **3. a.** 720 **b.** 120 **5.** 840

7. 56 **9.** 5 **11.** 2,162,160 **13.** 6,375,600

15. 1260 **17.** 14 **19.** 120 **21.** = **23.** 40,320

25. a. $\frac{1}{132}$ **b.** $\frac{11}{12}$

6.3 Exercise Set A (p. 349)

1. 70 **3.** 1 **5.** 1365 **7.** 6 **9.** 12,870

11. > **13.** = **15.** =

17. combinations; Order is not important; 43,949,268 **19.** 30

21. a. 6435 **b.** $\frac{1}{5}$; $\frac{1}{210}$; It is more likely that you and your friend are just part of the group.

6.3 Exercise Set B (p. 350)

1. 84 **3.** 1 **5.** 1287 **7.** 26,334 **9.** 19,448

11. $<$ **13.** $>$ **15.** $<$

17. permutations; Order is important; 55,440

19. 90

6.4 Exercise Set A (p. 353)

1. overlapping; $\frac{4}{9}$ **3.** overlapping; $\frac{5}{9}$

5. independent; $\frac{25}{121}$

7. a. $\frac{13}{25}$ **b.** $\frac{12}{25}$ **c.** The sum of the probabilities is 1.

6.4 Exercise Set B (p. 354)

1. mutually exclusive; $\frac{6}{11}$ **3.** overlapping; $\frac{9}{11}$

5. independent; $\frac{18}{169}$

6.5 Exercise Set A (p. 357)

1. 0.72 **3.** Player A: 0 points; Player B: 0 points

5. 21.5 lawns per day

7. a.

Amount	\$95,000	\$0	−\$65,000
Probability	0.6	0.2	0.2

b. \$44,000 **c.** The company can expect to gain an average of \$44,000 with venture. **9.** −\$.80

6.5 Exercise Set B (p. 358)

1. 400 **3.** player A: 2.48 points; player B: 0.52 point **5.** about 2.5 points per turn; 32 turns

7. about \$.006

6.6 Exercise Set A (p. 361)

1. music store customers; self-selected sample

3. Biased sample; Riders dissatisfied with biking conditions may be more likely to complete the survey than other riders.

5. The sample is biased because students in the drama club are more likely than other students to prefer performances such as school plays and concerts. The Student Council should use a random or stratified sampling method. **7.** not biased because a particular response is not encouraged

9. Biased; It suggests that taxes are already high; Would you use your taxes to fund a new highway?

11. *Sample answer:* You could survey 25 random students in each grade. The random sample is likely to be representative of all students.

6.6 Exercise Set B (p. 362)

1. all students in a school; stratified random sample

3. Biased sample; Customers at one store location may have stronger opinions than all customers in general. **5.** not biased because a particular response is not encouraged

7. biased because it suggests that two hot lunches are better than one hot lunch and one cold lunch; Do you think that the school should offer two hot lunches or a hot lunch and a cold lunch?

9. *Sample answer:* You could survey 40 random students in each grade. The random sample is likely to be representative of all students. What sport would you like added to the athletic program? The question is unbiased because it does not encourage a particular response.

6.7 Exercise Set A (p. 365)

1. mean: 5; median: 5; modes: 1, 5 **3.** mean: 16; median: 13.5; modes: 8, 28 **5.** median **7.** mean

9. range: 6; mean absolute deviation: 1.68

11. range: 13; mean absolute deviation: 4.67

13. range: 9; mean absolute deviation: 2.44

15. a. 24 **b.** mean: 41.25; median: 41.5; mode: none **c.** either the mean or the median because they are both close to all of the data

17. a. highs: mean: 85.3; median: 87; mode: 89; lows: mean: 64.1; median: 66; mode: none
b. both the medians because they are closer to all of the data **c.** The range of the lows is greater than the range of the highs, so the lows cover a wider interval than the highs.

d. The mean absolute deviation of the highs is greater, so the average variation from the mean is greater for the highs than the lows.

6.7 Exercise Set B (p. 366)

1. mean: 50; median: 48; mode: 48

3. mean: 329; median: 332.5; mode: 410

5. mean: 7.7; median: 7.65; mode: 7.5

7. median **9.** median

11. range: 26; mean absolute deviation: 8.48

13. range: 0.75; mean absolute deviation: 0.18

15. range: 29; mean absolute deviation: 7.54

17. Answers will vary.

19. a. $\frac{90 + 108 + 88 + 75 + 95 + 101 + x}{7} \leq 90$; $x \leq 73$ **b.** Yes; the median of the existing scores is 92.5; if the median is 95, then the last score must be at least 95, so you did not meet your goal.

6.8 Exercise Set A (p. 371)

1. mean = 8; median = 8; range = 9; lower quartile = 5.5; upper quartile = 11; interquartile range = 5.5

3. mean = 4.7; median = 4.9; range = 5.2; lower quartile = 3.1; upper quartile = 6.3; interquartile range = 3.2

5. The data were not ordered before the quartiles were found; median = 19; lower quartile = 15; upper quartile = 23 **7.** Sample A's mean and median are greater than Sample B's mean and median. Sample A's range is less than Sample B's range, so Sample A's data were less spread out than Sample B's data. Sample A's interquartile range is less than Sample B's interquartile range, so Sample A's middle 50% of the data showed less variation than the middle 50% of Sample B's data.

9. The average mean increases to 87.3 and is still greater than the population mean. The average median increases to 88.75 and is now greater than the population median. The average range decreases to 30.75 and is still less than the population range. The average interquartile range decreases to 11.25 and is still less than the population interquartile range.

6.8 Exercise Set B (p. 372)

1. mean = 14.5; median = 15; range = 10; lower quartile = 11; upper quartile = 17; interquartile range = 6 **3.** mean = 44.5; median = 44; range = 39; lower quartile = 35; upper quartile = 54.5; interquartile range = 19.5

5. Sample B's mean and median are greater than Sample A's mean and median. Sample B's range is less than Sample A's range, so Sample B's data are less spread out than Sample A's data. Sample B's interquartile range is less than Sample A's interquartile range, so Sample B's middle 50% of the data showed less variation than the middle 50% of Sample A's data.

7. average mean = 151.4; average median = 152.1; average range = 174.4; average lower quartile = 125.5; average upper quartile = 202.5; average interquartile range = 76.7